Real-Time Systems and Programming Languages

INTERNATIONAL COMPUTER SCIENCE SERIES
Consulting Editor **A D McGettrick** University of Strathclyde

Real-Time Systems and Programming Languages

Ada 95, Real-Time Java and Real-Time POSIX

Third Edition

Alan Burns and Andy Wellings

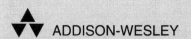 ADDISON-WESLEY

An imprint of **Pearson Education**

Harlow, England · London · New York · Reading, Massachusetts · San Francisco · Toronto · Don Mills, Ontario · Sydney
Tokyo · Singapore · Hong Kong · Seoul · Taipei · Cape Town · Madrid · Mexico City · Amsterdam · Munich · Paris · Milan

Pearson Education Limited
Edinburgh Gate
Harlow
Essex CM20 2JE
England

and Associated Companies around the world

Visit us on the World Wide Web at:
www.pearsoneduc.com

First published 1989
Second Edition 1997
Third Edition 2001

ISBN 0 201 72988 1

British Library Cataloguing-in-Publication Data
A catalogue record for this book can be obtained from the British Library

Library of Congress Cataloging-in-Publication Data
A catalog record for this book can be obtained from the Library of Congress

10   9   8   7   6   5   4   2   1
05   04   03   02   01

Typeset by 66
Printed and bound in Great Britain by Biddles Ltd., Guildford and King's Lynn

Preface

In 1981, a software error caused a stationary robot to move suddenly and with impressive speed to the edge of its operational area. A nearby worker was crushed to death.

This is just one example of the hazards of embedded real-time systems. It is, unfortunately, not an isolated incident. Every month the newsletter *Software Engineering Notes* has pages of examples of events in which the malfunctioning of real-time systems has put the public or the environment at risk. What these sobering descriptions illustrate is that there is a need to take a system-wide view of embedded systems. Indeed, it can be argued that there is a requirement for real-time systems to be recognized as a distinct engineering discipline. This book is a contribution towards the development of this discipline. It cannot, of course, cover all the topics that are apposite to the study of real-time systems engineering; it does, however, present a comprehensive description and assessment of the programming languages and operating system standards used in this domain. Particular emphasis is placed on language primitives and their role in the production of reliable, safe and dependable software.

Audience

The book is aimed at Final Year and Masters students in Computer Science and related disciplines. It has also been written with the professional software engineer and real-time systems engineer in mind. Readers are assumed to have knowledge of a sequential programming language, such as Pascal, and to be familiar with the basic tenets of software engineering. The material presented reflects the content of courses developed over a number of years by the authors at various universities and for industry. These courses specifically address real-time systems and programming languages.

Structure and content

In order to give the chapters continuity, four programming languages are considered in detail: Ada, Java, occam2 and C. These languages have been chosen because they are actually used for software production. As C is a sequential language, it is used in conjunction with the POSIX family of operating system interfaces (in particular, the real-time extensions). Other theoretical or experimental languages are discussed when they offer primitives not available within the core languages. Practitioners who are primarily interested in only one of these languages should find sufficient material for their needs. The authors believe that a full appreciation of a language like Ada or Java, say, can only be obtained through a comparative study of their facilities.

In all, the book contains 18 chapters, the first 13 of which are loosely organized into the following five groups. Chapters 1–4 represent an extended introduction. The characteristics and requirements of real-time systems are presented, and then an overview of the design of such systems is given. Design is not the primary focus of this book; nevertheless, it is important to discuss implementation within an appropriate context – Chapter 2 attempts to provide such a context. Also considered in this chapter are general criteria by which languages can be assessed. Chapters 3 and 4 consider basic language structures through discussions on *programming in the small* and *programming in the large*. These chapters also serve to introduce Ada, Java, occam2 and C. Readers familiar with these languages, and the basic properties of real-time systems, can progress quickly through these opening four chapters. For other readers, the material presented will help to make the book more self-contained.

Chapters 5 and 6 concern themselves with the production of reliable software components. Although consideration is given to fault prevention, attention is primarily focused on fault tolerance. Both forward and backward error recovery techniques are considered. The use of an exception handling facility is discussed in Chapter 6. Both resumption and termination models are described, as are the language primitives found in Ada, Java, CHILL, CLU, C++ and Mesa.

Real-time systems are inherently concurrent, and therefore the study of this aspect of programming languages is fundamental. Chapter 7 introduces the notion of process and reviews the many different models that are used by language and operating system designers. Communication between processes is considered in the following two chapters. Firstly, shared-variable methods are described, including the use of semaphores, monitors, mutexes and protected objects. Message-based models are also important in modern languages; combining as they do communication and synchronization. These models are covered in Chapter 9. Particular attention is given to the rendezvous primitives of Ada and occam2.

It is debatable whether issues of reliability or concurrency should have been considered first within the book. Both authors have experimented with reversing the order and have found little to choose between the two possible approaches. The book can in fact be used in either mode with only one or two topics being 'out of place'. The decision to cover reliability first reflects the authors' belief that safety is the predominant requirement of real-time systems.

The next grouping incorporates Chapters 10 and 11. In general, the relationship between system processes can be described as either cooperating (to achieve a common goal) or competing (to acquire a shared resource). Chapter 10 extends the earlier discussions on fault tolerance by describing how reliable process cooperation can be programmed. Central to this discussion is the notion of an *atomic action* and asynchronous event handling techniques. Competing processes are considered in the following chapter. An assessment is given of different language features. One important topic here is the distinction between conditional and avoidance synchronization within the concurrency model.

Temporal requirements constitute the distinguishing characteristic of real-time systems. Chapters 12 and 13 present a detailed discussion of these requirements, and the language facilities and implementation strategies that are used to satisfy them. Hard real-time systems have timing constraints that must be satisfied; soft systems can occasionally fail to perform adequately. Both are considered within the context of deadline scheduling. The notion of *priority* is discussed at length along with schedulability analysis for preemptive priority-based systems.

The remaining chapters are essentially self-contained. Recent advances in hardware and communications technology have made distributed computer systems a viable alternative to uniprocessor and centralized systems in many embedded application areas. Although, in some respects, distribution can be thought of as an implementation consideration, issues which arise when applications are distributed raise fundamental questions that go beyond mere implementation details. Chapter 14 considers four areas of interest: language support; reliability in the presence of processor and communication failure; algorithms for distributed control; and distributed scheduling. This chapter is specifically designed to be self-contained and can be omitted by students on shorter courses.

One important requirement of many real-time systems is that they incorporate external devices that must be programmed (that is, controlled) as part of the application software. This low-level programming is at variance with the abstract approach to software production that characterizes software engineering. Chapter 15 considers ways in which low-level facilities can be successfully incorporated into high-level languages.

A popular misconception surrounding real-time systems is that they must be highly efficient. This is not in itself true. Real-time systems must satisfy timing constraints (and reliability requirements); efficient implementation is one means of extending the realms of possibility, but it is not an end in itself. Chapter 16 reviews the role of the execution environment in obtaining efficient predictable implementations.

The final major chapter of the book is a case study programmed in Ada. An example from a mine control system is used. Inevitably a single scaled down study cannot illustrate all the issues covered in the previous chapters; in particular, factors such as size and complexity are not addressed. Nevertheless, the case study does cover many important aspects of real-time systems.

All chapters have summaries and further reading lists. Most also have lists of exercises. These have been chosen to help readers consolidate their understanding of the material presented in each chapter. They mostly represent exercises that have been used by the authors for assessment purposes.

Ada, Java, occam2 and C

The Ada 95 examples in this book conform to the ISO/ANSI standard. The Java examples conform to the Java 2 platform along with the Real-Time Specification for Java extensions (which will be called Real-Time Java in this book). The occam2 examples conform to the occam2 definition given by INMOS. The C examples conform to ANSI C, and the POSIX primitives are those given in the POSIX.1, POSIX.1b, POSIX.1c, POSIX.1d and POSIX.13 definitions.

To facilitate easy identification of the four languages, different presentation styles are used. Ada is presented with keywords in bold lower case; program identifiers are given in mixed case. Occam2 has keywords unbolded in upper case and identifiers in mixed case. C has keywords unbolded and identifiers in lower case. To distinguish Java from C, Java keywords are bolded and identifiers are mixed case.

Changes from the Second Edition

In the second edition, we moved from Ada 83 to Ada 95, and from Modula-2 to C and POSIX. The third edition was motivated by the following developments in the real-time domain.

- The emergence of Java as a real-time language through the Real-Time Java extensions. This has resulted in the treatment of Java as one of the core languages covered in the book.

- The addition of new real-time facilities into the POSIX standard; in particular Execution Time Monitoring and Sporadic Servers. Chapters 12 and 13 have been updated to reflect these changes to the Standard.

- The proposed extensions to CORBA to address real-time issues. CORBA is clearly a major topic in its own right, and it is beyond the scope of this book to address the topic in detail. However, Chapter 14 has been updated to reflect the CORBA approach.

We have also taken the advice of those using this book in teaching to include more scheduling material.

Teaching Aids

This text is supported by further material available via the following WWW site:

http://www.booksites.net/burns

Overhead projection foil layouts are available for many parts of the book. Also available are solutions to some of the exercises. We will, over time, add further exercises, and where appropriate new examples and additional teaching material. Teachers/lecturers who make us of this book are invited to contribute to these Web pages.

Real-Time Systems Research at York

Alan Burns and Andy Wellings are members of the Real-Time Systems Research Group in the Department of Computer Science at the University of York (UK). This group undertakes research into all aspects of the design, implementation and analysis of real-time systems. Specifically, the group is addressing: formal and structured methods for development, scheduling theories, reuse, language design, kernel design, communication protocols, distributed and parallel architectures, and program code analysis. The aim of the group is to undertake fundamental research, and to bring into engineering practice modern techniques, methods and tools. Areas of application of our work include space and avionic systems, engine controllers, vehicle control and multi-media systems. Further information about the group's activities can be found via:

http://www.cs.york.ac.uk/rts/

Acknowledgements for the First Edition

The material in this book has been developed over the last five years and presented to many third year and M.Sc. students at the Universities of Bradford and York, taking Computer Science or Electronics degrees. We would like to acknowledge their contribution to the end product, for without them this book would never have been written.

Many people have read and commented on a first draft of the book. In particular we would like to thank Martin Atkins, Chris Hoggarth, Andy Hutcheon, Andrew Lister and Jim Welsh. We would also like to thank our colleagues at our respective Universities for providing us with a stimulating environment and for many enlightening discussions, particularly Ljerka Beus-Dukic, Geoff Davies, John McDermid, Gary Morgan, Rick Pack, Rob Stone and Hussein Zedan.

During 1988 Alan Burns was on sabbatical at the Universities of Queensland and Houston. We would like to thank all staff at these institutions, particularly Andrew Lister, Charles McKay and Pat Rogers.

This book would not have been possible without the use of electronic mail over JANET. We would like to thank the Computer Board of the United Kingdom University Grants Council and the Science and Engineering Research Council for providing this invaluable service.

Finally, we would like to give special thanks to Sylvia Holmes and Carol Burns – Sylvia for the many hours she has spent painstakingly proofreading the final manuscript, and Carol for the many evenings she has tolerated our meetings and discussions.

Acknowledgements for the Second Edition

Many people have helped in the production of the Second Edition of this book. In particular we would like to thank Alejandro Alonse, Angel Alvarez, Sergio Arevalo, Neil Audsley, Martin Dorey, Michael Gonzalez Harbour, Stuart Mitchell, Gary Morgan, Offer Pazy and Juan de la Puente.

Acknowledgements for the Third Edition

We would like to thank the Real-Time Java Expert Group for the open manner in which they have developed the Real-Time Java Specification. Thanks are also due to Angel Alvarez, Jose Alvarez, Neil Audsley, Iain Bate, Jorge Diaz-Herrera, David Duke, Alan Grigg, Ian Hayes, George Lima, Greg Murphy, Peter Puschner and Pat Rogers, who all provided us with help of one form on another during the writing of this edition.

We also wish to acknowledge the very helpful comments given by the technical reviewers, Jorge Díaz-Herrera, Jörgen Hansson and Robert Holton, on the first draft of this edition.

Finally, we would like to thank all those people who gave us comments on the Second Edition of the book.

Alan Burns and Andy Wellings
York
November 2000

Contents

A companion website accompanies *Real-Time Systems and Programming Languages*, 3e by Alan Burns and Andy Wellings.

Visit the *Real-Time Systems and Programming Languages* companion website at www.booksites.net/burns

Here you will find valuable teaching and learning support material including:

- Supplementary OHT lecturing masters for the main teaching chapters in the book
- Selected solutions to exercises
- Source code for the substantial code extracts in the book

Chapter 1
Introduction to real-time systems

As computers become smaller, faster, more reliable and cheaper, so their range of application widens. Built initially as equation solvers, their influence has extended into all walks of life, from washing machines to air traffic control. One of the fastest expanding areas of computer exploitation is that involving applications whose prime function is *not* that of information processing, but which nevertheless require information processing in order to carry out their prime function. A microprocessor-controlled washing machine is a good example of such a system. Here, the prime function is to wash clothes; however, depending on the type of clothes to be washed, different 'wash programs' must be executed. These types of computer applications are generically called **real-time** or **embedded**. It has been estimated that 99% of the worldwide production of microprocessors is used in embedded systems. These embedded systems place particular requirements on the computer languages needed to program them, as they have different characteristics from the more traditional information processing systems.

This book is concerned with embedded computer systems and their programming languages. It studies the particular characteristics of these systems and discusses how modern real-time programming languages and operating systems have evolved.

1

1.1 Definition

Before proceeding fur   stem' more
precisely. There are   ne system;
however, they all ha   e taken for
the system to genera   *ctionary of*
Computing gives the

> Any system in   ficant.
> This is usuall   in the
> physical work   t. The
> lag from input   ;ptable
> timeliness.

Here, the word 'tin   For example,
in a missile guidance system, output is required within a few s, whereas in
a computer-controlled car assembly line, the response may be required only within a
second. To illustrate the various ways in which 'real-time' systems are defined, two
further definitions will be given. Young (1982) defines a real-time system to be:

> any information processing activity or system which has to respond to ex-
> ternally generated input stimuli within a finite and specified period.

The PDCS (Predictably Dependable Computer Systems) (Randell et al., 1995) project
gives the following definition:

> A real-time system is a system that is required to react to stimuli from the
> environment (including the passage of physical time) within time intervals
> dictated by the environment.

In their most general sense, all these definitions cover a very wide range of computer activities. For example, an operating system like Unix may be considered real-
time in that when a user enters a command he or she will expect a response within a
few seconds. Fortunately, it is usually not a disaster if the response is not forthcom-
ing. These types of system can be distinguished from those where *failure* to respond
can be considered just as bad as a wrong response. Indeed, for some, it is this aspect
that distinguishes a real-time system from others where response time is important but
not crucial. Consequently, *the correctness of a real-time system depends not only on
the logical result of the computation, but also on the time at which the results are produced.* Practitioners in the field of real-time computer system design often distinguish
between **hard** and **soft** real-time systems. Hard real-time systems are those where it is
absolutely imperative that responses occur within the specified deadline. Soft real-time
systems are those where response times are important but the system will still function
correctly if deadlines are occasionally missed. Soft systems can themselves be distinguished from interactive ones in which there are no explicit deadlines. For example, the
flight control system of a combat aircraft is a hard real-time system because a missed

deadline could lead to a catastrophe, whereas a data acquisition system for a process control application is soft, as it may be defined to sample an input sensor at regular intervals but to tolerate intermittent delays. Of course, many systems will have both hard and soft real-time subsystems. Indeed, some services may have both a soft and a hard deadline. For example, a response to some warning event may have a soft deadline of 50 ms (for an optimally efficient reaction) and a hard deadline of 200 ms (to guarantee that no damage to equipment or personnel takes place). Between 50 ms and 200 ms, the 'value' (or utility) of the output decreases.

As these definitions and examples illustrate, the use of the term 'soft' does not imply a single type of requirement, but incorporates a number of different properties. For example:

- the deadline can be missed occasionally (typically with an upper limit of misses within a defined interval)
- the service can occasionally be delivered late (again, with an upper limit on tardiness)

A deadline that can be missed occasionally, but in which there is no benefit from late delivery, is called **firm**. In some real-time systems, optional firm components may be given probabilistic requirements (for example, a hard service must produce an output every 300 ms; at least 80% of the time this output will be produced by a firm component, X; on other occasions, a hard, but functionally much simpler component, Y, will be used).

In this book, the term 'real-time system' is used to mean both soft and hard real-time. Where discussion is concerned specifically with hard real-time systems, the term 'hard real-time' will be used explicitly.

In a hard or soft real-time system, the computer is usually interfaced directly to some physical equipment and is dedicated to monitoring or controlling the operation of that equipment. A key feature of all these applications is the role of the computer as an information processing component within a larger engineering system. It is for this reason that such applications have become known as **embedded computer systems**.

1.2   Examples of real-time systems

Having defined what is meant by real-time and embedded systems, some examples of their use are now given.

1.2.1   Process control

The first use of a computer as a component in a larger engineering system occurred in the process control industry in the early 1960s. Nowadays, the use of microprocessors is the norm. Consider the simple example shown in Figure 1.1, where the computer performs a single activity: that of ensuring an even flow of liquid in a pipe by controlling a valve.

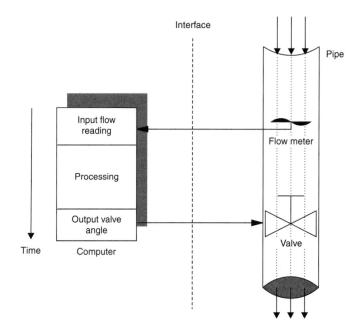

Figure 1.1   A fluid control system.

On detecting an increase in flow, the computer must respond by altering the valve angle; this response must occur within a finite period if the equipment at the receiving end of the pipe is not to become overloaded. Note that the actual response may involve quite a complex computation in order to calculate the new valve angle.

This example shows just one component of a larger control system. Figure 1.2 illustrates the role of a real-time computer embedded in a complete process control environment. The computer interacts with the equipment using sensors and actuators. A valve is an example of an actuator, and a temperature or pressure transducer is an example of a sensor. (A transducer is a device that generates an electrical signal that is proportional to the physical quantity being measured.) The computer controls the operation of the sensors and actuators to ensure that the correct plant operations are performed at the appropriate times. Where necessary, analogue to digital (and digital to analogue) converters must be inserted between the controlled process and the computer.

1.2.2 Manufacturing

The use of computers in manufacturing has become essential in order that production costs can be kept low and productivity increased. Computers have enabled the integration of the entire manufacturing process from product design to fabrication. It is in

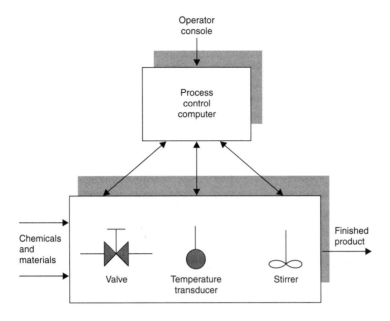

Figure 1.2   A process control system.

the area of production control that embedded systems are best illustrated. Figure 1.3 diagrammatically represents the role of the production control computer in the manufacturing process. The physical system consists of a variety of mechanical devices – such as machine tools, manipulators and conveyor belts – all of which need to be controlled and coordinated by the computer.

1.2.3   Communication, command and control

entirely dissimilar

Although **communication, command and control** is a military term, there is a wide range of disparate applications which exhibit similar characteristics; for example, airline seat reservation, medical facilities for automatic patient care, air traffic control and remote bank accounting. Each of these systems consists of a complex set of policies, information gathering devices and administrative procedures which enable decisions to be supported, and provide the means by which they can be implemented. Often, the information gathering devices and the instruments required for implementing decisions are distributed over a wide geographical area. Figure 1.4 diagrammatically represents such a system.

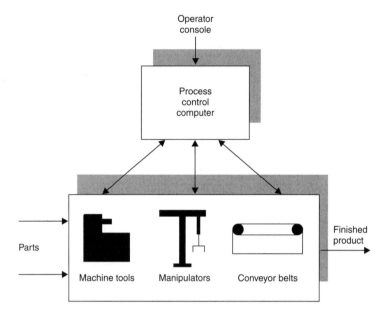

Figure 1.3   A production control system.

1.2.4 Generalized embedded computer system

In each of the examples shown, the computer is interfaced directly to physical equipment in the real world. In order to control these real-world devices, the computer will need to sample the measurement devices at regular intervals; a real-time clock is therefore required. Usually there is also an operator's console to allow for manual intervention. The human operator is kept constantly informed of the state of the system by displays of various types, including graphical ones.

questioned   Records of the system's state changes are also kept in an database which can be interrogated by the operators, either for post mortems (in the case of a system crash), or to provide information for administrative purposes. Indeed, this information is increasingly being used to support decision making in the day-to-day running of systems. For example, in the chemical and process industries, plant monitoring is essential for maximizing economic advantages rather than simply maximizing production. Decisions concerning production at one plant may have serious repercussions for other plants at remote sites, particularly when the products of one process are being used as raw material for another.

A typical embedded computer system can, therefore, be represented by Figure 1.5. The software which controls the operations of the system can be written in modules which reflect the physical nature of the environment. Usually there will be a module which contains the algorithms necessary for physically controlling the devices; a module responsible for recording the system's state changes; a module to retrieve and display those changes; and a module to interact with the operator.

Figure 1.4 A command and control system.

1.3 Characteristics of real-time systems

A real-time system possesses many special characteristics (either inherent or imposed) which are identified in the following sections. Clearly, not all real-time systems will exhibit all these characteristics; however, any general purpose language (and operating system) which is to be used for the effective programming of real-time systems must have facilities which support these characteristics.

1.3.1 Large and complex

Large – amoun of variety + continuous change

It is often said that most of the problems associated with developing software are those related to size and complexity. Writing small programs presents no significant problem as they can be designed, coded, maintained and understood by a single person. If that person leaves the company or institution using the software, then someone else can learn the program in a relatively short period of time. Indeed, for these programs, there is an *art* or *craft* to their construction and *small is beautiful*.

Unfortunately, not all software exhibits this most desirable characteristic of smallness. Lehman and Belady (1985), in attempting to characterize large systems, reject the simple and perhaps intuitive notion that largeness is simply proportional to the number

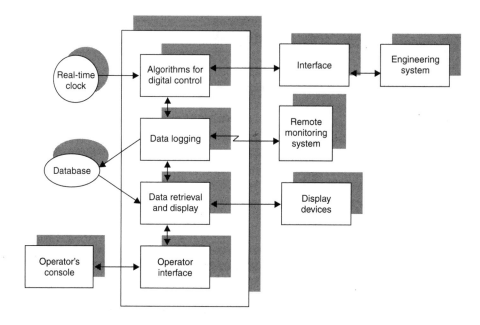

Figure 1.5   A typical embedded system

of instructions, lines of code or modules comprising a program. Instead, they relate largeness to **variety**, and the degree of largeness to the amount of variety. Traditional indicators, such as number of instructions and development effort are, therefore, just symptoms of variety.

> The variety is that of needs and activities in the real world and their reflection in a program. But the real world is continuously changing. It is evolving. So too are, therefore, the needs and activities of society. Thus large programs, like all complex systems, must continuously evolve.

Embedded systems by their definition must respond to real-world events. The variety associated with these events must be catered for; the programs will, therefore, tend to exhibit the undesirable property of largeness. Inherent in the above definition of largeness is the notion of **continuous change**. The cost of redesigning or rewriting software to respond to the continuously changing requirements of the real world is prohibitive. Therefore real-time systems undergo constant maintenance and enhancements during their lifetimes. They must be extensible.

Although real-time software is often complex, features provided by real-time languages and environments enable these complex systems to be broken down into smaller components which can be managed effectively. Chapters 2 and 4 will consider these features in detail.

Figure 1.6   A simple controller.

1.3.2 Manipulation of real numbers

As was noted earlier, many real-time systems involve the control of some engineering activity. Figure 1.6 exemplifies a simple control system. The controlled entity, the plant, has a vector of output variables, y, that change over time, hence $y(t)$. These outputs are compared with the desired (or reference) signal $r(t)$ to produce an error signal, $e(t)$. The controller uses this error vector to change the input variables to the plant, $u(t)$. For a very simple system, the controller can be an analogue device working on a continuous signal.

Figure 1.6 illustrates a feedback controller. This is the most common form, but feed-forward controllers are also used. In order to calculate what changes must be made to the input variables, so that a desirable effect on the output vector takes place, it is necessary to have a mathematical model of the plant. The derivation of these models is the concern of the distinct discipline of control theory. Often a plant is modelled as a set of first-order differential equations. These link the output of the system with the internal state of the plant and its input variables. Changing the output of the plant involves solving these equations to give required input values. Most physical systems exhibit inertia, so that change is not instantaneous. A real-time requirement to move to a new set point within a fixed time period will add to the complexity of the manipulations needed, both to the mathematical model and to the physical system. The fact that, in reality, linear first-order equations are only an approximation to the actual characteristics of the system also presents complications.

Because of these difficulties, the complexity of the model, and the number of distinct (but not independent) inputs and outputs, most controllers are implemented as computers. The introduction of a digital component into the system changes the nature of the control cycle. Figure 1.7 is an adaptation of the earlier model. Items marked with a * are now discrete values; the sample and hold operation being carried out by an analogue-to-digital converter, both converters being under the direct control of the computer.

Within the computer, the differential equations can be solved by numerical techniques, although the algorithms themselves need to be adapted to take into account the fact that plant outputs are now being sampled. The design of control algorithms is a topic outside the scope of this book; the implementation of these algorithms is, how-

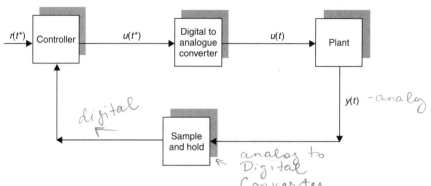

Figure 1.7   A simple computerized controller.

ever, of direct concern. They can be mathematically complex and require a high degree of precision. A fundamental requirement of a real-time programming language, therefore, is the ability to manipulate real or floating-point numbers. This is considered in Chapter 3, along with other data types.

1.3.3   Extremely reliable and safe

The more society relinquishes control of its vital functions to computers, the more imperative it becomes that those computers do not fail. The failure of a system involved in automatic fund transfer between banks can lead to millions of dollars being lost irretrievably; a faulty component in electricity generation could result in the failure of a vital life-support system in an intensive care unit; and the premature shutdown of a chemical plant could cause expensive damage to equipment or environmental harm. These somewhat dramatic examples illustrate that computer hardware and software must be reliable and safe. Even in hostile environments, such as those found in military applications, it must be possible to design and implement systems which will fail only in a controlled way. Furthermore, where operator interaction is required, care must be taken in the design of the interface in order to minimize the possibility of human error.

The sheer size and complexity of real-time systems exacerbates the reliability problem; not only must expected difficulties inherent in the application be taken into account, but also those introduced by faulty software design.

In Chapters 5 and 6, the problems of producing reliable and safe software will be considered along with the facilities that languages have introduced to cope with both expected and unexpected error conditions. The issue is examined further in Chapters 10–14.

1.3.4   Concurrent control of separate system components

An embedded system will tend to consist of computers and several coexisting external elements with which the computer programs must interact simultaneously. It is the very nature of these external real-world elements that they exist in parallel. In our typical embedded computer example, the program has to interact with an engineering system (which will consist of many parallel activities such as robots, conveyor belts, sensors, actuators and so on) and the computer's display devices, the operator's console, the database and the real-time clock. Fortunately, the speed of a modern computer is such that usually these actions may be carried out in sequence but give the illusion of being simultaneous. In some embedded systems, however, this may not be the case, for example where the data is to be collected and processed at various geographically distributed sites, or where the response time of the individual components cannot be met by a single computer. In these cases, it is necessary to consider distributed and multiprocessor embedded systems.

A major problem associated with the production of software for systems which exhibit concurrency is how to express that concurrency in the structure of the program. One approach is to leave it all up to the programmer who must construct his/her system so that it involves the cyclic execution of a program sequence to handle the various concurrent tasks. There are several reasons, however, why this is inadvisable:

- it complicates the programmer's already difficult task and involves him or her in considerations of structures which are irrelevant to the control of the tasks in hand;

- the resulting programs will be more obscure and inelegant;

- it makes proving program correctness more difficult;

- it makes decomposition of the problem more complex;

- parallel execution of the program on more than one processor will be much more difficult to achieve;

- the placement of code to deal with faults is more problematic.

Older real-time programming languages, for example, RTL/2 and Coral 66, relied on operating system support for concurrency; C is usually associated with Unix or POSIX. However, the more modern languages, such as Ada, Java, Pearl and occam, have direct support for concurrent programming. In Chapters 7, 8 and 9, various models of concurrent programming are considered in detail. Attention is then focused, in the following two chapters, on achieving reliable communication and synchronization between concurrent processes in the presence of design errors. In Chapter 14, issues of execution in a distributed environment are discussed, along with the problems of tolerating processor and communications failures.

1.3.5   Real-time facilities

Response time is crucial in any embedded system. Unfortunately, it is very difficult to design and implement systems which will guarantee that the appropriate output will be generated at the appropriate times under all possible conditions. To do this, and make full use of all computing resources at all times is often impossible. For this reason, real-time systems are usually constructed using processors with considerable spare capacity, thereby ensuring that 'worst-case behaviour' does not produce any unwelcome delays during critical periods of the system's operation.

Given adequate processing power, language and run-time support is required to enable the programmer to:

- specify times at which actions are to be performed,
- specify times at which actions are to be completed,
- respond to situations where *all* the timing requirements cannot be met,
- respond to situations where the timing requirements are changed dynamically (for example, mode changes).

These are called real-time control facilities. They enable the program to synchronize with time itself. For example, with direct digital control algorithms, it is necessary to sample readings from sensors at certain periods of the day, for example, 2 p.m., 3 p.m. and so on, or at regular intervals, for instance, every 5 seconds (with analogue to digital converters, sample rates can vary from a few hundred hertz to several hundred megahertz). As a result of these readings, other actions will need to be performed. For example, in an electric power station, it is necessary at 5 p.m. on Monday to Friday each week to increase the supply of electricity to domestic consumers. This is in response to the peak in demand caused by families returning home from work, turning on lights, cooking dinner and so on. In recent years in the UK, the demand for domestic electricity reached a peak after the end of the 1990 Soccer World Cup Final, when millions of viewers left their living rooms, turned on lights in the kitchen and switched on the kettle in order to make a cup of tea or coffee.

An example of a mode change can be found in aircraft flight control systems. If an aircraft has experienced depressurization, there is an immediate need for all computing resources to be given over to handling the emergency.

In order to meet response times, it is necessary for a system's behaviour to be predictable. This is discussed in Chapters 12 and 13 together with language facilities that assist in the programming of time critical operations.

1.3.6   Interaction with hardware interfaces

The nature of embedded systems requires the computer components to interact with the external world. They need to monitor sensors and control actuators for a wide variety of real-world devices. These devices interface to the computer via input and output registers, and their operational requirements are device- and computer-dependent. Devices may also generate interrupts to signal to the processor that certain operations have been performed or that error conditions have arisen.

In the past, interfacing to devices has either been left under the control of the operating system, or has required the application programmer to resort to assembly language inserts to control and manipulate the registers and interrupts. Nowadays, because of the variety of devices and the time-critical nature of their associated interactions, their control must often be direct, and not through a layer of operating system functions. Furthermore, reliability requirements argue against the use of low-level programming techniques.

In Chapter 15, the facilities provided by real-time programming languages which enable the specification of device registers and interrupt control will be considered.

1.3.7   Efficient implementation and the execution environment

Since real-time systems are time-critical, efficiency of implementation will be more important than in other systems. It is interesting that one of the main benefits of using a high-level language is that it enables the programmer to abstract away from implementation details, and to concentrate on solving the problem at hand. Unfortunately, the embedded computer systems programmer cannot afford this luxury. He or she must be constantly concerned with the cost of using particular language features. For example, if a response to some input is required within a microsecond there is no point in using a language feature whose execution takes a millisecond!

In Chapter 16, the role of the execution environment in providing efficient and predictable implementations will be examined.

Summary

In this chapter, a real-time system has been defined as

> any information processing activity or system which has to respond to externally generated input stimuli within a finite and specified delay.

Two main classes of such systems have been identified: hard real-time systems, where it is absolutely imperative that responses occur within the specified deadline; and soft real-time systems, where response times are important, but the system will still function correctly if deadlines are occasionally missed.

The basic characteristics of a real-time or embedded computer system have been considered. They were:

- largeness and complexity,
- manipulation of real numbers,
- extreme reliability and safety,

- concurrent control of separate system components,
- real-time control,
- interaction with hardware interfaces,
- efficient implementation.

Further reading

Bailey, D. L. and Buhr, R. J. A. (1998) *Introduction to Real-Time Systems: From Design to Networking with C/C++*. Upper Saddle River, NJ: Prentice Hall.

Buttazzo, G. C. (1997) *Hard Real-Time Computing Systems: Predictable Scheduling Algorithms and Applications*. New York: Kluwer Academic.

Joseph M. (1992) *Specification, Verification and Analysis*. Englewood Cliffs, NJ: Prentice Hall.

Kavi K. M. (1992) *Real-Time Systems: Abstractions, Languages and Design Methodologies*. Los Alamitos, CA: IEEE Computer Society Press.

Koptez H. (1997) *Real-time Systems*. New York: Kluwer Academic.

Laplante P. (1997) *Design and Application of Real-Time Systems*. New York: Institute of Electrical & Electronic Engineers.

Schneider, S. (1998). *Concurrent and Real-time Systems*. New York: John Wiley & Sons.

Chapter 2
Designing real-time systems

Clearly, the most important stage in the development of any real-time system is the generation of a consistent design that satisfies an authoritative specification of requirements. In this, real-time systems are no different from other computer applications, although their overall scale often generates quite fundamental design problems. The discipline of software engineering is now widely accepted as the focus for the development of methods, tools and techniques aimed at ensuring that the software production process is manageable, and that reliable and correct programs are constructed. It is assumed here that readers are familiar with the basic tenets of software engineering and consideration is thus restricted to the particular problems and requirements furnished by real-time embedded systems. Even within this restriction, it is not possible to give a comprehensive account of the many design methodologies proposed. Issues of design *per se* are not the main focus of attention in this book. Rather, the investigation of language and operating system primitives, which allow designs to be realized, is the central theme. Within this context, the languages Ada, (Real-Time) Java, occam2 and C (with Real-Time POSIX) will be considered in detail. Readers should consult the further reading list at the end of this chapter for additional material on the design process.

Although almost all design approaches are top-down, they are built upon an understanding of what is feasible at lower levels. In essence, all design methods involve a series of transformations from the initial statement of requirements to the executing code. This chapter gives an overview of some of the typical stages that are passed through on this route, that is:

- requirement specification,
- architectural design,
- detailed design,
- implementation,
- testing.

Other important activities are also discussed:

- prototyping prior to final implementation,
- the design of the human computer interface,
- criteria for assessing implementation languages.

As different activities are isolated, notations are required that enable each stage to be documented. Transformations from one stage to another are, therefore, nothing more than translations from one notation to another. For example, a compiler produces executable code from source code that is expressed in a programming language. Unfortunately, other translations (further up the design hierarchy) are less well defined; usually because the notations employed are too vague and imprecise, and cannot fully capture the semantics of the requirements or of the design.

2.1   Levels of notation

There are a number of ways of classifying forms of notation (or representation). For our purposes McDermid (1989), gives a useful decomposition. He names three techniques:

(1) informal

(2) structured

(3) formal

Informal methods usually make use of natural language and various forms of imprecise diagrams. They have the advantage that the notations are understood by a large group of people (that is, all those speaking the natural language). It is well known, however, that phrases in English, for example, are often open to a number of different interpretations.

   Structured methods often use a graphical representation, but unlike the informal diagrams these graphs are well defined. They are constructed from a small number of predefined components which are interconnected in a controlled manner. The graphical form may also have a syntactical representation in some well-defined language.

   Although structured methods can be made quite rigorous, they cannot, in themselves, be analyzed or manipulated. It is necessary for the notation to have a mathematical basis if such operations are to be carried out. Methods that have such mathematical properties are usually known as formal. They have the clear advantage that precise descriptions can be made in these notations. Moreover, it is possible to prove that necessary properties hold; for example, that the top-level design satisfies the requirement specification. The disadvantage with formal techniques is that they cannot easily be understood by those not prepared or able to become familiar with the notation.

The high reliability requirements in real-time systems have caused a movement away from informal approaches to the structured and, increasingly, the formal. Rigorous techniques of verification are beginning to be used in the real-time industry, but at present few software engineers have the necessary mathematical skills to exploit fully the potential of verification. In addition, formal techniques often do not possess adequate structuring facilities to cope with large specifications. As a consequence, it is becoming more popular to use a combination of structured and formal methods.

2.2 Requirement specification

Almost all computing projects start with an informal description of what is desired. This should then be followed by an extensive analysis of requirements. It is at this stage that the functionality of the system is defined. In terms of specific real-time factors, the temporal behaviour of the system should be made quite explicit, as should the reliability requirements and the desired behaviour of the software in the event of component failure. The requirements phase will also define which acceptance tests should apply to the software.

In addition to the system itself, it is necessary to build a model of the environment of the application. It is a characteristic of real-time systems that they have important interactions with their environment. Hence such issues as maximum rate of interrupts, maximum number of dynamic external objects (for example, aeroplanes in an air traffic control system) and failure modes are all important.

Some structured notations and techniques are used (such as PSL (Teichrow and Hershey, 1977) and CORE (Mullery, 1979)) in requirements analysis, for it is clearly advantageous to have an unambiguous set of requirements. Furthermore, object-oriented methods are becoming more widespread (Monarchi and Puhr, 1992) and an industrial standard, UML, has emerged – see Section 2.4.4. Some work has also been carried out on formal methods for requirement analysis, notably the FOREST project (Goldsack and Finkelstein, 1991) which has defined a logic scheme for dealing with requirements and a method for requirement elicitation. More recently, the Esprit II ICARUS project has been developing the ALBERT (Agent-oriented Language for Building and Eliciting Requirement for real-Time systems) language (Dubois et al., 1995; Bois, 1995). Notwithstanding these developments, no structured or formal notation will capture the requirements that the 'customer' has failed to mention.

The analysis phase provides an authoritative specification of requirements. It is from this that the design will emerge. There is no more critical phase in the software life cycle, and yet natural language documents are still the normal notation for this specification. To give one illustration, although the syntax of computer languages can be easily stated formally (using some form of BNF), the semantics are often left to wordy

English prose. The original version of Ada was so 'defined' and it was necessary to instigate a standing committee to pass judgement on what the defining document (which is an international standard) actually means. Compiler writers have found it necessary to forward thousands of queries to this committee. The current standard is still defined using natural language. By comparison, the semantics of occam have been defined using denotation semantics (Roscoe, 1985). This opens up the possibility of formally verified compilers and rigorous program manipulation (for example, transformation) tools.

Perhaps the most popular formal method that is now beginning to be used quite widely is VDM (Jones, 1986). Another technique that has gained much support is Z (Spivey, 1989). Both of these methods use set theory and predicate logic, and represent considerable improvements on informal and merely structured techniques. In their present form, however, they do not deal completely with the specification of real-time systems.

2.3   Design activities

The design of a large embedded system cannot be undertaken in one exercise. It must be structured in some way. To manage the development of complex real-time systems, two complementary approaches are often used: decomposition and abstraction. Together, they form the basis of most software engineering methods. Decomposition, as its name suggests, involves the systematic breakdown of the complex system into smaller and smaller parts until components are isolated that can be understood and engineered by individuals or small groups. At each level of decomposition, there should be an appropriate level of description and a method of documenting (expressing) this description. Abstraction enables the consideration of detail, particularly that appertaining to implementation, to be postponed. This allows a simplified view of the system and of the objects contained within it to be taken, which nevertheless still contains the essential properties and features. The use of abstraction and decomposition pervades the entire engineering process and has influenced the design of real-time programming languages and associated software design methods.

If a formal notation is used for the requirement specification then top-level designs may use the same notation and can thus be proven to meet the specification. Many structured notations are, however, advocated to either fill out the top-level design or to replace the formal notation altogether. Indeed, a structured top-level design may, in effect, be the authoritative specification of requirements.

2.3.1   Encapsulation

The hierarchical development of software leads to the specification and subsequent development of program subcomponents. The needs of abstraction dictate that these subcomponents should have well-defined roles, and clear and unambiguous interconnections and interfaces. If the specification of the entire software system can be verified just in terms of the specification of the immediate subcomponents then decomposition is said to be **compositional**. This is an important property when formally analyzing programs.

Sequential programs are particularly amenable to compositional methods, and a number of techniques have been used to encapsulate and represent subcomponents. Simula introduced the significant **class** construct. Modula-2 uses the less powerful, but still important, module structure. More recently *object-oriented* languages, such as C++, Java and Eiffel, have emerged to build upon the class construct. Ada uses a combinations of modules and type extensions to support object-oriented programming. Chapter 4 discusses these facilities further.

Objects, while providing an abstract interface, require extra facilities if they are to be used in a concurrent environment. Typically, this involves the addition of some form of process. The *process* abstraction is, therefore, the abstraction on which this book will focus. In Chapter 7, the notion of process is introduced, Chapter 8 then considers shared-variable process interaction. A more controlled and abstract interface is, however, provided by message-based process communication. This is discussed in Chapter 9.

Both object and process abstractions are important in the design and implementation of reliable embedded systems.

2.3.2   Cohesion and coupling

The above two forms of encapsulation lead to the use of modules with well-defined (and abstract) interfaces. But how should a large system be decomposed into modules? To a large extent, the answer to this question lies at the heart of all software design activities. However, before discussing some of these methods, it is appropriate to consider more general principles that lead to good encapsulation. Cohesion and coupling are two such metrics that describe the relationships between modules.

Cohesion is concerned with how well a module holds together – its internal strength. Allworth and Zobel (1987) give six measures of cohesion that range from the very poor to the strong:

- **coincidental** – elements of the module are not linked other than in a very superficial way, for example, written in the same month;
- **logical** – elements of the module are related in terms of the overall system, but not in terms of the actual software; for example all output device drivers;
- **temporal** – elements of the module are executed at similar times; for example, start-up routines;
- **procedural** – elements of the module are used together in the same section of the program; for example, user interface components;
- **communicational** (*sic*) – elements of the module work on the same data structure, for example, algorithms used to analyze an input signal;
- **functional** – elements of the module work together to contribute to the performance of a single system function; for example, the provision of a distributed file system.

Coupling, by comparison, is a measure of the interdependence of program modules. If two modules pass control information between them, they are said to possess high (or tight) coupling. Alternatively, the coupling is loose if only data is communicated. Another way of looking at coupling is to consider how easy it would be to remove a module (from a completed system) and replace it with an alternative one.

Within all design methods, a good decomposition is one that has strong cohesion and loose coupling. This principle is equally true in sequential and concurrent programming domains.

2.3.3   Formal approaches

The use of Place-Transition nets (Brauer, 1980) for modelling the behaviour of concurrent systems was proposed by C. A. Petri over thirty years ago. These nets are constructed as marked directed bipartite graphs from two types of node: S-elements, denoting local atomic states, and T-elements, denoting transitions. The arcs of the graph provide the relationship between the S and T elements. Markings on the graph represent tokens over the S-elements; the movement of a token represents a change in the state of the program. Rules are used to specify when and how a token may move from one S-element to another via a transition element. Petri nets are defined mathematically and are amenable to formal analysis.

Place-Transition nets have the useful characteristics of being simple, abstract and graphical, and provide a general framework for analyzing many kinds of concurrent and distributed systems. They have the disadvantage that they can produce very large and unwieldy representations. To allow for more concise modelling of such systems, Predicate-Transition nets have been introduced. With these nets, an S-element can model several normal S-elements (similarly T-elements) and the tokens, which originally had no internal structure, can be 'coloured' by tuples of data.

An alternative to Petri Nets is the use of Timed Automata and Model Checking. Here again, the concurrent system is represented by a collection of finite-state machines, and state exploration techniques are used to investigate the system's possible behaviours.

Petri Nets and Timed Automata represent one way of modelling concurrent systems. Other rigorous approaches require a formal description of the proposed implementation language. Having obtained these axioms, it is then possible to develop proof rules for analyzing the behaviour of concurrent systems. Unfortunately, few implementation languages are developed with a formal description in mind (occam being a notable exception). The Communicating Sequential Processes (CSP) notation was developed to enable concurrent systems to be specified and analyzed. In CSP, a process is described in terms of external *events*, that is, the communication it has with other processes. The history of a process is represented by a *trace*, which is a finite sequence of events.

A system represented in CSP can be analyzed to determine its behaviour. In particular, *safety* and *liveness* properties can be examined. Owicki and Lamport (1982) characterized these two concepts as:

- **safety** – 'something bad will not happen';
- **liveness** – 'something good will happen'.

Model checking techniques can also be used to verify safety and liveness properties.

Although real-time systems are concurrent, they also have timing requirements. Their analysis, therefore, needs an appropriate form of logic. Temporal logic is an extension to propositional and predicate calculi, with new operators being introduced in order to express properties relating to real time. Typical operators are: **always**, **sometime**, **until**, **since** and **leads-to**. For example, **sometime** (`<>`) means that the following property will hold true at some moment in the future – for instance, `<> (y > N)` implies that eventually `y` will take a value greater than `N`.

Many applications of temporal logic involve its use in verifying existing programs rather than in the hierarchical specification and rigorous development of new ones. It is possible to criticize the logic as being too global and non-modular, it usually being necessary to possess the complete program in order to analyze any part thereof. To overcome these difficulties, it is possible to extend the formalism so that the transitions themselves effectively become propositions in the logic. This approach has been advocated by Lamport (1983), and Barringer and Kuiper (1983) Further refinements to the temporal logic enable deadlines to be attached to these temporal operators. Thus, for example, not only will `y` become greater than `N`, but this will occur within bounded time. The formalism RTL (real-time logic) is a good example of a method that combines time with first-order predicate logic (Jahanian and Mok, 1986). The important issue of representing timing requirements and deadline scheduling is discussed again, in detail, in Chapters 12 and 13.

2.4   Design methods

It was noted earlier that most real-time practitioners advocate a process of object abstraction, and that formal techniques do exist that enable concurrent time-constrained systems to be specified and analyzed. Nevertheless, these techniques are not yet sufficiently mature to constitute 'tried and tested' design methods. Rather, the real-time industry uses, at best, structured methods and software engineering approaches that are applicable to all information processing systems. They do not give specific support to the real-time domain, and they lack the richness that is needed if the full power of implementation languages is to be exploited.

There are many structured design methods which are targeted toward real-time systems: MASCOT, JSD, Yourdon, MOON, OOD, RTSA, HOOD, DARTS, ADARTS, CODARTS, EPOS, MCSE, PAMELA, HRT-HOOD, Octopus etc. Gomaa (1994) suggests that there are four important objectives for a real-time design method. It should be capable of

(1) structuring a system in concurrent tasks

(2) supporting the development of reusable components through information hiding

(3) defining the behaviour aspects using finite-state machines

(4) analyzing the performance of a design to determine its real-time properties.

None of the above methods meets all these objectives. For example, RTSA is weak in task structuring and information hiding, and JSD does not support information hiding or finite state machines. Furthermore, few of the methods support directly the common hard real-time abstractions (such as periodic and sporadic activities) which are found in most hard real-time systems. Even fewer impose a computational model that will ensure that effective timing analysis of the final system can be undertaken. Consequently, their use is error-prone and can lead to systems whose real-time properties cannot be analyzed.

PAMELA (Process Abstraction Method for Embedded Large Application) (Cherry, 1986), HOOD V4 (Heitz, 1995), and HRT-HOOD (Burns and Wellings, 1994) are perhaps the three methods that fit the requirements best. PAMELA allows for the diagrammatic representation of cyclic activities, state machines and interrupt handlers. However, the notation is not supported by abstractions for resources, and therefore designs are not necessarily amenable to timing analysis. HRT-HOOD supports three of the four requirements; it is, however, lacking in its ability to define the behaviour aspects using finite-state machines. Also, being only object-based, its facilities for supporting reusable components is weak. HOOD V4 attempts to address the weaknesses of HOOD V3 and incorporate the strengths of HRT-HOOD. However, its support for reusable architectural design is weak and performance analysis of designs is not guaranteed.

EPOS (Lauber, 1989) is another method which supports the whole real-time system life cycle. It provides three specification languages: one for describing the customer requirements, one for describing the system specification, and one for describing project management, configuration management and quality assurance. Like HOOD and HRT-HOOD, the system specification has a graphical and a textual representation. Both periodic and sporadic activities can be represented (but they are not directly visible when manipulating the diagrams) and timing requirements can be specified. Furthermore, early recognition of the real-time behaviour of applications has been addressed within the context of EPOS (Lauber, 1989); however, this work relies on animating the system specification rather than timing analysis.

For a comparison of these methods, see Hull et al. (1991), Cooling (1991), Calvez (1993) and Gomaa (1994).

As outlined in the introduction, most traditional software development methods incorporate a life cycle model in which the following activities are recognized:

- requirements specification – during which an authoritative specification of the system's required functional and non-functional behaviour is produced;

- architectural design – during which a top-level description of the proposed system is developed;

- detailed design – during which the complete system design is specified;

- coding – during which the system is implemented;

- testing – during which the efficacy of the system is tested.

For hard real-time systems, this has the significant disadvantage that timing problems will only be recognized during testing, or worse, after deployment.

Typically a structured design method uses a diagram in which annotated arrows show the flow of data through the system and designated nodes represent points at which data is transformed (that is, processes). In the following sections, JSD and Mascot3 are briefly outlined; both of these techniques have been used extensively in the real-time domain. The Ada-specific method, HRT-HOOD, is then presented. This is a method which is specifically targeted at hard real-time systems. It will be used in Chapter 17. Finally, UML will be considered.

2.4.1   JSD

Jackson's system development method (Jackson, 1975) uses a precise notation for specification (top-level design) and implementation (detailed design). Interestingly, the implementation is not just a detailed re-statement of the specification, but is the result of applying transformations to the initial specification that are aimed at increasing efficiency.

A JSD graph consists of processes and a connection network. Processes are of three kinds:

- input processes that detect actions in the environment and pass them on to the system;
- output processes that pass system responses to the environment; and
- internal processes.

Processes can be linked in two distinct ways:

- by asynchronous data stream connections that are buffered; and
- by state vector connections (or inspections).

A state vector connection allows one process to see the internal state of another process without the need to communicate with it.

The JSD graph gives an architecture to the system. Yet to be added are the appropriate data structures for the information that is actually moving around the system, and the detail of the actions incorporated within each process. Unfortunately, JSD does not have a standard way of incorporating timing constraints and one must, therefore, add informal annotations to the diagrams.

Of course, what JSD provides is a facility for expressing a design – it does not do the design for you. Design inevitably incorporates human experience and creativity (as does programming). It is often said that structured and formal methods are aimed at stifling creativity; this is not true. What these techniques offer is a well-understood notation for expressing design, and techniques for checking that the creativity has been well placed, that is, that the design meets the specification, and the software implements the design.

The focus of design in JSD is the data flow. A 'good' design is, therefore, one that incorporates this natural flow. Earlier the factors that lead to good decomposition were discussed. These are precisely the issues that should influence a JSD design (and all other design methods). Processes themselves are categorized naturally into a few distinct types, and a top-down design approach that targets these types will result in a design that is easy to realize.

Another advantage of the dataflow focus is that timing constraints are often expressed as attributes of the data passing through the system. An interrupt generates a control signal; in essence, the control signal is a transformation of the interrupt. These transformations are undertaken within processes and they take time. An appropriate choice of processes will provide very visible deadlines that can be scheduled (although actual schedulability cannot be directly checked).

Having obtained the design, its implementation must be accomplished in a systematic manner. With a message-based concurrency model within the implementation language this is much easier, as design processes and buffered data flows can all be coded as program processes. Unfortunately, this can lead to a proliferation of processes and a very inefficient implementation. To counter this, two approaches are possible:

- transform the design so that fewer processes are necessary, or
- obtain the process-excessive program and transform it to reduce the number of concurrent objects.

Most languages are not amenable to transformation techniques. (Occam2 is again a notable exception, as its semantics are formally defined.) The approach advocated within the JSD method is a transformation known as **inversion**. In this, a design process is replaced by a procedure with a single scheduler process controlling the execution of a collection of these procedures; that is, rather than a pipeline of five processes, the scheduler would call five procedures each time a data item appeared (if the five processes were identical then obviously there would only be one procedure, which would be called five times). Time constraints do again cause a problem here, as they are difficult to preserve during inversion.

Although JSD was not originally used for real-time applications, it has been employed with success on some very large systems. From JSD, implementations in Ada or occam2 have been derived, with much of the code being generated automatically (Lawton and France, 1988).

2.4.2 Mascot3

Whereas JSD has only recently been used in the real-time domain, Mascot was developed specifically for the design, construction and execution of real-time software. Mascot1 appeared in the early 1970s but was quickly superseded by Mascot2 and in the 1980s by Mascot3.

Mascot3 is characterized by the use of graphical data flow networks and hierarchical design. Modularity is the key to this method, with identifiable modules being used for design, construction, implementation and testing. Importantly, a Mascot3 design can be expressed in an equivalent textual as well as graphical form.

In addition to the data flows, a Mascot3 description can contain:

- subsystems,
- general intercommunication data areas (IDAs),
- activities (processes),
- channels (an IDA which acts as a buffer),
- pools (an IDA which acts an information repository),
- servers (a design element that communicates with external hardware devices).

Necessary synchronizations on the use of channels and pools are given. Subsystems may contain collections of other elements, including further subsystems.

The implementation of a Mascot3 design can be achieved in two quite different ways. Either an appropriate concurrent programming language is used or a standard run-time executive. With Mascot2, the algorithmic coding was done in a sequential language such as Coral 66 or RTL2 (FORTRAN, Pascal, C and Algol 60 have also been used with Mascot2) and then this software was hosted on a Mascot run-time executive. The use of a concurrent language enables the complete system to be realized in the one language, thereby significantly easing integration.

Languages, such as Ada, that support decomposition and that have a message-based synchronization model (either predefined or programmable) clearly present a more favourable solution to the implementation activity. There is increasing support for using Ada with Mascot3, although their basic models of action are not completely compatible (Jackson, 1986). It should be noted, however, that the problem of process proliferation is also present with Mascot.

2.4.3 HRT-HOOD

HRT-HOOD (Burns and Wellings, 1995) is different from Mascot and JSD in that it directly addresses the concerns of hard real-time systems. It views the design process as a progression of increasingly specific *commitments* (Burns and Lister, 1991). These commitments define properties of the system design which designers operating at a more detailed level are not at liberty to change. Those aspects of a design to which no commitment is made at some particular level in the design hierarchy are effectively the subject of *obligations* that lower levels of design must address. Early in design there may already be commitments to the architectural structure of a system, in terms of object definitions and relationships. However, the detailed behaviour of the defined objects remains the subject of obligations which must be met during further design and implementation.

The process of refining a design – transforming obligations into commitments – is often subject to *constraints* imposed primarily by the execution environment. The execution environment is the set of hardware and software components (for example, processors, task dispatchers, device drivers) on top of which the system is built. It may impose both resource constraints (for example, processor speed, communication band-width) and constraints of mechanism (for example, interrupt priorities, task dispatch-ing, data locking). To the extent that the execution environment is immutable, these constraints are fixed.

Obligations, commitments and constraints have an important influence on the architectural design of any application. Therefore HRT-HOOD defines two activities of the architectural design:

- the logical architecture design activity;
- the physical architecture design activity.

The logical architecture embodies commitments which can be made independently of the constraints imposed by the execution environment, and is primarily aimed at satisfying the functional requirements (although the existence of timing requirements, such as end-to-end deadlines, will strongly influence the decomposition of the logical architecture). The physical architecture takes these functional requirements and other constraints into account, and embraces the non-functional requirements. The physical architecture forms the basis for asserting that the application's non-functional requirements will be met once the detailed design and implementation have taken place. It addresses timing and dependability requirements, and the necessary schedulability analysis that will ensure (guarantee) that the system, once built, will function correctly in both the value and time domains.

Although the physical architecture is a refinement of the logical architecture, its development will usually be an iterative and concurrent process in which both models are developed/modified. The analysis techniques embodied in the physical architecture can, and should, be applied as early as possible. Initial resource budgets can be defined that are then subject to modification and revision as the logical architecture is refined. In this way a 'feasible' design is tracked from requirements through to deployment.

More details on HRT-HOOD will be given in Chapter 17, where a case study is developed (in this design method) to illustrate a number of the issues covered in the intervening chapters.

2.4.4 The Unified Modeling Language (UML)

Over the last ten years there has been a plethora of object-oriented(OO) analysis and design methods developed (Graham (1994) puts the number at above 60!). Unfortunately, the industrial take up of these was hampered by the lack of a standardization process. In the real-time domain, the situation was exacerbated by the failure of the OO techniques to provide adequate support for hard real-time systems. This is in spite of an emerging theoretical underpinning for the analysis of real-time programs that is now capable of supporting most application requirements (see Chapter 13).

More recently there has been a significant effort by the Object Management Group to develop the Unified Modeling Language (UML) as the standard object-oriented notation. The UML is a graphical language for visualizing, specifying, constructing and documenting the artifacts in a software intensive system (Booch et al., 1999). It is clear that UML will become the dominant object-oriented analysis and design notation over the next ten years. Even other object-oriented methods, like Fusion (Coleman et al., 1994), are converting to the new notation.

The major features of UML suitable for modelling real-time embedded systems include (Douglass, 1999):

- an object model (incorporating data attributes, state, behaviour, identity and responsibility) allowing the structure of the system to be captured;

- use case scenarios – allowing key outputs to be identified from the system in response to user input;

- behavioral modelling – with finite-state machines (statecharts) facilitating the dynamic modelling of the system's behaviour;

- packaging – providing mechanisms to organize elements of the modelling into groups;

- representations for concurrency, communication and synchronization – for modelling real-world entities;

- models of physical topology – using deployment diagrams to show the devices and processors which comprise the system;

- support for object-oriented patterns and frameworks – allowing common solutions to common problems to be represented.

However, as the name implies, UML offers a language and not a method. Consequently, it is necessary to augment the notation with a design process. Douglass (1999) has proposed ROPES (Rapid Object-oriented Process for Embedded Systems) for use with UML. ROPES is based on an interactive life cycle oriented towards the rapid generation of prototypes. The activities are: analysis, design, implementation and testing. In common with other UML processes (Jacobson et al., 1999), ROPES is use-case driven. A set of use cases is identified and ordered according to priority, risk and commonality. These are then use to produce prototypes of the systems (where possible using automatic code generation facilities).

Current work on UML (Selic et al., 2000) is considering how to define standard paradigms for modelling real-time systems using a UML profile. Issues to be addressed include: how to model time and other resources, and how to to predict the performance of designs (using schedulability analysis).

2.5 Implementation

An important plateau between the top-level requirements specification and the executing machine code is the programming language. The development of implementation languages for real-time systems is the central theme of this book. Language design is still a very active research area. Although systems design should lead naturally into implementation, the expressive power of most modern languages is not matched by current design methodologies. Only by understanding what is possible at the implementation stage can appropriate design approaches be undertaken.

It is possible to identify three classes of programming languages which are, or have been, used in the development of real-time systems. These are assembly languages, sequential systems implementation languages and high-level concurrent languages.

2.5.1   Assembly

Initially, most real-time systems were programmed in the assembly language of the embedded computer. This was mainly because high-level programming languages were not well supported on most microcomputers and assembly language programming appeared to be the only way of achieving efficient implementations that could access hardware resources.

The main problem with the use of assembly languages is that they are machine-orientated rather than problem-orientated. The programmer can become encumbered with details which are unrelated to the algorithms being programmed, with the result that the algorithms themselves become obscure. This keeps development costs high and makes it very difficult to modify programs when errors are found or enhancements required.

Further difficulties arise because programs cannot be moved from one machine to another but must be rewritten. Also staff must be retrained if they are required to work with other machines.

2.5.2   Sequential systems implementation languages

As computers became more powerful, programming languages more mature, and compiler technology progressed, the advantages of writing real-time software in a high-level language outweighed the disadvantages. To cope with deficiencies in languages like FORTRAN, new languages were developed specifically for embedded programming. In the United States Air Force, for example, Jovial was in common use. In the UK, the Ministry of Defence standardized on Coral 66, and large industrial concerns like ICI standardized on RTL/2. More recently, the C and C++ programming languages have become popular.

All these languages have one thing in common – they are sequential. They also tend to be weak in the facilities they provide for real-time control and reliability. As a result of these shortcomings, it is often necessary to rely on operating system support and assembly code inserts.

2.5.3   High-level concurrent programming languages

In spite of the increasing use of application-tailored languages (such as sequential systems implementation languages for embedded computer applications, COBOL for data processing applications and FORTRAN for scientific and engineering applications), the production of computer software became progressively more difficult during the 1970s as computer-based systems became larger and more sophisticated.

It has been common to refer to these problems as the *software crisis*. There are several symptoms of this crisis which have been recognized (Booch, 1986):

- responsiveness – production systems which have been automated often do not meet users' needs;
- reliability – software is unreliable and will often fail to perform to its specification;
- cost – software costs are seldom predictable;
- modifiability – software maintenance is complex, costly and error prone;
- timeliness – software is often delivered late;
- transportability – software in one system is seldom used in another;
- efficiency – software development efforts do not make optimal use of the resources involved.

Perhaps one of the best illustrations of the impact of the software crisis can be found in the American Department of Defense's (DoD) search for a common high-order programming language for all its applications. As hardware prices began to fall during the 1970s, the DoD's attention was focused on the rising cost of its embedded software. It estimated that, in 1973, three thousand million dollars were spent on software alone. A survey of programming languages showed that at least 450 general-purpose programming languages and incompatible dialects were used in DoD embedded computer applications. An evaluation of existing languages occurred in 1976 against an emerging set of requirements. These evaluations resulted in four main conclusions (Whitaker, 1978):

(1) no current language was suitable,
(2) a single language was a desirable goal,
(3) the state-of-the-art of language design could meet the requirements,
(4) development should start from a suitable language base; those recommended were Pascal, PL/I and Algol 68.

The result was the birth of a new language in 1983 called Ada. In 1995, the language was updated to reflect 10 years of use and modern advances in programming language design.

Although the Ada programming language effort has dominated research in embedded computer programming languages since the early 1970s, other languages have emerged. For example, Modula-1 (Wirth, 1977b), was developed by Wirth for use in programming machine devices and was intended to

conquer that stronghold of assembly coding, or at least to attack it vigorously.

Perhaps the language that has been most successful in this area is C (Kernighan and Ritchie, 1978). Indeed, this language is arguably the most popular programming language in the world today.

Much of the experience gained from the implementation and use of Modula was fed into Modula-2 (Wirth, 1983), a more general-purpose systems implementation language. The C language has spawned many language variants; the most important being C++, which directly supports object-oriented programming. Other new languages of note include PEARL, used extensively in Germany for process control applications, Mesa (Xerox Corporation, 1985), used by Xerox in their office automation equipment, and CHILL (CCITT, 1980) which was developed in response to CCITT requirements for programming telecommunication applications. There is even a real-time version of Basic which, although lacking in many features normally associated with a high-level language (such as user-defined types), does provide concurrent programming facilities and other real-time related features.

With the advent of the Internet, the Java programming language has become popular. Although initially not suitable for real-time programming, recently much effort has been dedicated to producing real-time versions of Java (US National Institute of Standards and Technology, 1999; Bollella et al., 2000; J Consortium, 2000).

Modula, Modula-2, PEARL, Mesa, CHILL, Java and Ada are all high-level concurrent programming languages which include features aimed at aiding the development of embedded computer systems. The occam language, by comparison is a much smaller language. It provides no real support for programming large and complex systems, although the usual control structures are present and non-recursive procedures are provided. The development of occam has been closely associated with that of the *transputer* (May and Shepherd, 1984) (a processor with on-chip memory and link controllers that allow multi-transputer systems to be built easily). Occam had an important role in the emerging field of loosely coupled distributed embedded applications. However, in recent years it has faded in popularity.

2.5.4   General language design criteria

Although a real-time language may be designed primarily to meet the requirements of embedded computer system programming, its use is rarely limited to that area. Most real-time languages are also used as general-purpose systems implementation languages for applications such as compilers and operating systems.

Young (1982) lists the following six (sometimes conflicting) criteria as the basis of a real-time language design: security, readability, flexibility, simplicity, portability and efficiency. A similar list also appears in the original requirements for Ada.

Security

The security of a language design is a measure of the extent to which programming errors can be detected automatically by the compiler or language run-time support system. There is obviously a limit to the type and number of errors that can be detected by a language system; for example, errors in the programmer's logic cannot be detected automatically. A secure language must, therefore, be well structured and readable so that such errors can easily be spotted.

The benefits of security include:

- the detection of errors much earlier in the development of a program – generating an overall reduction in cost;
- compile-time checks have no overheads at run-time – a program is executed much more often than it is compiled.

The disadvantage of security is that it may result in a more complicated language with an increase in compilation time and compiler complexity.

Readability

The readability of a language depends on a variety of factors including the appropriate choice of keywords, the ability to define types and the facilities for program modularization. As Young points out:

> the aim is to provide a language notation with sufficient clarity to enable the main concepts of a particular program's operation to be assimilated easily by reading the program's text only, without resort to subsidiary flowcharts and written descriptions. (Young, 1982)

The benefits of good readability include:

- reduced documentation costs,
- increased security,
- increased maintainability.

The main disadvantage is that it usually increases the length of any given program.

Flexibility

A language must be sufficiently flexible to allow the programmer to express all the required operations in a straightforward and coherent fashion. Otherwise, as with older sequential languages, the programmer will often have to resort to operating system commands or machine code inserts to achieve the desired result.

Simplicity

Simplicity is a worthwhile aim of any design, be it of the proposed international space station or a simple calculator. In programming languages, simplicity has the advantages of:

- minimizing the effort required to produce compilers,
- reducing the cost associated with programmer training,
- diminishing the possibility of making programming errors as a result of misinterpretation of the language features.

Flexibility and simplicity can also be related to the **expressive power** (the ability to express the solutions to a wide range of problems) and **usability** (ease of use) of the language.

Portability

A program, to a certain extent, should be independent of the hardware on which it executes. One of the main claims of Java is that programs are compiled once and run anywhere. For a real-time system, this is difficult to achieve (even with the advent of portable binary codes (Venners, 1999; X/Open Company Ltd., 1996)), as a substantial part of any program will normally involve manipulation of hardware resources. However, a language must be capable of isolating the machine-dependent part of a program from the machine *independent* part.

Efficiency

In a real-time system, response times must be guaranteed; therefore the language must allow efficient and predictable programs to be produced. Mechanisms which lead to unpredictable run-time overheads should be avoided. Obviously, efficiency requirements must be balanced against security, flexibility and readability requirements.

2.6 Testing

With the high reliability requirements that are the essence of most real-time systems, it is clear that testing must be extremely stringent. A comprehensive strategy for testing involves many techniques, most of which are applicable to all software products. It is, therefore, assumed that the reader is familiar with these techniques.

The difficulty with real-time concurrent programs is that the most intractable system errors are usually the result of subtle interactions between processes. Often the errors are also time dependent and will only manifest themselves in rare states. Murphy's Law dictates that these rare states are also crucially important and only occur when the controlled system is, in some sense, critical. It should, perhaps, be emphasized here that appropriate formal design methods do not detract from the need for testing. They are complementary strategies.

Testing is, of course, not restricted to the final assembled system. The decomposition incorporated in the design and manifest within program modules (including processes) forms a natural architecture for component testing. Of particular importance (and difficulty) within real-time systems is that not only must correct behaviour in a correct environment be tested, but dependable behaviour in an arbitrarily incorrect environment must be catered for. All error recovery paths must be exercised and the effects of simultaneous errors investigated.

To assist in any complex testing activity, a realistic test bed presents many attractions. For software, such a test environment is called a simulator.

2.6.1   Simulators

A simulator is a program which imitates the actions of the engineering system in which the real-time software is embedded. It simulates the generation of interrupts and performs other I/O actions in real-time. Using a simulator, abnormal as well as 'normal' system behaviour can be created. Even when the final system has been completed, certain error states may only be safely experimented with via a simulator. The meltdown of a nuclear reactor is an obvious example.

Simulators are able to reproduce accurately the sequence of events expected in the real system. In addition, they can repeat experiments in a way that is usually impossible in a live operation. However, to faithfully recreate simultaneous actions it may be necessary to have a multiprocessor simulator. Moreover, it should be noted that with very complicated applications it may not be possible to build an appropriate simulator.

Although simulators do not have high reliability requirements, they are in all other ways real-time systems in their own right. They themselves must be thoroughly tested, although occasional errors can be tolerated. One technique that is often used in real-time systems that do not have reliability requirements (another example here is flight simulators) is to remove mutual exclusion protection from shared resources. This provides greater efficiency at the cost of intermittent failure. The construction of a simulator is also eased by the process model of the embedded system itself. Chapter 15 shows how external devices can be considered hardware processes with interrupts being mapped onto the available synchronization primitive. If this model has been followed then the replacement of a hardware process by a software one is relatively straightforward.

Notwithstanding these points, simulators are non-trivial and expensive systems to develop. They may even require special hardware. In the NASA Space Shuttle project, the simulators cost more than the real-time software itself. This money turned out to be well spent, with many system errors being found during hours of simulator 'flight'.

2.7   Prototyping

The standard 'waterfall' approach to software development, that is, requirements, specification, design, implementation, integration, testing and then delivery has the fundamental problem that faults within the initial requirements or specification phases are only recognized upon delivery of the product (or at best, during testing). To correct these faults at this late stage is time-consuming and very costly. Prototyping is an attempt to catch these faults earlier by presenting the customer with a 'mock-up' of the system.

The main purpose of a prototype is to help ensure that what the customer actually wanted has been captured in the requirements specification. This has two aspects:

- Is the requirements specification correct (in terms of what the customer desires)?

- Is the requirements specification complete (has the customer included everything)?

One of the benefits of running a prototype is that the customer can experience situations that were previously only vaguely understood. It is almost inevitable that changes to the requirements will be made during this activity. In particular, new error conditions and recovery paths may emerge.

Where specification techniques are not formal, prototyping can be used to build confidence that the overall design is consistent. Thus, with a large data flow diagram, a prototype may help to check that all the required connections are in place and that all pieces of data flowing through the system do actually visit the activities required.

To be cost effective, it must be possible to build the prototype more cheaply (much more cheaply) than the actual implementation software. It is, therefore, pointless to use the same design methods to the same standards as the final system. Significantly lower costs can be accomplished by using higher level languages. The language APL (Iverson, 1962) has been popular for prototyping; also functional and logic programming languages have been used. They have the advantage that they do in fact capture the important functional behaviour of the system without requiring the detailed non-functional aspects. More recently, design tools have integrated code generation facilities. However, these typically do not produce code of sufficient quality for the actual implementation, but can be used for prototyping. The clear drawback with such prototypes is that they do not exercise the real-time aspects of the application. To do this, requires a simulation of the system.

It was noted earlier that proving that a program will meet all time constraints under all operating conditions is very difficult. One method of examining a design to see if it is feasible is to try to simulate the behaviour of the software. By making assumptions about code structures and processor execution speed, it is possible to build a model that will emulate run-time characteristics. For example, it will show the maximum rate of interrupts that can be handled while still meeting time constraints.

The emulation of a large real-time system is expensive; its development is costly and each emulator run may take up considerable computing resources. Normally many hundreds of such runs are needed. Nevertheless, this cost must be balanced with the economic and social consequences of creating a faulty real-time system.

2.8   Human–computer interaction

If one takes a wide enough context, all real-time systems incorporate or affect humans. Most, in fact, involve direct communication between the executing software and one or more human operators. As human behaviour introduces the greatest source of variation in a running system, it follows that the design of the HCI (Human–Computer Interaction) component is one of the most critical in the entire structure. There are many examples of poor HCI design and the sometimes tragic consequences that follow from this weakness. For example, in the nuclear incident known as Three Mile Island, a number of the failures were put down to the operators being unable to cope with the sheer volume of information being displayed during a series of critical events (Kemeny et al., 1979).

The search for design principles on which to base HCI component construction is currently a very active one. Having spent too many years as a backwater, HCI is now appreciated to be central to the production of well-engineered software (all software). The first important issue is that of modularity; HCI activities should be isolated, and well-defined interfaces specified. These interfaces are themselves constructed in two parts, the functionality of each being quite different. Firstly it is important to define those objects that pass between the operator and the software. Secondly (and distinctly) it is necessary to specify how these objects are to be presented to, and extracted from, the user. A rigorous definition of the first kind of interface component must include predicates about the allowable action that an operator can take in any given state of the system. For example, certain commands may need authority, or can only sensibly, or safely, be carried out when the system is so disposed. To give an illustration here, a fly-by-wire plane would ignore a command that would lead to the plane moving outside its safe flight envelope.

A particularly important design question in all interactive systems is: who is in control? At one extreme, the human could explicitly direct the computer to perform particular functions, while at the other extreme the computer would be in full control (although it might occasionally ask the operator for information). Clearly, most real-time systems will incorporate a mixture of these extremes; they are known as **mixed initiative** systems. Sometimes the user is in control (for example, when giving a new command) and at other times the system is controlling the dialogue (for example, when extracting data necessary to perform a command that has been given).

The chief motivation for the design of the interface component is to capture all user-derived errors in the interface control software, not the application software or the rest of the real-time system. If this can be done then this application software can assume a **perfect user** and its design and implementation are simplified as a result (Burns, 1983). The term **error** in this discussion means an unintentional action. This is referred to as a **slip** by Reason (1979). He uses the term **mistake** to imply a deliberate error action. Although an interface may be able to block mistakes that would lead to hazards, it is not possible to recognize a 'sensible' change to an operating parameter as a mistake. Appropriate operator training and supervision are the only ways of eliminating these mistakes.

Although slips will inevitably occur (and therefore must be protected against), their frequency can be significantly reduced if the second component of the interface, the actual operator input/output module, is well defined. Within this context, however, the term 'well defined' is itself difficult to define. The specification of an I/O module is essentially in the domain of the psychologist. One must start with a model of the end-user or operator. Unfortunately, many different models exist; a useful review is given by Rouse (1981). From an understanding of these models, principles of design can be established, three important ones being:

(1) predictability – sufficient data should be supplied to the user so that the effect of a command is unambiguously derived from a knowledge of that command.

(2) commutativity – the order in which the user places parameters to a command should not affect the meaning of a command.

(3) sensitivity – if the system is subject to different modes of operation then the current mode should always be displayed.

The first two principles are reported by Dix et al. (1987). Real-time systems have the added difficulty that the human operators are not the only actors that are changing the state of the system. A mode change may be caused by an interrupt and the asynchronous nature of operator input could lead to a command that was valid when the operator initiated it being unavailable in a new mode.

Much of the work on HCI has been concerned with the design of screens so that the data presented is unambiguous and data entry can be accommodated with the minimum number of keystrokes. There are, however, other factors concerned with the ergonomics of the workstation and the wider issues of the working environment for the operators. Screen designs can be 'tested' with a prototype, but job satisfaction is a metric that can only be measured over much longer time intervals than are available for experimentation with a prototype. Operators may work an eight hour shift, five days a week, for year after year. If one adds stress to the work (as in air traffic control) then job satisfaction and performance become critically dependent upon

- the multitude of interdependent tasks that must be performed,
- the level of control the operator has,
- the degree to which the operator understands the operation of the complete system,
- the number of constructive tasks the operator is allowed to perform.

Understanding can be improved by always presenting the operator with a picture of 'what is happening'. Indeed, some process control systems can be made to illustrate the behaviour of the system in graphical, pictorial or spreadsheet form. The operator can experiment with the data to model ways in which performance can be improved. It is quite possible to incorporate such **decision support systems** into the control loop so that the operator can see the effect of minor changes to operation parameters. In this way, productivity can be increased and the working environment for the operators enhanced. It may also reduce the number of mistakes made!

2.9 Managing design

This chapter has attempted to give an overview of the important issues associated with the design of real-time software. A reliable and correct product will only result if the activities of specification, design, implementation and testing are carried out to a high quality throughout. There is now a wide range of techniques that can help achieve this quality. The appropriate use of a well-defined high-level language is the primary issue in this book. Programming and design both need to be managed in order to achieve the desired result. Modern concurrent programming languages have an important role in this management process.

The key to achieving quality lies in adequate verification and validation. At all stages of design and implementation there need to be well-defined procedures for ensuring that necessary techniques and actions have been carried out correctly. Where high assurance is needed, theorem provers and model checkers can be used to verify formally specified components. Many other structured activities, for example, hazard analysis, software fault-tree analysis, failure modes and effects analysis, and code inspections, are used more widely. Increasingly, there is a need for software tools to assist in verification and validation. Such tools perform an important role and their use may alleviate the need for human inspection. They themselves must, therefore, be of an extremely high quality.

Support tools are, however, not a substitute for well-trained and experienced staff. The application of rigorous software engineering techniques and the use of the language features that are described in this book do make a difference to the quality and cost of real-time systems. Practitioners have a responsibility to society at large to understand and apply whatever knowledge is necessary in order to ensure that embedded systems are safe. Many deaths have already been attributed to software errors. It is possible to stop a future epidemic, but only if the industry moves away from *ad hoc* procedures, informal methods and inadequate low-level languages.

Summary

This chapter has outlined the major stages involved in the design and implementation of real-time systems. These include, in general, requirements specification, systems design, detailed design, coding and testing. The high reliability requirements of real-time systems dictate that, wherever possible, rigorous methods should be employed.

To manage the development of complex real-time systems requires the appropriate application of decomposition, encapsulation and abstraction. A hierarchical design method, therefore, isolates subcomponents, or modules, that are either object-based or process-based. Both forms of module should exhibit strong cohesion and loose coupling.

Implementation, which is the primary focus of attention in this book, necessitates the use of a programming language. Early real-time languages lacked the expressive power to deal adequately with this application domain. More recent languages have attempted to incorporate concurrency and error-handling facilities. A discussion of these features is contained in subsequent chapters. The following general criteria were considered a useful basis for a real-time language design:

- security,
- readability,
- flexibility,
- simplicity,
- portability,
- efficiency.

Irrespective of the rigour of the design process, adequate testing is clearly needed. To aid this activity, prototype implementations, simulators and emulators all have an important role.

Finally in the chapter, attention was focused on the important human–computer interface. For too long, this subject has been viewed as containing little science, with the systematic application of engineering principles being conspicuous by its absence. This position is now changing, with a realization that the interface is a significant source of potential errors, and that these can be reduced in number by the application of current research and development activities.

In many ways, this chapter has been a divergent one. It has introduced more problem areas and engineering issues than can possibly be tackled in just one book. This broad sweep across the 'design process' has aimed at setting the rest of the book in context. By now focusing on language issues and programming activities, the reader will be able to understand the 'end product' of design, and judge to what extent current methodologies, techniques and tools are appropriate.

Further reading

Booch G., Rumbaugh J. and Jacobson I. (1999) *The Unified Modeling Language User Guide*. Harlow: Addison-Wesley.

Burns A. and Wellings A. J. (1995) *Hard Real-Time HOOD: A Structured Design Method for Hard Real-time Ada Systems*. New York: Elsevier.

Cooling J. E. (1995) *Software Design for Real-Time Systems*. London: International Thompson Computer Press.

Dix A. (1991) *Formal Methods for Interactive Systems*. New York: Academic Press.

Douglass B. P. (1999), *Doing Hard Time: Developing Real-Time Systems with UML, Objects, Frameworks and Patterns*. Harlow: Addison-Wesley.

Gomaa H. (1993) *Software Design Methods for Concurrent and Real-Time Systems*. Reading, MA: Addison-Wesley.

Jacobson I., Booch G. and Rumbaugh J. (1999) The Unified Software Development Process. Harlow: Addison Wesley Longman.

Jones C. B. (1990) *Systematic Software Development Using VDM*. New York: Prentice Hall.

Joseph M. (ed) (1996) *Real-Time Systems: Specification, Verification and Analysis*. London: Prentice Hall, 1996.

Levi S. T. and Agrawala A. K. (1990) *Real-Time Systems Design*. New York: McGraw-Hill.

Robinson P. (1992) *Hierarchical Object Oriented Design* New York: Prentice Hall.

Rosen J.-P. (1997) *HOOD: An Industrial Approach to Software Design*. HOOD Technical Group.

Schneider, S. (1999) *Concurrent and Real-time Systems: The CSP Approach*. New York: Wiley.

Woodcock J. (1994) *Using Standard Z*. Hemel Hempstead: Prentice Hall.

Exercises

2.1   To what extent should the choice of design method be influenced by:

(a) likely implementation language
(b) support tools
(c) reliability requirements of the application
(d) training requirements of staff
(e) marketing considerations
(f) previous experiences
(g) cost

2.2   In addition to the criteria given in this chapter, what other factors could be used in assessing programming languages?

2.3   At what stage in the design process should the views of the end-user be obtained?

2.4   Should software engineers be liable for the consequences of faulty real-time systems?

2.5   New medicines cannot be introduced until appropriate tests and trials have been carried out. Should real-time systems be subject to similar legislation? If a proposed application is too complicated to simulate, should it be constructed?

2.6   Should the Ada language be the only language used in the implementation of embedded real-time systems?

2.7   To what extent does UML allow hard real-time systems to be designed and analyzed?

2.8   Is UML a structured or a formal design notation?

Chapter 3
Programming in the small

In considering the features of high-level languages, it is useful to distinguish between those that aid the decomposition process and those that facilitate the programming of well-defined components. These two sets of features have been described as:

- support for programming in the large,
- support for programming in the small.

Programming in the small is a well-understood activity and will be discussed in this chapter within the context of an overview of the languages Ada 95 (called Ada throughout this book), Java 1.2 (called Java henceforth), ANSI C and occam2. Chapter 4 is concerned with programming in the large and will address the more problematic issue of managing complex systems.

3.1   Overview of Ada, Java, C and occam2

In a book on real-time systems and their programming languages, it is not possible to give a detailed description of all of the languages used in this computing domain. It has, therefore, been decided to limit detailed consideration to just four high-level programming languages. Ada is important because of its increasing use in safety-critical systems; Java has become the *de facto* standard language for programming Internet-based applications. C (and its derivative C++) is, perhaps, the most popular programming language in use today, and occam2 is the nearest a general-purpose language has got to embodying the formalisms of CSP. Occam2 is also specifically designed for multicomputer execution, which is of increasing application and importance in the real-time domain. Specific features of other languages will, however, be considered when appropriate.

The overview presented here will itself assume knowledge of a Pascal-like language. Sufficient detail on each language will be given to understand the example programs given later in the book. For a comprehensive description of each language, the reader must refer to the further reading section for books that specialize on each language.

3.2   Lexical conventions

Programs are written once but read many times; it follows that the lexical style of the language syntax should appeal to the reader rather than the writer. One simple aid to readability is to use names that are meaningful. Languages should not, therefore, restrict the lengths of identifiers; neither Ada, Java, C nor occam2 does so. The form of a name can also be improved by the use of a separator. Ada, Java and C allow a '_' to be included in identifiers; occam2 names can include a '.' (this is a somewhat unfortunate choice, as '.' is often used in languages to indicate a subcomponent, for example a field of a record). If a language does not support a separator, the technique of mixing upper- and lower-case characters is recommended. Although Java does allow a '_', the emerging style is to use a mixture of upper- and lower-case characters. The following are example identifiers.

```
Example_Name_In_Ada
exampleNameInJava
example_name_in_C
example.name.in.occam2
```

A classic illustration of poor lexical convention is provided by FORTRAN. This language allows the space character to be a separator. As a consequence, a simple typing error in a program (a '.' instead of a ',') reputedly resulted in an American Viking Venus probe being lost! Rather than the intended line:

```
DO 20 I = 1,100
```

which is a loop construct (loop to label 20 with I iterating from 1 to 100), an assignment was compiled (the assignment operator is '='):

```
DO 20 I = 1.100
```

or as spaces can be ignored in names:

```
DO20I = 1.100
```

Variables in FORTRAN need not be defined; identifiers beginning with 'D' are assumed to be reals, and 1.100 is a real literal!

Not surprisingly, all modern languages require variables to be explicitly defined.

3.3   Overall style

All four languages reviewed here are, to a greater or lesser extent, block structured. A block in Ada consists of

(1) the declaration of objects that are local to that block (if there are no such objects then this declaration part may be omitted),

(2) a sequence of statements, and

(3) a collection of exception handlers (again this part may be omitted if empty).

A schema for such a block is:

```
declare
  <declarative part>
begin
  <sequence of statements>
exception
  <exception handlers>
end;
```

Exception handlers catch errors that have occurred in the block. They are considered in detail in Chapter 6.

An Ada block may be placed in the program wherever an ordinary statement may be written. They can thus be used hierarchically and support decomposition within a program unit. The following simple example illustrates how a new integer variable Temp is introduced to swap the values contained by the two integers A and B. Note that a comment in Ada starts with the double hyphen and goes on to the end of that line.

```
declare
  Temp: Integer:= A; -- initial value given to
                     -- temporary variable
begin
  A:= B;             -- := is the assignment operator
  B:= Temp;
end;                 -- no exception part
```

In C and Java, a block (or compound statement) is delimited by a { and a }, and has the following structure

```
{
  < declarative part >

  < sequence of statements >
}
```

As with Ada, Java can have exception handlers at the end of a block if the block is labelled as a 'try' block (see Chapter 6). Each statement can itself be a compound statement. The swap code would be as follows:

```
{
    int temp = A; /* declaration and initialization */
    /* Note in C and Java (and occam2) the type name appears first */
    /* whereas in Ada, it appears after the variable name. */

    A = B;
    B = temp;
}
```

Note that the assignment operator in C and Java is '=' and that comments are delimited by '/*' and '*/'. Java also allows '//' for comments ending a line. Throughout the book, '//' will be used for Java comments so that they can be easily distinguished from C.

Before considering the occam2 equivalent of this program, some introductory remarks about this language must be made. Ada and Java are languages in which concurrent programs can be written. C is a sequential language which can be used with an operating system to create concurrent processes. In contrast, all programs in occam2 are concurrent. What would be a sequence of statements in Ada, Java or C is a sequence of processes in occam2. This distinction is a fundamental one in comparing the nature of the concurrency models in the four languages (see Chapters 7, 8 and 9), but it does not impinge upon the understanding of the primitive elements of the language.

Occam2, like Ada, is a fully block structured language. Any process can be preceded by the declaration of objects to be used in that process. To swap the two integers (INTs in occam2) requires a SEQ construct that specifies that the assignments that follow it must be executed in sequence:

```
INT temp: -- A declaration is terminated by a colon.
SEQ
    temp := A
    A := B
    B := temp
```

It is interesting to note the different ways in which the four languages separate actions. Unlike Pascal, Ada uses a semicolon as a statement terminator (hence there is one at the end of B := Temp;). C and Java also employ the semicolon as a statement terminator (but there is no semicolon after a compound statement, although Java will tolerate this). Occam2 does not use the semicolon at all! It requires each action (process) to be on a separate line. Moreover, the use of indentation, which merely (though importantly) improves readability in Ada, Java and C, is syntactically significant in occam2. The three assignments in the above code fragment have to start in the column under the Q of SEQ.

3.4 Data types

In common with all high-level languages, Ada, Java, C and occam2 require programs to manipulate objects that have been abstracted away from their actual hardware implementation. Programmers need not concern themselves about the representation or location of the entities that their programs manipulate. Moreover, by partitioning these entities into distinct types, the compiler can check for inconsistent usage, and thereby increase the security associated with using the languages.

Ada allows the declaration of constants, types, variables, subprograms (procedures and functions) and packages. Subprograms are considered later in this chapter and packages are described in the Chapter 4. The use of constants, types and variables is similar to that of Pascal, except that they may occur in any order, provided that an object is declared before it is referenced. Similarly, C and Java allow constants, types, variables and functions to be defined. Java also allows classes and packages to be defined – see also Chapter 4. By comparison with these languages, occam2's type model is more restrictive; in particular user-defined types are not allowed.

3.4.1 Discrete types

Table 3.1 lists the predefined discrete types supported in the four languages.

All the usual operators for these types are available. Note that Java's `char` type supports Unicode and, therefore, is equivalent to Ada's `Wide_Character` or C's `wchar_t`.

Ada, Java and occam2 are strongly typed (that is, assignments and expressions must involve objects of the same type), but explicit type conversions are supported. The C language is not so type secure; for example, an integer type can be assigned to a short without explicit type conversion. Java allows conversion only when no information is lost; for example integer to long, but not the other way around.

Both Ada and C also allow the basic integer types to be signed or unsigned. The default is signed, but unsigned (or modular) types can be created. Although not required by the language, an Ada implementation may support `Short_Integer` and `Long_Integer`.

In addition to these predefined types, Ada and C allow for the definition of enumeration types. Neither occam2 nor Java provides this facility, although proposals have been made to add it to the Java language (Cairns, 1999). In C, the enumerated constants must be uniquely determined and are really little more than integer constant definitions;

Ada	Java	C	Occam2
Integer	int	int	INT
	short	short	INT16
	long	long	INT32
			INT64
	byte		BYTE
Boolean	boolean		BOOL
Character		char	
Wide_Character	char	wchar_t	

Table 3.1   Discrete types.

however, the Ada model, by allowing names to be overloaded, is not so restrictive. Both languages provide means for manipulating objects of these enumeration types; C by the standard integer operations, Ada by the use of attributes. (Attributes are used throughout Ada to give information about types and objects.) The following examples illustrate these points.

```
/* C */
{
  typedef enum {xplane, yplane, zplane} dimension;
  /* typedef introduces a new name for a new type,   */
  /* enum indicates that it is an enumeration type; */
  /* dimension is the type's new name               */

  dimension line, force;
  line = xplane;
  force = line + 1;
  /* force now has the value yplane because the compiler */
  /* generates internal integer literals for xplane = 0, */
  /* yplane = 1, zplane = 2                               */
}
```

```
-- Ada
type Dimension is (Xplane,Yplane,Zplane);
type Map is (Xplane,Yplane);
Line,Force : Dimension;
Grid : Map;
begin
  Line := Xplane;
  Force := Dimension'Succ(Xplane);
  -- Force now has the value Yplane irrespective of the
  -- implementation technique

  Grid := Yplane; -- the name 'Yplane' is unambiguous as
                  -- Grid is of type 'map'
  Grid := Line; -- illegal - type clash
end;
```

Another facility that Ada supports is the use of subranges or subtypes to restrict the values of an object (of a particular base type). This allows for a closer association between objects in the program and the values, in the application domain, that could sensibly be taken by that object.

```
-- Ada
subtype Surface is Dimension range Xplane .. Yplane;
```

Note that Ada has predefined subtypes for positive and natural integers.

Importantly in Ada and C, all types can be duplicated by defining a type to be a new version of a previous type:

```
-- in Ada
type New_Int is new Integer;
type Projection is new Dimension range Xplane .. Yplane;
```

```
/* in C */
typedef int newint;
typedef dimension projection;
```

Whereas in Ada objects of a type and its subtypes can be mixed (in expressions), objects of a type and a derived type cannot. The two types are distinct:

```
-- Ada
D : Dimension;
S : Surface;
P : Projection;
begin
  D := S;   -- legal
  S := D;   -- legal but could cause run-time error if
            -- D has the value "Zplane"
  P := D;   -- illegal - type clash
  P := Projection(D);  -- legal, explicit type conversion
end;
```

This provision (and its use) significantly increases the security of Ada programs. In C, `typedef` does not provide this level of security.

In Java, new types are created using the object-oriented programming facilities, which are discussed in Section 4.4.

3.4.2   Real numbers

Many real-time applications (for example, signal processing, simulation and process control) require numerical computation facilities beyond those provided by integer arithmetic. There is a general need to be able to manipulate *real* numbers, although the sophistication of the arithmetic required varies widely between applications. In essence, there are two distinct ways of representing real values within a high-level language:

(1) floating-point, and

(2) scaled integer.

Floating-point numbers are a finite approximation to real numbers and are applicable to computations in which exact results are not needed. A floating-point number is represented by three values: a mantissa, M, an exponent, E, and a radix, R. It has a value of the form $M \times R^E$. The radix is (implicitly) implementation-defined and usually has the value 2. As the mantissa is limited in length, the representation has limited precision. The divergence between a floating-point number and its corresponding 'real' value is related to the size of the number (it is said to have **relative error**).

The use of scaled integers is intended for exact numeric computation. A scaled integer is a product of an integer and a scale. With the appropriate choice of scale, any value can be catered for. Scaled integers offer an alternative to floating-point numbers when non-integer calculations are required. The scale, however, must be known at compile time; if the scale of a value is not available until execution, a floating-point representation must be used. Although scaled integers provide exact values, not all numbers in the mathematical domain can be represented exactly. For example, 1/3 cannot be viewed as a finite scaled decimal integer. The difference between a scaled integer and its 'real' value is its **absolute error**.

Scaled integers have the advantage (over floating-point) of dealing with exact numerical values and of making use of integer arithmetic. Floating-point operations require either special hardware (a floating-point unit) or complex software that will result in numerical operations being many times slower than the integer equivalent. Scaled integers are, however, more difficult to use, especially if expressions need to be evaluated that contain values with different scales.

Traditionally, languages have supported a single floating-point type (usually known as **real**) which has an implementation-dependent precision. Use of scaled integers has normally been left to the user (that is, the programmer had to implement scaled integer arithmetic using the system-defined integer type).

Ada and C use the term `float` for an implementation-dependent 'real' type. There is, however, no equivalent in occam2; here the number of bits must be specified. The designers of occam2 took the view that the need for an abstract `real` type is not as great as the need for the programmer to be aware of the precision of the operations being carried out. The occam2 'reals' are REAL16, REAL32 and REAL64. C supports double and long double types for extra precision. Java provides `float` and `double` which support the 32 and 64 bit IEEE 754 floating-point values respectively. Note that Java floating-point literals are automatically considered to be of double precision. Consequently, they must either be explicitly converted to **float** or they can be followed by the letter `f`. For example,

```
float bodyTemperature = (float) 98.6;
// or
float bodyTemperature = 98.6f;
```

In addition to the predefined Float type, Ada provides the facilities for users to create both floating-point numbers with different precision and fixed point numbers. Fixed point numbers are implemented as scaled integers. The following are some examples of type definitions. To define a floating-point type requires a lower and upper bound, and a statement of the necessary precision (in decimal):

```
type New_Float is digits 10 range -1.0E18..1.0E18
```

A subtype of this type can restrict the range or the precision:

```
subtype Crude_Float is New_Float digits 2;
subtype Pos_New_Float is New_Float range 0.0..1000.0;
```

The statement of precision defines the minimum requirement, an implementation may give greater accuracy. If the minimum requirement cannot be accommodated, a compile-time error message is generated.

Ada's fixed point numbers remove from the programmer the details of implementing the necessary scaled integer operators; these are predefined. To construct a fixed point type requires range information and an absolute error bound called **delta**. For example, the following type definition gives a delta of 0.05 or 1/20:

```
type Scaled_Int is delta 0.05 range -100.00..100.00
```

To represent all these decimal values (−100.00, −99.95, −99.90 ... 99.95, 100.00) requires a specific number of bits. This can easily be calculated. The nearest (but smaller) power of 2 to 1/20 is 1/32, which is 2^{-5}. Thus 5 bits are needed to provide the fraction part. The range −100.00..100.00 is contained within −128..128 which requires 8 bits (including a sign bit). In total, therefore, 13 bits are required:

```
sbbbbbbb.fffff
```

where s is the sign bit, b denotes an integer bit and f denotes a fractional bit. Clearly, this fixed-point type can easily be implemented on a 16 bit architecture.

Note again that although a fixed-point type represents, exactly, a range of binary fractions, not all decimal constants within the correct range will have an exact representation. For instance, decimal 5.1 will be held as 00000101.00011 (binary) or 5.09375 (decimal) in the fixed-point type defined above.

3.4.3 Structured data types

The provision for structured data types within our four languages can be stated quite easily. Occam2 and Java support arrays; Ada and C support arrays and records. Arrays first and by example:

```
-- occam2
INT Max IS 10:    -- definition of a constant in occam2
[Max]REAL32 Reading:    -- Reading is an array with ten
                        -- elements Reading[0] .. Reading[9]
[Max][Max]BOOL Switches:   -- 2 dimensional array
```

All arrays in occam2 start at element zero.

```
/* C */
#define MAX 10 /* defines MAX to be 10 */
typedef float reading_t[MAX]; /* index is 0 .. max-1 */
typedef short int switches_t[MAX][MAX]; /* no boolean in C */

reading_t reading;
switches_t switches;
```

```java
// Java
static final int max = 10; // a constant

float reading[] = new float[max]; // index is 0 .. max-1
boolean switches[] [] = new boolean[max] [max];
```

```ada
-- Ada
Max: Const Integer:= 10;
type Reading_T is array(0 .. Max-1) of Float;
Size: Const Integer:= Max - 1;
type Switches_T is array(0 .. Size, 0 .. Size) of Boolean;
Reading: Reading_T;
Switches: Switches_T;
```

Note that Ada uses round brackets for arrays whereas occam2, Java and C use the more conventional square brackets. Also, Ada arrays can have any starting index, whereas in C, Java and occam2 it is always 0. Note that in Java, arrays are represented by objects. To create an object in Java requires the use of an allocator (see Section 3.4.4).

Although there is no fundamental reason why records have not been introduced into occam2, their present omission gives some indication as to the priorities of the language's designers and implementors. The Ada record types are quite straightforward:

```ada
-- Ada
type Day_T is new Integer range 1 .. 31;
type Month_T is new Integer range 1 .. 12;
type Year_T is new Integer range 1900 .. 2050;
type Date_T is
  record
    Day: Day_T:= 1;
    Month: Month_T:= 1;
    Year: Year_T;
  end record;
```

However, C's use of struct is confusing as it introduces a type without the use of typedef to give it a name (although typedef can also be used and is preferred).

```c
/* C */
typedef short int day_t;
typedef short int month_t;
typedef int year_t;
struct date_t {
  day_t day;
  month_t month;
  year_t year; };
/* as data_t has not been introduced by a typedef, */
/* its name is 'struct date_t' */

typedef struct {
  day_t day;
  month_t month;
```

```
  year_t year; } date2_t ;
/* here the type name 'data2_t' can be used */
```

In the C example, the fields are derived integers whereas the earlier Ada code has distinct new constrained types for the components. The Ada example also shows how initial values can be given to some (but not necessarily all) fields of a record. Both languages use the dot notation to address individual components and allow record assignments. Ada also supports complete record assignments using record aggregates (array aggregates are also available):

```
-- Ada
D: Data
begin
  D.Year:= 1989;    -- dot notation
  -- D now has value 1-1-1989 due to
  -- initialization
  D:= (3, 1, 1953);  -- complete assignment
  D:= (Year => 1974, Day => 4, Month => 7);
     -- complete assignment using name notation
  ...
end;
```

whereas C only allows complete record initialization for static data.

```
/* C */
struct date_t D = {1,1,1};
```

The use of name notation in Ada improves readability and removes the errors that could otherwise be introduced by positional faults; for example, writing (1, 3, 1953) rather than (3, 1, 1953).

Ada also allows a record type to be extended with new fields. This is to facilitate object-oriented programming, which is discussed in Section 4.4.

Java has no record structure as such. However, the same effect can be achieved using classes. The details of classes will be given in Section 4.4, but for now consider the following Java class for the date:

```
// Java
class Date
{
  int day, month, year;
}

Date birthday = new Date();

birthdate.day = 31;
birthdate.month = 1;
birthdate.year = 2000;
```

As with C, it is not possible to express range constraints on the values of the date's components. Note also that as a 'record' is a Java object, an allocator must be used to create an instance of the Date. Initialization of the object can be achieved using constructors (see Section 4.4.2).

3.4.4 Dynamic data types and pointers

There are many programming situations in which the exact size or organization of a collection of data objects cannot be predicted prior to the program's execution. Even though Ada and C support variable length arrays, a flexible and dynamic data structure can only be achieved if a memory allocation facility is provided using reference, rather than direct, naming. This was the case with Java arrays and 'records'.

The implementation of dynamic data types represents a considerable overhead to the run-time support system for a language. For this reason, occam2 does not have any dynamic structures. C allows pointers to any object to be declared. A linked list example is given below.

```
...
{
  typedef struct node {
    int value;
    struct node *next; /* a pointer to the enclosing structure*/
  } node_t;

  int V;
  node_t *Ptr;

  Ptr = malloc(sizeof(node_t));
  Ptr->value = V; /* -> de-references the pointer */
  Ptr->next = 0;
  ...
}
```

The procedure malloc is a standard library procedure which dynamically allocates memory. The sizeof operator returns the number of storage units allocated by the compiler to the struct node_t.

In Ada, an access type is used rather than a pointer (though the concept is similar).

```
type Node;    -- incomplete declaration
type Ac is access Node;
type Node is
  record
    Value: Integer;
    Next: Ac;
  end record;
V: Integer;
A1: Ac;
begin
  A1:= new (Node);   -- construct first node
  A1.Value:= V; -- the access variable is de-referenced
```

```
                    -- and the component identified
  A1.Next:= null;   -- predefined
  ...
end;
```

The above program fragment illustrate the use of a 'new' facility for dynamically allocating an area of memory (from the heap). In contrast with C, the Ada 'new' is an operator defined in the language; there is, however, no dispose operator. Rather, a generic procedure is provided that removes storage from designated objects. This procedure (called Unchecked_Deallocation) does not check to see if there are outstanding references to the object.

Neither Ada nor C requires a garbage collector to be supported. This omission is not surprising as garbage collectors usually result in heavy and unpredictable overheads in execution time. These overheads may well be unacceptable in real-time systems (see Section 15.9.1).

Pointers can also be taken to static object or objects on the stack. The next example shows how C allows pointers to static types and allows the programmer to do pointer arithmetic:

```
{
  typedef date_t events_t[MAX], *next_event_t;

  events_t history;
  next_event_t next_event;

  next_event = &history[0];
  /*takes the address of the 1st element of the array */

  next_event++;
  /* increment the pointer next_event;        */
  /* the increment adds the sizeof the date  */
  /* record to the pointer and so next_event */
  /* points at the next element of the array */
}
```

The disadvantage of the C approach is that pointers can be set up which point to objects which subsequently go out of scope. This is the so called **dangling pointer** problem. Ada provides a secure solution to this pointer with its aliased types. Only aliased types can be references:

```
Object : aliased Some_Type;
   -- aliased to say that it may be
   -- referenced by an access type

type General_Ptr is access all Some_Type;
   -- access all indicates that an access variable of this
   -- type can point to either static or dynamic objects

Gp : General_Ptr := Object'Access;
   -- assigns Object reference to Gp
```

A final form of access type definition, in Ada, allows a read-only restriction to be imposed on the use of accesses:

```
Object1 : aliased Some_Type;
Object2 : aliased constant Some_Type := ...;

type General_Ptr is access constant Some_Type;

Gp1 : General_Ptr := Object1'Access;
   -- Gp1 can now only read the value of Object1

Gp2 : General_Ptr := Object2'Access;
   -- Gp2 is a reference to a constant
```

In contrast to Ada and C, all objects in Java are references to the actual object containing the data; hence no addition access or pointer type is required. Furthermore, unlike Ada, no forward declaration of the Node type is required.

```
// Java
{
  class Node
  {
     int value;
     Node next;
  }

  Node Ref = new Node();

}
```

Note that as a result of representing objects as reference values, comparing two objects in Java is a comparison between their pointers, *not* their values. Hence,

```
Node Ref1 = new Node();
Node Ref2 = new Node();

. . .

if(Ref1 == Ref2) { ... }
```

will compare the locations of the objects, not the values encapsulated by the objects (in this case, the values of the value and next fields). To compare values requires a class to implement an explicit compareTo method. Of course, the same is true of access variables in Ada. However, Ada allows a **.all** suffix to access variables to indicate the object's data, not its reference.

A similar situation occurs with object assignment. In Java, the assignment operator assigns to the pointer. To create an actual copy of an object requires the class to provide methods to clone the object.

3.4.5   Files

None of Ada, Java, C or occam2 has a file type constructor like that of Pascal. Instead, each language allows an implementation to support files via libraries. Ada, for example, requires all compilers to provide sequential and direct access files.

3.5   Control structures

Although there are some variations in the data structures supported (particularly between occam2 and the other languages), there is much closer agreement about which control structures are required. As programming languages progressed from machine code through assembly languages to higher-level languages, control instructions evolved into control statements. There is now common agreement on the control abstractions needed in a sequential programming language. These abstractions can be grouped together into three categories: sequences, decisions and loops. Each will be considered in turn. The necessary control structures for the concurrent parts of languages will be considered in Chapters 7, 8 and 9.

3.5.1   Sequence structures

The sequential execution of statements is the normal activity of a (non-concurrent) programming language. Most languages, including Ada, Java and C, implicitly require sequential execution, and no specific control structure is provided. The definitions of a block in both Ada and Java (and C) indicate that between 'begin' ({) and 'end' (}) there is a sequence of statements. Execution is required to follow this sequence.

In occam2, the normal execution of statements (called processes in occam2) could quite reasonably be concurrent, and it is therefore necessary to state explicitly that a collection of actions must follow a defined sequence. This is achieved by using the SEQ construct that was illustrated earlier. For example:

```
SEQ
  action 1
  action 2
  .
  .
  .
```

If a sequence is, in a particular circumstance, empty, Ada requires the explicit use of the null statement:

```
begin   -- Ada
  null;
end;
```

Java and C allow an empty block:

```
{ /* Java/C */
}
```

and occam2 uses a SKIP process to imply no action:

```
SEQ
   SKIP -- occam2
```

or just:

```
SKIP
```

At the other extreme from a null action is one that causes the sequence to make no further progress. Java and C provide a special predefined procedure named exit that causes the entire program to terminate. The occam2 STOP process has a similar effect. Ada does not have an equivalent primitive, but an exception can be programmed to have the same result (see Chapter 6) or the main program can be aborted. In all four languages, the severe action of prematurely terminating the program is only used to respond to the detection of an error condition that cannot be repaired. After bringing the controlled system into a safe condition, the program has no further useful action to perform other than termination.

3.5.2 Decision structures

A decision structure provides a choice as to the route that execution takes from some point in a program sequence to a later point in that sequence. The decision as to which route is taken will depend upon the current values of relevant data objects. The important property of a decision control structure is that all routes eventually come back together. With such abstract control structures there is no need to use a goto statement, which often leads to programs that are difficult to test, read and maintain. Java and occam2 do not possess a goto statement. Ada and C do, but it should be used sparingly.

The most common form of decision structure is the if statement. Although the requirements for such a structure are clear, earlier languages, such as Algol-60, suffered from a poor syntactical form which could lead to confusion. In particular, with a nested if construct, it was not clear to which if a trailing single else applied. Unfortunately, C still suffers from this problem, whereas Ada and occam2 have clear unambiguous structures. To illustrate, consider a simple problem; find out if $B/A > 10$ – checking first to make sure that A is not equal to zero! An Ada solution is given below; although the code has the shortcoming that the boolean variable High is not assigned a value if $A = 0$, the meaning of the program fragment is clear due to the explicit **end if** token:

```
if A /= 0 then
   if B/A > 10 then
      High:= True;
   else
      High:= False;
```

```
  end if;
end if;
```

Ada also supports two short-circuit control forms **and then** and **or else** which allow more concise expression of the above code.

The C structure need not have an explicit 'end':

```
if (A != 0)
  if (B/A > 10) high = 1;
  else high = 0;
```

However, the structure can be made much clearer if the statements are bracketed:

```
if (A != 0) {
  if (B/A > 10) {
    high = 1;
  }
  else {
    high = 0;
  }
}
```

Java follows the C structure; however, the trailing else problem is avoided by disallowing ambiguous statements.

The occam2 IF has a somewhat different style from the other three languages, although the functionality is the same. Consider first the general structure. In the following schema, let B1 .. Bn be boolean expressions and A1 .. An be actions :

```
IF
  B1
    A1
  B2
    A2
  .

  .
  Bn
    An
```

Firstly, it is important to remember that the layout of occam2 programs is syntactically significant. The boolean expressions are on separate lines (indented two spaces from the IF), as are the actions (indented a further two spaces). Like C, no 'then' token is used. On execution of this IF construct, the boolean expression B1 is evaluated. If it evaluates to TRUE then A1 is executed and that completes the action of the IF. However, if B1 is FALSE then B2 is evaluated. All the boolean expressions are evaluated until one is found TRUE and then the associated action is undertaken. If no boolean expression is TRUE then this is an error condition and the IF construct behaves like the STOP discussed in the last section.

With this form of IF statement, no distinct ELSE part is required; the boolean expression TRUE as the final test is bound to be taken if all other choices have failed. The b/a > 10 example in occam2, therefore, takes the form:

```
IF
  a /= 0
    IF
      b/a > 10
        high := TRUE
      TRUE
        high := FALSE
  TRUE         -- These last two lines are needed so
    SKIP       -- that the IF does not become STOP when
               -- a has the value 0
```

To give another illustration of the important 'if' construct, consider a multiway branch. The following example (firstly in Ada) finds the number of digits in a positive integer variable Number. A maximum of 5 digits is assumed:

```
if Number < 10 then
  Num_Digits := 1;
else
  if Number < 100 then
    Num_Digits := 2;
  else
    if Number < 1000 then
      Num_Digits := 3;
    else
      if Number < 10000 then
        Num_Digits := 4;
      else
        Num_Digits := 5;
      end if;
    end if;
  end if;
end if;
```

This form, which is quite common, involves nesting on the else part and results in a trail of end ifs at the end. To remove this clumsy structure, Ada provides an elsif statement. The above can therefore be written more concisely as:

```
-- Ada
if Number < 10 then
  Num_Digits := 1;
elsif Number < 100 then
  Num_Digits := 2;
elsif Number < 1000 then
  Num_Digits := 3;
elsif Number < 1000 then
  Num_Digits := 4;
else
  Num_Digits := 5;
end if;
```

In occam2, the code is quite clear:

```
IF
  number < 10
    digits := 1
  number < 100
    digits := 2
  number < 1000
    digits := 3
  number < 10000
    digits := 4
  TRUE
    digits := 5
```

The above is an example of a multiway branch constructed from a series of binary choices. In general, a multiway decision can be more explicitly stated and efficiently implemented using a case (or switch) structure. All four languages have such a structure, although the occam2 version is somewhat more restricted. To illustrate, consider a character (byte) value 'command' which is used to decide upon four possible actions:

```
-- Ada
case Command is
  when 'A' | 'a'       => Action1;        -- A or a
  when 't'             => Action2;
  when 'e'             => Action3;
  when 'x' .. 'z'      => Action4;        -- x, y or z
  when others          => null;          -- no action
end case;
```

```
/* C and Java */
switch(command) {
  case 'A'   :
  case 'a'   : action1; break;           /* A or a */
  case 't'   : action2; break;
  case 'e'   : action3; break;
  case 'x'   :
  case 'y'   :
  case 'z'   : action4; break;           /* x, y or z */
  default    : break;                    /* no action */
}
```

Note that with Java and C it is necessary to insert statements to break out of the switch once the required command has been identified. Without these, control continues to the next option (as with the case of 'A').

In occam2, alternative values and ranges are not supported; the code is, therefore, more protracted:

```
CASE command
  'A'
    action1
  'a'
    action1
```

```
  't'
    action2
  'e'
    action3
  'x'
    action4
  'y'
    action4
  'z'
    action4
ELSE
   SKIP
```

3.5.3 Loop structures

A loop structure allows the programmer to specify that a statement, or collection of statements, is to be executed more than once. There are two distinct forms for constructing such loops:

(1) iteration, and

(2) recursion.

The distinctive characteristic of iteration is that each execution of the loop is completed before the next is begun. With a recursive control structure, the first loop is interrupted to begin a second loop, which may be interrupted to begin a third loop and so on. At some point, loop n will be allowed to complete, this will then allow loop $n - 1$ to complete, then loop $n - 2$ and so on, until the first loop has also terminated. Recursion is usually implemented via recursive procedure calls. Attention here is focused on iteration.

   Iteration comes in two forms: a loop in which the number of iterations is usually fixed prior to the execution of the loop construct; and a loop in which a test for completion is made during each iteration. The former is known generally as the for statement, the latter as the while statement. Most languages' for constructs also provide a counter that can be used to indicate which iteration is currently being executed.

   The following example code illustrates the for construct in our four languages; the code assigns into the first ten elements of array A the value of their position in the array:

```
-- Ada
for I in 0 .. 9 loop      -- I is defined by the loop
   A(I):= I;               -- I is read only in the loop
end loop;                  -- I is out of scope after the loop


/* C and Java  */
for(i = 0; i <= 9; i++) {   /* i must be a previously defined */
   A[i]= i;                 /* i can be read/written in the loop */
}                           /* the value of i is defined */
                            /* after the loop */
```

```
-- occam2
SEQ i = 0 FOR 10            -- i is defined by the construct
  A[i]:= i                  -- i is read only in the loop
                           -- i is out of scope after the loop
-- note that the range of i is 0 to 9,
-- as in the Ada and C example
```

Note that Ada and occam2 have restricted the use of the loop variable. The free use of this variable in Java and C can be the cause of many errors. Java also allows a local variable to be declared inside the for loop for this reason.

```
// Java
for(int i = 0; i <= max; i++) {
  A[i]= i;
}
```

In addition to the above forms, Ada allows the loop to be executed in reverse order.

The main variation with while statements concerns the point at which the test for exit from the loop is made. The most common form involves a test upon entry to the loop and subsequently before each iteration is made:

```
-- Ada
while <Boolean Expression> loop
   <Statements>
end loop;
```

```
/* Java and C */
while(<expression>) {
   /* expression evaluating to 0 implies loop termination */
   <statement>
}
```

```
-- occam2
WHILE <boolean expression>
   SEQ
      <statements>
```

Java also supports a variant where the test occurs at the end of the loop:

```
do {
   < sequence of statements>
} while (<expression>);
```

Ada, Java and C increase the flexibility of the construct by allowing control to pass out of the loop (that is, the loop to terminate) from any point within it:

```
-- Ada
loop
   .
   .
   exit when <Boolean Expression>;
   .
   .
end loop;
```

```
/* C and Java */
while(1) {
   .
   .
   if(<expression>) break;
   .
   .
}
```

A common programming error is a loop that either does not terminate (when it is meant to) or terminates in the wrong state. Fortunately, formal methods of analyzing loop structures are now well understood. They involve defining the pre- and post-conditions for the loop; the termination condition and the loop invariant. The loop invariant is a statement that is true at the end of each iteration but may not be true during the iteration. In essence, the analysis of the loop involves showing that the pre-condition will lead to loop termination and that, upon termination, the loop invariant will lead to a proof that the post-condition is satisfied. To facilitate the use of these formal approaches, exiting from the loop during an iteration is not advised. Where possible, the standard while construct is the best to use.

The final point to make about loops is that in real-time systems it is often required that a loop does not terminate. A control cycle will be expected to run indefinitely (that is, until the power is turned off). Although **while** True would facilitate such a loop, it may be inefficient and it does not capture the essence of an infinite loop. For this reason, Ada provides a simple loop structure:

```
-- Ada
loop
   <Statements>
end loop;
```

3.6 Subprograms

Even in the construction of a component or module, further decomposition is usually desirable. This is achieved by the use of procedures and functions; known collectively as *subprograms*.

Subprograms not only aid decomposition but also represent an important form of abstraction. They allow arbitrary complex computations to be defined and then invoked by the use of a simple identifier. This enables such components to be reused both within a program and between programs. The generality, and therefore usefulness, of subprograms is, of course, increased by the use of parameters.

3.6.1 Parameter-passing modes and mechanisms

A parameter is a form of communication; it is a data object being transferred between the subprogram user and the subprogram itself. There are a number of ways of describing the mechanisms used for this transfer of data. Firstly, one can consider the way parameters are transferred. From the invoker's point of view, there are three distinct modes of transfer.

(1) Data is passed into the subprogram.

(2) Data is passed out from the subprogram.

(3) Data is passed into the subprogram, is changed and is then passed out of the subprogram.

These three modes are often called: **in**, **out** and **in out**.

The second mechanism of describing the transfer is to consider the binding of the formal parameter of the subprogram and the actual parameter of the call. There are two general methods of interest here: a parameter may be bound by value or by reference. A parameter that is bound by value only has the value of the parameter communicated to the subprogram (often by copying into the subprogram's memory space); no information can return to the caller via such a parameter. When a parameter is bound by reference, any updates to that parameter from within the subprogram is defined to have an effect on the memory location of the actual parameter.

A final way of considering the parameter-passing mechanism is to examine the methods used by the implementation. The compiler must satisfy the semantics of the language, be these expressed in terms of modes or binding, but is otherwise free to implement a subprogram call as efficiently as possible. For example, a large array parameter that is 'pass by value' need not be copied if no assignments are made to elements of the array in the subprogram. A single pointer to the actual array will be more efficient but behaviourally equivalent. Similarly, a call by reference parameter may be implemented by a copy in and copy out algorithm.

Ada uses parameter modes to express the meaning of data transfer to and from a subprogram. For example, consider a procedure which returns the real roots (if they exist) of a quadratic equation.

```
procedure Quadratic (A, B, C : in Float;
                     R1, R2  : out Float;
                     Ok      : out Boolean);
```

An in parameter (which is the default) acts as a local constant within the subprogram – a value is assigned to the formal parameter upon entry to the procedure or function. This is the only mode allowed for functions. Within the procedure, an out parameter can be written and read. A value is assigned to the calling parameter upon termination of the procedure. An 'in out' parameter acts as a variable in the procedure. Upon entry, a value is assigned to the formal parameter; upon termination of the procedure, the value attained is passed back to the calling (actual) parameter.

C passes parameters (or **arguments** as C calls them) by value. If results are to be returned, pointers must be used. C, like Java, only supports functions; a procedure is considered to be a function with no return value (indicated by void in the function definition).

```
void quadratic(float A, float B, float C,
               float *R1, float *R2, int *OK);
```

Note that there is no function keyword. Also, even though A, B and C above have been copied into the function they can still be written to within the function. However, any updated values are **not** copied back.

In Java, primitive arguments are passed by copy. Variables of class type are reference variables. Hence, when they are passed as arguments they are copied, but the effect is as if the variable was passed by reference. If an argument is not to be written to by a Java function, it should be declared as final in the function specification.

```
public class Roots {
   float R1, R2;
}
boolean quadratic(final float A, final float B, final float C,
                  Roots R);
```

Note in this Java example that the boolean flag is returned via the function return value. Also, Java requires that the roots of the equation to be passed as a class type as primitive types (including float) are passed by copy and there are no pointer types.

In occam2, parameters by default are passed by reference; a VAL tag is used to imply pass by value. Significantly, within the procedure (called a PROC in occam2) a VAL parameter acts as a constant and, therefore, the errors that can occur in Pascal by missing out the VAR tag are caught by the compiler.

```
PROC quadratic(VAL REAL32 A, B, C,
               REAL32 R1, R2, BOOL OK)
  -- note, as with C and Java, the parameter separator
  -- is not a semicolon
```

3.6.2 Procedures

The procedure bodies in all four languages are quite straightforward and are illustrated by completing the 'quadratic' definitions given above. All procedures assume that a sqrt function is in scope.

```ada
-- Ada
procedure Quadratic (A, B, C : in Float;
                     R1, R2 : out Float;
                     Ok : out Boolean) is
  Z : Float;
begin
  Z:= B*B - 4.0*A*C;
  if Z < 0.0 or A = 0.0 then
    Ok:= False;
    R1:= 0.0;        -- arbitrary values
    R2:= 0.0;
    return;          -- return from a procedure before
                     -- reaching logical end
  end if;
  Ok:= True;
  R1:= (-B + Sqrt(Z)) / (2.0*A);
  R2:= (-B - Sqrt(Z)) / (2.0*A);
end Quadratic;
```

```c
/* C */
void quadratic(float A, float B, float C, float *R1,
               float *R2, int *OK)
{
  float Z;

  Z= B*B - 4.0*A*C;
  if(Z < 0.0 || A == 0.0) {
    *OK = 0;
    *R1 = 0.0;       /*  arbitrary values */
    *R2 = 0.0;
    return;          /*  return from a procedure before */
                     /*  reaching logical end */
  }
  *OK = 1;
  *R1 = (-B + SQRT(Z)) / (2.0*A);
  *R2 = (-B - SQRT(Z)) / (2.0*A);
}
```

```java
// Java
public class Roots {
  float R1, R2;
}

boolean quadratic(final float A, final float B, final float C, Roots R) {

  // Note that explicit conversions to float are required

  float Z;

  Z = (float) (B*B - 4.0*A*C);
  if(Z < 0.0 || A == 0.0) {
    R.R1 = 0f;       // arbitrary values
```

```
    R.R2 = 0f;
    return false;
  }
  R.R1 = (float) ((-B + Math.sqrt(Z)) / (2.0*A));
  R.R2 = (float) ((-B - Math.sqrt(Z)) / (2.0*A));
  return true;
};
```

```
--occam2
PROC quadratic(VAL REAL32 A, B, C,
                   REAL32 R1, R2, BOOL OK)
  REAL32 Z:
  SEQ
    Z:= (B*B) - (4.0*(A*C))     -- brackets are needed
                                -- to fully specify expression
    IF
      (Z < 0) OR (A = 0.0)
        SEQ
          OK:= FALSE
          R1:= 0.0              -- arbitrary values
          R2:= 0.0
      TRUE                      -- no return statement in occam2
        SEQ
          OK:= TRUE
          R1:= (-B + SQRT(Z)) / (2.0*A)
          R2:= (-B - SQRT(Z)) / (2.0*A)
  :   -- colon needed to show end of PROC declaration
```

The invoking of these procedures, in all four languages, merely involves naming the procedure and giving the appropriately typed parameters in parenthesis.

In addition to these basic features, there are two extra facilities available in Ada that improve readability. Consider an enumeration type Setting and an integer type that delineates 10 distinct valves:

```
type Setting is (Open, Closed);
type Valve is new Integer range 1 .. 10;
```

The following procedure specification gives a subprogram for changing the setting of one valve:

```
procedure Change_Setting (Valve_Number : Valve;
                          Position : Setting := Closed;
                          );
```

Note that one of the parameters has been given a default value. Calls to this procedure could take a number of forms:

```
Change_Setting(6, Open);       -- normal call
Change_Setting(3);             -- default value 'Closed' used
Change_Setting(Position => Open,
               Valve_Number => 9);  -- name notation
```

```
Change_Setting (Valve_Number => 4);  -- name notation and
                                      -- default value
```

Default values are useful if some of the parameters are nearly always given the same value. The use of name notation removes positional errors and increases readability.

Recursive (and mutually recursive) procedure calls are allowed in Ada, Java and C. They are not supported in occam2 because of the dynamic overhead they create at run-time. Procedures (and functions) can be nested in Ada but not in Java, C or occam2.

3.6.3 Functions

Ada supports functions in a manner that is similar to procedures. Consider a simple example of a function that returns the smallest of two integer values:

```
-- Ada
function Minimum (X, Y : in Integer) return Integer is
begin
   if X > Y then
      return Y;
   else
      return X;
   end if;
end Minimum;
```

```
/* C and Java */
int minimum (int X, int Y)
{
   if(X > Y) return Y;
   else return X;
}
```

Ada, Java and C allow functions to return any valid type including structured types.

The misuse of functions is a source of many errors within programs; the golden rule about functions is that they should not have side effects. An expression should mean what it says:

```
A := B + F(C)
```

The value of A becomes the value of B plus a value obtained from C by the application of the function F. In the execution of the above, only A should have its value changed.

Side effects can be introduced into the above expression in three ways.

(1) F could change the value of C as well as returning a value.
(2) F could change the value of B so that the expression has a different value if evaluated left to right as opposed to right to left.
(3) F could change the value of D, where D is any other variable in scope.

Ada and Java restrict side effects by only allowing parameters to functions to have 'in' mode. Of course, as these parameters may reference other objects, side effects are entirely possible. Occam2, however, goes much further and defines the semantics of a function so that no side-effects are possible.

As with Ada, the parameters to an occam2 function are passed by value. In addition, the body of a function is defined to be a VALOF. A VALOF is the sequence of statements necessary to compute the value of an object (which will be returned from the function). The important property of the VALOF is that the only other variables whose values can be changed are those defined locally within the VALOF. This prohibits side effects. The simple minimum function defined earlier would therefore have the form:

```
INT FUNCTION minimum (VAL INT X, Y)
   INT Z:      -- Z will be the value returned
   VALOF
     IF
       X > Y
         Z := Y
       TRUE
         Z := X
     RESULT Z
:
```

In concurrent languages, another form of side effect is hidden concurrency; this can have a number of unfortunate consequences. The VALOF of occam2 is further restricted to disallow any concurrency within it.

Finally, it should be noted that functions (and procedures) in Java can only be declared within the context of a class definition (see Section 4.4.2).

3.6.4   Subprogram pointers

Both Ada and C allows pointers to procedures and functions. For example, the following Ada type declaration (Error_Report) defines an access variable to a procedure which takes a string parameter. A procedure is then declared which has a parameter of this type, and a call is made to this procedure passing a pointer to the Operator_Warning procedure.

```
type Error_Report is access procedure (Reason: in String);

procedure Operator_Warning(Message: in String) is
begin
   -- inform Operator of error
end Operator_Warning;

procedure Complex_Calculation(Error_To : Error_Report; ... ) is
begin
   -- if error detected during the complex calculation
   Error_To("Giving Up");
end Complex_Calculation;
```

```
...
  Complex_Calculation(Operator_Warning'Access, ...);
...
```

In C, the equivalent of the error reporting pointer is:

```
void (*error_report)(char *Message);
```

and the address of a function is obtained by using

```
error_report = operator_warning;
```

Java does not allow pointers to functions (procedures) as they can only occur within the context of a class which is accessed by reference anyway.

3.6.5   Inline expansion

Although the use of subprograms is clearly beneficial in terms of decomposition, reuse and readability, for some real-time applications the overhead of implementing the actual call may be unacceptably high. One means of reducing the overhead is to substitute the code for the subprogram 'inline' whenever a call of that subprogram is made. This technique is known as **inline expansion** and has the advantage that it still allows the programmer to use subprograms but not to incur the run-time overhead.

Interestingly, occam2, whose semantics are formally specified, uses text substitution as the method of specifying what is meant by a procedure call. All four languages, however, allow the implementor to deal with subprograms as they see fit. The only exception to this appears in Ada where the programmer can, by use of the pragma Inline, request that inline expansion is used for the specified subprogram whenever possible. Pragmas are used in Ada to give instructions to the compiler – they are not executable statements.

Summary

In the title of his seminal book, Wirth expressed the now famous adage:

```
"Algorithms + Data Structures = Programs"
```

Perhaps, now that the difficulties presented by very large programs are apparent, the adage would be better phrased as Algorithms + Data Structures = Modules; where a module is the component program being designed and developed by an individual or a small, closely working, group of software engineers.

In this chapter, the necessary language features for expressing algorithms and representing data structures for Ada, Java, C and occam2 have been given. Although these languages differ, they present the programmer with very similar semantic models. Indeed, for imperative languages the necessary primitives for supporting programming in the small now seem well understood.

To express algorithms, blocks and well-constructed loop and decision structures are needed. The `goto` statement is now totally discredited. To give a concrete realization of the distinct logical units found in most non-trivial modules, subprograms are also required. Procedure semantics are relatively un-controversial (although different parameter-passing models exist), but functions are still problematic because of side effects. Occam2 has shown the lead here by constructing a form of function that cannot have side effects (occam1 had a more radical solution to side effects: it did not have functions at all!).

The provision of a rich variety of data structures and the rules of typing are visible in Ada, Java, C and occam2, although the occam2 facilities are not as comprehensive and the typing in C is not as strong. Strong typing is now universally accepted as a necessary aid to the production of reliable code. The restrictions it imposes can lead to difficulties, but the provision of a controlled means of doing explicit type conversions removes these problems. The absence of strong typing in C is one drawback to the use of that language in high-integrity systems.

The data types themselves can be classified in a number of different ways. There is a clear division between scalar and structured data types. Scalar types can then be subdivided into discrete types (integer types and enumeration types) and real types. The structured data types can be classified in terms of three attributes: homogeneity, size and access method. A structured data type is said to be homogeneous if its subcomponents are all of the same type (for example, arrays). Alternatively, if the subcomponents can be of different types (for example, records) then the data structure is known as heterogeneous. The size attribute can be either fixed or variable. Records are fixed as are arrays in some languages. Dynamic data structures such as linked lists, trees or graphs are variable in size and are usually constructed by the programmer from a pointer (or reference) type and a memory allocator. Finally, there are several access methods for getting at the subcomponents of the structure. The two most im-portant methods are direct and indirect. Direct access, as its name implies, allows the immediate referencing of a subcomponent (for example, an element of an array or a field of a record). Indirect access means that the addressing of a subcomponent may require a chain of accesses through other components. Most dynamic structures have only indirect access.

The attributes, homogeneity, size and access method, could theoretically give rise to at least eight different structures. In reality, the attributes are related (for example, a fixed size implies direct access) and only the following categories are necessary:

- arrays with arbitrary bounds and dimensions;
- records (or classes);
- pointers for constructing arbitrary dynamic data structures with indirect addressing.

Any language that provides appropriate control structures and all of these categories (as Ada, Java and C do) is well able to support programming in the small. The extra facilities for programming in the large are considered in Chapter 4.

Notwithstanding the discussion above, real-time languages may have to restrict the features available to the programmer. It is difficult, if not impossible, to make estimates of the time required to access dynamic data structures. Moreover, it is desirable to be able to guarantee before execution begins that there is sufficient memory available for the program. For this reason, dynamic arrays and pointers may need to be missing from the 'authorized' list of language features for real-time applications. Additionally, recursion and unbounded loop structures may need to be restricted.

Further reading

Barnes J. G. P. (1998) *Programming in Ada 1995*. Reading, MA: Addison-Wesley.

Bishop J. (2001) *Java Gently*, 3rd Edition. Reading, MA: Addison-Wesley.

Burns A. (1988) *Programming in occam2*. Reading, MA: Addison-Wesley.

Galletly J. (1990). *Occam2*. London: Pitman.

Hatton L. (1995). *Safer C: Developing Software for High-Integrity and Safety-Critical Systems*. London: McGraw-Hill.

INMOS Limited (1988) *occam2 Reference Manual*. Chichester: Prentice Hall.

Kernighan B. W. and Ritchie D. M. (1988) *The C Programming Language*. Englewood Cliffs, NJ: Prentice Hall.

Exercises

3.1   Ada ends each construct with **end** <construct name>; C does not use an end marker. What are the pros and cons of these language designs?

3.2   Occam2, Java and C are case-sensitive; Ada is not. What are the arguments for and against case sensitivity?

3.3   Occam2 has removed the need for operator precedence rules by requiring parentheses around all sub-expressions. What is the effect of this on readability and efficiency?

3.4   Should a language always require that initial values be given to variables?

3.5   Does the use of the **exit** statement in Ada lead to readable and reliable programs?

3.6   Why is recursion not allowed in occam2?

3.7   List the language features that are desirable for secure programming.

3.8   Why does Java not support pointer types?

3.9   To what extent can C be used in high-integrity systems?

Chapter 4
Programming in the large

In Chapter 3, it was noted that decomposition and abstraction are the two most important methods that can be used to manage the complexity characteristic of large embedded systems. This complexity is due not just to the amount of code, but to the variety of activities and requirements that are commensurate with real world interaction. As was observed in Section 1.3.1, the real world is also subject to continuous change. Furthermore, the design, implementation and maintenance of software is often poorly managed and results in unsatisfactory products. This chapter considers those language features that help to embody and support decomposition and the use of abstraction. These features are said to aid *programming in the large*.

The key structure that is missing from older languages, such as Pascal, is the module. A module can be described, informally, as a collection of logically related objects and operations. The technique of isolating a system function within a module and providing a precise specification for the interface to the module is called **encapsulation**. Consequently, with a module structure, it is possible to support:

- information hiding,

- separate compilation,

- abstract data types.

In the following sections, the major motivations for a module structure are described. These needs are illustrated by examples coded in Ada, Java and C. Ada and Java support modules explicitly in the form of **packages**. The support for modules in C is weak; it only provides indirect modules by allowing separate compilations of files. Occam2, by comparison, does not support modular decomposition.

Although the module allows encapsulation, it is essentially a static structuring mechanism and not part of the type model of a language. A more dynamic encapsulation mechanism is provided in the form of classes and objects (which are supported by Java).

4.1   Information hiding

In simple languages, all permanent variables have to be global. If two or more procedures wish to share data then that data must be visible to all other parts of the program. Even if a single procedure wishes to update some variable each time it is called, this variable must be declared outside the procedure, and therefore the possibility of misuse and error exists.

A module structure supports reduced visibility by allowing information to be hidden inside the module's 'body'. All module structures (of which there are many different models) allow the programmer to control access to module variables. To illustrate information hiding, consider the implementation of a FIFO dynamic queue. The interface of the queue manager (to the rest of the program) is via three procedures that allow elements to be added to or removed from the queue, and to provide a test for the queue being empty. It is not desirable that internal information about the queue (such as the queue pointer) should be visible outside the module. The following provides a package, in Ada, for this list structure. The main points to note are:

- An Ada package is always declared in two parts: a *specification* and a *body*. Only entities declared in the specification are visible externally.
- Ada uses 'open scope'. All identifiers visible at the point of the package declaration can be accessed within the package. There is no import list as in some languages, like Modula-2 and Java.
- All exported Ada identifiers are accessed from outside the package by quoting both the package name and the required identifier, for example, Queue-mod.Empty.
- Only a single instance of the queue is supported; it is created in the package initialization section by calling Create.

```
package Queuemod is
   -- assume type Element is in scope
   function Empty return Boolean;
   procedure Insert (E : Element);
   procedure Remove (E : out Element);
end Queuemod;
```

```
package body Queuemod is

  type Queue_Node_T;  -- forward declaration
  type Queue_Node_Ptr_T is access Queue_Node_T;

  type Queue_Node_T is
    record
      Contents : Element;
      Next : Queue_Node_Ptr_T;
    end record;

  type Queue_T is
    record
      Front : Queue_Node_Ptr_T;
      Back : Queue_Node_Ptr_T;
    end record;

  type Queue_Ptr_T is access Queue_T;

  Q : Queue_Ptr_T;

  procedure Create is
  begin
    Q := new Queue_T;
    Q.Front := null; -- strictly not necessary as pointers
    Q.Back := null;  -- are always initialized to null
  end Create;

  function Empty return Boolean is
  begin
    return Q.Front = null;
  end Empty;

  procedure Insert(E : Element) is
    New_Node : Queue_Node_Ptr_T;
  begin
    New_Node := new Queue_Node_T;
    New_Node.Contents := E;
    New_Node.Next := null;
    if Empty then
      Q.Front := New_Node;
    else
      Q.Back.Next := New_Node;
    end if;
    Q.Back := New_Node;
  end Insert;

  procedure Remove(E : out Element) is
    Old_Node : Queue_Node_Ptr_T;
  begin
    Old_Node := Q.Front;
    E := Old_Node.Contents;
    Q.Front := Q.Front.Next;
    if Q.Front = null then
      Q.Back := null;
```

```
      end if;
      -- free up old_node, see Section 4.5.1
   end Remove;
begin
   Create; -- create the queue
end Queuemod;
```

Both the specification and the body of a package must be placed within the same declarative part, although other entities may be defined between the two parts. In this way, two packages can call subprograms in each other without the need of forward declarations.

Any package can be used if it is in scope. To reduce the need for excessive naming, a 'use' statement is provided:

```
declare
   use Queuemod;
begin
   if not Empty then
      Remove(E);
   end if;
end;
```

Java's packaging facilities are best explained in the context of its object-oriented programming model, which is discussed in Section 4.4.

In C, modules are not so well formalized. Instead, the programmer must make use of separate files: a header file (usually with a file extension of '.h') and a body file (usually with a file extension of '.c'). Consider the queue module again; first the header (queuemod.h).

```
/* assume element is in scope */

int empty();

void insertE(element E);
void removeE(element *E);
```

This defines the functional interface to the module. The user of the module simply uses this file. The body of the module is given below:

```
. . .
#include "queuemod.h" /* make the module specification */
                       /* visible to the body */

   struct queue_node_t {
       element contents;
       struct queue_node_t *next;
   };

   struct queue_t {
     struct queue_node_t *front;
     struct queue_node_t *back;
   } *Q; /* Q is now a pointer to struct queue_t */
```

```
void create()
{
  Q = (struct queue_t *)malloc(sizeof(struct queue_t));
  Q->front = NULL;
  Q->back = NULL;
};

int empty()
{
  return(Q->front == NULL);
}

void insertE(element E)
{
  struct queue_node_t *new_node;

  new_node = (struct queue_node_t *)
             malloc(sizeof(struct queue_node_t));
  new_node->contents = E;
  new_node->next = NULL;
  if(empty) {
    Q->front = new_node;
  } else {
    Q->back->next = new_node;
  };
  Q->back = new_node;
}

void removeE(element *E)
{
  struct queue_node_t *old_node;

  old_node = Q->front;
  *E = old_node->contents;
  Q->front = Q->front->next;
  if(Q->front == NULL) {
    Q->back = NULL;
  }
  free(old_node);
}
```

It should be noted that there is no formal relationship between a '.h' and a '.c' file in the C language. Indeed, the specification given in queuemod.h need have no relationship at all with the code given in queuemod.c. Their use is purely a convention. In contrast, the package is an integral part of the Ada language and for every subprogram specification there must be a subprogram body. An error caused by a missing subprogram body will be caught at compiler time in Ada. In C, a missing function body will not be caught until link time.

The importance of the module construct to real-time programming cannot be over-emphasized. However, as previously mentioned, modules are, typically, not first class language entities. Module types cannot be defined, pointers to modules cannot be created and so on. Advocates of the dynamic language Simula are never slow to point out that the class concept has been available within that language since the late 1960s. Furthermore, Smalltalk-80 has shown the power of a dynamic module structure. The issue of dynamic modules is closely tied to that of object-oriented programming, which is discussed in Section 4.4.

4.2 Separate compilation

If a program is constructed from modules, there are obvious advantages in having these modules compiled separately. Such a program is said to be compiled within the context of a library. Programmers can therefore concentrate on the current module but be able to construct, at least in part, the complete program so that their module can be tested. Once tested, and possibly authorized, the new unit can be added to the library in a precompiled form. As well as supporting project management, there are clearly resource savings if the entire program does not have to be recompiled for each minor edit.

In Ada (and C), the package (module) specification and body, as outlined in the previous section, can be precompiled in a straightforward manner. If a library unit wishes to have access to any other library unit then it must indicate this, explicitly, using a **with** clause (#include):

```
package Dispatcher is
  -- new visible objects
end Dispatcher;

with Queuemod;
package body Dispatcher is
  -- hidden objects
end Dispatcher;
```

In this way, a hierarchy of dependencies between library units is constructed. The main program itself uses **with** clauses to gain access to the library units it requires.

An important feature of the Ada (and to a lesser extent the C) model is that the module specification and body are seen as distinct entities in the library. Obviously both must be present for the final program compilation. (To be completely accurate, some module specifications do not require a body; for example, if they only define types or variables.) During program development, however, a library may contain only specifications. These can be used to check the logical consistency of the program prior to the detailed implementation work. Within the context of project management, specifications may well be done by more senior staff. This is because the specification represents an interface between software modules. An error in such code is more serious than one within a package body, as a change to the specification requires all users of the module to be potentially changed and recompiled, whereas a change to a body requires only the body to be recompiled.

Separate compilation supports bottom-up programming. Library units are built up from other units until the final program can be coded. Bottom-up programming, within the context of top-down design, is quite acceptable, especially as it is bottom-up in terms of specifications (definitions), not implementations (bodies). Nevertheless,

Ada has included a further feature of separate compilation that more directly supports top-down design. Within a program unit, a 'stub' can be left for inclusion later by using the **is separate** keywords. For example, the following schema shows how the procedure Convert can be left unimplemented until after the main program has been defined:

```
procedure Main is
   type Reading is ...
   type Control_Value is ...
   procedure Convert (R : Reading; Cv : out Control_Value)
            is separate;
begin
   loop
      Input (Rd);
      Convert(Rd, Cv);
      Output (Cv);
   end loop;
end;
```

Later the procedure body is added:

```
separate (Main)
procedure Convert (R : Reading; Cv : out Control_Value) is
   -- actual required code
end Convert;
```

In Ada, separate compilation is integrated into the language specification. Most importantly, the strong typing rules that would apply if the program was constructed as a single unit apply equally across library units. This is a much more reliable mechanism than the linking together of precompiled units as supported in C (and some implementations of FORTRAN and Pascal). With this latter approach, comprehensive type-checking is not possible. However, C does have a specific support tool, called lint, to check consistency across compilation units.

4.3   Abstract data types

In Chapter 3, it was noted that one of the major advantages of high-level languages is that programmers do not have to concern themselves with the physical representation of the data in the computer. From this separation comes the idea of data types. Abstract data types (ADT) are a further extension of this concept. To define an ADT, a module will name a new type and then give all the operations that can be applied to that type. The structure of the ADT is hidden within the module. Note that more than one instance of the type is now supported, and therefore a create routine is required in the interface of the module.

The facility for ADTs is complicated by the requirement for the separate compilation of a module specification from its body. As the structure of an ADT is meant to be hidden, the logical place for it to be defined is in the body. But then the compiler will not know the size of the type when it is compiling code which is using the specification. One way of getting around this problem is to force the programmer to use a level of indirection. For example, in C the interface to the queuemod module would become.

```
typedef struct queue_t *queue_ptr_t;

queue_ptr_t create();

int empty(queue_ptr_t Q);

void insertE(queue_ptr_t Q, element E);
void removeE(queue_ptr_t Q, element *E);
```

Although this is an acceptable approach, it is not always appropriate. For this reason, Ada also allows part of the implementation to appear in the specification but to be accessible only from the package body. This is called the **private** part of the specification.

Keeping with the queue example, for comparison, the Ada definition of an ADT for queue is as follows:

```
package Queuemod is
   type Queue is limited private;
   procedure Create (Q : in out Queue);
   function Empty (Q : Queue) return Boolean;
   procedure Insert (Q : in out Queue; E : Element);
   procedure Remove (Q : in out Queue; E : out Element);
private
   -- none of the following declarations are externally visible
   type Queuenode;
   type Queueptr is access Queuenode;
   type Queuenode is
     record
       Contents : Element;
       Next : Queueptr;
     end record;
   type Queue is
     record
       Front : Queueptr;
       Back : Queueptr;
     end record;
end Queuemod;

package body Queuemod is
   -- essentially the same as the original code
end Queuemod;
```

The keywords **limited private** mean that only those subprograms defined in this package can be applied to the type. A limited private type is, therefore, a true abstract data type. However, Ada recognizes that many ADTs need the assignment operator and tests for equality. Therefore, rather than have these be defined on all occasions that they are needed, a type can be declared as just **private**. If this is the case, then in addition to the defined subprograms, assignment and the equality test are available to the user.

The following gives a common example of an ADT in Ada. It provides a package for complex arithmetic. Note that the subprograms defined with the type Complex take the form of overloaded operations and so allow 'normal' arithmetic expressions to be written:

```
package Complex_Arithmetic is
  type Complex is private;
  function "+" (X,Y : Complex) return Complex;
  function "-" (X,Y : Complex) return Complex;
  function "*" (X,Y : Complex) return Complex;
  function "/" (X,Y : Complex) return Complex;
  function Comp (A,B : Float) return Complex;
  function Real_Part (X: Complex) return Float;
  function Imag_Part (X: Complex) return Float;
private
  type Complex is
    record
      Real_Part: Float;
      Imag_Part: Float;
    end record;
end Complex_Arithmetic;
```

4.4 Object-oriented programming

It has become fashionable to call variables of an ADT *objects* and to designate the programming paradigm that leads to their use *object-oriented programming* (OOP). There is, however, a stricter definition of an object abstraction (Wegner, 1987) that draws a useful distinction between objects and ADTs. In general, ADTs lack four properties that would make them suitable for object-oriented programming. They are

(1) type extensibility (inheritance),

(2) automatic object initialization (constructors),

(3) automatic object finalization (destructors),

(4) run-time dispatching of operations (polymorphism).

All of which are supported, in some form, by Ada and Java. In the queue example given earlier, it was necessary to declare a queue variable and then call a create procedure to initialize it. Using OOP, this initialization (using a constructor routine) is done automatically on each queue object as it is declared. Similarly, as an object goes out of scope, a destructor procedure is executed.

Properties (2) and (3) are useful, but the significant concept in an object abstraction is extensibility. This enables a type to be defined as an extension of a previously defined type. The new type inherits the 'base' type but may include new fields and new operations. Once the type has been extended, run-time dispatching of operation is required to ensure the appropriate operation is called for a particular instance of the family of types.

C does not support OOP, but an extension of C called C++ has become very popular and is an ISO standard.

It is beyond the scope of this book to address the full implications of object-oriented software development. However, it is necessary to have a good grasp of OOP principles in order to understand the facilities provided by Java for concurrency and real-time.

4.4.1 OOP and Ada

Ada supports object-oriented programming through two complementary mechanisms which provide type extensions and dynamic polymorphism: tagged types and class-wide types. Child packages and controlled types are also important features of the support that Ada provides.

Tagged types

In Ada, a new type can be *derived* from an old type and some of the properties of the type changed using subtyping. For example, the following declares a new type and a subtype called Setting which has the same properties as the Integer type but a restricted range. Setting and Integer are distinct and cannot be interchanged:

```
type Setting is new Integer range 1 .. 100;
```

New operations manipulating Setting can be defined; however, no new components can be added. Tagged types remove this restriction and allow extra components to be added to a type. Any type that might potentially be extended in this way must be declared as a tagged type. Because extending the type inevitably leads to the type becoming a record, only record types (or private types which are implemented as records) can be tagged. For example, consider the following type and a primitive operation:

```
type Coordinates is tagged
  record
    X : Float;
    Y : Float;
  end record;

procedure Plot(P: Coordinates);
```

This type can then be extended:

```
type Three_D is new Coordinates with
  record
    Z : Float;
  end record;
```

```
procedure Plot(P: Three_D);  -- overrides the Plot subprogram
Point : Three_D := (X => 1.0, Y => 1.0, Z => 0.0);
```

All types derived in this way (including the original **root**) are said to belong to the same **class** hierarchy. When a type is extended, it automatically inherits any primitive operations (those defined with the type) available for the parent type.

The fields of the Three_D class in the above example are directly visible to users of the type. Ada 95 also allows these attributes to be fully encapsulated by using private types:

```
package Coordinate_Class is
   type Coordinates is tagged private;

   procedure Plot(P: Coordinates);

   procedure Set_X(P: Coordinates; X: Float);
   function Get_X(P: Coordinates) return Float;
   -- similarly for Y
private
   type Coordinates is tagged
   record
     X : Float;
     Y : Float;
   end record;
end Coordinate_Class;
```

Other facilities include the notion of abstract tagged types and abstract primitive operations. These are similar to the Java facilities which are considered in Section 4.4.2. Note that Ada supports only inheritance from a single parent, although an element of multiple inheritance can be achieved using the generic facilities of the language.

Class-wide types

Tagged types provide the mechanism by which types can be extended incrementally. The result is that a programmer can create a hierarchy of related types. Other parts of the program may now wish to manipulate any member of that hierarchy for their own purposes without being too concerned which member it is processing at any one time. Ada is a strongly typed language, and therefore a mechanism is needed by which an object from any member of the hierarchy can be passed as a parameter. For example, a subprogram may wish to take a coordinate as a parameter without being too concerned whether it is a two-dimensional or three-dimensional one.

Class-wide programming is the technique which enables programs to be written which manipulate families of types. Associated with each tagged type, T, there is a type T'Class which comprises all the types which are in the family of types starting at T. Hence, the following subprogram will allow either a two-dimensional or three-dimensional coordinate to be passed.

```
procedure General_Plot(P : Coordinates'Class);
```

Any call to a primitive operation on a class-wide type will result in the correct operation for the actual type being called; a process known as **run-time dispatching**.

```
procedure General_Plot(P : Coordinates'Class) is
begin
  -- do some house keeping
  Plot(P);
  -- depending on the actual value of P
  -- one of the defined Plot procedures
  -- will be called
end General_Plot;
```

Although run-time dispatching is a powerful mechanism, it does cause some problems for real-time systems. In particular, it is not possible to know from examining statically the code which operations are called. This makes static timing analysis difficult (see Section 13.7).

Child packages

The main motivation for child packages is to add more flexibility to the single-level packaging facility. Without them, changes to a package which resulted in modifications to the specification require recompilation of all clients using that package. This is at odds with object-oriented programming, which facilitates incremental changes. Furthermore, extending private tagged types is not feasible without further language additions, as access to data in private types can only be made from within the package body.

Consider the following example given in the previous section:

```
package Coordinate_Class is
  type Coordinates is tagged private;

  procedure Plot(P: Coordinates);

  procedure Set_X(P: Coordinates; X: Float);
  function Get_X(P: Coordinates) return Float;
  -- similarly for Y
private
  type Coordinates is tagged
  record
    X : Float;
    Y : Float;
  end record;
end Coordinate_Class;
```

To extend this class and have visibility of the parent data attributes would require the package to be edited.

Child packages allow direct access to the parents' private components without going through the parents' interfaces. Hence, the following code

```
package Coordinate_Class.Three_D is
  -- "." indicates that package Three_D is a child of Coordinate_Class

  type Three_D is new Coordinates with private;

  -- new primitive operations
  procedure Set_Z(P: Coordinates; Z: Float);
  function Get_Z(P: Coordinates) return Float;

  procedure Plot(P: Three_D); -- overrides the Plot subprogram
private

  type Three_D is new Coordinates with
  record
    Z : Float;
  end record;
end Coordinate_Class.Three_D;
```

allows the implementation of the new and overridden primitive operations to have access to the original class's data attributes.

Controlled types

Further support for object-oriented programming is provided by *controlled* types. With these types, it is possible to define subprograms that are called (automatically) when objects of the type:

- are created – *initialize*;
- cease to exist – *finalize*;
- are assigned a new value – *adjust*.

To gain access to these features, the type must be derived from `Controlled`, a pre-defined type declared in the library package `Ada.Finalization`, that is, it must be part of the `Controlled` class hierarchy. The package `Ada.Finalization` defines procedures for `Initialize`, `Finalize` and `Adjust`. When a type is derived from `Controlled`, these procedures may be overridden. As objects typically cease to exist when they go out of scope, the exiting of a block may involve a number of calls of `Finalize`.

4.4.2   OOP and Java

In general there are at least two ways of introducing object-oriented programming facilities into a language. One is the approach advocated by programming language Oberon, (Wirth, 1988) which provides a type extension mechanism. It was this approach that was chosen by Ada. The alternative (and more popular approach) is to introduce the notion of *class* directly into the language.

In Chapter 3, a simple Java class for the date was introduced.

```
class Date
{
  int day, month, year;
}
```

This example only illustrates how data items can be grouped together. The full facilities of a class allow the data items (or instance variables or fields as Java calls them) to be encapsulated and, hence, an abstract data type to be easily produced.

The class for a queue abstraction will now be developed in Java. First, a package to contain the queue can be declared (if there is no named package, then the system assumes an unnamed package). Items from other packages can be imported. Then classes to be declared inside the package are given. One of these classes (Queue) is declared as 'public', and it is only this that can be accessed outside the package. The keyword **public** is termed a 'modifier' in Java, the other ones for classes being **abstract** and **final**. An **abstract** class is one from which no objects can be created. Hence the class has to be extended (to produce a subclass) and made non-abstract before objects can exist. A **final** modifier indicates that the class cannot be subclassed. No modifier indicates that the class is only accessible within the package.

Each class can declare local instance variables (or fields), constructor methods and ordinary (member) methods. Constructor methods have the same name as their associated class. An appropriate constructor method is called when objects of the class are created. All methods of the object can also have associated modifiers. These dictate the accessibility of the method; **public, protected** and **private** are allowed: **public** allows full access, **protected** allows access only from within the same package or from within a subclass of the defining class, and **private** allows access only from within the defining class. Instance variables can also have these modifiers. Member methods and instance variables can have other modifiers which will be introduced throughout this book.

The code for the queue abstract data type can now be given.

```
import somepackage.Element; // import element type
package queues; // package name

class QueueNode // class local to package
{
  Element data;
  QueueNode next;
}

public class Queue // class available from outside the package
{

  QueueNode front, back; // instance variables

  public Queue() // public constructor
  {
    front = null;
```

```
    back = null;
  }

  public void insert(Element E) //  visible method
  {
    QueueNode newNode = new QueueNode();

    newNode.data = E;
    newNode.next = null;
    if(empty()) {
      front.next = newNode;
    } else {
      back.next = newNode;
    }
    back = newNode;
  }

  public void remove(Element E) //visible method
  {
    if(!empty()) {
      E = front.data;
      front = front.next;
    }
    // garbage collection will free up the QueueNode object
    //  which is now dangling
  }

  public boolean empty() // visible method
  {
    return (front == null);
  }
}
```

Note that there is no concept of a package specification as in Ada. However, a similar functionality can be provided using interfaces. See Section 4.5.2.

4.4.3 Inheritance and Java

Inheritance in Java is obtained by deriving one class from another. Multiple inheritance is not supported, although similar effects can be achieved using interfaces (see Section 4.5.2).

Consider again the coordinate example; a class structure for this abstract type is

```
package coordinate;

public class Coordinate  // remember Java is case sensitive
{
  float X;
  float Y;
```

```
public Coordinate(float initial_X, float initial_Y) // constructor
{
  X = initial_X;
  Y = initial_Y;
};

public void set(float F1, float F2)
{
  X = F1;
  Y = F2;
};

public float getX()
{
  return X;
};

public float getY()
{
  return Y;
};
};
```

This class can now be extended to produce a new class by naming the base class in the declaration of the derived class with the 'extends' keyword. The new class is placed in the same package.[1]

```
package coordinate;
public class ThreeDimension extends Coordinate {
  // subclass of Coordinate

  float Z; // new field

  public ThreeDimension(float initialX, float initialY,
         float initialZ) // constructor
  {
    super(initialX, initialY); // call superclass constructor
    Z = initialZ;
  };

  public void set(float F1, float F2, float F3) //overridden method
  {
    set(F1, F2); // call superclass set
    Z = F3;
  };

  public float getZ() // new method
  {
    return Z;
  };
};
```

---

[1] In Java, public classes must reside in their own file. Hence a package can be distributed across one or more files, and can be continually augmented.

A new field Z has been added and the constructor class has been defined, the set function has been overridden, and a new operation provided. Here, the constructor calls the base class constructor (via the **super** keyword) and then initializes the final dimension. Similarly, the set function calls the base class.

Unlike Ada, all method calls in Java are potentially dispatching (dynamically bound). For example, consider again the above example:

```
package coordinate;

public class Coordinate
{
   float X;
   float Y;

   public Coordinate(float initial_X, float initial_Y)
   {
     X = initial_X;
     Y = initial_Y;
   };

   public void set(float F1, float F2)
   {
     X = F1;
     Y = F2;
   };

   public float getX()
   {
     return X;
   };

   public float getY()
   {
     return Y;
   };

   public void plot()
   {
   // plot a two dimension point
   };
};
```

Here the method plot has been added. Now if plot is overridden in a child (sub) class:

```
package coordinate;
public class ThreeDimension extends Coordinate
{
   public ThreeDimension(float initialX, float initialY,
                  float initialZ)
   {
     super(initialX, initialY);
     Z = initialZ;
   };
```

```
  float Z;

  void set (float F1, float F2, float F3)
  {
    set (F1, F2);
    Z = F3;
  };

  float getZ ()
  {
    return Z;
  };

  public void plot ()
  {
    // plot a three dimension point
  };
};
```

Then the following:

```
{
  Coordinate A = new Coordinate(0f, 0f);
  A.plot ();
}
```

would plot a two dimension coordinate; where as

```
{
  Coordinate A = new Coordinate(0f, 0f);
  ThreeDimension B = new ThreeDimension(0f, 0f, 0f);

  A = B;
  A.plot ();
}
```

would plot a three-dimension coordinate even though A was originally declared to be of type Coordinate. This is because A and B are reference types. By assigning B to A only the reference has changed not the object itself.

4.4.4 The Object class

All classes in Java are implicit subclasses of a root class called Object. The definition of this class is given in Program 4.1 – (throw will be discussed in Section 6.3.2).

There are six methods in the Object class which are of interest in this book. The three wait and two notify methods are used for concurrency control and will be considered in Section 8.8. The sixth method is the finalize method. It is this method that gets called just before the object is destroyed. Hence by overriding this

Program 4.1   The Java Object class.

```
public class Object {
  public final class getClass();

  public String toString();
  public boolean equals(Object obj);
  public int hashCode();

  protected Object clone()
    throws CloneNotSupportedException;

  public final void wait()
    throws IllegalMonitorStateException,
      InterruptedException;
  public final void wait(long millis)
    throws IllegalMonitorStateException,
      InterruptedException;
  public final void wait(long millis, int nanos)
    throws IllegalMonitorStateException,
      InterruptedException;
  public final void notify()
    throws IllegalMonitorStateException;
  public final void notifyAll()
    throws IllegalMonitorStateException;

  protected void finalize()
    throws Throwable;
}
```

method, a child class can provide finalization for objects that are created from it. Of course, when a class overrides the `finalize` method, its last action should be to call the `finalize` method in its parent. However, it should be noted that `finalize` is only called when garbage collection is about to take place, and this may be sometime after the object is no longer in use; there are no destructor methods as in, say, C++. Hence this facility should not be used for reclaiming resources. An alternative approach using the exception handling facilities is preferred (see Section 6.3.2).

4.5 Reusability

Software production is an expensive business, with costs rising inexorably every year. One reason for the high costs is that software always seems to be constructed 'from scratch'. By comparison, the hardware engineer has a rich choice of well tried and tested components from which systems can be built. It has been a long held quest of software engineers to have a similar supply of software components. Unfortunately, apart from some specific areas (for example, numerical analysis) this quest has been largely unfulfilled. And yet reusable code would clearly have a beneficial effect on both the reliability and productivity of software construction.

Modern programming language techniques such as modular programming and object-oriented programming provide the foundations on which reusable software libraries can be constructed.

One inhibition to reusability is the strong typing model that was commended in Chapter 3. With such a model, a module for sorting integers, for example, cannot be used for sorting reals or records even though the basic algorithms are identical. This type of restriction, although necessary for other reasons, severely restricts reusability. The designers of Ada and Java have addressed this issue and have provide facilities that aids reuse without undermining the typing model. In Ada, the facility is based on the concept of generic modules. (A similar facility is provided by C++, where generic classes called **templates** can be defined.) In Java, a different method is employed using the notion of an interface. These are discussed in the next two subsections.

4.5.1   Generic programming in Ada

A **generic** is a template from which actual components can be **instantiated**. In essence, a generic will manipulate objects without regard to their type. An instantiation specifies an actual type. The language model ensures that any assumptions made about the type within the generic are checked against the type named in the instantiation. For example, a generic may assume that a **generic parameter** is of a discrete type. When an instantiation is made, the compiler will check that the specified type is discrete.

A measure of a generic's reusability can be derived from the restrictions placed on the generic parameters. At one extreme, if the instantiated type has to be, for example, a one-dimensional array of an integer type, then the generic is not particularly reusable. Alternatively, if any type can be used at instantiation then a high level of reuse has been obtained.

The parameter model for Ada generics is comprehensive and will not be described in detail here; rather, a couple of examples will be given that have high reusability.

Generic parameters are defined in a way that specifies what operations are applied to them within the generic body. If no operations at all are applied then the parameters are said to be **limited private**. If only assignments and equality tests are performed then the parameters are **private**. Components with high reuse have limited private or private parameters. For a first example, consider the Queuemod package. As so far given, although an abstract data type for queue is provided, all such queues must only hold objects of type Element. There is, clearly, a need for a generic in which the type of the object being manipulated is a parameter. Within the package body for Queuemod, objects of type Element were only assigned in and out of queues. The parameter can therefore be private.

```
generic
  type Element is private;
package Queuemod_Template is
  type Queue is limited private;
  procedure Create (Q : in out Queue);
```

```
   function Empty (Q : Queue) return Boolean;
   procedure Insert (Q : in out Queue; E : Element);
   procedure Remove (Q : in out Queue; E : out Element);
private
   type Queuenode;
   type Queueptr is access Queuenode;
   type Queuenode is
     record
       Contents : Element;
       Next : Queueptr;
     end record;
   type Queue is
     record
       Front : Queueptr;
       Back : Queueptr;
     end record;
end Queuemod_Template;

package body Queuemod_Template is
   -- the same as before
end Queuemod_Template;
```

An instantiation of this generic creates an actual package:

```
declare
   package Integer_Queues is new Queuemod_Template(Integer);
   type Processid is
     record
       . . .
     end record;
   package Process_Queues is new Queuemod_Template(Processid);
   Q1, Q2 : Integer_Queues.Queue;
   Pid : Process_Queues.Queue;
   P : Processid;
   use Integer_Queues;
   use Process_Queues;
begin
   Create(Q1);
   Create(Pid);
   . . .
   Insert(Pid,P);
   . . .
end;
```

Each of these packages defines an abstract data type for queue. But they are different as the element types are distinct.

The above discussion has concentrated upon generic parameters as types. Three other forms are available: constants, subprograms and packages. Buffers are often an important construct within real-time programs. They differ from queues in that they have a fixed size. The following shows the specification of a generic package for an abstract data type for buffers. Again, the element type is a generic parameter. In addition, the size of the buffer is a generic constant parameter; it has a default value of 32:

```ada
generic
  Size : Natural := 32;
  type Element is private;
package Buffer_Template is
  type Buffer is limited private;
  procedure Create(B : in out Buffer);
  function Empty(B : Buffer) return Boolean;
  procedure Place(B : in out Buffer; E : Element);
  procedure Take(B : in out Buffer; E : out Element);
private
  subtype Buffer_Range is Natural range  0..Size-1;
  type Buff is array(Buffer_Range) of Element;
  type Buffer is
    record
      Bf : Buff;
      Top : Buffer_Range := 0;
      Base: Buffer_Range := 0;
    end record;
end Buffer_Template;
```

An integer buffer of size 32 is instantiated as follows:

```ada
package Integer_Buffers is new Buffer_Template(Integer);
```

A buffer with 64 elements of some record type Rec is constructed with a similar instantiation:

```ada
package Rec_Buffers is new Buffer_Template(64,Rec);
```

As with parameters to subprograms, greater readability is furnished by using name association:

```ada
package Rec_Buffers is new Buffer_Template(Size => 64,
                                      Element => Rec);
```

An example of a generic subprogram parameter is given below. The generic package defines two procedures which both act upon an array of Elements. One procedure finds the largest Element; the other sorts the array. To implement these procedures it is necessary to compare any two Elements to see which is the greater. For scalar types the '>' operator is available; for general private types it is not. It follows that the generic package must import a '>' function.

```ada
generic
  Size : Natural;
  type Element is private;
  with function ">"(E1, E2 : Element) return Boolean;
package Array_Sort is
  type Vector is array(1..Size) of Element;
  procedure Sort(V: in out Vector);
  function Largest(V: Vector) return Element;
end Array_Sort;
```

The implementation of this generic is left as an exercise (Exercise 4.8) for the reader.

More sophisticated generic packages can be created by using packages (possibly themselves generic instantiations) as generic parameters. However, these will not be discussed, as they are not required for the material presented in the remaining chapters.

4.5.2   Interfaces in Java

Interfaces in Java augment classes to increase the reusability of code. An interface is a special form of class that defines the specification of a set of methods and constants. They are by definition abstract, so no instances of interfaces can be declared. Instead, one or more classes can implement an interface, and objects implementing interfaces can be passed as arguments to methods by defining the parameter to be of the interface type. What interfaces do, in effect, is to allow relationships to be constructed between classes outside of the class hierarchy.

Consider a 'generic' algorithms to sort arrays of objects. What is common about all classes that can be sorted is that they support a '<' or '>' operator. Consequently, this feature is encapsulated in an interface.

The Ordered interface defines a single method lessThan which takes as an argument an object whose class implements the Ordered interface. Any class which implements the Ordered interface must compare its object ordering with the argument passed and return whether it is less than the object.[2]

```
package interfaceExamples;

public interface Ordered {
  boolean lessThan (Ordered O);
};
```

The class for complex numbers is such a class.

```
import interfaceExamples.*;
class ComplexNumber implements Ordered
{
  // the class implements the Ordered interface

  protected float realPart;
  protected float imagPart;

  public boolean lessThan(Ordered O) // the interface implementation
  {
    ComplexNumber CN = (ComplexNumber) O; // cast the parameter

    if((realPart*realPart + imagPart*imagPart) <
        (CN.getReal()*CN.getReal() + CN.getImag()*CN.getImag()))
    {
```

---

[2]Compare this to the Ada style, where the comparison of two objects is performed by a function which takes **both** objects as parameters.

```
      return true;
    }
    return false;
  };

  public ComplexNumber (float I, float J) // constructor
  {
    realPart = I;
    imagPart = J;
  };

  public float getReal ()
  {
    return realPart;
  };

  public float getImag ()
  {
    return imagPart;
  };

}
```

Now it is possible to write algorithms which will sort this and any other class which implements the interface. For example, in Section 4.5.1 an Ada generic was given for an Array_Sort. The equivalent package in Java would be:

```
package interfaceExamples;

public class ArraySort
{
  public static void sort (Ordered oa[], int size) //sort method
  {
    Ordered tmp;
    int pos;

    for (int i = 0; i < size - 1;  i++) {
      pos = i;
      for (int j = i + 1; j < size; j++) {
        if (oa[j].lessThan(oa[pos])) {
          pos = j;
        }
      }
      tmp = oa[pos];
      oa[pos] = oa[i];
      oa[i] = tmp;
    };
  };

  public static Ordered largest(Ordered oa[], int size) // largest method
  {
    Ordered tmp;
    int pos;
```

```
    pos = 0;
    for (int i = 1; i < size; i++) {
      if (! oa[i].lessThan(oa[pos])) {
        pos = i;
      };
    };
    return oa[pos];
  };
}
```

The `sort` method takes two arguments: the first is an array of objects which implement the `Ordered` interface; the second is the number of items in the array. The implementation performs an exchange sort. The important point about this example is that when two objects are exchanged, it is the reference values that are exchanged; hence it does not matter what the type of object is (as long as it supports the `Ordered` interface).

To use the above classes and interfaces simply requires the following:

```
{
  ArraySort AR = new ArraySort();
  ComplexNumber arrayComplex[] = { // say
                  new ComplexNumber(6f,1f),
                  new ComplexNumber(1f, 1f),
                  new ComplexNumber(3f,1f),
                  new ComplexNumber(1f, 0f),
                  new ComplexNumber(7f,1f),
                  new ComplexNumber(1f, 8f),
                  new ComplexNumber(10f,1f),
                  new ComplexNumber(1f, 7f)
  };
  // array unsorted
  AR.sort(arrayComplex, 8);
  // array sorted
}
```

In fact, the package `java.lang` already defines an interface called `Comparable` with a function called `compareTo` which could be used in place of `Ordered`. Furthermore, there is a static method in `java.util.Arrays` called `sort` which implements a merge sort of objects.

Interfaces have three further properties which should be noted. Firstly, like classes, they can participate in single inheritance relationships with other interfaces. Secondly, a class can implement more than one interface, and hence much of the functionality of multiple inheritance can be achieved. Finally, interfaces also provide the mechanisms by which call-backs can be implemented. This is when a server needs to call a method defined in the caller's class.

Summary

In the evolution of programming languages, one of the most important constructs to have emerged is the module. This structure enables the complexity inherent in large real-time systems to be contained and managed. In particular, it supports

(1) information hiding

(2) separate compilation

(3) abstract data types

Both Ada and C have a static module structure. Ada uses 'open scope' so that all objects in scope at the declaration of a module are visible within it. C only informally supports modules, whereas Java supports a dynamic module structure in the form of a class. Both packages in Ada (and Java) and classes in Java have well-defined specifications which act as the interface between the module and the rest of the program.

Separate compilation enables libraries of precompiled components to be constructed. This encourages reusability and provides a repository for project software. This repository must, however, be subject to appropriate project management so that issues such as version control do not become a source of unreliability.

The decomposition of a large program into modules or classes is the essence of programming in the large. It is, however, important that this decomposition process does lead to well-defined modules.

The use of abstract data types (ADTs), or object-oriented programming, provides one of the main tools that programmers can use to manage large software systems. Again it is the module construct in both Ada and Java that enables ADTs to be built and used.

Languages that are strongly typed suffer from the restriction that modules cannot easily be reused as their behaviour is tied to the types of their parameters and subcomponents. This dependency is often more than is required. Ada's and C++'s provision of a generic primitive is an attempt to improve the reusability of software. Generic packages and procedures can be defined which act as templates from which real code can be instantiated. In Java, the same effect is achieved through interfaces. The appropriate use of these facilities should reduce the cost, while improving the reliability, of real-time programs.

Further reading

Ben-Ari, M. (1998) *Ada for Software Engineers*. Chichester: Wiley.

Darnell, P. A. and Margolis, P. E. (1996) *C: A Software Engineering Approach*. London: Springer-Verlag.

Meyer, B. (1992) *Eiffel: The Language*. New York: Prentice Hall.

Sommerville, I. (2001) *Software Engineering*, 6th Edition. Reading, MA: Addison-Wesley.

Horstmann, C. S. and Cornell, G. (1999) *Core Java Fundamentals*. Sun Microsystems.

Schach, S. R. (1997) *Software Engineering with Java*. Chicago, IL: Richard Irwin.

Exercises

4.1   Why is the procedure not sufficient as a program module?

4.2   Distinguish between separate compilation, independent compilation and multi-programming.

4.3   Evaluate the C approach to modular programming.

4.4   What advantages and disadvantages would there be to having Ada packages as first-class language objects?

4.5   Compare and contrast the Ada and C mechanisms for passing functions as parameters to other functions.

4.6   Compare and contrast the Ada and Java OOP facilities.

4.7   Define an abstract data type for time. What operations are applicable on time values?

4.8   Implement the Ada generic package given in Section 4.5.1. Illustrate its use by showing how to sort any array of buffers (assume that one buffer is 'greater than' another if it has more elements in it).

4.9   OOP allows the run-time dispatching of operations. Should a real-time programming language only use static binding?

4.10 In Java, all objects are dynamically allocated. Discuss the implication of garbage collection for real-time programming.

4.11 To what extent do Ada 95 and Java support multiple inheritance?

4.12 Ada 95 supports the notion of child packages. Discuss the role they play in Ada's overall support for OOP.

Chapter 5
Reliability and fault tolerance

Reliability and safety requirements are usually much more stringent for real-time and embedded systems than for other computer systems. For example, if an application which computes the solution to some scientific problem fails then it may be reasonable to abort the program, as only computer time has been lost. However, in the case of an embedded system, this may not be an acceptable action. A process control computer, for instance, responsible for the operation of a large gas furnace, cannot afford to close down the furnace as soon as a fault occurs. Instead, it must try to provide a degraded service and prevent a costly shutdown operation. More importantly, real-time computer systems may endanger human lives if they abandon control of their application. An embedded computer controlling a nuclear reactor must not let the reactor run out of control, as this may result in a core meltdown and an emission of radiation. An avionics system should at least allow the pilot to eject before permitting the plane to crash!

Nowadays, more and more control functions previously performed by human operators or proven analogue methods, are being administered by digital computers. In 1955, only 10% of US weapons systems required computer software; by the early 1980s, this figure had risen to 80% (Leveson, 1986). There are many examples where faults in software have resulted in mission failures. In the early 1970s, the software in a French meteorological satellite responsible for controlling high-altitude weather balloons issued an 'emergency self-destruct' request instead of a 'read data' request. The outcome was that 72 out of 141 balloons were destroyed (Leveson, 1986). Many similarly alarming examples have been documented, and it is reasonable to assume that far more have not. In 1986, Hecht and Hecht (1986b) studied large software systems and concluded that, typically, for every million lines of code, 20 000 bugs entered the software; normally 90% of these were found by testing. A further 200 faults would surface during the first year of operation, leaving 1800 bugs undetected. Routine maintenance would usually result in 200 bug fixes and 200 new faults!

The more society relinquishes control of its vital functions to computer systems, the more imperative it becomes that those systems do not fail. Without wishing to define precisely what is meant by a system failure or a fault (at the moment), there are, in general, four sources of faults which can result in an embedded system failure.

(1) Inadequate specification. It has been suggested that the great majority of software faults stem from inadequate specification (Leveson, 1986).

(2) Faults introduced from design errors in software components.

(3) Faults introduced by failure of one or more processor components of the embedded systems.

(4) Faults introduced by transient or permanent interference in the supporting communication subsystem.

It is these last three types of fault which impinge on the programming language used in the implementation of an embedded system. The errors introduced by design faults are, in general, unanticipated (in terms of their consequences), whereas those from processor and network failure are, in some senses, predictable. One of the main requirements, therefore, for any real-time programming language, is that it must facilitate the construction of highly dependable systems. In this chapter, some of the general design techniques that can be used to improve the overall reliability of embedded computer systems are considered. Chapter 6 will show how **exception handling** facilities can be used to help implement some of these design philosophies, particularly those based on **fault tolerance**. Issues concerning processor and communication failure are deferred until Chapter 14.

5.1   Reliability, failure and faults

Before proceeding, more precise definitions of reliability, failures and faults are necessary. Randell et al. (1978) define the **reliability** of a system to be

Figure 5.1   Fault, error, failure, fault chain.

a measure of the success with which the system conforms to some authoritative specification of its behaviour.

Ideally, this specification should be complete, consistent, comprehensible and unambiguous. It should also be noted that the *response times* of the system are an important part of the specification, although discussion of the meeting of deadlines will be postponed until Chapter 13. The above definition of reliability can now be used to define a system **failure**. Again, quoting from Randell et al.

> When the behaviour of a system deviates from that which is specified for it, this is called a failure.

Section 5.9 will deal with the metrics of reliability; for the time being, *highly reliable* will be considered synonymous with a *low failure rate*.

The alert reader will have noticed that our definitions, so far, have been concerned with the *behaviour* of a system; that is, its *external* appearance. Failures result from unexpected problems internal to the system which eventually manifest themselves in the system's external behaviour. These problems are called **errors** and their mechanical or algorithmic cause are termed **faults**. A faulty component of a system is, therefore, a component which, under a particular set of circumstances during the lifetime of the system, will result in an error. Viewed in terms of state transitions, a system can be considered as a number of *external* and *internal* states. An external state which is not specified in the behaviour of the system is regarded as a failure of the system. The system itself consists of a number of components, each with their own states, all of which contribute to the system's external behaviour. The combined states of these components are termed the internal state of the system. An internal state which is not specified is called an error and the component which produced the illegal state transition is said to be faulty.

Of course, a system is usually composed of components; each of these may be considered as a system in its own right. Hence a failure in one system will lead to a fault in another which will result in an error and potential failure of that system. This in turn will introduce a fault into any surrounding system and so on (as illustrated in Figure 5.1).

Three types of fault can be distinguished.

(1) **Transient faults** A transient fault starts at a particular time, remains in the system for some period and then disappears. Examples of such faults occur in hardware components which have an adverse reaction to some external interference, such

as electrical fields or radioactivity. After the disturbance disappears so does the fault (although not necessarily the induced error). Many faults in communication systems are transient.

(2) **Permanent faults** Permanent faults start at a particular time and remain in the system until they are repaired; for example, a broken wire or a software design error.

(3) **Intermittent faults** These are transient faults that occur from time to time. An example is a hardware component that is heat sensitive, it works for a time, stops working, cools down and then starts to work again.

To create reliable systems, all these types of fault must be prevented from causing erroneous system behaviour (that is failure). The difficulty this presents is compounded by the indirect use of computers in the *construction* of safety-critical systems. For example, in 1979 an error was discovered in a program used to design nuclear reactors and their supporting cooling systems. The fault that this caused in the reactor design had not been found during installation tests as it concerned the strength and structural support of pipes and valves. The program had supposedly guaranteed the attainment of earthquake safety standards in operating reactors. The discovery of the bug led to the shutting down of five nuclear power plants (Leveson, 1986).

5.2 Failure modes

A system can fail in many different ways. A designer who is using system X to implement another system, Y, usually makes some assumptions about X's expected failure modes. If X fails differently from that which was expected then system Y may fail as a result.

A system provides services. It is, therefore, possible to classify a system's failure modes according to the impact they have on the services it delivers. Two general domains of failure modes can be identified:

- Value failure – the value associated with the service is in error;
- Time failure – the service is delivered at the wrong time.

Combinations of value and timing failures are often termed **arbitrary**.

In general, a value error might still be within the correct range of values or be outside the range expected from the service. The latter is equivalent to a typing error in programming languages and is called a **constraint error**. It is usually easy to recognize this type of failure.

Failures in the time domain can result in the service being delivered:

- too early – the service is delivered earlier than required
- too late – the service is delivered later than required (often called a **performance error**)

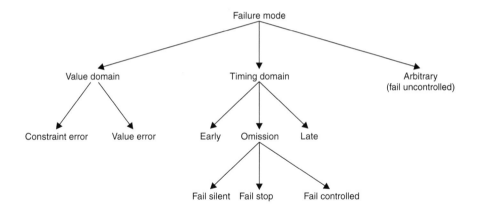

Figure 5.2   Failure mode classification.

- infinitely late – the service is never delivered (often called an **omission failure**).

One further failure mode should be identified, which is where a service is delivered which is not expected. This is often called a **commission** or **impromptu** failure. It is, of course, often difficult to distinguish between a failure in both the value and the time domain from an commission failure followed by an omission failure. Figure 5.2 illustrates the failure mode classification.

Given the above classification of failure modes, it is now possible to make some assumptions about how a system might fail:

- **Fail uncontrolled** – a system which can produce arbitrary errors in both the value and the time domains (including impromptu errors).

- **Fail late** – a system which produces correct services in the value domain but may suffer from a 'late' timing error.

- **Fail silent** – a system which produces correct services in both the value and time domains until it fails; the only failure possible is an omission failure and when this occurs all following services will also suffer an omission failure.

- **Fail stop** – a system which has all the properties of fail silent, but also permits other systems to detect that it has entered the fail-silent state.

- **Fail controlled** – a system which fails in a specified controlled manner.

- **Fail never** – a system which always produces correct services in both the value and the time domain.

Other assumptions are clearly possible, but the above list will suffice for this book.

5.3   Fault prevention and fault tolerance

Two approaches that can help designers improve the reliability of their systems can
be distinguished (Anderson and Lee, 1990). The first is known as **fault prevention**;
this attempts to eliminate any possibility of faults creeping into a system before it goes
operational. The second is **fault tolerance**; this enables a system to continue functioning
even in the presence of faults. Both approaches attempt to produce systems which have
well-defined failure modes.

5.3.1   Fault prevention

There are two stages to fault prevention: **fault avoidance** and **fault removal** .
     Fault avoidance attempts to limit the introduction of potentially faulty components
during the construction of the system. For hardware this may entail (Randell et al.,
1978):

- the use of the most reliable components within the given cost and performance
  constraints;
- the use of thoroughly-refined techniques for the interconnection of components
  and the assembly of subsystems;
- packaging the hardware to screen out expected forms of interference.

The software components of large embedded systems are nowadays much more complex
than their hardware counterparts. Although software does not deteriorate with use, it is
virtually impossible in all cases to write fault-free programs. It was noted in Chapters 2
and 4, however, that the quality of software can be improved by:

- rigorous, if not formal, specification of requirements;
- the use of proven design methodologies;
- the use of languages with facilities for data abstraction and modularity;
- the use of software engineering tools to help manipulate software components
  and thereby manage complexity.

In spite of fault avoidance techniques, faults will inevitably be present in the system
after its construction. In particular, there may be design errors in both hardware and
software components. The second stage of fault prevention, therefore, is *fault removal*.
This normally consists of procedures for finding and then removing the causes of errors.
Although techniques such as design reviews, program verification, and code inspections
may be used, emphasis is usually placed on system testing. Unfortunately, system testing can never be exhaustive and remove all potential faults. In particular, the following
problems exist.

- A test can only be used to show the presence of faults, not their absence.

- It is sometimes impossible to test under realistic conditions – one of the major causes for concern over the American Strategic Defense Initiative was the impossibility of testing any system realistically except under battle conditions. Most tests are done with the system in simulation mode and it is difficult to guarantee that the simulation is accurate. The last French nuclear testing in the Pacific was allegedly to allow data to be collected so that future tests could be simulated more accurately.

- Errors that have been introduced at the requirements stage of the system's development may not manifest themselves until the system goes operational. For example, in the design of the F18 aircraft an erroneous assumption was made concerning the length of time taken to release a wing-mounted missile. The problem was discovered when the missile failed to separate from the launcher after ignition, causing the aircraft to go violently out of control (Leveson, 1986).

In spite of all the testing and verification techniques, hardware components will fail; the fault prevention approach will, therefore, be unsuccessful when either the frequency or duration of repair times are unacceptable, or the system is inaccessible for maintenance and repair activities. An extreme example of the latter is the crewless spacecraft Voyager.

5.3.2 Fault tolerance

Because of the inevitable limitations of the fault prevention approach, designers of embedded systems must consider the use of fault tolerance. Of course, this does not mean that attempts at preventing faulty systems from becoming operational should be abandoned. However, this book will focus on fault tolerance rather than fault prevention.

Several different levels of fault tolerance can be provided by a system.

- **Full fault tolerance** – the system continues to operate in the presence of faults, albeit for a limited period, with no significant loss of functionality or performance.

- **Graceful degradation** (or fail soft) – the system continues to operate in the presence of errors, accepting a partial degradation of functionality or performance during recovery or repair.

- **Fail safe** – the system maintains its integrity while accepting a temporary halt in its operation.

The level of fault tolerance required will depend on the application. Although in theory most safety-critical systems require full fault tolerance, in practice many settle for graceful degradation. In particular, those systems which can suffer physical damage, such as combat aircraft, may provide several degrees of graceful degradation. Also, with highly complex applications which have to operate on a continuous basis (they have *high availability* requirements) graceful degradation is a necessity, as full fault tolerance is not achievable for indefinite periods. For example, the Federal Aviation Administration's Advanced Automation System, which provides automated services to

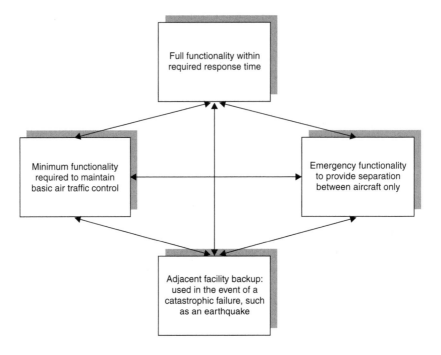

Figure 5.3   Graceful degradation and recovery in an air traffic control system.

both *en route* and terminal air traffic controllers throughout the USA, has three levels of graceful degradation for its area control computer couplers (Avizienis and Ball, 1987). This is illustrated in Figure 5.3.

In some situations, it may simply be necessary to shut down the system in a safe state. These fail-safe systems attempt to limit the amount of damage caused by a failure. For example, the A310 Airbus's slat and flap control computers, on detecting an error on landing, restore the system to a safe state and then shut down. In this situation, a safe state is having both wings with the same settings; only asymmetric settings are hazardous in landing (Martin, 1982).

Early approaches to the design of fault-tolerant systems made three assumptions:

(1) the algorithms of the system have been correctly designed,

(2) all possible failure modes of the components are known,

(3) all possible interactions between the system and the environment have been fore-
seen.

However, the increasing complexity of computer software and the introduction of VLSI hardware components mean that it is no longer possible to make these assumptions (if it ever was). Consequently, both anticipated and unanticipated faults must be catered for. The latter include both hardware and software design faults.

5.3.3 Redundancy

All techniques for achieving fault tolerance rely on extra elements introduced into the system to detect and recover from faults. These components are redundant in the sense that they are not required for the system's normal mode of operation. This is often called **protective redundancy**. The aim of fault tolerance is to minimize redundancy while maximizing the reliability provided, subject to the cost and size constraints of the system. Care must be taken in structuring fault-tolerant systems because the added components inevitably increase the complexity of the overall system. This itself can lead to *less* reliable systems. For example, the first launch of the Space Shuttle was aborted because of a synchronization difficulty with the replicated computer systems (Garman, 1981). To help reduce problems associated with the interaction between redundant components, it is therefore advisable to separate out the fault-tolerant components from the rest of the system.

There are several different classifications of redundancy, depending on which system components are under consideration and which terminology is being used. Software fault tolerance is the main focus of this chapter and therefore only passing reference will be made to hardware redundancy techniques. For hardware Anderson and Lee (1990), distinguish between *static* (or masking) and *dynamic* redundancy. With static redundancy, redundant components are used inside a system (or subsystem) to hide the effects of faults. An example of static redundancy is **Triple Modular Redundancy** (TMR). TMR consists of three identical subcomponents and majority voting circuits. The circuits compare the output of all the components, and if one differs from the other two that output is masked out. The assumption here is that the fault is not due to a common aspect of the subcomponents (such as a design error), but is either transient or due to component deterioration. Clearly, to mask faults from more than one component requires more redundancy. The general term *N Modular Redundancy* (NMR) is therefore used to characterize this approach.

Dynamic redundancy is the redundancy supplied inside a component which indicates explicitly or implicitly that the output is in error. It therefore provides an *error detection* facility rather than an error-masking facility; recovery must be provided by another component. Examples of dynamic redundancy are checksums on communication transmissions and parity bits on memories.

For fault tolerance of software design errors, two general approaches can be identified. The first is analogous to hardware masking redundancy and is called N-version programming. The second is based on error detection and recovery; it is analogous to dynamic redundancy in the sense that the recovery procedures are brought into action after an error has been detected. This issue of tolerating hardware faults will be returned to in Section 14.5 where software techniques will be used.

5.4 *N*-version programming

The success of hardware TMR and NMR have motivated a similar approach to software fault tolerance. However, software does not deteriorate with use, so the approach is used to focus on detecting design faults. In fact, this approach (which is now know as N-version programming) was first advocated by Babbage in 1837(Randell, 1982):

> When the formula is very complicated, it may be algebraically arranged for computation in two or more distinct ways, and two or more sets of cards may be made. If the same constants are now employed with each set, and if under these circumstances the results agree, we may then be quite secure of the accuracy of them all.

N-version programming is defined as the independent generation of N (where N is greater than or equal to 2) functionally equivalent programs from the same initial specification (Chen and Avizienis, 1978). The independent generation of N programs means that N individuals or groups produce the required N versions of the software *without interaction* (for this reason N-version programming is often called **design diversity**). Once designed and written, the programs execute concurrently with the same inputs and their results are compared by a **driver process**. In principle, the results should be identical, but in practice there may be some difference, in which case the consensus result, assuming there is one, is taken to be correct.

N-version programming is based on the assumptions that a program can be completely, consistently and unambiguously specified, and that programs which have been developed independently will fail independently. That is, there is no relationship between the faults in one version and the faults in another. This assumption may be invalidated if each version is written in the same programming language, because errors associated with the implementation of the language may be common between versions. Consequently, different programming languages and different development environments should be used. Alternatively, if the same language is used, compilers and support environments from different manufacturers should be employed. Furthermore, in either case, to protect against physical faults, the N versions must be distributed to separate machines which have fault-tolerant communication lines. On the Boeing 777 flight control system, a single Ada program was produced but three different processors and three distinct compilers were used to obtain diversity.

The N-version program is controlled by a driver process which is responsible for

- invoking each of the versions,
- waiting for the versions to complete,
- comparing and acting on the results.

So far it has been implicitly assumed that the programs or processes run to completion before the results are compared, but for embedded systems this often will not be the case; such processes may never complete. The driver and N versions must, therefore, communicate during the course of their executions.

It follows that these versions, although independent, must interact with the driver program. This interaction is specified in the requirements for the versions. It consists of three components (Chen and Avizienis, 1978):

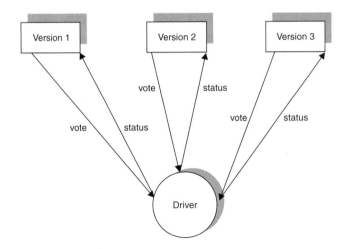

Figure 5.4   *N*-version programming.

(1) comparison vectors,

(2) comparison status indicators,

(3) comparison points.

How the versions communicate and synchronize with the driver will depend on the programming language used and its model of concurrency (see Chapters 7, 8 and 9). If different languages are used for different versions, then a real-time operating system will usually provide the means of communication and synchronization. The relationship between the *N* versions and the driver for an *N* = 3 version system is shown diagrammatically in Figure 5.4.

Comparison vectors are the data structures which represent the outputs, or votes, produced by the versions plus any attributes associated with their calculation; these must be compared by the driver. For example, in an air traffic control system, if the values being compared are the positions of aircraft, an attribute may indicate whether the values were the result of a recent radar reading or calculated on the basis of old readings.

The comparison status indicators are communicated from the driver to the versions; they indicate the actions that each version must perform as a result of the driver's comparison. Such actions will depend on the outcome of the comparison: whether the votes agreed and whether they were delivered on time. Possible outcomes include:

- continuation,
- termination of one or more versions,
- continuation after changing one or more votes to the majority value.

The comparison points are the points in the versions where they must communicate their votes to the driver process. As Hecht and Hecht (1986a) point out, an important design decision is the frequency with which the comparisons are made. This is the **granularity** of the fault tolerance provision. Fault tolerance of large granularity, that is, infrequent comparisons, will minimize the performance penalties inherent in the comparison strategies and permit a large measure of independence in the version design. However, a large granularity will probably produce a wide divergence in the results obtained because of the greater number of steps carried out between comparisons. The problems of vote comparison or voting (as it is often called) are considered in the next subsection. Fault tolerance of a fine granularity requires commonality of program structures at a detailed level, and therefore reduces the degree of independence between versions. A frequent number of comparisons also increases the overheads associated with this technique.

5.4.1   Vote comparison

Crucial to N-version programming is the efficiency and the ease with which the driver program can compare votes and decide whether there is any disagreement. For applications which manipulate text or perform integer arithmetic there will normally be a single correct result; the driver can easily compare votes from different versions and choose the majority decision.

Unfortunately, not all results are of an exact nature. In particular, where votes require the calculation of real numbers, it will be unlikely that different versions will produce exactly the same result. This might be due to the inexact hardware representation of real numbers or the data sensitivity of a particular algorithm. The techniques used for comparing these types of results are called **inexact voting**. One simple technique is to conduct a range check using a previous estimation or a median value taken from all N results. However, it can be difficult to find a general inexact voting approach.

Another difficulty associated with finite-precision arithmetic is the so-called **consistent comparison problem** (Brilliant et al., 1987). The trouble occurs when an application has to perform a comparison based on a finite value given in the specification; the result of the comparison then determines the course of action to be taken. As an example, consider a process control system which monitors temperature and pressure sensors and then takes appropriate actions according to their values to ensure the integrity of the system. Suppose that when either of these readings passes a threshold value some corrective course of action must be taken. Now consider a 3-version software system (V_1, V_2, V_3) each of which must read both sensors, decide on some action and then vote on the outcome (there is no communication between the versions until they vote). As a result of finite-precision arithmetic, each version will calculate different values (say T_1, T_2, T_3 for the temperature sensor and P_1, P_2, P_3 for the pressure sensor). Assuming that the threshold value for temperature is T_{th} and for pressure P_{th}, the consistent comparison problem occurs when both readings are around their threshold values.

The situation might occur where T_1 and T_2 are just below T_{th} and T_3 just above; consequently V_1 and V_2 will follow their normal execution paths and V_3 will take some

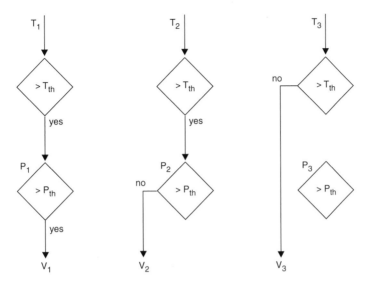

Figure 5.5 Consistent comparison problem with three versions.

corrective action. Now if versions V_1 and V_2 proceed to another comparison point, this time with the pressure sensor, then it is possible that P_1 could be just below and P_2 just above P_{th}. The overall result will be that all three versions will have followed different execution paths, and therefore produce different results, each of which is valid. This process is represented diagrammatically in Figure 5.5.

At first sight, it might seem appropriate to use inexact comparison techniques and assume that the values are equal if they differ by a tolerance Δ, but as Brilliant et al. (1987) point out, the problem reappears when the values are close to the threshold value $\pm\Delta$.

Still further problems exist with vote comparison when multiple solutions to the same problem naturally exist. For example, a quadratic equation may have more than one solution. Once again disagreement is possible, even though no fault has occurred (Anderson and Lee, 1990).

5.4.2 Principal issues in *N*-version programming

It has been shown that the success of *N*-version programming depends on several issues, which are now briefly reviewed.

(1) **Initial specification** – It has been suggested that the great majority of software faults stem from inadequate specification (Leveson, 1986). Current techniques

are a long way from producing complete, consistent, comprehensible and un-ambiguous specifications, although formal specification methods are proving a fruitful line of research. Clearly a specification error will manifest itself in all N versions of the implementation.

(2) **Independence of design effort** – Some experiments (Knight et al., 1985; Avizie-nis et al., 1988; Brilliant et al., 1990; Eckhardt et al., 1991; Hatton, 1997) have been undertaken to test the hypothesis that independently produced software will display distinct failures; however, they produce conflicting results. Knight et al. (1985) have shown that for a particular problem with a thoroughly refined specifi-cation, the hypothesis had to be rejected at the far from adequate 99% confidence level. In contrast, Avizienis et al. (1988) found that it was very rare for iden-tical faults to be found in two versions of a six-version system. In comparing their results and those produced by Knight et al., they concluded that the problem addressed by Knight et al. had limited potential for diversity, the programming process was rather informally formulated, testing was limited, and the acceptance test was totally inadequate according to common industrial standards. Avizienis et al. claim that the rigorous application of the N-version programming paradigm would have led to the elimination of all of the errors reported by Knight et al. before the acceptance of the system. However, there is concern that where part of a specification is complex this will inevitably lead to a lack of understanding of the requirements by all the independent teams. If these requirements also refer to rarely occurring input data, then common design errors may not be caught during system testing. In more recent years, studies by Hatton (1997) found that a three-version system is still around 5 to 9 times more reliable than a single-version high-quality system.

(3) **Adequate budget** – With most embedded systems, the predominant cost is soft-ware. A three-version system will therefore almost triple the budget requirement and cause problems for maintenance personnel. In a competitive environment, it is unlikely that a potential contractor will propose an N-version technique unless it is mandatory. Furthermore, it is unclear whether a more reliable system would be produced if the resources potentially available for constructing N version were instead used to produce a single version.

It has also been shown that in some instances it is difficult to find inexact voting algo-rithms, and that unless care is taken with the consistent comparison problem, votes will differ even in the absence of faults.

Although N-version programming may have a role in producing reliable software it should be used with care and in conjunction with other techniques; for example, those discussed below.

5.5   Software dynamic redundancy

N-version programming is the software equivalent of static or masking redundancy, where faults inside a component are hidden from the outside. It is static because each version of the software has a fixed relationship with every other version and the driver; and because it operates whether or not faults have occurred. With **dynamic** redundancy, the redundant components only come into operation *when* an error has been detected.

This technique of fault tolerance has four constituent phases (Anderson and Lee, 1990).

(1) **Error detection** – Most faults will eventually manifest themselves in the form of an error; no fault tolerance scheme can be utilized until that error is detected.

(2) **Damage confinement and assessment** – When an error has been detected, it must be decided to what extent the system has been corrupted (this is often called *error diagnosis*); the delay between a fault occurring and the manifestation of the associated error means that erroneous information could have spread throughout the system.

(3) **Error recovery** – This is one of the most important aspects of fault tolerance. Error recovery techniques should aim to transform the corrupted system into a state from which it can continue its normal operation (perhaps with degraded functionality).

(4) **Fault treatment and continued service** – An error is a symptom of a fault; although the damage may have been repaired the fault may still exist, and therefore the error may recur unless some form of maintenance is undertaken.

Although these four phases of fault tolerance are discussed under software dynamic redundancy techniques, they can clearly be applied to *N*-version programming. As Anderson and Lee (1990) have noted: error detection is provided by the driver which does the vote checking; damage assessment is not required because the versions are independent; error recovery involves discarding the results in error, and fault treatment is simply ignoring the version determined to have produced the erroneous value. However, if all versions have produced differing votes then error detection takes place, but there are *no* recovery facilities.

The next sections briefly cover the above phases of fault tolerance. For a fuller discussion, the reader is referred to Anderson and Lee (1990).

5.5.1 Error detection

The effectiveness of any fault tolerant system depends on the effectiveness of its error detection techniques. Two classes of error detection techniques can be identified.

- **Environmental detection**. These are the errors which are detected in the environment in which the program executes. They include those that are detected by the hardware, such as 'illegal instruction executed', 'arithmetic overflow' and 'protection violation'. They also include errors detected by the run-time support system for the real-time programming language; for example, 'array bounds error', 'null pointer referenced' and 'value out of range'. These type of error will be considered in the context of the Ada and Java programming languages in Chapter 6.

- **Application detection**. These are the errors that are detected by the application itself. The majority of techniques that can be used by the application fall into the following broad categories.

  - **Replication checks**. It has been shown that N-version programming can be used to tolerate software faults and that the technique can be used to provide error detection (by using two-version redundancy).
  - **Timing checks**. Two types of timing check can be identified. The first involves a **watchdog timer** process that, if not reset within a certain period by a component, assumes that the component is in error. The software component must continually reset the timer to indicate that it is functioning correctly.

    In embedded systems, where timely responses are important, a second type of check is required. These enable the detection of faults associated with missed deadlines. Where deadline scheduling is performed by the underlying run-time support system, the detection of missed deadlines can be considered to be part of the environment. (Some of the problems associated with deadline scheduling will be covered in Chapter 13.)

    Of course, timing checks do *not* ensure that a component is functioning correctly, only that it is functioning on time! Time checks should therefore be used in conjunction with other error detection techniques.
  - **Reversal checks**. These are feasible in components where there is a one-to-one (isomorphic) relationship between the input and the output. Such a check takes the output, calculates what the input should be, and then compares the value with the actual input. For example, for a component which finds the square root of a number, the reversal check is simply to square the output and compare it with the input. (Note that inexact comparison techniques may have to be used when dealing with real numbers.)
  - **Coding checks**. Coding checks are used to test for the corruption of data. They are based on redundant information contained within the data. For example, a value (checksum) may be calculated and sent with the actual data to be transmitted over a communication network. When the data is received, the value can be recalculated and compared with the checksum.
  - **Reasonableness checks**. These are based on knowledge of the internal design and construction of the system. They check that the state of data or value of an object is reasonable, based on its intended use. Typically with modern real-time languages, much of the information necessary to perform these checks can be supplied by programmers, as type information associated with data objects. For example, integer objects which are constrained to be within certain values can be represented by subtypes of integers which have explicit ranges. Range violation can then be detected by the run-time support system.

    Sometimes explicit reasonableness checks are included in software components; these are commonly called **assertions** and take a logical expression which evaluates at run-time to true if no error is detected.

- **Structural checks**. Structural checks are used to check the integrity of data objects such as lists or queues. They might consist of counts of the number of elements in the object, redundant pointers, or extra status information.
- **Dynamic reasonableness checks**. With output emitted from some digital controllers, there is usually a relationship between any two consecutive outputs. Hence an error can be assumed if a new output is too different from the previous value.

Note that many of the above techniques may be applied also at the hardware level and therefore may result in 'environmental errors'.

5.5.2   Damage confinement and assessment

As there can be some delay between a fault occurring and an error being detected, it is necessary to assess any damage that may have occurred. While the type of error that was detected will give the error handling routine some idea of the damage, erroneous information could have spread throughout the system and into its environment. Thus damage assessment will be closely related to the damage confinement precautions that were taken by the system's designers. Damage confinement is concerned with structuring the system so as to minimize the damage caused by a faulty component. It is also known as **firewalling**.

There are two techniques that can be used for structuring systems which will aid damage confinement: **modular decomposition** and **atomic actions**. The merits of modular decomposition were discussed in Chapter 4. Here, the emphasis is simply that the system should be broken down into components where each component is represented by one or more modules. Interaction between components then occurs through well-defined interfaces, and the internal details of the modules are hidden and not directly accessible from the outside. This makes it more difficult for an error in one component to be indiscriminately passed to another.

Modular decomposition provides a *static* structure to the software system in that most of that structure is lost at run-time. Equally important to damage confinement is the *dynamic* structure of the system as it facilitates reasoning about the run-time behaviour of the software. One important dynamic structuring technique is based on the use of atomic actions.

> The activity of a component is said to be atomic if there are *no* interactions between the activity and the system for the duration of the action.

That is, to the rest of the system an atomic action appears to be *indivisible* and takes place *instantaneously*. No information can be passed from within the atomic action to the rest of the system and vice versa. Atomic actions are often called **transactions** or **atomic transactions**. They are used to move the system from one consistent state to another and constrain the flow of information between components. Where two or more components share a resource then damage confinement will involve constraining access to that resource. The implementation of this aspect of atomic actions, using the communication and synchronization primitives found in modern real-time languages, will be considered in Chapter 10.

Other techniques which attempt to restrict access to resources are based on **protection mechanisms**, some of which may be supported by hardware. For example, each resource may have one or more modes of operation each with an associated access list (for example, read, write and execute). An activity of a component, or process, will also have an associated mode. Every time a process accesses a resource the intended operation can be compared against its **access permissions** and, if necessary, access is denied.

5.5.3 Error recovery

Once an error situation has been detected and the damage assessed, error recovery procedures must be initiated. This is probably the most important phase of any fault-tolerance technique. It must transform an erroneous system state into one which can continue its normal operation, although perhaps with a degraded service. Two approaches to error recovery have been proposed: **forward** and **backward** recovery.

Forward error recovery attempts to continue from an erroneous state by making selective corrections to the system state. For embedded systems, this may involve making safe any aspect of the controlled environment which may be hazardous or damaged because of the failure. Although forward error recovery can be efficient, it is system specific and depends on accurate predictions of the location and cause of errors (that is, damage assessment). Examples of forward recovery techniques include redundant pointers in data structures and the use of self-correcting codes, such as Hamming Codes. An abort, or asynchronous exception, facility may also be required during the recovery action if more than one process is involved in providing the service when the error occurred.

Backward error recovery relies on restoring the system to a safe state previous to that in which the error occurred. An alternative section of the program is then executed. This has the same functionality as the fault-producing section, but uses a different algorithm. As with N-version programming, it is hoped that this alternative approach will *not* result in the same fault recurring. The point to which a process is restored is called a **recovery point** and the act of establishing it is usually termed **checkpointing**. To establish a recovery point, it is necessary to save appropriate system state information at run-time.

State restoration has the advantage that the erroneous state has been cleared and that it does not rely on finding the location or cause of the fault. Backward error recovery can therefore be used to recover from unanticipated faults including design errors. However, its disadvantage is that it cannot undo any effects that the fault may have had in the environment of the embedded system; it is difficult to undo a missile launch, for example. Furthermore, backward error recovery can be time-consuming in execution, which may preclude its use in some real-time applications. For instance, operations involving sensor information may be time dependent, therefore costly state restoration

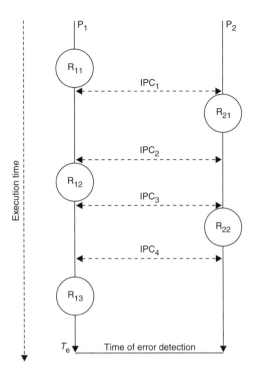

Figure 5.6   The domino effect.

techniques may simply not be feasible. Consequently, to improve performance **incremental checkpointing** approaches have been considered. The **recovery cache** is an example of such a system (Anderson and Lee, 1990). Other approaches include audit trails or logs; in these cases, the underlying support system must undo the effects of the process by reversing the actions indicated in the log.

With concurrent processes that interact with each other, state restoration is not as simple as so far portrayed. Consider two processes depicted in Figure 5.6. Process P_1 establishes recovery points R_{11}, R_{12} and R_{13}. Process P_2 establishes recovery points R_{21} and R_{22}. Also, the two processes communicate and synchronize their actions via IPC_1, IPC_2, IPC_3 and IPC_4. The abbreviation IPC is used to indicate interprocess Communication.

If P_1 detects an error at T_e then it is simply rolled back to recovery point R_{13}. However, consider the case where P_2 detects an error at T_e. If P_2 is rolled back to R_{22} then it must undo the communication IPC_4 with P_1; this requires P_1 to be rolled back to R_{12}. But if this is done, P_2 must be rolled back to R_{21} to undo communication IPC_3, and so on. The result will be that both processes will be rolled back to the beginning of their interaction with each other. In many cases, this may be equivalent to aborting both processes! This phenomenon is known as the **domino effect**.

Obviously, if the two processes do not interact with each other then there will be no domino effect. When more than two processes interact, the possibility of the effect occurring increases. In this case, consistent recovery points must be designed into the system so that an error detected in one process will not result in a total rollback of all the processes with which it interacts; instead, the processes can be restarted from a consistent set of recovery points. These **recovery lines**, as they are often called, are closely linked with the notion of atomic actions, introduced earlier in this section. The issue of error recovery in concurrent processes will be revisited in Chapter 10. For the remainder of this chapter, sequential systems only will be considered.

The concepts of forward and backward error recovery have been introduced; each has its advantages and disadvantages. Not only do embedded systems have to be able to recover from unanticipated errors but they also must be able to respond in finite time; they may therefore require *both* forward and backward error recovery techniques. The expression of backward error recovery in sequential experimental programming languages will be considered in the next section. Mechanisms for forward error recovery will not be considered further in this chapter because it is difficult to provide in an application-independent manner. However, in the next chapter the implementation of both forms of error recovery is considered within the common framework of exception handling.

5.5.4   Fault treatment and continued service

An error is a manifestation of a fault, and although the error recovery phase may have returned the system to an error-free state, the error may recur. Therefore the final phase of fault tolerance is to eradicate the fault from the system so that normal service can be continued.

The automatic treatment of faults is difficult to implement and tends to be system-specific. Consequently, some systems make no provision for fault treatment, assuming that all faults are transient; others assume that error recovery techniques are sufficiently powerful to cope with recurring faults.

Fault treatment can be divided into two stages: fault location and system repair. Error detection techniques can help to trace the fault to a component. For a hardware component this may be accurate enough and the component can simply be replaced. A software fault can be removed in a new version of the code. However, in most non-stop applications it will be necessary to modify the program while it is executing. This presents a significant technical problem, but will not be considered further here.

5.6   The recovery block approach to software fault tolerance

Recovery blocks(Horning et al., 1974) are **blocks** in the normal programming language sense except that, at the entrance to the block is an automatic **recovery point** and at the exit an **acceptance test**. The acceptance test is used to test that the system is in an acceptable state after the execution of the block (or **primary module** as it is often

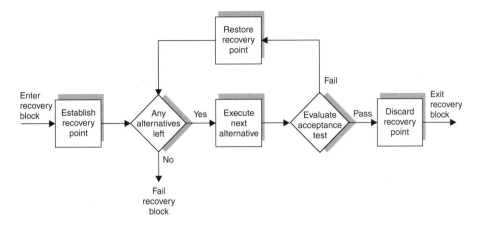

Figure 5.7   Recovery block mechanism.

called). The failure of the acceptance test results in the program being restored to the recovery point at the beginning of the block and an **alternative module** being executed. If the alternative module also fails the acceptance test then again the program is restored to the recovery point and yet another module is executed, and so on. If all modules fail then the block fails and recovery must take place at a higher level. The execution of a recovery block is illustrated in Figure 5.7.

In terms of the four phases of software fault tolerance: error detection is achieved by the acceptance test, damage assessment is not needed as backward error recovery is assumed to clear all erroneous states, and fault treatment is achieved by use of a stand-by spare.

Although no commercially available real-time programming language has language features for exploiting recovery blocks, some experimental systems have been developed (Shrivastava, 1978) (Purtilo and Jalote, 1991). A possible syntax for recovery blocks is illustrated below

```
ensure <acceptance test>
by
   <primary module>
else by
   <alternative module>
else by
   <alternative module>
   ...
else by
   <alternative module>
else error
```

Like ordinary blocks, recovery blocks can be nested. If a block in a nested recovery block fails its acceptance tests and all its alternatives also fail, then the outer level recovery point will be restored and an alternative module to that block executed.

To show the use of recovery blocks, the various methods used to find the numerical solution of a system of differential equations are considered. As such methods do not give exact solutions, but are subject to various errors, it may be found that some approaches will perform better for certain classes of equations than for others. Unfortunately, methods which give accurate results across a wide range of equations are expensive to implement (in terms of the time needed to complete the method's execution). For example, an **explicit Kutta** method will be more efficient than an **implicit Kutta** method. However, it will only give an acceptable error tolerance for particular problems. There is a class of equations called **stiff** equations whose solution using an explicit Kutta leads to an accumulation of rounding errors; the more expensive implicit Kutta method can more adequately deal with this problem. The following illustrates an approach using recovery blocks which enables the cheaper method to be employed for non-stiff equations but which does not fail when stiff equations are given.

```
ensure rounding_error_within_acceptable_tolerance
by
   Explicit Kutta Method
else by
   Implicit Kutta Method
else error
```

In this example, the cheaper explicit method is usually used; however, when it fails the more expensive implicit method is employed. Although this error is anticipated, this approach also gives tolerance to an error in the design of the explicit algorithm. If the algorithm itself is in error and the acceptance test is general enough to detect both types of error result, the implicit algorithm will be used. When the acceptance test cannot be made general enough, nested recovery blocks can be used. In the following, full design redundancy is provided; at the same time the cheaper algorithm is always used if possible.

```
ensure rounding_error_within_acceptable_tolerance
by
   ensure sensible_value
   by
     Explicit Kutta Method
   else by
     Predictor-Corrector K-step Method
   else error
else by
   ensure sensible_value
   by
     Implicit Kutta Method
   else by
     Variable Order K-Step Method
   else error
else error
```

In the above, two explicit methods are given; when both methods fail to produce a sensible result, the implicit Kutta method is executed. The implicit Kutta method will, of course, also be executed if the value produced by the explicit methods is sensible but not within the required tolerance. Only if all four methods fail will the equations remain unsolved.

The recovery block could have been nested the other way around as shown below. In this case, different behaviour will occur when a non-sensible result is also not within acceptable tolerance. In the first case, after executing the explicit Kutta algorithm, the Predictor Corrector method would be attempted. In the second, the implicit Kutta algorithm would be executed.

```
ensure sensible_value
by
  ensure rounding_error_within_acceptable_margin
  by
    Explicit Kutta Method
  else by
    Implicit Kutta Method
  else error
else by
  ensure rounding_error_within_acceptable_margin
  by
    Predictor-Corrector K-step Method
  else by
    Variable Order K-Step Method
  else error
else error
```

5.6.1   The acceptance test

The acceptance test provides the error detection mechanism which then enables the redundancy in the system to be exploited. The design of the acceptance test is crucial to the efficacy of the recovery block scheme. As with all error detection mechanisms, there is a trade-off between providing comprehensive acceptance tests and keeping the overhead this entails to a minimum, so that normal fault-free execution is affected as little as possible. Note that the term used is **acceptance** not **correctness**; this allows a component to provide a degraded service.

All the error detection techniques discussed in Section 5.5.1 can be used to form the acceptance tests. However, care must be taken in their design as a faulty acceptance test may lead to residual errors going undetected.

5.7   A comparison between *N*-version programming and recovery blocks

Two approaches to providing fault-tolerant software have been described: *N*-version programming and recovery blocks. They clearly share some aspects of their basic philosophy, and yet at the same time they are quite different. This section briefly reviews and compares the two.

- **Static versus dynamic redundancy**

  N-version programming is based on static redundancy; all versions run in parallel irrespective of whether or not a fault occurs. In contrast, recovery blocks are dynamic in that alternative modules only execute when an error has been detected.

- **Associated overheads**

  Both *N*-version programming and recovery blocks incur extra development cost, as both require alternative algorithms to be developed. In addition, for *N*-version programming, the driver process must be designed and recovery blocks require the design of the acceptance test.

  At run-time, *N*-version programming in general requires *N* times the resources of a single version. Although recovery blocks only require a single set of resources at any one time, the establishment of recovery points and the process of state restoration is expensive. However, it is possible to provide hardware support for the establishment of recovery points (Lee et al., 1980), and state restoration is only required when a fault occurs.

- **Diversity of design**

  Both approaches exploit diversity in design to achieve tolerance of unanticipated errors. Both are, therefore, susceptible to errors that originate from the requirements specification.

- **Error detection**

  N-version programming uses vote comparison to detect errors whereas recovery blocks use an acceptance test. Where exact or inexact voting is possible there is probably less associated overhead than with acceptance tests. However, where it is difficult to find an inexact voting technique, where multiple solutions exist or where there is a consistent comparison problem, acceptance tests may provide more flexibility.

- **Atomicity**

  Backward error recovery is criticized because it cannot undo any damage which may have occurred in the environment. *N*-version programming avoids this problem because all versions are assumed not to interfere with each other: they are atomic. This requires each version to communicate with the driver process rather than directly with the environment. However, it is entirely possible to structure a program such that unrecoverable operations do not appear in recovery blocks.

It perhaps should be stressed that although *N*-version programming and recovery blocks have been described as competing approaches, they also can be considered as complementary ones. For example, there is nothing to stop a designer using recovery blocks within each version of an *N*-version system.

5.8 Dynamic redundancy and exceptions

In this section, a framework for implementing software fault tolerance is introduced which is based on dynamic redundancy and the notion of exceptions and exception handlers.

So far in this chapter, the term 'error' has been used to indicate the manifestation of a fault, where a fault is a deviation from the specification of a component. These errors can be either anticipated, as in the case of an out of range sensor reading due to hardware malfunction, or unanticipated, as in the case of a design error in the component. An **exception** can be defined as the occurrence of an error. Bringing an exception condition to the attention of the invoker of the operation which caused the exception, is called **raising** (or **signalling** or **throwing**) the exception and the invoker's response is called **handling** (or **catching**) the exception. Exception handling can be considered a *forward error recovery* mechanism, as when an exception has been raised the system is not rolled back to a previous state; instead, control is passed to the handler so that recovery procedures can be initiated. However, as will be shown in Section 6.5, the exception handling facility can be used to provide backward error recovery.

Although an exception has been defined as the occurrence of an error, there is some controversy as to the true nature of exceptions and when they should be used. For example, consider a software component or module which maintains a compiler symbol table. One of the operations it provides is to look up a symbol. This has two possible outcomes: *symbol present* and *symbol absent*. Either outcome is an anticipated response *and* may or may not represent an error condition. If the *lookup* operation is used to determine the interpretation of a symbol in a program body, *symbol absent* corresponds to 'undeclared identifier', which is an error condition. If, however, the *lookup* operation is used during the declaration process, the outcome *symbol absent* is probably the normal case and *symbol present*, that is 'duplicate definition', the exception. What constitutes an error, therefore, depends on the context in which the event occurs. However, in either of the above cases it could be argued that the error is not an error of the symbol table component or of the compiler, in that either outcome is an anticipated result and forms part of the functionality of the symbol table module. Therefore neither outcome should be represented as an exception.

Exception-handling facilities were *not* incorporated into programming languages to cater for programmer design errors; however, it will be shown in Section 6.5 how they can be used to do just that. The original motivation for exceptions came from the requirement to handle abnormal conditions arising in the environment in which a program executes. These exceptions could be termed rare events in the functioning of the environment, and it may or may not be possible to recover from them within the program. A faulty valve or a temperature alarm might cause an exception. These are rare events which, given enough time, might well occur and must be tolerated.

Despite the above, exceptions and their handlers will inevitably be used as a general-purpose error-handling mechanism. To conclude, exceptions and exception handling can be used to:

- cope with abnormal conditions arising in the environment,
- enable program design faults to be tolerated,

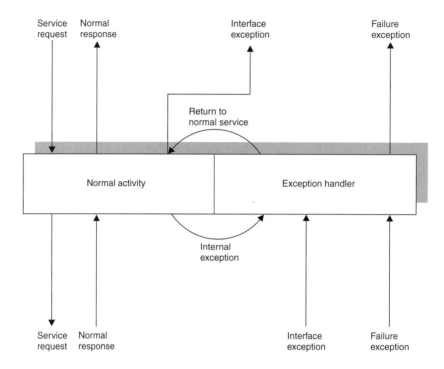

Figure 5.8   An ideal fault-tolerant component.

- provide a general-purpose error-detection and recovery facility.

Exceptions are considered in more detail in Chapter 6.

5.8.1   Ideal fault-tolerant system components

Figure 5.8 shows the ideal component from which to build fault-tolerant systems (Anderson and Lee, 1990). The component accepts service requests and, if necessary, calls upon the services of other components before yielding a response. This may be a normal response or an exception response. Two types of fault can occur in the ideal component: those due to an illegal service request, called **interface exceptions**, and those due to a malfunction in the component itself, or in the components required to service the original request. Where the component cannot tolerate these faults, either by forward or backward error recovery, it raises **failure exceptions** in the calling component. Before raising any exceptions, the component must return itself to a consistent state, if possible, in order that it may service any future request.

5.9   Measuring and predicting the reliability of software

Reliability metrics for hardware components have long been established. Traditionally, each component is regarded as a representative of a population of identical members whose reliability is estimated from the proportion of a sample that fail during testing. For example, it has been observed that, following an initial settling period, electronic components fail at a constant rate and their reliability at a time t can be modelled by

$$R(t) = Ge^{-\lambda t}$$

where G is a constant and λ is the sum of the failure rates of all constituent components. A commonly used metric is Mean Time Between Failures (MTBF) which for a system without redundancy is equal to $1/\lambda$.

Software reliability prediction and measurement is not yet a well-established discipline. It was ignored for many years by those industries requiring extremely reliable systems because software does not deteriorate with use; it was regarded as either reliable or not. Also, in the past, particular software components were used once only, in the systems for which they were originally intended; consequently, although any errors found during testing were removed, this did not lead to the development of more reliable components which could be used elsewhere. This can be contrasted with hardware components, which are mass produced; any errors found in the design can be corrected, making the next batch more reliable. However, it is now recognized that software reliability can be improved and software costs reduced by reuse of components. Unfortunately, our understanding of how to build reusable software components is far from comprehensive (see Section 4.5.1).

The view that software is either correct or not correct is still commonly held. If it is not correct, program testing or program proving will indicate the location of faults which can then be corrected. This chapter has tried to illustrate that the traditional approach of software testing, although indispensable, can never ensure that programs are fault-free, especially with very large and complicated systems where there may be residual specification or design errors. Furthermore, in spite of the rapid advances made in the field of proof of correctness, the application of these techniques to non-trivial systems, particularly those involving the concept of time, is still beyond the *state of the art* . It is for all these reasons that methods of improving reliability through the use of redundancy have been advocated. Unfortunately, even with this approach, it cannot be guaranteed that systems containing software will not fail. It is therefore essential that techniques for predicting or measuring their reliability are developed.

Software reliability can be considered as *the probability that a given program will operate correctly in a specified environment for a specified length of time* . Several models have been proposed which attempt to estimate software reliability. These can be broadly classified as (Goel and Bastini, 1985)

- software reliability growth models,

- statistical models.

Growth models attempt to predict the reliability of a program on the basis of its error history. Statistical models attempt to estimate the reliability of a program by determining its success or failure response to a random sample of test cases, without correcting any errors found. Growth models, in particular, are now quite mature and there is an extensive body of literature and industrial experience concerning their application (Littlewood and Strigini, 1993; Bennett, 1994; Lytz, 1995). However, Littlewood and Strigini (1993) have argued that testing alone can only provide evidence for reliability estimates of at best 10^{-4} (that is 10^{-4} errors per hour of operation). This should be compared with the often quoted reliability requirement of 10^{-9} for avionics and nuclear power applications.

5.10   Safety, reliability and dependability

The term 'safety' (which was defined informally in Chapter 2) can have its meaning extended to incorporate the issues raised in this chapter. Safety can thus be defined as *freedom from those conditions that can cause death, injury, occupational illness, damage to (or loss of) equipment (or property), or environmental harm* (Leveson, 1986). However, as this definition would consider most systems which have an element of risk associated with their use as unsafe, software safety is often considered in terms of **mishaps** (Leveson, 1986). A mishap is an **unplanned event** or **series of events** that can result in death, injury, occupational illness, damage to (or loss of) equipment (or property), or environmental harm.

Although reliability and safety are often considered as synonymous, there is a difference in their emphasis. Reliability has been defined as a measure of the success with which a system conforms to some authoritative specification of its behaviour. This is usually expressed in terms of probability. Safety, however, is the probability that conditions that can lead to mishaps do not occur *whether or not the intended function is performed*. These two definitions can conflict with each other. For example, measures which increase the likelihood of a weapon firing when required may well increase the possibility of its accidental detonation. In many ways, the only safe aeroplane is one that never takes off; however, it is not very reliable.

As with reliability, to ensure the safety requirements of an embedded system, system safety analysis must be performed throughout all stages of its life cycle development. It is beyond the scope of this book to enter into details of safety analysis; for a general discussion of software fault tree analysis – a technique used to analyze the safety of software design – the reader is referred to Leveson and Harvey (1983).

5.10.1   Dependability

Over the last decade much research has been carried out under the general name of reliable and fault-tolerant computing. Consequently, the terms have become overloaded and researchers have looked for new words and phrases to express the particular aspect they wish to emphasize. The terms 'safety' and 'security' are examples of this new

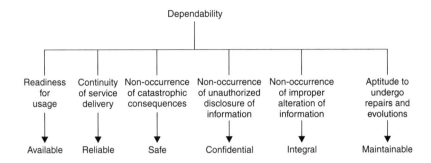

Figure 5.9   Aspects of dependability.

terminology. To this end, an attempt has been made to produce clear and widely accept-able definitions of the basic concepts found within this field. To this end, the notion of **dependability** has been introduced (Laprie, 1985) (Laprie, 1995).

The dependability of a system is that property of the system which allows reliance to be justifiably placed on the service it delivers. Dependability, therefore, includes as special cases the notions of reliability, safety and security. Figure 5.9, based on that given by Laprie (1995), illustrates these and other aspects of dependability (where se-curity is viewed in terms of integrity and confidentiality). In this figure, the term 'reli-ability' is used as a measure of the continuous delivery of a proper service; availability is a measure of the frequency of periods of improper service.

Dependability itself can be described in terms of three components (Laprie, 1995).

- *impairments* – circumstances causing or resulting from non-dependability;
- *means* – the methods, tools and solutions required to deliver a dependable service with the required confidence;
- *attributes* – the way and measures by which the quality of a dependable service can be appraised.

Figure 5.10 summarizes the concept of dependability in terms of these three compo-nents.

Although there is some agreement on dependability terminology, this is far from unanimous, and the terminology is still being refined. This book, therefore, will con-tinue with the established names used for the main part of this chapter.

Summary

This chapter has identified reliability as a major requirement for any real-time system. The reliability of a system has been defined as a measure of the suc-cess with which the system conforms to some authoritative specification of its

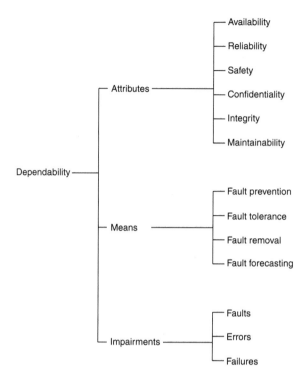

Figure 5.10   Dependability terminology.

behaviour. When the behaviour of a system deviates from that which is specified for it, this is called a failure. Failures result from faults. Faults can be accidentally or intentionally introduced into a system. They can be transient, permanent or intermittent.

There are two approaches to system design which help ensure that potential faults do not cause system failure: fault prevention and fault tolerance. Fault prevention consists of fault avoidance (attempting to limit the introduction of faulty components into the system) and fault removal (the process of finding and removing faults). Fault tolerance involves the introduction of redundant components into a system so that faults can be detected and tolerated. In general, a system will provide either full fault tolerance, graceful degradation or fail-safe behaviour.

Two general approaches to software fault tolerance have been discussed: *N*-version programming (static redundancy) and dynamic redundancy using forward and backward error recovery. *N*-version programming is defined as the independent generation of *N* (where *N* is greater than or equal to 2) functionally equivalent programs from the same initial specification. Once designed and written, the programs execute concurrently with the same inputs and their results are compared. In principle, the results should be identical, but in practice there may be some difference, in which case the consensus result, assuming there is one, is taken to be correct. N-version programming is based on the assumptions that a program can be completely, consistently and unambiguously specified, and that programs which have been developed independently will fail independently. These assumptions may not always be valid, and although N-version programming may have a role in producing reliable software it should be used with care and in conjunction with techniques based on dynamic redundancy.

Dynamic redundancy techniques have four constituent phases: error detection, damage confinement and assessment, error recovery, and fault treatment and continued service. Atomic actions were introduced as an important structuring technique to aid damage confinement. One of the most important phases is error recovery for which two approaches have been proposed: backward and forward. With backward error recovery, it is necessary for communicating processes to reach consistent recovery points to avoid the domino effect. For sequential systems, the recovery block has been introduced as an appropriate language concept for expressing backward error recovery. Recovery blocks are blocks in the normal programming language sense except that, at the entrance to the block is an automatic recovery point and at the exit an acceptance test. The acceptance test is used to test that the system is in an acceptable state after the execution of the primary module. The failure of the acceptance test results in the program being restored to the recovery point at the beginning of the block and an alternative module being executed. If the alternative module also fails the acceptance test, the program is restored to the recovery point again and yet another module is executed, and so on. If all modules fail then the block fails. A comparison between N-version programming and recovery blocks illustrated the similarities and differences between the approaches.

Although forward error recovery is system-specific, exception handling has been identified as an appropriate framework for its implementation. The concept of an ideal fault tolerant component was introduced which used exceptions.

Finally in this chapter, the notions of software safety and dependability were introduced.

Further reading

Anderson, T. and Lee, P. A. (1990) *Fault Tolerance, Principles and Practice*, 2nd edn. Englewood Cliffs, NJ: Prentice Hall.

Laprie J.-C. et al. (1995) *Dependability Handbook*. Toulouse: Cépaduès (in French).

Leveson, N. G. (1995) *Safeware: System Safety and Computers*. Reading, MA: Addison-Wesley.

Mili A. (1990) *An Introduction to Program Fault Tolerance*. New York: Prentice Hall.

Neumann, P. G. (1995) *Computer-Related Risks*. Reading, MA: Addison-Wesley.

Powell, D. (ed.) (1991) *Delta-4: A Generic Architecture for Dependable Distributed Computing*. London: Springer-Verlag.

Randell, B., Laprie, J.-C. , Kopetz, H. and Littlewood, B., (eds) (1995) *Predictable Dependable Computing Systems*. London: Springer.

Redmill, F. and Rajan, J. (eds) (1997) *Human Factors in Safety-Critical Systems*. Oxford: Butterworth-Heinemann.

Storey, N. (1996) *Safety-Critical Computer Systems*. Reading, MA: Addison-Wesley.

There is also a series of books published by Kluwer Academic Publishers and edited by G. M. Koob and C. G. Lau on the 'Foundations of Dependable Systems'.

Exercises

5.1   Is a program reliable if it conforms to an erroneous specification of its behaviour?

5.2   What would be the appropriate levels of degraded service for a computer-controlled automobile?

5.3   Write a recovery block for sorting an array of integers.

5.4   To what extent is it possible to detect recovery lines at run-time? (See Anderson and Lee (1990), Chapter 7.)

5.5   Figure 5.11 illustrates the concurrent execution of four communicating processes (P1, P2, P3 and P4) and their associated recovery points (for example, R11 is the first recovery point for process P1).

Figure 5.11   Concurrent execution of four processes for Exercise 5.5.

Explain what happens when an error is detected by

- Process P1 at time t.
- Process P2 at time t.

5.6 Should the end of file condition that occurs when sequentially reading a file be signalled to the programmer as an exception?

5.7 Data diversity is a fault-tolerance strategy that complements design diversity. Under what conditions might data diversity be more appropriate than design diversity? (Hint: see Ammann and Knight (1988)).

5.8 Should the dependability of a system be judged by an independent assessor?

Chapter 6
Exceptions and exception handling

Chapter 5 considered how systems can be made more reliable and introduced exceptions as a framework for implementing software fault tolerance. In this chapter, exceptions and exception handling are considered in more detail and their provision in particular real-time programming languages is discussed.

There are a number of general requirements for an exception handling facility:

(R1) As with all language features, the facility must be simple to understand and use.

(R2) The code for exception handling should not be so obtrusive as to obscure understanding of the program's normal error-free operation. A mechanism which intermingles code for normal processing and exceptional processing will prove difficult to understand and maintain. It may well lead to a less reliable system.

(R3) The mechanism should be designed so that run-time overheads are incurred only when handling an exception. Although the majority of applications require that the performance of a program which uses exceptions is not adversely affected under normal operating conditions, this may not always be the case. Under some circumstances, in particular where speed of recovery is of prime importance, an application may be prepared to tolerate a little overhead on the normal error-free operation.

(R4) The mechanism should allow the uniform treatment of exceptions detected both by the environment and by the program. For example, an exception such as **arithmetic overflow**, which is detected by the hardware, should be handled in exactly the same manner as an exception raised by the program as a result of an assertion failure.

(R5) As already mentioned in Chapter 5, the exception mechanism should allow recovery actions to be programmed.

6.1   Exception handling in older real-time languages

Although the terms 'exception' and 'exception handling' have only recently come into fashion, they simply express an approach to programming which attempts to contain and handle error situations. Consequently, most programming languages have facilities which enable at least some exceptions to be handled. This section briefly appraises these facilities in terms of the requirements set out above.

6.1.1   Unusual return value

One of the most primitive forms of an exception handling mechanism is the *unusual return value* or *error return* from a procedure or a function. Its main advantage is that it is simple and does not require any new language mechanism for its implementation. C supports this approach, and typically it would be used as follows:

```
if(function_call(parameters) == AN_ERROR) {
  /* error handling code */
} else {
  /* normal return code */
};
```

As can be seen, although this meets the simplicity requirement R1 and allows recovery actions to be programmed (R5), it fails to satisfy R2, R3 and R4. The code is obtrusive, it entails overheads every time it is used, and it is not clear how to handle errors detected by the environment.

Throughout this book, C is used in conjunction with POSIX. Error conditions from POSIX are indicated by the return of a non-zero value (each with a symbolic name). For reliability, every call to a system function should test the return to ensure no unexpected errors have occurred. However, as illustrated above, this can obscure the structure of the code. Consequently for pedagogically purposes, this book will use a stylized interface to POSIX. For every POSIX system call, it is assumed that there is a macro defined which undertakes an error check. For example, a system call named sys_call which takes one parameter will have the following macro automatically defined.

```
#define SYS_CALL(A) if(sys_call(A) != 0) error()
```

where error is a function which undertakes error processing. Hence the code shown will simply be SYS_CALL(param).

6.1.2 Forced branch

In assembly languages, the typical mechanism for exception handling is for subroutines to *skip return*. In other words, the instruction immediately following the subroutine call is skipped to indicate the presence (or the absence) of an error. This is achieved by the subroutine incrementing its return address (program counter) by the length of a simple jump instruction to indicate an error-free (or error) return. In the case where more than one exceptional return is possible, the subroutine will assume that the caller has more than one jump instruction after the call, and will manipulate the program counter accordingly.

For example, assuming two possible error conditions, the following might be used to call a subroutine which outputs a character to a device.

```
jsr pc, PRINT_CHAR
jmp IO_ERROR
jmp DEVICE_NOT_ENABLED
# normal processing
```

The subroutine, for a normal return, would increment the return address by two `jmp` instructions.

Although this approach incurs little overhead (R3) and enables recovery actions to be programmed (R5), it can lead to obscure program structures, and therefore violates requirements R1 and R2. R4 also cannot be satisfied.

6.1.3 Non-local `goto`

A high-level language version of a forced branch might require different labels to be passed as parameters to procedures or to have standard label variables (a label variable is an object to which a program address can be assigned and which can be used to transfer control). RTL/2 is an example of an early real-time language which provides the latter facility in the form of a non-local `goto`. RTL/2 uses **bricks** to structure its programs: a brick can be data (surrounded by the keywords `data enddata`), a procedure (surrounded by `proc endproc`) or a stack (identified by the `stack` keyword). A special type of data brick defined by the system is called `svc data`. One such brick (`rrerr`) provides a standard error-handling facility which includes an error label variable called `erl`.

The following example shows how the error label may be used in RTL/2.

```
svc data rrerr
  label erl; %a label variable %
  ...
enddata

proc WhereErrorIsDetected();
  ...
  goto erl;
  ...
endproc;
```

```
proc Caller();
  ...
  WhereErrorIsDetected();
  ...
endproc;

proc main();
  ...
restart:
  ...
  erl := restart;
  ...
  Caller();
  ...
end proc;
```

Notice that, when used in this way, the goto is more than just a jump; it implies an abnormal return from a procedure. Consequently, the stack must be unwound until the environment restored is that of the procedure containing the declaration of the label. The penalty of unwinding the stack is only incurred when an error has occurred, so requirement R3 has been satisfied. Although the use of gotos is very flexible (satisfying R4 and R5), they can lead to very obscure programs. They therefore fail to satisfy the requirements R1 and R2.

6.1.4 Procedure variable

Although the RTL/2 example shows how to recover from errors using the error label, the control flow of the program has been broken. In RTL/2, the error label is generally used for unrecoverable errors and an *error procedure variable* used when control should be returned to the point where the error originated. The following example illustrates this approach.

```
svc data rrerr;
  label erl;
  proc(int) erp; % erp is a procedure variable %
enddata;

proc recover(int);
  ...
  ...
endproc;

proc WhereErrorIsDetected();
  ...
  if recoverable then
    erp(n)
  else
    goto erl
  end;
```

```
  ...
endproc;

proc Caller();
  ...
  WhereErrorIsDetected();
  ...
endproc;

proc main();
  ...
  erl := fail;
  erp := recover;
  ...
  Caller();
  ...
fail:
  ...
end proc;
```

Again, the main criticism of this approach is that programs can become very difficult to understand and maintain.

6.2   Modern exception handling

It has been shown that the traditional approaches to exception handling often result in the handling code being intermingled with the program's normal flow of execution. The modern approach is to introduce exception-handling facilities directly into the language and thereby provide a more structured exception handling mechanism. The exact nature of these facilities varies from language to language; however, there are several common threads that can be identified. These are discussed in the following sections.

6.2.1   Exceptions and their representation

In Section 5.5.1, it was noted that there are two types of error detection technique: environmental detection and application detection. Also, depending on the delay in detecting the error, it may be necessary to raise the exception synchronously or asynchronously. A synchronous exception is raised as an immediate result of a section of code attempting an inappropriate operation. An asynchronous exception is raised some time after the operation that resulted in the error occurring. It may be raised in the process that originally executed the operation or in another process. There are therefore four classes of exceptions:

(1) Detected by the environment and raised synchronously – an array bounds violation or divide by zero are examples of such an exceptions.

(2) Detected by the application and raised synchronously – for example, the failure of a program-defined assertion check.

(3) Detected by the environment and raised asynchronously – an exception raised as the result of power failure or the failure of some health monitoring mechanism.

(4) Detected by the application and raised asynchronously – for example, one process may recognize that an error condition has occurred, which will result in another process not meeting its deadline or not terminating correctly.

Asynchronous exceptions are often called asynchronous notifications or signals and are usually considered in the context of concurrent programming. This chapter will therefore focus on synchronous exception handling and leave the topic of asynchronous exception handling until Chapter 10.

With synchronous exceptions, there are several models for their declaration. For example, they can be viewed as:

- a constant name which needs to be explicitly declared, or
- an object of a particular type which may or may not need to be explicitly declared,

Ada requires exceptions to be declared like constants; for example, the exceptions that can be raise by the Ada run-time environment are declared in package Standard:

```
package Standard is
   . . .
   Constraint_Error : exception;
   Program_Error : exception;
   Storage_Error : exception;
   Tasking_Error : exception;
   . . .
end Standard;
```

This package is visible to all Ada programs.

Java and C++ take a more object-oriented view of exceptions. In Java, exceptions are objects whose class is a subclass of the Throwable class. They can be **thrown** by the run-time systems and the application (see Section 6.3.2). In C++, exceptions of any object type may be thrown without predeclaration.

6.2.2   The domain of an exception handler

Within a program, there may be several handlers for a particular exception. Associated with each handler is a domain which specifies the region of computation during which, if an exception occurs, the handler will be activated. The accuracy with which a domain can be specified will determine how precisely the source of the exception can be located. In a block structured language, like Ada, the domain is normally the block. For example, consider a temperature sensor whose value should fall in the range 0 to 100 °C. The following Ada block defines temperature to be an integer between 0 and 100. If the calculated value falls outside that range, the run-time support system for Ada raises a Constraint_Error exception.   The invocation of the associated handler enables any necessary corrective action to be performed.

```
declare
  subtype Temperature is Integer range 0 .. 100;
begin
  -- read temperature sensor and calculate its value
exception
  -- handler for Constraint_Error
end;
```

The Ada details will be filled in shortly.

Where blocks form the basis of other units, such as procedures and functions, the domain of an exception handler is usually that unit.

In some languages, such as Java, C++ and Modula-3, not all blocks can have exception handlers. Rather, the domain of an exception handler must be explicitly indicated and the block is considered to be **guarded**; in Java this is done using a 'try-block':

```
try {
  // statements which may raise exceptions
}
catch (ExceptionType e) {
  // handler for e
}
```

As the domain of the exception handler specifies how precisely the error can be located, it can be argued that the granularity of the block is inadequate. For example consider the following sequence of calculations, each of which possibly could cause Constraint_Error to be raised.

```
declare
  subtype Temperature is Integer range 0 .. 100;
  subtype Pressure is Integer range 0 .. 50;
  subtype Flow is Integer range 0 .. 200;
begin
  -- read temperature sensor and calculate its value
  -- read pressure sensor and calculate its value
  -- read flow sensor and calculate its value

  -- adjust temperature, pressure and flow
  -- according to requirements
exception
  -- handler for Constraint_Error
end;
```

The problem for the handler is to decide which calculation caused the exception to be raised. Further difficulties arise when arithmetic overflow and underflow can occur.

With exception handler domains based on blocks, one solution to this problem is to decrease the size of the block and/or nest them. Using the sensor example:

```
declare
  subtype Temperature is Integer range 0 .. 100;
  subtype Pressure is Integer range 0 .. 50;
```

```
  subtype Flow is Integer range 0 .. 200;
begin
  begin
    -- read temperature sensor and calculate its value
  exception
    -- handler for Constraint_Error for temperature
  end;
  begin
    -- read pressure sensor and calculate its value
  exception
    -- handler for Constraint_Error for pressure
  end;
  begin
    -- read flow sensor and calculate its value
  exception
    -- handler for Constraint_Error for flow
  end;
  -- adjust temperature, pressure and flow according
  -- to requirements
exception
  -- handler for other possible exceptions
end;
```

Alternatively, procedures containing handlers could be created for each of the nested blocks. However, in either case this can become long-winded and tedious. A different solution is to allow exceptions to be handled at the statement level. Using such an approach the above example would be rewritten thus:

```
-- NOT VALID Ada
declare
  subtype Temperature is Integer range 0 .. 100;
  subtype Pressure is Integer range 0 .. 50;
  subtype Flow is Integer range 0 .. 200;
begin
  Read_Temperature_Sensor;
    exception -- handler for Constraint_Error;

  Read_Pressure_Sensor;
    exception -- handler for Constraint_Error;

  Read_Flow_Sensor;
    exception -- handler for Constraint_Error;

  -- adjust temperature, pressure and flow
  -- according to requirements

end;
```

The CHILL programming language (CCITT, 1980) has such a facility. Although this enables the cause of the exception to be located more precisely, it intermingles the exception handling code with the normal flow of operation, which may result in less clear programs and violate Requirement R2 (given at the beginning of this chapter).

The preferred approach to this problem is to allow parameters to be passed with the exceptions. With Java this is automatic, as the exception is an object, and therefore can contain as much information as the programmer wishes. In contrast, Ada provides a predefined procedure `Exception_Information` which returns implementation-defined details on the occurrence of the exception.

6.2.3   Exception propagation

Closely related to the concept of an exception domain is the notion of exception propagation. So far it has been implied that if a block or procedure raises an exception, then there is a handler associated with that block or procedure. However, this may not be the case, and there are two possible methods for dealing with a situation where no immediate exception handler can be found.

The first approach is to regard the absence of a handler as a programmer error which should be reported at compile time. However, it is often the case that an exception raised in a procedure can only be handled within the context from which the procedure was called. In this situation, it is not possible to have the handler local to the procedure. For example, an exception raised in a procedure as a result of a failed assertion involving the parameters can only be handled in the calling context. Unfortunately, it is not always possible for the compiler to check whether the calling context includes the appropriate exception handlers, as this may require complex flow control analysis. This is particularly difficult when the procedure calls other procedures which may also raise exceptions. Consequently, languages which require compile-time error generation for such situations require that a procedure specifies which exceptions it may raise (that is, not handle locally). The compiler can then check the calling context for an appropriate handler and if necessary generate the required error message. This is the approach taken by the CHILL language. Java and C++ allow a function to define which exceptions it can raise. However, unlike CHILL, they do not require a handler to be available in the calling context.

The second approach, which can be adopted when no local handler for an exception can be found, is to look for handlers up the chain of invokers at run-time; this is called **propagating** the exception. Ada and Java allow exception propagation, as do languages such as C++ and Modula-2/3.

A potential problem with exception propagation occurs when the language requires exceptions to be declared and thus given scope. Under some circumstances it is possible for an exception to be propagated outside its scope, thereby making it impossible for a handler to be found. To cope with this situation, most languages provide a 'catch all' exception handler. This handler is also used to save the programmer enumerating many exception names.

An unhandled exception causes a sequential program to be aborted. If the program contains more than one process and a particular process does not handle an exception it has raised, then usually that process is aborted. However, it is not clear whether the exception should be propagated to the parent process. Exceptions in multi-process programs will be considered in detail in Chapter 10.

Another way of considering the exception propagation issue is in terms of whether the handlers are statically or dynamically associated with exceptions. Static association, as in CHILL, is done at compile time, and therefore cannot allow propagation because the chain of invokers is unknown. Dynamic association is performed at run-time, and therefore can allow propagation. Although dynamic association is more flexible, it does entail more run-time overhead as the handler must be searched for; with static association a compile time address can be generated.

6.2.4   Resumption versus termination model

A crucial consideration in any exception-handling facility is whether the invoker of the exception should continue its execution after the exception has been handled. If the invoker can continue, then it may be possible for the handler to cure the problem that caused the exception to be raised and for the invoker to resume as if nothing has happened. This is referred to as the **resumption** or **notify** model. The model where control is not returned to the invoker is called **termination** or **escape**. Clearly it is possible to have a model in which the handler can decide whether to resume the operation which caused the exception, or to terminate the operation. This is called the **hybrid** model.

The resumption model

To illustrate the resumption model, consider three procedures P, Q and R. Procedure P invokes Q which in turn invokes R. Procedure R raises an exception r which is handled by Q, assuming there is no local handler in R. The handler for r is Hr. In the course of handling r, Hr raises exception q which is handled by Hq in procedure P (the caller of Q). Once this has been handled Hr continues its execution and when finished R continues. Figure 6.1 represents this sequence of events diagrammatically by arcs numbered 1 to 6.

The resumption model is most easily understood by viewing the handler as an implicit procedure which is called when the exception is raised.

The problem with this approach is that it is often difficult to repair errors which are raised by the run-time environment. For example, an arithmetic overflow occurring in the middle of a sequence of complex expressions may result in several registers containing partial evaluations. As a consequence of calling the handler, these registers may be overwritten.

The languages Pearl and Mesa both provide a mechanism whereby a handler can return to the context from which the exception was raised. Both languages also support the termination model.

Although implementing a strict resumption model is difficult, a compromise is to re-execute the block associated with the exception handler. The Eiffel language (Meyer, 1992) provides such a facility, called **retry**, as part of its exception handling model. The handler is able to set a local flag to indicate that an error has occurred and the block is able to test that flag. Note that for such a scheme to work, the local variables of the block must not be re-initialized on a retry.

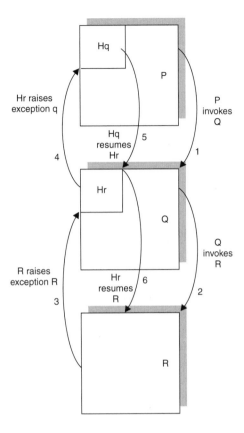

Figure 6.1   The resumption model.

The advantage of the resumption model comes when the exception has been raised asynchronously, and therefore has little to do with the current process execution. Asynchronous event handling is discusses in detail in Section 10.5.

The termination model

In the termination model, when an exception has been raised and the handler has been called, control does not return to the point where the exception occurred. Instead, the block or procedure containing the handler is terminated, and control passed to the calling block or procedure. An invoked procedure may therefore terminate in one of a number of conditions. One of these is the **normal condition**, while the others are **exception conditions**.

When the handler is inside a block, control is given to the first statement following the block after the exception has been handled; as the following example shows.

```
declare
  subtype Temperature is Integer range 0 .. 100;
begin
  ...
  begin
    -- read temperature sensor and calculate its value,
    -- may result in an exception being raised
  exception
    -- handler for Constraint_Error for temperature,
    -- once handled this block terminates
  end;

    -- code here executed when block exits normally
    -- or when an exception has been raised and handled.

exception
  -- handler for other possible exceptions
end;
```

With procedures, as opposed to blocks, the flow of control can change quite dramatically, as Figure 6.2 illustrates. Again procedure *P* has invoked procedure *Q*, which has in turn called procedure *R*. An exception is raised in *R* and handled in *Q*.

Ada, Java, C++, Modula-2/3 and CHILL all have the termination model of exception handling.

The hybrid model

With the hybrid model, it is up to the handler to decide whether the error is recoverable. If it is, the handler can return a value and the semantics are the same as in the resumption model. If the error is not recoverable, the invoker is terminated. The signal mechanisms of Mesa and Real-Time Basic (Bull and Lewis, 1983) provide such a facility. As noted before, Eiffel also supports the restricted 'retry' model.

Exception handling and operating systems

In many cases, a program in a language like Ada or Java will be executed on top of an cperating system such as POSIX or NT. These systems will detect certain synchronous error conditions; for example, memory violation or illegal instruction. Typically, this will result in the executing process being terminated. However, many systems allow the programmer to attempt error recovery. The recovery model supported by POSIX, for instance, allows the programmer to handle these synchronous exceptions (via *signals* in POSIX) by associating a handler with the exception. This handler is called by the system when the error condition is detected. Once the handler is finished, the process is resumed at the point where it was 'interrupted' – hence POSIX supports the resumption model.

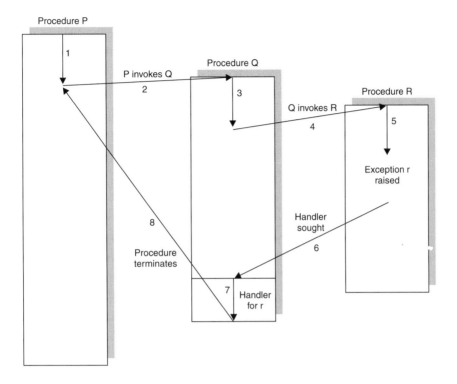

Figure 6.2   The termination model.

If a language supports the termination model, it is the responsibility of the run-time support system for that language to catch the error and undertake the necessary manipulation of program state so that the programmer can use the termination model.

POSIX signals will be considered in detail in Chapter 10, as they are really an asynchronous concurrency mechanism.

6.3   Exception handling in Ada, Java and C

Exception handling in sequential Ada, Java and C is now considered. The three languages all have different philosophies. Exception handling in concurrent systems will be described in Chapter 10.

6.3.1 Ada

The Ada language supports explicit exception declaration, the termination model of exception handling with propagation of unhandled exceptions, and a limited form of exception parameters.

Exception declaration

Exceptions in Ada are declared in one of two ways. The first way is in the same fashion as constants; the type of constant being defined by the keyword **exception**. The following example declares an exception called Stuck_Valve.

```
Stuck_Valve : exception;
```

The alternatively way is to use the predefined package Ada.Exceptions (see Program 6.1) which defines a private type called Exception_Id. Every exception declared using the keyword **exception** has an associated Exception_Id which can be obtained using the pre-defined attribute Identity. The identity of the Stuck_Valve exception, given above, can be found by:

```
with Ada.Exceptions;
with Valves;
package My_Exceptions is
  Id : Ada.Exceptions.Exception_Id :=
         Valves.Stuck_Valve'Identity;
end My_Exceptions;
```

assuming that Stuck_Valve is declared in package Valves. Note that applying the function Exception_Name to Id will now return the string My_Exceptions.Id and not Stuck_Valve.

An exception can be declared in the same place as any other declaration and, like every other declaration, it has scope.

The language has several standard exceptions whose scopes are the whole program. These exceptions may be raised by the language's run-time support system in response to certain error conditions. They include:

- Constraint_Error
  This is raised, for example, when an attempt is made to assign a value to an object which is outside its declared range, when an access to an array is outside the array bounds, or when access using a null pointer is attempted. It is also raised by the execution of a predefined numeric operation that cannot deliver a correct result within the declared accuracy for real types. This includes the familiar divide by zero error.

- Storage_Error
  This is raised when the dynamic storage allocator is unable to fulfil a demand for storage because the physical limitations of the machine have been exhausted.

Program 6.1 Package Ada.Exceptions.

```
package Ada.Exceptions is
  type Exception_Id is private;
    -- each exception has an associated identifier
  Null_Id : constant Exception_Id;
  function Exception_Name(Id : Exception_Id) return String;
    -- returns the name of the object which
    -- has the Exception_Id Id

  type Exception_Occurrence is limited private;
    -- each exception occurrence has an associated identifier
  type Exception_Occurrence_Access is
      access all Exception_Occurrence;
  Null_Occurrence : constant Exception_Occurrence;

  procedure Raise_Exception(E : in Exception_Id;
          Message : in String := "");
    -- raises the exception E and associates Message with
    -- the exception occurrence

  function Exception_Message(X : Exception_Occurrence)
          return String;
    -- allows the string passed by Raise_Exception to be accessed
    -- in the handler; if the exception was raised by the raise
    -- statement, the string contains implementation-defined
    -- information about the exception

  procedure Reraise_Occurrence(X : in Exception_Occurrence);
    -- reraises the exception identified by the exception
    -- occurrence parameter

  function Exception_Identity(X : Exception_Occurrence)
          return Exception_Id;
    -- returns the exception identifier of the exception
    -- occurrence passed as a parameter

  function Exception_Name(X : Exception_Occurrence)
          return String;
    -- same as Exception_Name(Exception_Identity(X)).

  function Exception_Information(X : Exception_Occurrence)
          return String;
    -- the same as Exception_Message(X) but contains more details
    -- if the message comes from the implementation

  procedure Save_Occurrence(Target : out Exception_Occurrence;
                            Source : in Exception_Occurrence);
    -- allows assignment to objects of type Exception_Occurrence

  function Save_Occurrence(Source : Exception_Occurrence)
                            return Exception_Occurrence_Access;
    -- allows assignment to objects of type Exception_Occurrence
```

```
private
   ... -- not specified by the language
end Ada.Exceptions;
```

Raising an exception

As well as exceptions being raised by the environment in which the program executes, they may also be raised explicitly by the program using the **raise** statement. The following example raises the exception Io_Error (which must have been previously declared and be in scope) if an I/O request produces device errors.

```
begin
   ...
   -- statements which request a device to perform some I/O
   if Io_Device_In_Error then
      raise Io_Error;
   end if;
   ...
end;
```

Notice that no else part of the if statement is required because control is *not* returned to the statement following the raise.

If Io_Error had been declared as an Exception_Id, it would have been necessary to raise the exception using the procedure Ada.Exceptions.Raise_Exception. This would have allowed a textual string to be passed as a parameter to the exception.

Each individual raising of an exception is called an exception **occurrence** and is represented by a value of type Ada.Exceptions.Exception_Occurrence. When an exception is handled, the value of the Exception_Occurrence can be found and used to determine more information about the cause of the exception.

Exception handling

As shown in Chapter 3, every block in Ada (and every subprogram, accept statement or task) can contain an optional collection of exception handlers. These are declared at the end of the block (or subprogram, accept statement or task). Each handler is a sequence of statements. Preceding the sequence are: the keyword **when**, an optional parameter to which the identity of the exception occurrence will be assigned, the names of the exceptions which are to be serviced by the handler, and the symbol =>. For example the following block declares three exceptions and provides two handlers.

```
declare
   Sensor_High, Sensor_Low, Sensor_Dead : exception;
   -- other declarations
```

```
begin
   -- statements which may cause the above exceptions
   -- to be raised
exception
   when E: Sensor_High | Sensor_Low =>
      -- Take some corrective action
      -- if either Sensor_High or Sensor_Low is raised.
      -- E contains the exception occurrence
   when Sensor_Dead =>
      -- sound an alarm if the exception
      -- Sensor_Dead is raised
end;
```

To avoid enumerating all possible exception names, Ada provides a **when others** handler name. This is only allowed as the last exception-handling choice and stands for all exceptions not previously listed in the current collection of handlers. For example, the following block prints out information about the exception, and sounds an alarm when any exception except Sensor_Low or Sensor_High is raised (including Sensor_Dead).

```
declare
   Sensor_High, Sensor_Low, Sensor_Dead : exception;
   -- other declarations
   use Text_Io;
begin
   -- statements which may cause the above exceptions
   -- to be raised
exception
   when Sensor_High | Sensor_Low =>
      -- take some corrective action
   when E: others  =>
      Put(Exception_Name(E));
      Put_Line(" caught. The following information is available ");
      Put_Line(Exception_Information(E));
      -- sound an alarm
end;
```

An exception raised in an exception handler cannot be handled by that handler or other handlers in the same block (or procedure). Instead, the block is terminated and a handler sought in the surrounding block or at the point of call for a subprogram.

Exception propagation

If there is no exception handler in the enclosing block (or subprogram or accept statement), the exception is raised again. Ada thus **propagates** exceptions. In the case of a block, this results in the exception being raised in the enclosing block, or subprogram. In the case of a subprogram, the exception is raised at its point of call.

A common misconception with Ada is that exception handlers can be provided in the initialization section of packages to handle exceptions that are raised in the execution of their nested subprograms. An exception raised and *not* handled by a subprogram is propagated to the caller of the subprogram. Therefore, such an exception will only be handled by the initialization code if it itself called the subprogram. The following example illustrates this point.

```
package Temperature_Control is
   subtype Temperature is Integer range 0 .. 100;
   Sensor_Dead, Actuator_Dead : exception;

   procedure Set_Temperature(New_Temp : in Temperature);
   function Read_Temperature return Temperature;
end Temperature_Control;

package body Temperature_Control is
   procedure Set_Temperature(New_Temp : in Temperature) is
   begin
      -- inform actuator of new temperature
      if No_Response then
        raise Actuator_Dead;
      end if;
   end Set_Temperature;

   function Read_Temperature return Temperature is
   begin
      -- read sensor
      if No_Response then
        raise Sensor_Dead;
      end if;
      -- calculate temperature
      return Reading;
   exception
      when Constraint_Error =>
        -- the temperature has gone outside
        -- its expected range;
        -- take some appropriate action
   end Read_Temperature;
begin
   -- initialization of package
   Set_Temperature(Initial_Reading);
exception
   when Actuator_Dead =>
      -- take some corrective action
end Temperature_Control;
```

In this example, the procedure Set_Temperature, which can be called from outside the package, is also called during the initialization of the package. This procedure may raise the exception Actuator_Dead. The handler for Actuator_Dead given in the initialization section of the package *will only catch the exception when the procedure is called from the initialization code.* It will not catch the exception when the procedure is called from outside the package.

   If the code which initialized a package body itself raises an exception which is not handled locally, the exception is propagated to the point where the package came into scope.

Last wishes

An exception can also be propagated by a program re-raising the exception in the local handler. The statement **raise** (or the procedure Ada.Exceptions.Reraise_Occurrence) has the effect of re-raising the last exception (or the specific exception occurrence). This facility is useful in the programming of **last wishes**. Here it is often the case that the significance of an exception is unknown to the local handler, but must be handled in order to clean up any partial resource allocation that may have occurred previous to the exception being raised. For example, consider a procedure which allocates several devices. Any exception raised during the allocation routine which is propagated to the caller may leave some devices allocated. The allocator, therefore, wishes to deallocate the associated devices if it has not been possible to allocate the full request. The following illustrates this approach.

```
subtype Devices is Integer range 1 .. Max;

procedure Allocate (Number :  Devices) is
begin
   -- request each device be allocated in turn
   -- noting which requests are granted
exception
  when others  =>
     -- deallocate those devices allocated
     raise; -- re-raise the exception
end Allocate;
```

Used in this way, the procedure can be considered to implement the failure atomicity property of an atomic action; all the resources are allocated or none are (see Chapter 10).

As a further illustration, consider a procedure which sets the positions of slats and flaps on the wings of a fly-by-wire aircraft during its landing phase. These alter the amount of lift on the plane; asymmetrical wing settings on landing (or take-off) will cause the plane to become unstable. Assuming that the initial settings are symmetrical, the following procedure ensures that they remain symmetrical, even if an exception is raised – either as a result of a failure of the physical system or because of a program error. [1]

```
procedure Wing_Settings ( -- relevant parameters) is
begin
   -- carry out the required setting
   -- of slats and flaps;
   -- exceptions may be raised
exception
  when others  =>
     -- ensure the settings are symmetrical
     -- re-raise exception to indicate
     -- a slatless and flapless landing
```

---

[1] This, of course, is a crude example used to illustrate an approach; it is not necessarily the approach that would be taken in practice.

```
    raise;
end Wing_Settings;
```

Ada allows an alternative mechanism for programming last wishes. Essentially, a dummy controlled variable is declared in the procedure. All controlled variables have procedures that are called automatically when they go out of scope. This finalization procedure can ensure a termination condition in the presence of exceptions. In the above example, it would ensure that the slats and flaps have a symmetrical setting. See Section 4.4.1.

Exceptions raised during elaboration of declarations

It is possible for an exception to be raised during the elaboration of a declarative part of a subprogram, block, task or package (for example by initializing a variable to a value outside its specified range). In general, when this occurs, the declarative part is abandoned and the exception is raised in the block, subprogram, task or package that caused the elaboration in the first place.

The full definition of the exception handling rules in all these cases is a little more complicated than outlined here. The reader is referred to the *Ada 95 Reference Manual*, Chapter 11, for full details.

Suppressing exceptions

There is an aphorism which has become popular with programmers over the last decade; it normally takes the form: 'there is no such thing as a free lunch!'. One of the requirements for exception handling facilities was that they should not incur run-time overheads unless exceptions were raised (R3). The facilities provided by Ada have been described, and on the surface they appear to meet this requirement. However, there will always be some overhead associated with detecting possible error conditions.

For example, Ada provides a standard exception called `Constraint_Error` which is raised when a null pointer is used, or where there is an array bound error, or where an object is assigned a value outside its permissible range. In order to catch these error conditions, a compiler must generate appropriate code. For instance, when an object is being accessed through a pointer, a compiler will, in the absence of any global flow control analysis (or hardware support), insert code which tests to see if the pointer is null before accessing the object. Although hidden from the programmer, this code will be executed even when no exception is to be raised. If a program uses many pointers, this can result in a significant overhead both in terms of execution time and code size. Furthermore, the presence of the code may require it to be tested during any validation process, and this may be difficult to do.

The Ada language does recognize that the standard exceptions raised by the run-time environment may be too costly for a particular application. Consequently, it provides a facility by which these checks can be suppressed. This is achieved by use of the

`Suppress` pragma which eliminates a whole range of run-time checks. The pragma affects only the compilation unit in which it appears. Of course, if a run-time error check is suppressed and subsequently the error occurs, then the language considers the program to be 'erroneous' and the subsequent behaviour of the program is undefined.

A full example

The following package illustrates the use of exceptions in an abstract data type which implements a single `Stack`. This example was chosen as it enables the full specification and body to be given without leaving anything to the reader's imagination.

The package is generic and, therefore, can be instantiated for different types.

```
generic
  Size : Natural := 100;
  type Item is private;
package Stack is

  Stack_Full, Stack_Empty : exception;

  procedure Push(X:in Item);
  procedure Pop(X:out Item);

end Stack;


package body Stack is

  type Stack_Index is new Integer range 0..Size-1;
  type Stack_Array is array(Stack_Index) of Item;
  type Stack is
    record
      S : Stack_Array;
      Sp : Stack_Index := 0;
    end record;
  Stk : Stack;

  procedure Push(X:in Item) is
  begin
    if Stk.Sp = Stack_Index'First then
      raise Stack_Full;
    end if;
    Stk.Sp :=Stk.Sp + 1;
    Stk.S(Stk.Sp) := X;
  end Push;

  procedure Pop(X:out Item) is
  begin
    if Stk.Sp = 0 then
      raise Stack_Empty;
    end if;
```

```
   X := Stk.S(Stk.Sp);
   Stk.Sp := Stk.Sp - 1;
 end Pop;

end Stack;
```

It may be used as follows:

```
with Stack;
with Text_Io;
procedure Use_Stack is
  package Integer_Stack is new Stack(Item => Integer);
  X : Integer;
  use Integer_Stack;
begin
  . . .
  Push(X);
  . . .
  Pop(X);
  . . .
exception
  when Stack_Full =>
    Text_Io.Put_Line("stack overflow!");
  when Stack_Empty =>
    Text_Io.Put_Line("stack empty!");
end Use_Stack;
```

Difficulties with the Ada model of exceptions

Although the Ada language provides a comprehensive set of facilities for exception handling, there are some difficulties with its ease of use.

(1) **Exceptions and packages**. Exceptions which can be raised by the use of a package are declared in the package specification along with any subprograms that can be called. Unfortunately, it is not obvious which subprograms can raise which exceptions. If the users of the package are unaware of its implementation, they must attempt to associate the names of exceptions with the subprogram names. In the stack example given above, the user could assume that the exception Stack_Full is raised by the procedure Pop and not Push! For large packages, it may not be obvious which exceptions can be raised by which subprograms. The programmer in this case must resort to either enumerating all possible exceptions every time a subprogram is called, or to the use of **when others**. Writers of packages should therefore indicate which subprograms can raise which exceptions using comments.

(2) **Parameter passing**. Ada does not allow a full range of parameters to be passed to handlers only a character string. This can be inconvenient if an object of a particular type needs to be passed.

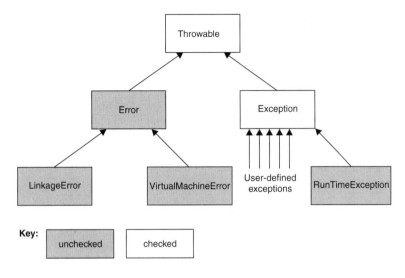

Figure 6.3   The Java predefined `Throwable` class hierarchy.

(3) **Scope and propagation**. It is possible for exceptions to be propagated outside the scope of their declaration. Such exceptions can only be trapped by **when others**. However, they may go back into scope again when propagated further up the dynamic chain. This is disconcerting, although probably inevitable when using a block structured language and exception propagation.

6.3.2   Java

Java is similar to Ada in that it supports a termination model of exception handling. However, Java exceptions, unlike Ada, are integrated into the object-oriented model.

Exception declaration

In Java, all exceptions are subclasses of the predefined class `java.lang.Throwable`. The language also defines other classes, for example: `Error`, `Exception`, and `RuntimeException`. The relationship between these is depicted in Figure 6.3. Throughout this book, the term Java exception is used to denote any class derived from `Throwable` not just those derived from `Exception`.

Objects derived from `Error` describe internal errors and resource exhaustion in the Java run-time support system. Although these errors clearly have a major impact on the program, there is little that the program can do when they are thrown (raised) as no assumptions can be made concerning the integrity of the system.

Objects derived from the Exception hierarchy represent errors that programs can handle and potentially throw themselves. RuntimeExceptions are those exceptions that are raised by the run-time support system as a result of a program error. They include errors such as those resulting from a bad cast ClassCastException, array bounds error (IndexOutOfBoundException), a null pointer access (NullPointerException), integer divide by zero (ArithmeticException) etc.

Throwable objects which are derived from Error or RuntimeExceptions are called **unchecked** exceptions. This means that the Java compiler will not expect them to be identified in the throws clause of a method's declaration (see below).

Consider, for example, the temperature controller example given in Section 6.3.1. In Java, this might be written as follows. First a class has to be declared to represent a constraint error for integer subtypes. As this is a general error condition, it may have already been provided in a library. The public variables of the class will contain information about the cause of the error.

```java
public class IntegerConstraintError extends Exception
{

  private int lowerRange, upperRange, value;

  public IntegerConstraintError(int L, int U, int V)
  {
    super(); // call constructor on parent class
    lowerRange = L;
    upperRange = U;
    value = V;
  }

  public String getMessage()
  {
    return ("Integer Constraint Error: Lower Range " +
            java.lang.Integer.toString(lowerRange) + " Upper Range " +
            java.lang.Integer.toString(upperRange) + " Found " +
            java.lang.Integer.toString(value));
  }

};
```

Now the temperature type can be introduced.

```java
import exceptionLibrary.IntegerConstraintError;

public class Temperature
{
  private int T;

  public Temperature(int initial) throws IntegerConstraintError
    // constructor
  {
    ...;
  }
```

```
public void setValue(int V) throws IntegerConstraintError
{
  ...;
};

public int readValue()
{
  return T;
};

// both the constructor and setValue can throw an
// IntegerConstraintError
};
```

In the above code, member functions which can throw the `IntegerConstraint-Error` exception are formally labelled. Contrast this with the Ada approach, which relies on comments.

Now the class `TemperatureController` can be defined. It declares a type to represent the failed actuator exception. In this case, no data is passed with the object.

```
class ActuatorDead extends Exception
{
  public String getMessage()
  {
    return ("Actuator Dead");
  }
};

class TemperatureController
{
  public TemperatureController(int T)
        throws IntegerConstraintError
  {
    currentTemperature = new Temperature(T);
  };

  Temperature currentTemperature;

  public void setTemperature(int T)
        throws ActuatorDead, IntegerConstraintError
  {
    currentTemperature.setValue(T);
  };

  int readTemperature()
  {
    return currentTemperature.readValue();
  }
};
```

In general, each function must specify a list of throwable checked exceptions **throws**
A, B, C – in which case the function may throw any exception in this list and any
of the unchecked exceptions. A, B, and C must be subclasses of Exception. If a
function attempts to throw an exception which is not allowed by its throws list, then a
compilation error occurs.

Throwing an exception

Raising an exception in Java is called **throwing** the exception. For example, consider
now the full implementation of the Temperature class outlined in the previous section.

```
import exceptionLibrary.IntegerConstraintError;

class Temperature
{
  int T;

  void check(int value) throws IntegerConstraintError
  {
    if(value  > 100 || value  < 0) {
      throw new IntegerConstraintError(0, 100, value);
    };
  }

  public Temperature(int initial) throws IntegerConstraintError
    // constructor
  {
    check(initial);
    T = initial;
  }

  public void setValue(int V) throws IntegerConstraintError
  {
    check(V);
    T = V;
  };

  public int readValue()
  {
    return T;
  };
};
```

Here **throw new** IntegerConstraintError(0, 100, value)   creates
and throws an object of type (IntegerConstraintError) with the appropriate
values for its instance variables.

Exception handling

An exception can only be handled in Java from within a **try-block**. Each handler is specified using a **catch** statement. Consider the following:

```
// given TemperatureController

try {
  TemperatureController TC = new TemperatureController(20);

  TC.setTemperature(100);
  // statements which manipulate the temperature
}
catch (IntegerConstraintError error) {
  // exception caught, print error message on
  // the standard output
  System.out.println(error.getMessage());
}
catch (ActuatorDead error) {
  System.out.println(error.getMessage());
}
```

The **catch** statement is like a function declaration, the parameter of which identifies the exception type to be caught. Inside the handler, the object name behaves like a local variable.

A handler with parameter type T will catch a thrown object of type E if:

(1) T and E are the same type, or

(2) T is a parent (super) class of E at the throw point.

It is this last point that makes the Java exception-handling facility very powerful. In the above example, two exceptions are derived from the Exception class. IntegerConstraintError and ActuatorDead. The following try block will catch both exceptions:

```
try {
  // statements which might raise the exception
  // IntegerConstraintError or ActuatorDead
}
catch(Exception E) {
  // handler will catch all exceptions of type exception and
  // any derived type; but from within the handler only the
  // methods of Exception are accessible
}
```

Of course, a call to E.getMessage will dispatch to the appropriate routine for the type of object thrown. Indeed, the catch(Exception E) is equivalent to Ada's **when others**.

Exception propagation

As with Ada, if no exception is found in the calling context of a function, the calling context is terminated and a handler is sought in its calling context. Hence, Java supports exception propagation.

Last wishes

Section 6.3.1 discussed how **when others** could be used to program last wishes in Ada. Clearly a catch(Exception E) can also be used to achieve this effect. However, Java also supports a **finally** clause as part of a try statement. The code attached to this clause is guaranteed to execute whatever happens in the try statement irrespective of whether exceptions are thrown, caught or propagated, or, indeed, even if there are no exceptions thrown at all.

```
try
{
  ...
}
catch(..)
{
...
}
finally
{
 // code that will be executed under all circumstances
}
```

The same effect can be achieved in Ada using controlled variables and finalization (see Section 4.4.1).

A full example

The following is the stack example in Java that was previously given for Ada. There are two points about this example which are of interest.

Firstly, the stack is generic in that any object can be passed as a parameter to push. Hence, there is no need to instantiate the stack (as in the Ada case). Furthermore, each stack can handle more than one object type (unlike the Ada case). Of course, this is because the Java stack is actually a stack of references to objects. It would be possible to explicitly program this in Ada.

The second point is that the Java example will only handle objects and not the primitive types like integer. This is in contrast to the Ada example, which will handle all types.

```java
public class EmptyStackException extends Exception
{
    public EmptyStackException() {
    }
}

public class FullStackException extends Exception
{
    public FullStackException() {
    }
}
public class Stack {

  public Stack(int capacity)
  {
     stackArray = new Object[capacity];
     stackIndex = 0;
     stackCapacity = capacity;
  }

  public void push(Object item) throws FullStackException
  {
    if(stackIndex == stackCapacity) throw new FullStackException();
    stackArray[stackIndex++] = item;
  }

  public synchronized Object pop() throws EmptyStackException
  {
    if(stackIndex == 0) throw new EmptyStackException();
    return stackArray[--stackIndex];
  }

  protected Object stackArray[];
  protected int stackIndex;
  protected int stackCapacity;
}
```

The above classes can be used as follows:

```java
import Stack;
import FullStackException;
import EmptyStackException;

public class UseStack
{

  public static void main(...)
  {
    Stack S = new Stack(100);

    try {
      ...
      S.push(SomeObject);
      ...
      SomeObject = S.pop();
```

```
    . . .
  }
  catch (FullStackException F)   ...
  catch (EmptyStackException E)   ... ;
 }
}
```

Finally, it should be noted that Java provides a standard Stack class in its util package.

6.3.3 C

C does not define any exception-handling facilities within the language. Such an omission clearly limits the usefulness of the language in the structured programming of reliable systems. However, it is possible to provide some form of exception-handling mechanism by using the macro facility of the language. To illustrate this approach, the implementation of a simple Ada-like exception-handling macros will be considered. The approach is based on that given by Lee (1983).

      To implement a termination model in C, it is necessary to save the status of a program's registers, and so on, on entry to an exception domain and then restore them if an exception occurs. Traditionally C has been associated with Unix, and the POSIX facilities of setjmp and longjmp can be used for this purpose. The routine setjmp saves the program status and returns a 0; the routine longjmp restores the program status and results in the program abandoning its current execution and restarting from the position where setjmp was called. This time, however, setjmp returns the value passed by longjmp. The following code structure is needed:

```
/* begin exception domain */

typedef char *exception;
  /* a pointer type to a character string */
exception error ="error";
  /* the representation of an exception named "error" */

if((current_exception =  (exception) setjmp(save_area)) == 0) {
  /* save the registers and so on in save_area */
  /* 0 is returned */

 /* the guarded region */

 /* when an exception "error" is identified */
 longjmp(save_area, (int) error);
 /* no return */

}
else {
  if(current_exception == error) {
    /* handler for "error" */
  }
  else {
```

```
    /* re-raise exception in surrounding domain */
  }
}
```

The above code is clearly difficult to understand. However, a set of macros can be defined to help structure the program.

```
#define NEW_EXCEPTION(name) ...
  /* code for declaring an exception */
#define BEGIN ...
  /* code for entering an exception domain */
#define EXCEPTION ...
  /* code for beginning exception handlers */
#define END ...
  /* code for leaving an exception domain */
#define RAISE(name) ...
  /* code for raising an exception */
#define WHEN(name) ...
  /* code for handler */
#define OTHERS ...
  /* code for catch all exception handler */
```

Consider now the following example:

```
  NEW_EXCEPTION(sensor_high);
  NEW_EXCEPTION(sensor_low);
  NEW_EXCEPTION(sensor_dead);
  /* other declarations */

BEGIN
  /* statements which may cause the above exceptions */
  /* to be raised; for example */
  RAISE(sensor_high);

EXCEPTION
  WHEN(sensor_high)
    /* take some corrective action */
  WHEN(sensor_low)
    /* take some corrective action */
  WHEN(OTHERS)
    /* sound an alarm */
END;
```

The above provides a simple termination model similar to Ada's.

6.4   Exception handling in other languages

Within this book, attention is primarily focused on the languages Ada, Java, C and occam2. There are, of course, many other languages that are used for real-time applications, but it would be impossible to comprehensively cover them all within a single volume. It is nevertheless one of the aims of this book to discuss particular features of other languages if they are distinctive and/or important. Consequently, in this section, exception handling in CHILL, CLU, Mesa and C++ is briefly reviewed.

6.4.1 CHILL

CHILL is similar to Ada in that exceptions are part of the language definition and that the termination model of exception handling is supported. However, the other facilities that it provides are significantly different from Ada. CHILL has a slightly different syntax for its type names and object declarations than any of the other languages considered in detail in this book; an Ada-like syntax will, therefore, be used in the examples given here.

As indicated in Section 6.2.1, the domain of an exception handler in CHILL is the statement, block or process. The main difference between CHILL and Ada is, therefore, that exception handlers can be appended to the end of statements in CHILL. Instead of the keyword *exception*, CHILL uses *on* and *end* to surround a handler. In between, the syntax is rather like a *case* statement. The following example illustrates a CHILL exception handler.

```
-- Ada-like syntax used to illustrate concepts
-- not valid CHILL syntax
declare
  subtype temperature is integer range 0 .. 100;

  A : temperature;
  B,C : integer;
begin
  ...
  A := B + C on
               (overflow):   .....;
               (rangefail): .....;
               else      ....;
            end;
  ...
end on
      -- exception handlers for the block
      (overflow):   .....;
      (rangefail): .....;
      else      ....;
    end;
```

CHILL defines several standard exceptions similar to those of Ada. In the above example, (arithmetic) *overflow* may be raised when B and C are added together; furthermore, a *rangefail* exception may occur if the result assigned to A is outside the range 0 to 100. The *else* option is equivalent to Ada's **when others**.

The association between an exception and its handler is static, and therefore must be known at compile time. Consequently, exceptions need not be predeclared. They can, however, be returned from a procedure by appropriate declarations in the procedure header. Again, using an Ada-like syntax:

```
procedure push(x:in item)   exceptions (stack_full);
procedure pop(x:out item)   exceptions (stack_empty);
```

The rule for statically determining a handler for an exception E which occurs during the execution of statement S is:

- it must be appended to S, or
- it must be appended to a block directly enclosing S, or
- it must be appended to the procedure directly enclosing S, or
- the directly enclosing procedure must have E defined in its specification, or
- it is appended to the process directly enclosing S.

When no exception can be found using the above rules, the program is in error. There is *no* propagation of exceptions.

6.4.2   CLU

CLU is an experimental language which, although not a 'real-time' language as such, does have some interesting features, one of which is its exception handling mechanism (Liskov and Snyder, 1979). It is similar to C++ and CHILL in that a procedure declares the exceptions it can raise. It also allows parameters to be passed to the handler.

For example, consider the function sum_stream which reads in a sequence of signed decimal integers from a character stream and returns the sum of those integers. The following exceptions are possible: overflow – the sum of the number is outside the implemented range of integers, unrepresentable_integer – a number in the stream is outside the implemented range of integers, and bad_format – the stream contains a non-integer field. With the last two exceptions, the offending string is passed to the handler.

```
sum_stream = proc(s : stream) return(int)
             signals
               (overflow,
                unrepresentable_integer(string),
                bad_format(string)
               )
```

As with CHILL, there is no propagation of exceptions; an exception must be handled at the point of call.

```
x = sum_stream
      except
        when overflow:
          S1
```

```
    when unrepresentable_integer(f : string):
      S2
    when bad_format(f:string):
      S3
  end
```

where `S1`, `S2` and `S3` are arbitrary sequences of statements.

6.4.3 Mesa

In Mesa, exceptions are called **signals**. They are dynamic in that they can be propagated, and their handlers adhere to the hybrid model. Like Ada's exceptions, signals must be declared, but, unlike Ada, their declaration is analogous to a procedure type rather than a constant declaration. Consequently, they can take parameters and return values. The body of the signal procedure is, of course, the exception handler. Unlike procedure bodies which are *statically* bound to the procedure at compile time, exception handlers are *dynamically* bound to the signal at run time.

Handlers can be associated with blocks, as with Ada, C++ and CHILL. Like Ada, Mesa procedures and functions cannot specify which signals they will return; however, handlers can be associated with a procedure call giving a similar effect.

There are two types of signal declaration: those using the keyword *signal* and those using *error*. Signals which are declared as errors cannot be resumed by their corresponding handlers.

6.4.4 C++

C++ is similar to Java except it does not require the explicit declaration of exceptions. Rather, any instance of a class can be thrown as an exception. There are no predefined exceptions.

In general, each function may specify

- a list of throwable objects, `throw(A, B, C)` – in which case the function may throw any object in the list
- an empty list of throwable objects, `throw()` – in which case the function will not throw any objects
- no list of throwable objects – in which case the function can throw *any* object.

If a function attempts to throw an object which is not allowed by its throw list, then the function `unexpected` is automatically called. The default for `unexpected` is to call the `terminate` function whose default action is to abort the program. Both these functions may have their default operations overridden by calling:

```
typedef void(*PFV)();

PFV set_unexpected(PFV new_handler);
/* sets the default action to new_handler and */
/* returns the previous action               */

PFV set_terminate(PFV new_handler);
/* sets the default action to new_handler and */
/* returns the previous action               */
```

Like Java, C++ has a **catch** statement, the parameter of which identifies the type of object to be caught.

A handler with parameter type T will catch a thrown object of type E if:

(1) T and E are the same type;

(2) T is a pointer type and E is a pointer type that can be converted to T by a C++ standard pointer conversion at the throw point;

(3) T is a pointer type and E is an object of the type that T points to – in this case a pointer to the thrown object is created; both pointer and object persist until the exception handler is exited;

(4) T is a base class of E at the throw point.

Exception hierarchies can be constructed like in Java.

6.5   Recovery blocks and exceptions

In Chapter 5, the notion of recovery blocks was introduced as a mechanism for fault-tolerant programming. Its main advantage over forward error recovery mechanisms is that it can be used to recover from unanticipated errors, particularly from errors in the design of software components. So far in this chapter, only anticipated errors have been considered, although catch-all exception handlers can be used to trap unknown exceptions. In this section, the implementation of recovery blocks using exceptions and exception handlers is described.

As a reminder, the structure of a recovery block is shown below:

```
ensure   <acceptance test>
by
  <primary module>
else by
  <alternative module>
else by
  <alternative module>
  .
  .
  .
else by
  <alternative module>
else error
```

The error detection facility is provided by the acceptance test. This test is simply the negation of a test which would raise an exception using forward error recovery. The only problem is the implementation of state saving and state restoration. In the example below, this is shown as an Ada package which implements a recovery cache. The procedure Save stores the state of the global and local variables of the program in the recovery cache; this does not include the values of the program counter, stack pointer and so on. A call of Restore will reset the program variables to the states saved.

```
package Recovery_Cache is
   procedure Save;
   procedure Restore;
end Recovery_Cache;
```

Clearly, there is some magic going on inside the package which will require support from the run-time system and possibly even hardware support for the recovery cache. Also, this may not be the most efficient way to perform state restoration. It may be more desirable to provide more basic primitives, and to allow the program to use its knowledge of the application to optimize the amount of information saved (Rogers and Wellings, 2000).

The purpose of the next example is to show that given recovery cache implementation techniques, recovery blocks can be used in an exception handling environment. Notice also that by using exception handlers, forward error recovery can be achieved before restoring the state. This overcomes a criticism of recovery blocks: that it is difficult to reset the environment.

The recovery block scheme can, therefore, be implemented using a language with exceptions plus a bit of help from the underlying run-time support system. For example, in Ada the structure for a triple redundant recovery block would be:

```
procedure Recovery_Block is
   Primary_Failure, Secondary_Failure,
         Tertiary_Failure: exception;
   Recovery_Block_Failure : exception;
   type Module is (Primary, Secondary, Tertiary);
   function Acceptance_Test return Boolean is
   begin
      -- code for the acceptance test
   end Acceptance_Test;

   procedure Primary is
   begin
      -- code for primary algorithm
      if not Acceptance_Test then
        raise Primary_Failure;
      end if;
   exception
      when Primary_Failure  =>
         -- forward recovery to return environment
         -- to the required state
         raise;
```

```
    when others  =>
      -- unexpected error
      -- forward recovery to return environment
      -- to the required state
      raise Primary_Failure;
  end Primary;

  procedure Secondary is
  begin
    -- code for secondary algorithm
    if not Acceptance_Test then
      raise Secondary_Failure;
    end if;
  exception
    when Secondary_Failure  =>
      -- forward recovery to return environment
      -- to the required state
      raise;
    when others  =>
      -- unexpected error
      -- forward recovery to return environment
      -- to the required state
      raise Secondary_Failure;
  end Secondary;

  procedure Tertiary is
  begin
    -- code for tertiary algorithm
    if not Acceptance_Test then
      raise Tertiary_Failure;
    end if;
  exception
    when Tertiary_Failure  =>
      -- forward recovery to return environment
      -- to the required state
      raise;
    when others  =>
      -- unexpected error
      -- forward recovery to return environment
      -- to the required state
      raise Tertiary_Failure;
  end Tertiary;

begin
  Recovery_Cache.Save;
  for Try in Module loop
    begin
      case Try is
        when Primary => Primary; exit;
        when Secondary => Secondary; exit;
        when Tertiary => Tertiary;
      end case;
    exception
      when Primary_Failure =>
        Recovery_Cache.Restore;
```

```
      when Secondary_Failure =>
         Recovery_Cache.Restore;
      when Tertiary_Failure =>
         Recovery_Cache.Restore;
         raise Recovery_Block_Failure;
      when others =>
         Recovery_Cache.Restore;
         raise Recovery_Block_Failure;
   end;
 end loop;
end Recovery_Block;
```

Summary

This chapter has studied the various models of exception handling for sequential processes. Although many different models exist they all address the following issues.

- Exception representation – an exception may, or may not, be explicitly represented in a language.
- The domain of an exception handler – associated with each handler is a domain which specifies the region of computation during which, if an exception occurs, the handler will be activated. The domain is normally associated with a block, subprogram or a statement.
- Exception propagation – this is closely related to the idea of an exception domain. It is possible that when an exception is raised there is no exception handler in the enclosing domain. In this case, either the exception can be propagated to the next outer level enclosing domain, or it can be considered to be a programmer error (which can often be flagged at compilation time).
- Resumption or termination model – this determines the action to be taken after an exception has been handled. With the resumption model, the invoker of the exception is resumed at the statement after the one at which the exception was invoked. With the termination model, the block or procedure containing the handler is terminated, and control is passed to the calling block or procedure. The hybrid model enables the handler to choose whether to resume or to terminate.
- Parameter passing to the handler – may or may not be allowed.

The exception handling facilities of various languages are summarized in Table 6.1.

It is not unanimously accepted that exception-handling facilities should be provided in a language. The C and the occam2 languages, for example, have none. To sceptics, an exception is a `goto` where the destination is undeterminable and the source is unknown. They can, therefore, be considered to be

Language	Domain	Propagation	Model	Parameters
Ada	Block	Yes	Termination	Limited
Java	Block	Yes	Termination	Yes
C++	Block	Yes	Termination	Yes
CHILL	Statement	No	Termination	No
CLU	Statement	No	Termination	Yes
Mesa	Block	Yes	Hybrid	Yes

Table 6.1   The exception-handling facilities of various languages.

the antithesis of structured programming. This, however, is not the view taken in this book.

Further reading

Cristian, F. (1982) Exception Handling and Software Fault Tolerance. *IEEE Transactions on Computing*, c-31(6), 531–540.

Cui, Q. and Gannon, J. (1992) Data-oriented Exception Handling. *IEEE Transactions on Software Engineering*, 18(5), 393–401.

Lee, P. A. (1983) Exception Handling in C Programs. *Software – Practice and Experience*, 13(5), 389–406.

Papurt, D. M. (1998) The Use of Exceptions. *JOOP*, 11(2), 13–17.

Exercises

6.1   Compare and contrast the exception handling and recovery block approaches to software fault tolerance.

6.2   Give examples of:

(1) a synchronous exception detected by the application
(2) an asynchronous exception detected by the application
(3) a synchronous exception detected by the execution environment
(4) an asynchronous exception detected by the execution environment

6.3   The package `Character_Io` whose specification is given below, provides a function for reading characters from the terminal. It also provides a procedure for throwing away all the remaining characters on the current line. The package may raise the exception `Io_Error`.

```
package Character_Io is
  function Get return Character;
    -- reads a character from the terminal

  procedure Flush;
    -- throw away all character on the current line

  Io_Error : exception;
end Character_Io;
```

Another package Look contains the function Read which scans the current input line looking for the punctuation characters comma (,) period (.) and semicolon (;). The function will return the next punctuation character found or raise the exception Illegal_Punctuation if a non-alphanumeric character is found. If, during the process of scanning the input line, an Io_Error is encountered, then the exception is propagated to the caller of Read. The specification of Look is given below.

```
with Character_Io; use Character_Io;
package Look is
  type Punctuation is (Comma, Period, Semicolon);
  function Read return Punctuation;
    -- reads the next , . or ; from the terminal

  Illegal_Punctuation : exception;
end Look;
```

Sketch the package body of Look using the Character_Io package for reading characters from the terminal. On receipt of a legal punctuation character, an illegal punctuation character or an Io_Error exception, the remainder of the input line should be discarded. You may assume that an input line will always have a legal or illegal punctuation character and that Io_Errors occur at random.

Using the Look package, sketch the code of a procedure Get_Punctuation which will always return the next punctuation character in spite of the exceptions that Look raises. An infinite input stream may be assumed.

6.4   In a process control application, gas is heated in an enclosed chamber. The chamber is surrounded by a coolant which reduces the temperature of the gas by conduction. There is also a valve which when open releases the gas into the atmosphere. The operation of the process is controlled by an Ada package whose specification is given below. For safety reasons, the package recognizes several error conditions; these are brought to the notice of the user of the package by the raising of exceptions. The exception Heater_Stuck_On is raised by the procedure Heater_Off when it is unable to turn the heater off. The exception Temperature_Still_Rising is raised by the Increase_Coolant procedure if it is unable to decrease the temperature of the gas by increasing the flow of the coolant. Finally, the exception Valve_Stuck is raised by the Open_Valve procedure if it is unable to release the gas into the atmosphere.

```
package Temperature_Control is
   Heater_Stuck_On, Temperature_Still_Rising,
          Valve_Stuck : exception;

   procedure Heater_On;
      -- turn on heater

   procedure Heater_Off;
      -- turn off heater
      -- raises Heater_Stuck_On

   procedure Increase_Coolant;
      -- Causes the flow of coolant which surrounds the
      -- chamber to increase until the temperature reaches
      -- a safe level raises Temperature_Still_Rising

   procedure Open_Valve;
      -- opens a valve to release some of the gas thereby
      -- avoiding an explosion
      -- raises Valve_Stuck

   procedure Panic;
      -- sounds an alarm and calls the fire,
      -- hospital and police services
end Temperature_Control;
```

Write an Ada procedure which when called will attempt to turn off the heater in the gas chamber. If the heater is stuck on then the flow of coolant surrounding the chamber should be increased. If the temperature still rises then the escape valve should be opened to release the gas. If this fails then the alarm must be sounded and the emergency services informed.

6.5 Write a general purpose generic Ada package to implement nested recovery blocks. (Hint – the primary, secondary modules, acceptance test and so on, should be encapsulated in a package and passed as a parameter to the generic.)

6.6 To what extent could the Ada exception-handling facilities be implemented outside the language by a standard package?

6.7 How would you defend the statement that an Ada exception is a `goto` where the destination is undeterminable and the source is unknown. Would the same argument hold for (a) the resumption model of exception handling and (b) the CHILL termination model?

6.8 Compare the exception domains of the following apparently identical pieces of code (the variable `Initial` is of type integer).

```
procedure Do_Something is
   subtype Small_Int is Integer range -16..15;
   A : Small_Int := Initial;
begin
   ...
end Do_Something;
```

```
procedure Do_Something is
  subtype Small_Int is Integer range -16..15;
  A : Small_Int;
begin
  A := Initial;
  ...
end Do_Something;

procedure Do_Something is
  subtype Small_Int is Integer range -16..15;
  A : Small_Int;
begin
  begin
    A := Initial;
    ...
  end;
end Do_Something;
```

6.9 Show how the C macros given in Section 6.3.3 can be implemented.

6.10 Consider the following program:

```
I : Integer := 1;
J : Integer := 0;
K : Integer := 3;

procedure Primary is
begin
  J := 20;
  I := K*J/2
end Primary;

procedure Secondary is
begin
  I := J;
  K := 4;
end Secondary;

procedure Tertiary is
begin
  J := 20;
  I := K*J/2
end Tertiary;
```

This code is to be executed in a recovery block environment and in an exception handling environment. The following is the recovery block environment:

```
ensure I = 20
by
  Primary;
else by
  Secondary;
else by
  Tertiary;
```

```
else
   I := 20;
end;
```

The following is the exception handling environment:

```
Failed : exception;
type Module is (P,S,T);

for Try in Module loop
  begin
    case Try is
      when P =>
          Primary;
          if I /= 20 then
             raise Failed;
          end if;
          exit;
      when S =>
          Secondary;
          if I /= 20 then
             raise Failed;
          end if;
          exit;
      when T =>
          Tertiary;
          if I /= 20 then
             raise Failed;
          end if;
          exit;
      end case;
    exception
      when Failed =>
         if Try = T then
            I := 20;
         end if;
    end;
end loop;
```

Assuming the *termination model* of exception handling, compare and contrast the execution of *both* the recovery block environment and the exception handling environment code fragments.

6.11 Illustrate how recovery blocks can be implemented using C++ and Java. Hint see Rubira-Calsavara and Stroud (1994).

6.12 Redo the answer to Exercise 6.3 using Java.

6.13 Redo the answer to Exercise 6.4 using Java.

6.14 Explain under what circumstances **when others** (e: Exception_Id) in Ada is not equivalent to **catch**(Exception e) in Java.

6.15 What are the advantages and disadvantages of having exceptions integrated into the OOP model?

6.16 A subset of Ada 95 has been defined for use in safety-critical embedded systems. The language has formal semantics and a set of tools that allow static analysis techniques to be performed. It has no exception-handling facility. The designers argue that exceptions cannot occur if the program has been proved correct. What arguments can be put forward for the introduction of exception-handling facilities into the language?

Chapter 7
Concurrent programming

Virtually all real-time systems are inherently concurrent. Languages intended for use in this domain have greater expressive power if they provide the programmer with primitives that match the application's parallelism.

> Concurrent programming is the name given to programming notation and techniques for expressing potential parallelism and solving the resulting synchronization and communication problems. Implementation of parallelism is a topic in computer systems (hardware and software) that is essentially independent of concurrent programming. Concurrent programming is important because it provides an abstract setting in which to study parallelism without getting bogged down in the implementation details. (Ben-Ari, 1982)

This, and the following two chapters, concentrate on the issues associated with general concurrent programming. The topic of time and how it can be represented and manipulated in programs is deferred until Chapter 12.

7.1   The notion of process

Any language, natural or computer, has the dual property of enabling expression while at the same time limiting the framework within which that expressive power may be applied. If a language does not support a particular notion or concept then those that use the language cannot apply that notion and may even be totally unaware of its existence.

Pascal, C, FORTRAN and COBOL share the common property of being sequential programming languages. Programs written in these languages have a single thread

179

of control. They start executing in some state and then proceed, by executing one statement at a time, until the program terminates. The path through the program may differ
due to variations in input data but for any particular execution of the program there is
only one path. This is not adequate for the programming of real-time systems.

Following the pioneering work of Dijkstra (1968a), a concurrent program is con-
ventionally viewed as consisting of a collection of autonomous sequential processes,
executing (logically) in parallel. Concurrent programming languages all incorporate,
either explicitly or implicitly, the notion of process; each process itself has a single
thread of control.[1]

The actual implementation (that is, execution) of a collection of processes usually
takes one of three forms. Processes can either:

(1) multiplex their executions on a single processor,

(2) multiplex their executions on a multiprocessor system where there is access to
    shared memory,

(3) multiplex their executions on several processors which do not share memory
    (such systems are usually called distributed systems).

Hybrids of these three methods are also possible.

Only in cases (2) and (3) is there the possibility of true parallel execution of more
than one process. The term **concurrent** indicates potential parallelism. Concurrent
programming languages thus enable the programmer to express logically parallel activities without regard to their implementation. Issues that are pertinent to true parallel
execution are considered in Chapter 14.

The life of a process is illustrated, simply, in Figure 7.1. A process is created,
moves into the state of initialization, proceeds to execution and termination. Note that
some processes may never terminate and that others, which fail during initialization,
pass directly to termination without ever executing. After termination, a process goes
to non-existing when it can no longer be accessed (as it has gone out of scope). Clearly,
the most important state for a process is executing; however, as processors are limited
not all processes can be executing at once. Consequently, the term **executable** is used
to indicate that the process could execute if there is a processor available.

From this consideration of a process, it is clear that the execution of a concurrent
program is not as straightforward as the execution of a sequential program. Processes
must be created and terminated, and dispatched to and from the available processors.
These activities are undertaken by the Run-Time Support System (RTSS) or Run-Time
Kernel. The RTSS has many of the properties of the scheduler in an operating system
and sits logically between the hardware and the application software. In reality, it may
take one of a number of forms:

(1) A software structure programmed as part of the application (that is, as one com-
    ponent of the concurrent program). This is the approach adopted by the Modula-2
    language.

---

[1] Recent work in operating systems has led to the explicit notion of a thread and multithreaded processes.
This issue will be returned to later in this section.

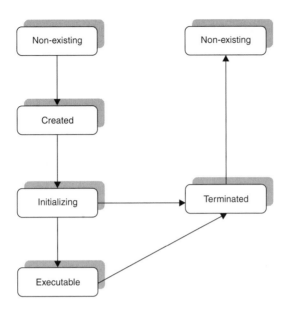

Figure 7.1   Simple state diagram for a process.

(2) A standard software system generated with the program object code by the compiler. This is normally the structure with Ada and Java programs.

(3) A hardware structure microcoded into the processor for efficiency. An occam2 program running on the transputer has such a run-time system.

The algorithm used for scheduling by the RTSS (that is, to decide which process to execute next if there is more than one executable) will affect the time behaviour of the program, although, for well-constructed programs, the logical behaviour of the program will not be dependent on the RTSS. From the program's point of view, the RTSS is assumed to schedule processes non-deterministically. For real-time systems, the characteristics of the scheduling are significant. They are considered further in Chapter 13.

Although this book is focusing on concurrent real-time languages, it is clear that an alternative approach is to use a sequential language and a real-time operating system. All operating systems provide facilities for creating concurrent processes. Usually, each process executes in its own virtual machine to avoid interference from other, unrelated, processes. Each process is, in effect, a single program. However, in recent years there has been a tendency to provide the facilities for processes to be created within programs. Modern operating systems allow processes created within the same program to have unrestricted access to shared memory (such processes are often called **threads**). Hence, in operating systems like those conforming to POSIX, it is necessary to distinguish between the concurrency between programs (processes) and the concurrency within a program (threads). Often, there is also a distinction between threads which are visible to the operating system and those that are supported solely by library routines. For example, Windows 2000 supports threads and **fibers**, the latter being invisible to the kernel.

There has been a long debate among programmers, language designers and operating system designers as to whether it is appropriate to provide support for concurrency in a language or whether this should be provided by the operating system only. Arguments in favour of including concurrency in the programming languages include the following:

(1) It leads to more readable and maintainable programs.

(2) There are many different types of operating system; defining the concurrency in the language makes the program more portable.

(3) An embedded computer may not have any resident operating system available.

These arguments were clearly the ones which held the most weight with the designers of Ada and Java. Arguments against concurrency in a language include the following:

(1) Different languages have different models of concurrency; it is easier to compose programs from different languages if they all use the same operating system model of concurrency.

(2) It may be difficult to implement a language's model of concurrency efficiently on top of an operating system's model.

(3) Operating system standards are beginning to emerge, and therefore programs become more portable.

The need to support multiple languages was one of the main reasons why the civil aircraft industry when developing its Integrated Modular Avionics programme opted for a standard applications–kernel interface (called APEX) supporting concurrency rather than adopting the Ada model of concurrency (ARINC AEE Committee, 1999). The debate will no doubt continue for some time.

7.1.1   Concurrent programming constructs

Although constructs for concurrent programming vary from one language (and operating system) to another, there are three fundamental facilities that must be provided. These allow the following:

(1) the expression of concurrent execution through the notion of process;

(2) process synchronization

(3) interprocess communication.

In considering the interaction of processes, it is useful to distinguish between three types of behaviour:

- independent
- cooperating
- competing

Independent processes do not communicate or synchronize with each other. Cooperating processes, by comparison, regularly communicate and synchronize their activities in order to perform some common operation. For example, a component of an embedded computer system may have several processes involved in keeping the temperature and humidity of a gas in a vessel within certain defined limits. This may require frequent interactions.

A computer system has a finite number of resources which may be shared between processes; for example, peripheral devices, memory, and processor power. In order for processes to obtain their fair share of these resources, they must compete with each other. The act of resource allocation inevitably requires communication and synchronization between the processes in the system. But although these processes communicate and synchronize in order to obtain resources, they are, essentially, independent.

Discussion of the facilities which support process creation and process interaction is the focus of the next three chapters.

7.2   Concurrent execution

Although the notion of process is common to all concurrent programming languages, there are considerable variations in the models of concurrency adopted. These variations appertain to:

- Structure
- Level
- Granularity
- Initialization
- Termination
- Representation

The *structure* of a process may be classified as follows.

- Static: the number of processes is fixed and known at compile-time.
- Dynamic: processes are created at any time. The number of extant processes is determined only at run-time.

Another distinction between languages comes from the *level* of parallelism supported. Again, two distinct cases can be identified:

(1) Nested: processes are defined at any level of the program text; in particular, processes are allowed to be defined within other processes.

Language	Structure	Level
Concurrent Pascal	static	flat
occam2	static	nested
Modula-1	dynamic	flat
Modula-2	dynamic	flat
Ada	dynamic	nested
Java	dynamic	nested
Mesa	dynamic	nested
C/POSIX	dynamic	flat

Table 7.1.   The structure and level characteristics of a number of concurrent programming languages.

(2) Flat: processes are defined only at the outermost level of the program text.

Table 7.1 gives the structure and level characteristics for a number of concurrent programming languages.   In this table, the language C is considered to incorporate the POSIX 'fork' and 'wait' primitives.

Within languages that support nested constructs, there is also an interesting distinction between what may be called **coarse** and **fine grain** parallelism. A coarse grain concurrent program contains relatively few processes, each with a significant life history. By comparison, programs with a fine grain of parallelism will have a large number of simple processes, some of which will exist for only a single action. Most concurrent programming languages, typified by Ada, display coarse grain parallelism. Occam2 is a good example of a concurrent language with fine grain parallelism.

When a process is created, it may need to be supplied with information pertinent to its execution (much as a procedure may need to be supplied with information when it is called). There are two ways of performing this **initialization**. The first is to pass the information in the form of parameters to the process; the second is to communicate explicitly with the process after it has commenced its execution.

Process **termination** can be accomplished in a variety of ways. The circumstances under which processes are allowed to terminate can be summarized as follows:

(1) completion of execution of the process body;

(2) suicide, by execution of a 'self-terminate' statement;

(3) abortion, through the explicit action of another process;

(4) occurrence of an untrapped error condition;

(5) never: processes are assumed to execute non-terminating loops;

(6) when no longer needed.

With nested levels, hierarchies of processes can be created and interprocess relationships formed. For any process, it is useful to distinguish between the process (or

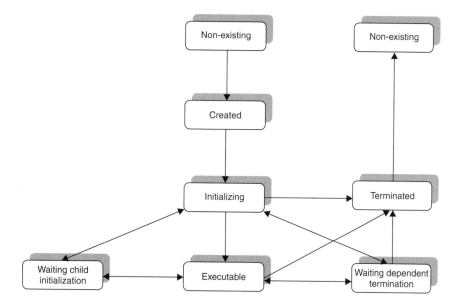

Figure 7.2   State diagram for a process.

block) that is responsible for its creation and the process (or block) which is affected by its termination. The former relationship is know as **parent/child** and has the attribute that the parent may be delayed while the child is being created and initialized. The latter relationship is termed **guardian/dependant**. A process may be dependent on the guardian process itself or on an inner block of the guardian. The guardian is not allowed to exit from a block until all dependent processes of that block have terminated (that is, a process cannot exist outside its scope). It follows that a guardian cannot terminate until all its dependents have also terminated. This rule has the particular consequence that a program itself will not be able to terminate until all processes created within it have also terminated.

In some situations, the parent of a process will also be its guardian. This will be the case when using languages which allow only static process structures (for example, occam2). With dynamic process structures (that are also nested), the parent and guardian may or may not be identical. This will be illustrated later in the discussion of Ada.

Figure 7.2 includes the new states that have been introduced in the above discussion.

One of the ways a process may terminate (point (3) in the above list) is by the application of an abort statement. The existence of abort in a concurrent programming language is a question of some contention and is considered in Chapter 11 within the context of resource control. For a hierarchy of processes, it is usually necessary for the abort of a guardian to imply the abort of all dependents (and their dependents and so on).

The final circumstance for termination, in the above list, is considered in more detail when process communication methods are described. In essence, it allows a server process to terminate if all other processes that could communicate with it have already terminated.

7.2.1 Processes and objects

The object-oriented programming paradigm encourages system (and program) builders to consider the artifact under construction as a collection of cooperating objects (or, to use a more neutral term, *entities*). Within this paradigm, it is constructive to consider two kinds of object – active and reactive. **Active** objects undertake spontaneous actions (with the help of a processor): they enable the computation to proceed. **Reactive** objects, by comparison, only perform actions when 'invoked' by an active object. Other programming paradigms, such as data-flow or real-time networks, identify active agents and passive data.

Only active entities give rise to spontaneous actions. Resources are reactive but can control access to their internal states (and any real resources they control). Some resources can only be used by one agent at a time; in other cases the operations that can be carried out at a given time depend on the resources' current states. A common example of the latter is a data buffer whose elements cannot be extracted if it is empty. The term **passive** will be used to indicate a reactive entity that can allow open access.

The implementation of resource entities requires some form of control agent. If the control agent is itself passive (such as a semaphore), then the resource is said to be **protected** (or **synchronized**). Alternatively, if an active agent is required to program the correct level of control, then the resource is in some sense active. The term **server** will be used to identify this type of entity, and the term **protected resource** to indicate the passive kind. These, together with **active** and **passive**, are the four abstract program entities used in this book.

In a concurrent programming language, active entities are represented by processes. Passive entities can be represented either directly as data variables or they can be encapsulated by some module/package/class construct that provides a procedural interface. Protected resources may also be encapsulated in a module-like construct and require the availability of a low-level synchronization facility. Servers, because they need to program the control agent, require a process.

A key question for language designers is whether to support primitives for both protected resources and servers. Resources, because they typically use a low-level control agent (for example a semaphore), are normally implemented efficiently (at least on single-processor systems). But they can be inflexible and lead to poor program structures for some classes of problems (this is discussed further in Chapter 8). Servers, because the control agent is programmed using a process, are eminently flexible. The drawback of this approach is that it can lead to proliferation of processes, with a resulting high number of context switches during execution. This is particularly problematic if the language does not support protected resources and hence servers must be used for all such entities. As will be illustrated in this chapter and Chapters 8 and 9, Ada, Java, and POSIX support the full range of entities. Occam2, in contrast, supports only servers.

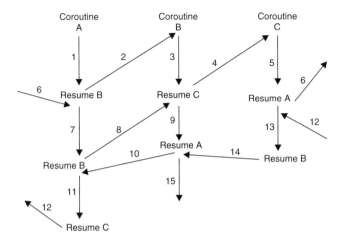

Figure 7.3   Coroutine flow of control.

7.3   Process representation

There are three basic mechanisms for representing concurrent execution: fork and join, cobegin and explicit process declaration. Coroutines are also sometimes included as a mechanism for expressing concurrent execution.

7.3.1   Coroutines

Coroutines are like subroutines but they allow control to pass explicitly between them in a symmetric rather than strictly hierarchical way. Control is passed from one coroutine to another by means of the **resume** statement which names the coroutine to be resumed. When a coroutine executes a resume, it stops executing but retains local state information so that if another coroutine subsequently 'resumes' it, it can and will continue its execution. Figure 7.3 illustrates the execution of three coroutines; the numbered arrows represent the flow of control which starts in coroutine A and completes in coroutine B (having twice visited coroutine C).

Each coroutine may be viewed as implementing a process; however, no run-time support system is needed, as the coroutines themselves sort out their order of execution. Clearly, coroutines are not adequate for true parallel processing as their semantics allow for execution of only one routine at a time. Modula-2 is an example of a language that supports coroutines.

7.3.2 Fork and join

This simple approach does not provide a visible entity for a process but merely supports two statements. The fork statement specifies that a designated routine should start executing concurrently with the invoker of the fork. The join statement allows the invoker to synchronize with the completion of the invoked routine. For example:

```
function F return ... ;
 .
 .
 .
end F;

procedure P;
  ...
  C:= fork F;
    .
    .
    .
  J:= join C;
  ...
end P;
```

Between the execution of the fork and the join, procedure P and function F will be executing concurrently. At the point of the join, the procedure will wait until the function has finished (if it has not already done so). Figure 7.4 illustrates the execution of fork and join.

The fork and join notation can be found in the Mesa language. A version of fork and join can also be found in POSIX; here `fork` is used to create a copy of the invoker and the `wait` system call provides the effective join.

Fork and join allow for dynamic process creation and provide a means of passing information to the child process via parameters. Usually only a single value is returned by the child on its termination. Although flexible, fork and join do not provide a structured approach to process creation and are error prone in use. For example, a guardian must explicitly 'rejoin' all dependants rather than merely wait for their completion.

7.3.3 Cobegin

The cobegin (or parbegin or par) is a structured way of denoting the concurrent execution of a collection of statements:

```
cobegin
  S1;
  S2;
  S3;
    .
    .
    .
  Sn
coend
```

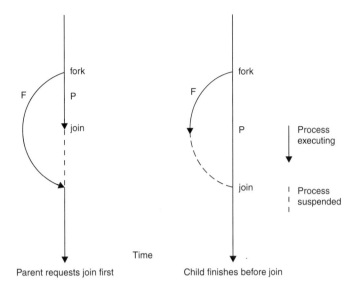

Figure 7.4   Fork and join

This code causes the statements S1, S2 and so on to be executed concurrently. The cobegin statement terminates when all the concurrent statements have terminated. Each of the Si statements may be any construct allowed within the language, including simple assignments or procedure calls. If procedure calls are used, data can be passed to the invoked process via the parameters of the call. A cobegin statement could even include a sequence of statements that itself has a cobegin within it. In this way, a hierarchy of processes can be supported. Figure 7.5 illustrates the execution of the cobegin statement.

Cobegin can be found in occam2.

7.3.4   Explicit process declaration

Although sequential routines may be executed concurrently by means of the cobegin or fork, the structure of a concurrent program can be made much clearer if the routines themselves state whether they will be executed concurrently. Explicit process declaration provides such a facility. The following example is in Modula-1. It presents a simple structure for a robot arm controller. A distinct process is used to control each dimension of movement. These processes loop around, each reading a new setting for its dimension and then calling a low-level procedure move_arm to cause the arm to move.

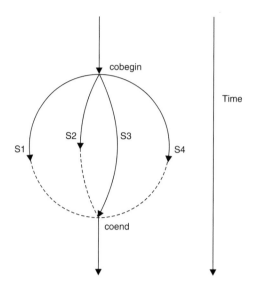

Figure 7.5   Cobegin.

```
MODULE main;
  TYPE dimension = (xplane, yplane, zplane);

  PROCESS control(dim : dimension);
    VAR position : integer;        (* absolute position *)
        setting : integer;         (* relative movement *)
  BEGIN
    position := 0;                 (* rest position *)
    LOOP
      move_arm(dim, position);
      new_setting(dim, setting);
      position := position + setting
    END
  END control;

BEGIN
  control(xplane);
  control(yplane);
  control(zplane)
END main.
```

In the above, the process control is declared with a parameter to be passed on creation. The example then creates three instances of this process, passing each a distinct
parameter.

Other languages that support explicit process declaration, for example Ada, also
have implicit task creation. All processes declared within a block start executing, con-

currently, at the end of the declarative part of that block.

In the above discussions, the basic models for concurrent execution have been outlined and references have been made to the languages that support particular features. To give concrete examples of actual programming languages, concurrent execution in occam2, Ada and Java will now be considered. This is followed by consideration of concurrent execution in POSIX.

7.3.5   Concurrent execution in occam2

Occam2 uses a cobegin structure called PAR. For example, consider the concurrent execution of two simple assignments (A:=1 and B:=1):

```
PAR
   A := 1
   B := 1
```

This PAR structure, which can be nested, can be compared to the sequential form:

```
SEQ
   A := 1
   B := 1
```

Note that a collection of actions must be explicitly defined to be either executing in sequence or parallel; there is no default. Indeed, it can be argued that PAR is the more general form and should be the natural structure to use unless the actual code in question requires a SEQuence.

If the process designated by a PAR is an instance of a parameterized PROC (procedure) then data can be passed to the process upon creation. For example, the following code creates three processes from a single PROC and passes an element of an array to each:

```
PAR
   ExampleProcess(A[1])
   ExampleProcess(A[2])
   ExampleProcess(A[3])
```

A greater collection of processes can be created from the same PROC by the use of a 'replicator' to increase the power of the PAR:

```
PAR i=1 FOR N
   ExampleProcess(A[i])
```

In Chapter 3, a replicator was used with a SEQ to introduce a standard 'for' loop. The only distinction between a replicated SEQ and a replicated PAR is that the number of replications (N in the above example) must be a constant in the PAR; that is, known at compile time. It follows that occam2 has a static process structure.

The following program fragment in occam2 is the robot arm example given earlier for Modula-1. Note that occam2 does not support enumeration types and so the
dimensions are represented by the integers 1, 2 and 3.

```
PROC control(VAL INT dim)
  INT  position,                  -- absolute position
       setting:                   -- relative movement
  SEQ
    position := 0                 -- rest position
    WHILE TRUE
      SEQ
        MoveArm(dim,position)
        NewSetting(dim,setting)
        position := position + setting
:
PAR
  control(1)
  control(2)
  control(3)
```

Process termination is quite straightforward in occam2. There is no abort facility nor
are there any exceptions. A process must either terminate normally or not terminate at
all (as in the above example).

    In general, occam2 has a fine grain view of concurrency. Most concurrent pro-
gramming languages have the notion of process added to an essentially sequential framework. This is not the case with occam2; the concept of process is basic to the language.
All activities, including the assignment operations and procedure calls, are considered
to be processes. Indeed, the notion of statement is missing from occam2. A program
is a single process that is built from a hierarchy of other processes. At the lowest level,
all primitive actions are considered to be processes and the constructors (IF, WHILE,
CASE and so on) are themselves constructor processes.

7.3.6 Concurrent execution in Ada

The conventional unit of parallelism, the sequential process, is called a **task** in Ada.
Tasks may be declared at any program level; they are created implicitly upon entry to
the scope of their declaration. The following example illustrates a procedure containing
two tasks (A and B)

```
procedure Example1 is
  task A;
  task B;

  task body A is
  -- local declarations for task A
  begin
  -- sequence of statement for task A
  end A;
```

```
task body B is
-- local declarations for task B
begin
-- sequence of statements for task B
end B;

begin
  -- tasks A and B start their executions before
  -- the first statement of the sequence of
  -- statements belonging to the procedure
  .
  .
  .
end Example1;   -- the procedure does not terminate
                -- until tasks A and B have terminated.
```

Tasks, like packages, consist of a specification and a body. They can, however, be passed initialization data upon creation.

In the above, tasks A and B (which are created when the procedure is called) are said to have anonymous type, as they do not have a type declared for them (compared with anonymous array types). Types could easily have been given for A and B:

```
task type A_Type;
task type B_Type;
A : A_Type;
B : B_Type;
task body A_Type is
  -- as before for task body A
task body B_Type is
  -- as before for task body B
```

With task types, a number of instances of the same process can easily be declared using an array:

```
task type T;
A,B : T;
type Long is array (1..100) of T;
type Mixture is
record
  Index : Integer;
  Action : T;
end record;
L : Long; M : Mixture;
task body T is ...
```

A more concrete example of the use of tasks in an Ada program is the robot arm system introduced earlier for both Modula-1 and occam2.

```
procedure Main is
  type Dimension is (Xplane, Yplane, Zplane);
  task type Control(Dim : Dimension);
```

```
C1 : Control(Xplane);
C2 : Control(Yplane);
C3 : Control(Zplane);

task body Control is
   Position : Integer;      -- absolute position
   Setting : Integer;       -- relative movement
begin
   Position := 0;                -- rest position
   loop
      Move_Arm(Dim, Position);
      New_Setting(Dim, Setting);
      Position := Position + Setting;
   end loop;
end Control;
begin
   null;
end Main;
```

It is, perhaps, worth noting that Ada only allows discrete types and access types to be passed as initialization parameters to a task.

By giving non-static values to the bounds of an array (of tasks), a dynamic number of tasks is created. Dynamic task creation can also be obtained explicitly using the 'new' operator on an access type (of a task type):

```
procedure Example2 is
   task type T;
   type A is access T;
   P : A;
   Q : A := new T;
begin
   ...
   P := new T;
   Q := new T;
   ...
end Example2;
```

Q is declared to be of type A and is given a 'value' of a new allocation of T. This creates a task that immediately starts its initialization and execution; the task is designated Q.all (all is an Ada naming convention used to indicate the task itself, not the access pointer). During execution of the procedure, P is allocated a task (P.all) followed by a further allocation to Q. There are now three tasks active within the procedure; P.all, Q.all and the task that was created first. This first task is now anonymous as Q is no longer pointing to it. In addition to these three tasks, there is the task or main program executing the procedure code itself; in total, therefore, there are four distinct threads of control.

Tasks created by the operation of an allocator ('new') have the important property that the block that acts as its guardian (or **master** as Ada calls it) is not the block in which it is created but the one that contains the declaration of the access type. To illustrate this point, consider the following:

```
declare
  task type T;
  type A is access T;
begin
  .
  .
  .
  declare              -- inner block
    X : T;
    Y : A:= new T;
  begin
    -- sequence of statements
  end;   -- must wait for X to terminate but not Y.all
  .
  .        -- Y.all could still be active although the name Y is
           -- out of scope
  .
end;      -- must wait for Y.all to terminate
```

Although both X and Y.**all** are created within the inner block, only X has this block as its master. Task Y.**all** is considered to be a dependent of the outer block, and it therefore does not affect the termination of the inner block.

If a task fails while it is being initialized (an exercise called **activation** in Ada) then the parent of that task has the exception Tasking_Error raised. This could occur, for example, if an inappropriate initial value is given to a variable. Once a task has started its true execution, it can catch any raised exceptions itself.

Task identification

One of the main uses of access variables is in providing another means of naming tasks. All task types in Ada are considered to be limited private. It is therefore not possible to pass a task by assignment to another data structure or program unit. For example, if Robot_Arm and New_Arm are two variables of the same access type (the access type being obtained from a task type) then the following is illegal:

```
Robot_Arm.all := New_Arm.all;   -- not legal Ada
```

However,

```
Robot_Arm := New_Arm;
```

is quite legal and means that Robot_Arm is now designating the same task as New_Arm. Care must be exercised here, as duplicated names can cause confusion and lead to programs that are difficult to understand. Furthermore, tasks may be left without any access pointers; such tasks are said to be **anonymous**. For example, if Robot_Arm pointed to a task, when it was overwritten with New_Arm, the previous task will have become anonymous if there were no other pointers to it.

In some circumstances it is useful for a task to have a unique identifier (rather than a name).   For example, a server task is not usually concerned with the type of the client tasks. Indeed, when communication and synchronization are discussed in the next chapter, it will be seen that the server has no direct knowledge of who its clients are. However, there are occasions when a server needs to know that the client task it is communicating with is the same client task that it previously communicated with. Although the core Ada language provides no such facility, the Systems Programming Annex provides a mechanism by which a task can obtain its own unique identification. This can then be passed to other tasks:

```
package Ada.Task_Identification is

  type Task_Id is private;
  Null_Task_Id : constant Task_Id;

  function "=" (Left, Right : Task_Id) return Boolean;

  function Current_Task return Task_Id;
    -- returns unique id of calling task

  -- other functions not relevant to this discussion
private
  ...
end Ada.Task_Identification;
```

As well as this package, the Annex supports two attributes:

(1) For any prefix T of a task type, T'Identity returns a value of type Task_Id that equals the unique identifier of the task denoted by T.

(2) For any prefix E that denotes an entry declaration, E'Caller returns a value of type Task_Id that equals the unique identifier of the task whose entry call is being serviced. The attribute is only allowed inside an entry body or an accept statement (see Chapters 8 and 9).

Care must be taken when using task identifiers since there is no guarantee that, at some later time, the task will still be active or even in scope.

Task termination

Having considered creation and representation, one is left with task termination. Ada provides a range of options; a task will terminate if

(1) it completes execution of its body (either normally or as the result of an unhandled exception);

(2) it executes a 'terminate' alternative of a select statement (this is explained in Section 9.4.2) thereby implying that it is no longer required;

(3) it is aborted.

If an unhandled exception has caused the task's demise then the effect of the error is isolated to just that task. Another task can enquire (by the use of an attribute) if a task has terminated:

```
if T'Terminated then    -- for some task T
  -- error recovery action
end if;
```

However, the enquiring task cannot differentiate between normal or error termination of the other task.

Any task can abort any other task whose name is in scope. When a task is aborted, all its dependents are also aborted. The abort facility allows wayward tasks to be removed. If, however, a rogue task is anonymous then it cannot be named and hence aborted (unless its master is aborted). It is desirable, therefore, that only terminated tasks are made anonymous.

7.3.7   Concurrent execution in Java

Java has a predefined class, java.lang.Thread which provides the mechanism by which threads (processes) are created. However, to avoid all threads having to be child classes of Thread, Java also has a standard interface, called Runnable:

```
public interface Runnable {
  public abstract void run();
}
```

Hence any class which wishes to express concurrent execution must implement this interface and provide the run method. The Thread class given in Program 7.1 does just this.

Thread is a subclass of Object. It provides several constructor methods and a run method. Using these constructors, threads can be created in two ways. (Thread groups will be considered later in this section.)

The first is to declare a class to be a subclass of Thread and override the run method. An instance of the subclass can then be allocated and started. For instance, in the robot arm example assume that the following classes and objects are available:

```
public class UserInterface
{
  public int newSetting (int Dim) { ... }
  ...
}

public class Arm
{
  public void move(int dim, int pos) { ... }
}

UserInterface UI = new UserInterface();
Arm Robot = new Arm();
```

Program 7.1 The Java `Thread` class.

```
public class Thread extends Object implements Runnable
{
  // Constructors

  public Thread();
  public Thread(String name);
  public Thread(Runnable target);
  public Thread(Runnable target, String name);


  public Thread(ThreadGroup group, String name);
  //           throws SecurityException, IllegalThreadStateException
  public Thread(ThreadGroup group, Runnable target);
  //           throws SecurityException, IllegalThreadStateException
  public Thread(ThreadGroup group, Runnable target, String name);
  //           throws SecurityException, IllegalThreadStateException


  public void run();
  public native synchronized void start();
  //           throws IllegalThreadStateException

  public static Thread currentThread();

  public final void join() throws InterruptedException;

  public final native boolean isAlive();

  public void destroy();
  //       throws SecurityException;

  public final void stop();
  //       throws SecurityException
  // DEPRECATED

  public final synchronized void stop(Throwable o);
  //       throws SecurityException, NullPointerException
  // DEPRECATED

  public final void setDaemon();
  //       throws SecurityException, IllegalThreadStateException

  public final boolean isDaemon();

  // other methods etc will be introduced throughout this
  // book -- see Appendix A for the full class description

  // Note, RuntimeExceptions are not listed as part of the method
  // specification. Here, they are shown as comments
}
```

Given the above classes, in scope, the following will declare a class which can be used to represent the three controllers.

```
public class Control extends Thread
{

  private int dim;

  public Control(int Dimension) // constructor
  {
    super();
    dim = Dimension;
  }

  public void run()
  {

    int position = 0;
    int setting;

    while(true)
    {
      Robot.move(dim, position);
      setting = UI.newSetting(dim);
      position = position + setting;
    }
  }
}
```

The three controllers can now be created:

```
final int xPlane = 0;   // final indicates a constant
final int yPlane = 1;
final int zPlane = 2;

Control C1 = new Control(xPlane);
Control C2 = new Control(yPlane);
Control C3 = new Control(zPlane);
```

At this point, the threads have been created, any variables declared have been initialized and the constructor methods for the Control and Thread class have been called (Java calls this the *new* state). However, the thread does not begin its execution until the start method[2] is called:

---

[2] The start method has both native and synchronize modifiers. The native modifier indicates that the body of the method is provided in a different language. The synchronize modifier is used to obtain mutual exclusive access to the object. It will be considered in detail in Section 8.8.

```
C1.start();
C2.start();
C3.start();
```

Note that if the run method is called explicitly then the code is executed sequentially.

The second way to create a thread is to declare a class that implements the Runnable interface. An instance of the class can then be allocated and passed as an argument during the creation of a thread object. Remember, Java threads are not created automatically when their associated objects are created, but must be explicitly created and started using the start method.

```
public class Control implements Runnable
{

  private int dim;

  public Control(int Dimension)   // constructor
  {
    dim = Dimension;
  }

  public void run()
  {
    int position = 0;
    int setting;

    while(true)
    {
      Robot.move(dim, position);
      setting = UI.newSetting(dim);
      position = position + setting;
    }
  }
}
```

The three controllers can now be created:

```
final int xPlane = 0;
final int yPlane = 1;
final int zPlane = 2;

Control C1 = new Control(xPlane); // no thread created yet
Control C2 = new Control(yPlane);
Control C3 = new Control(zPlane);
```

and then associated with threads and started:

```
// constructors passed a Runnable interface and threads created
Thread X = new Thread(C1);
Thread Y = new Thread(C2);
Thread Z = new Thread(C2);
```

```
X.start(); // thread started
Y.start();
Z.start();
```

Like Ada, Java allows dynamic thread creation. In contrast to Ada, Java (by means of constructor methods) allows arbitrary data to be passed as parameters (of course, all objects are passed by references which are similar to Ada's access variables).

Although Java allows thread hierarchies and thread groups to be created, there is no master or guardian concept. This is because Java relies on garbage collection to clean up objects which can no longer be accessed. The exception to this is the main program. The main program in Java terminates when all its user threads have terminated (see later).

One thread can wait for another thread (the target) to terminate by issuing the `join` method call on the target's thread object. Furthermore, the `isAlive` method allows a thread to determine if the target thread has terminated.

Thread identification

There are two ways that threads can be identified. If the code of the thread is a subclass of the `Thread` class, then the following will define a thread identifier.

```
Thread threadID;
```

Any subclass of `Thread` can be assigned to this object (because of the reference semantics of Java). Note that where the code of a thread is passed through a constructor with the `Runnable` interface, the thread identifier would be the thread object not the object providing the `Runnable` interface. To define an identifier which would identify the object providing the code requires a `Runnable` interface to be defined.

```
Runnable threadCodeID;
```

However, once a reference to the `Runnable` object has been obtained there is little explicitly that can be done with it. All the thread-related operations are provided by the `Thread` class.

The identity of the currently running thread can be found using the `current-Thread` method. This method has a `static` modifier which means that there is only one method for all instances of `Thread` objects. Hence the method can always be called using the `Thread` class.

Thread termination

There are several ways in which a Java thread can terminate:

(1) it completes execution of its `run` method either normally or as the result of an unhandled exception;

(2) by having its `stop` method called, in which case the `run` method is simply stopped and the thread class cleans up before terminating the thread (releases the locks it holds and executes any finally clauses); the thread object is now eligible for garbage collection. If a `Throwable` object is passed as a parameter to the `stop` method, then this exception is thrown in the target thread. This allows the run method to exit more gracefully and clean up after itself.[3] The `stop` method is inherently unsafe as it releases locks on objects and can leave those objects in inconsistent states. For this reason, the method is now deemed obsolete (what Java calls 'deprecated') and, therefore, should not be used.

(3) by its `destroy` method being called (either by another thread or by itself) – destroy terminates the thread without the thread object having any chance to cleanup. This method seems to have never been implemented in the Java virtual machine.

Although (3) above seems to imply that an arbitrary thread can destroy another thread, the program can provide some protection against this by several mechanisms:

- overriding the method when creating the new thread and undertaking some alternative action inside the method;
- by using thread groups to restrict the access;
- by enclosing the thread inside another class and only allowing certain operations to be passed through to the thread.

Only the latter two approaches can be used with the `stop` method as they are labelled as being `final` and hence cannot be overridden.

Java threads can be of two types: **user** threads or **daemon** threads. Daemon threads are those threads which provide general services and typically never terminate. Hence when all user threads have terminated, daemon threads can also be terminated and the main program terminates. (Daemon threads provide the same functionality as the Ada 'or terminate' option on the select statement – see Section 9.4.2). The `setDaemon` method must be called before the thread is started.

Thread groups

Thread groups allow collections of threads to be grouped together and manipulated as a group rather than as individuals. They also provide a means of restricting who does what to which thread. Every thread in Java is a member of a thread group. There is a default group associated with the main program, and hence unless otherwise specified, all created threads are placed in this group. Thread groups are represented by the class given in Program 7.2.

---

[3] In fact, when no parameter is passed to the `stop` method, the exception `ThreadDeath` is thrown. This is a subclass of `Error` and, therefore, should not be caught by the program (see Section 6.3.2).

Program 7.2 An excerpt of the Java Class for thread groups.

```
public class ThreadGroup {

    // Constructs a new thread group. The parent of this new group is
    // the thread group of the currently running thread.
    public ThreadGroup(String name);

    // Creates a new thread group. The parent of this new group is the
    // specified thread group.
    public ThreadGroup(ThreadGroup parent, String name);
    //         throws SecurityException

    // Returns the parent of this thread group.
    public final ThreadGroup getParent();

    // Tests if this thread group is a daemon thread group.
    public final boolean isDaemon();

    // Tests if this thread group has been destroyed.
    public synchronized boolean isDestroyed();

    // Changes the daemon status of this thread group.
    public final void setDaemon(boolean daemon);
    //                 throws SecurityException

    // Tests if this thread group is either the thread group
    // argument or one of its ancestor thread groups.
    public final boolean parentOf(ThreadGroup g);

    // Determines if the currently running thread has permission to
    // modify this thread group.
    public final void checkAccess();

    // Returns an estimate of the number of active threads in this
    // thread group.
    public int activeCount();

    // Returns an estimate of the number of active groups in this
    // thread group.
    public int activeGroupCount();

    // Stops all processes in this thread group.
    public final void stop();
    //                 throws SecurityException

    // Destroys this thread group and all of its subgroups.
    public final void destroy();
    //                 throws  IllegalThreadStateException

// other methods etc will be introduced throughout this
// book -- See Appendix A for full class specification
}
```

When a thread creates a new thread group, it does so from within a thread group. Hence the new thread group is a child of the current thread group unless a different thread group is passed as a parameter to the constructor. Using these two constructor methods allows hierarchies of thread groups to be created.

When threads are created they can be placed into explicit thread groups using the appropriate `Thread` class construction. Requests to `stop` or `destroy` a thread group will (if permitted by the security manager) be applied to all threads in the group.

Thread-related exceptions

In Chapter 6, Java `RuntimeExceptions` were introduced. The following `RuntimeExceptions` are relevant to threads.

The `IllegalThreadStateException` is thrown when:

- the `start` method is called and the thread has already been started;
- the `setDaemon` method has been called and the thread has already been started;
- an attempt is made to destroy a non-empty thread group;
- an attempt is made to place a thread into a thread group (via the `Thread` constructor) and the thread group has already been destroyed.

The `SecurityException` is thrown by the security manager[4] when:

- the `Thread` constructor has been called and it is requested that the thread to be created be placed into a thread group for which it has no permissions;
- a `stop` or `destroy` method has been called on a thread for which the caller does not have the correct permissions for the operation requested;
- the `ThreadGroup` constructor has been called and requested that the parent group of the newly created group is one for which the calling group has no permissions;
- a `stop` or `destroy` method has been called on a thread group for which the caller does not have the correct permissions for the operation requested.

The `NullPointerException` is thrown when:

- a null pointer is passed to the `stop` method;
- a null pointer is passed to the `ThreadGroup` constructor for the parent group.

The `InterruptedException` is thrown if a thread which has issued a `join` method is woken up by the thread being interrupted rather than the target thread terminating (see Section 10.9).

---

[4]The Java security manager will not be discussed in this book as it relates to issues associated with the use of Java in an open distributed system.

Real-time threads

The Java programming language lacks many facilities for programming real-time systems; hence the development of Real-Time Java. Real-Time Java produces several new thread classes. These will be considered in Sections 12.7.3.

7.3.8 Ada, Java and occam2 comparison

In the previous sections, the basic structure of the process models of occam2, Ada and Java have been given. Unfortunately, without communication between processes, meaningful programs cannot be presented; this will be remedied later. Nevertheless, it is possible to illustrate some of the differences between the occam2, Ada, and Java process models. In occam2, two procedure calls are explicitly executed either sequentially or concurrently:

```
SEQ        -- sequential form
   proc1
   proc2

PAR        -- concurrent form
   proc1
   proc2
```

To achieve concurrency in Ada requires the introduction of two tasks:

```
begin      -- sequential form
   Proc1;
   Proc2;
end;


declare    -- concurrent form
   task One;
   task Two;
   task body One is
   begin
      Proc1;
   end One;
   task body Two is
   begin
      Proc2;
   end Two;
begin
   null;
end;
```

Actually it would be possible in Ada to use only one task and have the block itself make the other call.

```
declare
  task One;
  task body One is
  begin
    Proc1;
  end One;
begin
  Proc2;
end;
```

This form, however, has lost the logical symmetry of the algorithm and is not recommended.

In Java, it is necessary to create an object for each procedure which implements the Runnable interface.

```
public class Proc1 implements Runnable
{
  public void run()
  {
    // code for proc1
  }
}
```

```
public class Proc2 implements Runnable
{
  public void run()
  {
    // code for proc2
  }
}
```

```
Proc1 P1 = new Proc1();
Proc2 P2 = new Proc2();
```

```
// sequential form
{
  P1.run;
  P2.run;
}
```

```
//concurrent form
Thread T1 = new Thread(P1);
Thread T2 = new Thread(P2)
```

```
T1.start();
T2.start();
```

7.3.9 Concurrent execution in POSIX

Real-time POSIX provides three mechanisms for creating concurrent activities. The first is the traditional Unix fork mechanism (and its associated wait system call). This

Program 7.3   A C POSIX interface to threads.

```
typedef ... pthread_t;   /* details not defined */
typedef ... pthread_attr_t;
typedef ... size_t;

int pthread_attr_init(pthread_attr_t *attr);
  /* initializes a thread attribute pointed at by attr to
     their default values */

int pthread_attr_destroy(pthread_attr_t *attr);
  /* destroys a thread attribute pointed at by attr*/

int pthread_attr_setstacksize(pthread_attr_t *attr,
                              size_t stacksize);
  /* set the stack size of a thread attribute */

int pthread_attr_getstacksize(const pthread_attr_t *attr,
                              size_t *stacksize);
 /* get the stack size of a thread attribute */

int pthread_attr_setstackaddr(pthread_attr_t *attr,
                              void *stackaddr);

  /* set the stack address of a thread attribute */

int pthread_attr_getstackaddr(const pthread_attr_t *attr,
                              void **stackaddr);
  /* get the stack address of a thread attribute */

int pthread_attr_setdetachstate(pthread_attr_t *attr,
                                int detachstate);
  /* set the detach state of the attribute */

int pthread_attr_getdetachstate(const pthread_attr_t *attr,
                                int *detachstate);
  /* get the detach state of the attribute */

int pthread_create(pthread_t *thread, const pthread_attr_t *attr,
                   void *(*start_routine)(void *), void *arg);
  /* create a new thread with the given attributes and call the
     given start_routine with the given argument */

int pthread_join(pthread_t thread, void **value_ptr);
  /* suspends the calling thread until the named thread has
     terminated, any returned values are pointed at by value_ptr */

int pthread_exit(void *value_ptr);
  /* terminate the calling thread and make the pointer value_ptr
     available to any joining thread */

int pthread_detach(pthread_t thread);
  /* the storage space associated with the given thread may be
     reclaimed when the thread terminates */
```

```
pthread_t pthread_self(void);
 /* return the thread id of the calling thread */

int pthread_equal(pthread_t t1, pthread_t t2);
/* compare two thread ids */


/* All the above integer functions returns 0 if successful,
   otherwise an error number is returned  */
```

causes a copy of the entire process to be created and executed. The details of fork can be found in most textbooks on operating systems (for example, Silberschatz and Galvin (1994)) and will not be discussed here. (An example of process creation using fork is given in Section 9.5.) The second is the spawn system call which is equivalent in function to a combined fork and join.

Real-time POSIX also allows for each process to contain several 'threads' of execution. These threads all have access to the same memory locations and run in a single address space. Thus, they can be compared with Ada's tasks, Java's threads and occam2's processes. Program 7.3 illustrates the primary C interface for thread creation in POSIX.

All threads in POSIX have attributes (for example, their stack size). To manipulate these attributes, it is necessary to define an attribute object (of type pthread_attr_t) and then call functions to set and get the attributes. Once the correct attribute object has been established, a thread can be created and the appropriate attribute object passed. Every created thread has an associated identifier (of type pthread_t) which is unique with respect to other threads in the same process. A thread can obtain its own identifier (via pthread_self).

A thread becomes eligible for execution as soon as it is created by pthread_create; there is no equivalent to the Ada activation state or the Java new state. This function takes four pointer arguments: a thread identifier (returned by the call), a set of attributes, a function that represents the code of the thread when it executes, and the set of parameters to be passed to this function when it is called. The thread can terminate normally by returning from its start_routine or by calling pthread_exit or by receiving a signal sent to it (see Section 10.6). It can also be aborted by the use of pthread_cancel. One thread can wait for another thread to terminate via the pthread_join function.

Finally, the activity of cleaning up after a thread's execution and reclaiming its storage is termed **detaching**. There are two ways to achieve this: by calling the pthread_join function and waiting until the thread terminates, or by setting the detached attribute of the thread (either at creation time or dynamically by calling the pthread_detach function). If the detached attribute is set, the thread is not joinable and its storage space may be reclaimed automatically when the thread terminates.

In many ways, the interface provided by POSIX threads is similar to that which would be used by a compiler to interface to its run-time support systems. Indeed, the run-time support system for Ada may well be implemented using POSIX threads. The advantage of providing higher-level language abstractions (such as those of Ada, Java and occam2) is that it removes the possibility of errors in using the interface.

To illustrate the simple use of the POSIX thread creation facility, the robot arm program is shown below.

```
#include <pthread.h>

pthread_attr_t attributes;
pthread_t xp, yp, zp;

typedef enum {xplane, yplane, zplane} dimension;

int new_setting(dimension D);
void move_arm(dimension D, int P);

void controller(dimension *dim)
{
  int position, setting;

  position = 0;
  while (1) {
    move_arm(*dim, position);
    setting = new_setting(*dim);
    position = position + setting;
  }
  /* note, no call to pthread_exit, process does not terminate */
}

#include <stdlib.h>
int main() {
  dimension X, Y, Z;
  void *result;

  X = xplane,
  Y = yplane;
  Z = zplane;
  if(pthread_attr_init(&attributes) != 0)
    /* set default attributes */
    exit(EXIT_FAILURE);
  if(pthread_create(&xp, &attributes,
                    (void *)controller, &X) != 0)
    exit(EXIT_FAILURE);
  if(pthread_create(&yp, &attributes,
                    (void *)controller, &Y) != 0)
    exit(EXIT_FAILURE);
  if(pthread_create(&zp, &attributes,
                    (void *)controller, &Z) != 0)
    exit(EXIT_FAILURE);
  pthread_join(xp, (void **)&result);
  /* need to block main program */

  exit(EXIT_FAILURE);
  /* error exit, the program should not terminate */
}
```

A thread attribute object is created with default attributes set. Calls to `pthread_create` create each instance of the `controller` thread and pass a parameter indicating its domain of operation. If any errors are returned from the operating system, the program terminates by calling the `exit` routine. Note that a program which terminates with threads still executing results in those threads being terminated. Hence it is necessary for the main program to issue a `pthread_join` system call even though the threads do not terminate.

In Section 6.1.1, a style of handling the error returns from POSIX was given. It assumes that each call has a macro defined which tests the return value and calls, if appropriate, an error handling routine. It is therefore possible to write the above code in the following more readable way:

```
int main() {
  dimension X, Y, Z;
  void *result;

  X = xplane,
  Y = yplane;
  Z = zplane;

  PTHREAD_ATTR_INIT(&attributes);

  PTHREAD_CREATE(&xp, &attributes, (void *)controller, &X);
  PTHREAD_CREATE(&yp, &attributes, (void *)controller, &Y);
  PTHREAD_CREATE(&zp, &attributes, (void *)controller, &Z);

  PTHREAD_JOIN(xp, (void **)&result);

}
```

Finally, it should be noted that conceptually forking a process (program) which contains multiple threads is not straightforward, as some threads in the process may hold resources or be executing system calls. The POSIX standard specifies that the child process will only have one thread (see POSIX 1003.1c (IEEE, 1995)).

7.4   A simple embedded system

In order to illustrate some of the advantages and disadvantages of concurrent programming, a simple embedded system will now be considered. Figure 7.6 outlines this simple system: a process T takes readings from a set of thermocouples (via an analogue to digital converter, ADC) and makes appropriate changes to a heater (via a digitally controlled switch). Process P has a similar function, but for pressure (it uses a digital to analogue converter, DAC). Both T and P must communicate data to S, which presents measurements to an operator via a screen. Note that P and T are active; S is a resource (it just responds to requests from T and P): it may be implemented as a protected resource or a server if it interacts more extensively with the user.

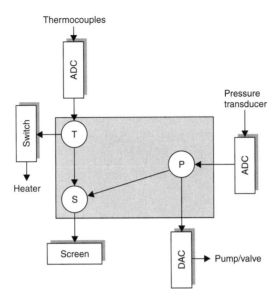

Figure 7.6   A simple embedded system.

The overall objective of this embedded system is to keep the temperature and pressure of some chemical process within defined limits. A real system of this type would clearly be more complex – allowing, for example, the operator to change the limits. However, even for this simple system, the implementation could take one of three forms:

(1) A single program is used which ignores the logical concurrency of T, P and S. No operating system support is required.

(2) T, P and S are written in a sequential programming language (either as separate programs or distinct procedures in the same program) and operating system primitives are used for program/process creation and interaction.

(3) A single concurrent program is used which retains the logical structure of T, P and S. No direct operating system support is required by the program although a run-time support system is needed.

To illustrate these solutions, consider the Ada code to implement the simple embedded system. In order to simplify the structure of the control software, the following passive packages will be assumed to have been implemented:

```
package Data_Types is
  -- necessary type definitions
```

```
  type Temp_Reading is new Integer range 10..500;
  type Pressure_Reading is new Integer range 0..750;
  type Heater_Setting is (On, Off);
  type Pressure_Setting is new Integer range 0..9;
end Data_Types;
```

```
with Data_Types; use Data_Types;
package IO is
  -- procedures for data exchange with the environment
  procedure Read(TR : out Temp_Reading); -- from ADC
  procedure Read(PR : out Pressure_Reading);
    -- note, this is an example of overloading; two reads
    -- are defined but they have a different parameter type;
    -- this is also the case with the following writes
  procedure Write(HS : Heater_Setting);   -- to switch.
  procedure Write(PS : Pressure_Setting); -- to DAC
  procedure Write(TR : Temp_Reading);     -- to screen
  procedure Write(PR : Pressure_Reading); -- to screen
end IO;
```

```
with Data_Types; use Data_Types;
package Control_Procedures is
  -- procedures for converting a reading into
  -- an appropriate setting for output to
  procedure Temp_Convert(TR : Temp_Reading;
                         HS : out Heater_Setting);
  procedure Pressure_Convert(PR : Pressure_Reading;
                             PS : out Pressure_Setting);
end Control_Procedures;
```

Sequential solution

A simple sequential control program could have the following structure:

```
with Data_Types; use Data_Types;
with IO; use IO;
with Control_Procedures; use Control_Procedures;
procedure Controller is
  TR : Temp_Reading;
  PR : Pressure_Reading;
  HS : Heater_Setting;
  PS : Pressure_Setting;
begin
  loop
    Read(TR);      -- from ADC
    Temp_Convert(TR,HS); -- convert reading to setting
    Write(HS);     -- to switch
```

```
      Write(TR);    -- to screen
      Read(PR);     -- as above for pressure
      Pressure_Convert(PR,PS);
      Write(PS);
      Write(PR);
   end loop; -- infinite loop, common in embedded software
end Controller;
```

This code has the immediate handicap that temperature and pressure readings must be taken at the same rate, which may not be in accordance with requirements. The use of counters and appropriate **if** statements will improve the situation, but it may still be necessary to split the computationally intensive sections (the conversion procedures Temp_Convert and Pressure_Convert) into a number of distinct actions, and interleave these actions so as to meet a required balance of work. Even if this were done, there remains a serious drawback with this program structure: while waiting to read a temperature no attention can be given to pressure (and vice versa). Moreover, if there is a system failure that results in, say, control never returning from the temperature Read, then in addition to this problem, no further pressure Reads would be taken.

An improvement on this sequential program can be made by including two boolean functions in the package IO, Ready_Temp and Ready_Pres, to indicate the availability of an item to read. The control program then becomes

```
with Data_Types; use Data_Types;
with IO; use IO;
with Control_Procedures; use Control_Procedures;
procedure Controller is
   TR : Temp_Reading;
   PR : Pressure_Reading;
   HS : Heater_Setting;
   PS : Pressure_Setting;
   Ready_Temp, Ready_Pres : Boolean;
begin
   loop
      ...
      if Ready_Temp then
        Read(TR);
        Temp_Convert(TR,HS);
        Write(HS);    -- assuming write to be reliable
        Write(TR);
      end if;
      if Ready_Pres then
        Read(PR);
        Pressure_Convert(PR,PS);
        Write(PS);
        Write(PR);
      end if;
   end loop;
end Controller;
```

This solution is more reliable; unfortunately the program now spends a high proportion of its time in a 'busy loop' polling the input devices to see if they are ready. Busy-waits are, in general, unacceptably inefficient. They tie up the processor and make it difficult to impose a queue discipline on waiting requests. Moreover, programs that rely on busy waiting are difficult to design, understand or prove correct.

The major criticism that can be levelled at the sequential program is that no recognition is given to the fact that the pressure and temperature cycles are entirely independent subsystems. In a concurrent programming environment, this can be rectified by coding each system as a process (or in Ada terms, a task).

Using operating system primitives

Consider a POSIX-like operating system which allows a new process/thread to be created and started by calling the following Ada subprogram:

```
package Operating_System_Interface is
   type Thread_ID is private;
   type Thread is access procedure; -- a pointer type

   function Create_Thread(Code : Thread) return Thread_ID;
   -- other subprograms for thread interaction
private
   type Thread_ID is ...;
end Operating_System_Interface;
```

The simple embedded system can now be implemented as follows. First, the two controller procedures are placed in a package:

```
package Processes is
   procedure Pressure_Controller;
   procedure Temp_Controller;
end Processes;

with Data_Types; use Data_Types;
with IO; use IO;
with Control_Procedures; use Control_Procedures;
package body Processes is
   procedure Temp_Controller is
      TR : Temp_Reading;
      HS : Heater_Setting;
   begin
      loop
         Read(TR);
         Temp_Convert(TR,HS);
         Write(HS);
         Write(TR);
      end loop;
   end Temp_Controller;

   procedure Pressure_Controller is
      PR : Pressure_Reading;
      PS : Pressure_Setting;
```

```
  begin
    loop
       Read(PR);
       Pressure_Convert(PR,PS);
       Write(PS);
       Write(PR);
    end loop;
  end Pressure_Controller;
end Processes;
```

Now the `Controller` procedure can be given:

```
with Operating_System_Interface; use Operating_System_Interface;
with Processes; use Processes;

procedure Controller is
  Tc, Pc: Thread_Id;
begin
  -- create the threads
  -- 'Access returns a pointer to the procedure
  Tc := Create_Thread(Temp_Controller'Access);
  Pc := Create_Thread(Pressure_Controller'Access);
end Controller;
```

Procedures `Temp_Controller` and `Pressure_Controller` execute concurrently and each contains an indefinite loop within which the control cycle is defined. While one thread is suspended waiting for a read, the other may be executing; if they are both suspended a busy loop is not executed.

     Although this solution does have advantages over the sequential solution, the lack of language support for expressing concurrency means that the program can become difficult to write and maintain. For the simple example given above, the added complexity is manageable. However, for large systems with many concurrent processes and potentially complex interactions between them, having a procedural interface obscures the structure of the program. For example, it is not obvious which procedures are really procedures or which ones are intended to be concurrent activities.

Using a concurrent programming language

In a concurrent programming language, concurrent activities can be identified explicitly in the code:

```
with Data_Types; use Data_Types;
with IO; use IO;
with Control_Procedures; use Control_Procedures;
procedure Controller is
  task Temp_Controller;
  task Pressure_Controller;
```

```
task body Temp_Controller is
  TR : Temp_Reading; HS : Heater_Setting;
begin
  loop
    Read(TR);
    Temp_Convert(TR,HS);
    Write(HS);
    Write(TR);
  end loop;
end Temp_Controller;

task body Pressure_Controller is
  PR : Pressure_Reading; PS : Pressure_Setting;
begin
  loop
    Read(PR);
    Pressure_Convert(PR,PS);
    Write(PS);
    Write(PR);
  end loop;
end Pressure_Controller;

begin
  null;    -- Temp_Controller and Pressure_Controller
           -- have started their executions
end Controller;
```

The logic of the application is now reflected in the code; the inherent parallelism of the domain is represented by concurrently executing tasks in the program.

Although an improvement, one major problem remains with this two-task solution. Both Temp_Controller and Pressure_Controller send data to the screen, but the screen is a resource that can only sensibly be accessed by one process at a time. In Figure 7.6, control over the screen was given to a third entity (S) which will need a representation in the program – Screen_Controller. This entity may be a server or a protected resource (depending on the complete definition of the required behaviour of Screen_Controller). This has transposed the problem from one of concurrent access to a passive resource to one of inter-task communication, or at least communication between a task and some other concurrency primitive. It is necessary for tasks Temp_Controller and Pressure_Controller to pass data to Screen_Controller. Moreover, Screen_Controller must ensure that it deals with only one request at a time. These requirements and difficulties are of primary importance in the design of concurrent programming languages, and are considered in the following chapters.

Summary

The application domains of most real-time systems are inherently parallel. It follows that the inclusion of the notion of process within a real-time programming language makes an enormous difference to the expressive power and ease of use of the language. These factors in turn contribute significantly to reducing the software construction costs whilst improving the reliability of the final system.

Without concurrency, the software must be constructed as a single control loop. The structure of this loop cannot retain the logical distinction between system components. It is particularly difficult to give process-oriented timing and reliability requirements without the notion of a process being visible in the code.

The use of a concurrent programming language is not, however, without its costs. In particular, it becomes necessary to use a run-time support system (or operating system) to manage the execution of the system processes.

The behaviour of a process is best described in terms of states. In this chapter, the following states are discussed:

- non-existing
- created
- initialized
- executable
- waiting dependent termination
- waiting child initialization
- terminated

Within concurrent programming languages, there are a number of variations in the process model adopted. These variations can be analyzed under six headings.

(1) structure – static or dynamic process model

(2) level – top-level processes only (flat) or multilevel (nested)

(3) initialization – with or without parameter passing

(4) granularity – fine or coarse grain

(5) termination –

- natural
- suicide
- aborted
- untrapped error
- never
- when no longer needed

(6) representation – coroutines, fork/join, cobegin; explicit process declarations

Occam2 employs a cobegin (PAR) representation with nested static processes; initialization data can be given to a process, although neither abortion nor 'no longer needed' termination is supported. Ada and Java provide a dynamic model with support for nested tasks and a range of termination options. POSIX allows dynamic threads to be created with a flat structure; threads must explicitly terminate or be killed.

Further reading

Andrews, G. A. (1991) *Concurrent Programming Principles and Practice*. Redwood City, CA: Benjamin/Cummings.

Ben-Ari, M. (1990) *Principles of Concurrent and Distributed Programming*. New York: Prentice Hall.

Burns, A. and Wellings, A. J. (1995) *Concurrency in Ada*. Cambridge: Cambridge University Press.

Burns, A. (1998) *Programming in occam2*. Reading: Addison-Wesley.

Butenhof, D. R. (1997) *Programming With Posix Threads*. Reading, MA: Addison-Wesley.

Galletly, J. (1990) *Occam2*. London: Pitman.

Hyde, P. (1999) *Java Thread Programming*. Indianapolis, IN: Sams Publishing.

Lea, D. (1999) *Concurrent Programming in Java: Design Principles and Patterns*. Reading, MA: Addison-Wesley.

Oaks, A. and Wong, H. (1997) *Java Threads*. Sebastopol, CA: O'Reilly.

Nichols, B., Buttlar, D. and Farrell, J. (1996) *POSIX Threads Programming*. Sebastopol, CA: O'Reilly.

Silberschatz, A. and Galvin, P. A. (1998) *Operating System Concepts*. New York: John Wiley & Sons.

Exercises

7.1   A particular operating system has a system call (*RunConcurrently*) which takes an unconstrained array. Each element of the array is a pointer to a parameterless procedure. The system call executes all the procedures concurrently and returns when all have terminated. Show how this system call can be implemented in Ada using the Ada tasking facilities. Assume that the operating system and the application run in the same address space.

7.2   Write Ada code to create an array of tasks where each task has a parameter which indicates its position in the array.

7.3   Show how a *cobegin* can be implemented in Ada.

7.4   Can the *fork* and *join* method of process creation be implemented in Ada without using intertask communication?

7.5   How many POSIX processes are created with the following procedure?

```
for(i=0; i<=10;i++) {
   fork();
}
```

7.6 Rewrite the simple embedded system illustrated in Section 7.4 in Java, C and POSIX, and occam2.

7.7 If a multithread process executes a POSIX-like fork system call, how many threads should the created process contain?

7.8 Show, using concurrent processes, the structure of a program to control access to a simple car park. Assume that the car park has a single entrance and a single exit barrier, and a full sign.

7.9 Explain, with the help of the following program, the interactions between Ada's rules for task termination and its exception propagation model. Include a consideration of the program's behaviour (output) for initial values of the variable C of 2, 1 and 0.

```ada
with Ada.Text_Io; use Ada.Text_Io;
procedure Main is
   task A;

   task body A is
      C : Positive := Some_Integer_Value;
      procedure P(D : Integer) is
         task T;
         A : Integer;
         task body T is
         begin
            delay 10.0;
            Put("T Finished"); New_Line;
         end T;
      begin
         Put("P Started"); New_Line;
         A := 42/D;
         Put("P Finished"); New_Line;
      end P;

   begin
      Put("A Started"); New_Line;
      P(C-1);
      Put("A Finished"); New_Line;
   end A;

begin
   Put("Main Procedure Started"); New_Line;
exception
   when others =>
      Put("Main Procedure Failed"); New_Line;
end Main;
```

7.10 For every task in the following Ada program indicate its parent and guardian (master) and if appropriate its children and dependants. Also indicate the dependants of the Main and Hierarchy procedures.

```ada
procedure Main is
  procedure Hierarchy is
    task A;
    task type B;

    type Pb is access B;
    Pointerb : Pb;

    task body A is
      task C;
      task D;
      task body C is
      begin
        -- sequence of statements including
        Pointerb := new B;
      end C;
      task body D is
        Another_Pointerb : Pb;
      begin
        -- sequence of statements including
        Another_Pointerb := new B;
      end D;
    begin
      -- sequence of statements
    end A;

    task body B is
    begin
      -- sequence of statements
    end B;

  begin
    -- sequence of statements
  end Hierarchy;

begin
  -- sequence of statements
end Main;
```

7.11 To what extent can Figure 7.2 be used to represent the state transition diagram of (a) POSIX pthreads, (b) occam2 processes and (c) Java threads?

7.12 Given the following:

```java
public class Calculate implements Runnable

{

  public void run()
  {
```

```
    /* long calculation */
  }
}
```

```
Calculate MyCalculation = new Calculate();
```

what is the difference between:

```
MyCalculation.run();
```

and

```
new Thread(MyCalculation).start();
```

7.13 Explain how a Java thread can be protected against being destroyed by an arbitrary thread.

Chapter 8
Shared variable-based synchronization and communication

The major difficulties associated with concurrent programming arise from process interaction. Rarely are processes as independent of one another as they were in the simple example at the end of Chapter 7. The correct behaviour of a concurrent program is critically dependent on synchronization and communication between processes. In its widest sense, synchronization is the satisfaction of constraints on the interleaving of the actions of different processes (for example, a particular action by one process only occurring after a specific action by another process). The term is also used in the narrower sense of bringing two processes simultaneously into predefined states. Communication is the passing of information from one process to another. The two concepts are linked, since some forms of communication require synchronization, and synchronization can be considered as contentless communication.

Interprocess communication is usually based upon either **shared variables** or **message passing**. Shared variables are objects that more than one process has access to; communication can therefore proceed by each process referencing these variables when appropriate. Message passing involves the explicit exchange of data between two processes by means of a message that passes from one process to another via some agency. Note that the choice between shared variables and message passing is one for the language or operating systems designers; it does not imply that any particular implementation method should be used. Shared variables are easy to support if there is shared memory between the processes, but they can still be used even if the hardware incorporates a communication medium. Similarly, a message-passing primitive can be supported via shared memory or a physical message-passing network. Furthermore, an application can arguably be programmed in either style and ob-

tain the same functionality (Lauer and Needham, 1978). Message-based synchronization and communication is discussed in the Chapter 9. This chapter
will concentrate on shared variable-based communication and synchronization
primitives. In particular, busy waiting, semaphores, conditional critical regions,
monitors, protected types and synchronized methods are discussed.

8.1   Mutual exclusion and condition synchronization

Although shared variables appear to be a straightforward way of passing information
between processes, their unrestricted use is unreliable and unsafe due to multiple update
problems. Consider two processes updating a shared variable, X, with the assignment:

```
X:= X+1
```

On most hardware this will not be executed as an **indivisible** (atomic) operation, but
will be implemented in three distinct instructions:

(1) load the value of X into some register (or to the top of the stack);

(2) increment the value in the register by 1; and

(3) store the value in the register back to X.

As the three operations are not indivisible, two processes simultaneously updating the
variable could follow an interleaving that would produce an incorrect result. For example, if X was originally 5, the two processes could each load 5 into their registers,
increment and then store 6.

A sequence of statements that must appear to be executed indivisibly is called
a **critical section**. The synchronization required to protect a critical section is known
as **mutual exclusion**. Atomicity, although absent from the assignment operation, is
assumed to be present at the memory level. Thus, if one process is executing X : =
5, simultaneously with another executing X := 6, the result will be either 5 or 6
(not some other value). If this were not true, it would be difficult to reason about
concurrent programs or implement higher levels of atomicity, such as mutual exclusion
synchronization. Clearly, however, if two processes are updating a structured object,
this atomicity will only apply at the single word element level.

The mutual exclusion problem itself was first described by Dijkstra (1965). It lies
at the heart of most concurrent process synchronizations and is of great theoretical as
well as practical interest. Mutual exclusion is not the only synchronization of importance; indeed, if two processes do not share variables then there is no need for mutual
exclusion. Condition synchronization is another significant requirement and is needed
when a process wishes to perform an operation that can only sensibly, or safely, be
performed if another process has itself taken some action or is in some defined state.

An example of condition synchronization comes with the use of buffers. Two
processes that exchange data may perform better if communication is not direct but
via a buffer. This has the advantage of de-coupling the processes and allows for small

fluctuations in the speed at which the two processes are working. For example, an input process may receive data in bursts that must be buffered for the appropriate user process. The use of a buffer to link two processes is common in concurrent programs and is known as a **producer–consumer** system.

Two condition synchronizations are necessary if a finite (bounded) buffer is used. Firstly, the producer process must not attempt to deposit data into the buffer if the buffer is full. Secondly, the consumer process cannot be allowed to extract objects from the buffer if the buffer is empty. Moreover, if simultaneous deposits or extractions are possible, mutual exclusion must be ensured so that two producers, for example, do not corrupt the 'next free slot' pointer of the buffer.

The implementation of any form of synchronization implies that processes must at times be held back until it is appropriate for them to proceed. In Section 8.2, mutual exclusion and condition synchronization will be programmed (in a Pascal-like language with explicit process declaration) using **busy-wait** loops and **flags**. From this analysis, it should be clear that further primitives are needed to ease the coding of algorithms that require synchronization.

8.2 Busy waiting

One way to implement synchronization is to have processes set and check shared variables that are acting as flags. This approach works reasonably well for implementing condition synchronization, but no simple method for mutual exclusion exists. To signal a condition, a process sets the value of a flag; to wait for this condition, another process checks this flag and proceeds only when the appropriate value is read:

```
process P1;   (* waiting process *)
  . . .
  while flag = down do
    null
  end;
  . . .
end P1;

process P2;   (* signalling process *)
  . . .
  flag := up;
  . . .
end P2;
```

If the condition is not yet set (that is, flag is still down) then P1 has no choice but to loop round and recheck the flag. This is **busy waiting**; also known as **spinning** (with the flag variables called **spin locks**).

Busy-wait algorithms are in general inefficient; they involve processes using up processing cycles when they cannot perform useful work. Even on a multiprocessor system, they can give rise to excessive traffic on the memory bus or network (if distributed). Moreover, it is not possible to impose queuing disciplines easily if there is more than one process waiting on a condition (that is, checking the value of a flag).

Mutual exclusion presents even more difficulties as the algorithms required are more complex. Consider two processes (P1 and P2 again) that have mutual critical sections. In order to protect access to these critical sections, it can be assumed that each process executes an entry protocol before the critical section and an exit protocol afterwards. Each process can therefore be considered to have the following form:

```
process P;
  loop
    entry protocol
      critical section
    exit protocol
    non-critical section
  end
end P;
```

Before giving a solution that adequately provides for mutual exclusion, three inappropriate approaches will be discussed. First, consider a two-flag solution that is an (almost) logical extension of the busy-wait condition synchronization algorithm:

```
process P1;
  loop
    flag1 := up;       (* announce intent to enter *)
    while flag2 = up do
      null             (* busy wait if the other process is in *)
    end;               (* its critical section *)
    <critical section>
    flag1 := down;     (* exit protocol *)
    <non-critical section>
  end
end P1;

process P2;
  loop
    flag2 := up;
    while flag1 = up do
      null
    end;
    <critical section>
    flag2 := down;
    <non-critical section>
  end
end P2;
```

Both processes announce their intention to enter their critical sections and then check to see if the other process is in its critical section. Unfortunately, this 'solution' suffers from a not insignificant problem. Consider an interleaving that has the following progression:

```
P1 sets its flag (flag1 now up)
P2 sets its flag (flag2 now up)
P2 checks flag1 (it is up therefore P2 loops)
P2 enters its busy wait
```

```
P1 checks flag2 (it is up therefore P1 loops)
P1 enters its busy wait
```

The result is that both processes will remain in their busy waits. Neither can get out because the other cannot get out. This phenomenon is known as **livelock** and is a severe error condition.

The difficulty with the above approach arises because each process announces its intention to enter its critical section before checking to see whether it is acceptable for it to do so. Another approach is to reverse the order of these two actions:

```
process P1;
  loop
    while flag2 = up do
      null            (* busy wait if the other process is in *)
    end;              (* its critical section *)
    flag1 := up;      (* announce intent to enter *)
    <critical section>
    flag1 := down;    (* exit protocol *)
    <non-critical section>
  end
end P1;

process P2;
  loop
    while flag1 = up do
      null
    end;
    flag2 := up;
    <critical section>
    flag2 := down;
    <non-critical section>
  end
end P2;
```

Now we can produce an interleaving that actually fails to give mutual exclusion.

```
P1 and P2 are in their non-critical section (flag1 = flag2 = down)
P1 checks flag2 (it is down)
P2 checks flag1 (it is down)
P2 sets its flag (flag2 now up)
P2 enters critical section
P1 sets it flag (flag1 now up)
P1 enters critical section
(P1 and P2 are both in their critical sections).
```

The difficulty with the two structures given so far is that the setting of one's own flag and the checks on the other processes cannot be done as an indivisible action. One might, therefore, consider that the correct approach is to use just one flag that indicates which process should next enter its critical section. As this flag decides whose turn it is to enter, it will be called `turn`.

```
process P1;
  loop
    while turn = 2 do
      null
    end
    <critical section>
    turn:= 2
    <non-critical section>
  end
end P1;

process P2;
  loop
    while turn = 1 do
      null
    end
    <critical section>
    turn:=1;
    <non-critical section>
  end
end P2;
```

With this structure, the variable `turn` must have either the value 1 or 2. If it is 1 then P1 cannot be indefinitely delayed and P2 cannot enter its critical section. Moreover, `turn` cannot become 2 while P1 is in its critical section, as the only place that turn can be assigned 2 is by P1 and that is while it is in its exit protocol. A symmetric argument for `turn` having the value 2 implies that mutual exclusion is provided and livelock is not possible if both processes are cycling round.

Unfortunately, this latter point is significant. If P1 fails in its non-critical section then `turn` will eventually obtain the value 1 and will stay with that value (that is, P2 will be prohibited from entering its critical section even though P1 is no longer executing). Even when executing normally, the use of a single turn variable requires the processes to cycle round at the same rate. It is not possible for P1 (say) to enter its critical section three times between visits by P2. This constraint is unacceptable for autonomous processes.

Finally, an algorithm is presented that does not give rise to the close coupling of the previous example but provides mutual exclusion and absence of livelock. It was first presented by Peterson (1981). Another famous algorithm, Dekker's, is discussed by Ben-Ari (1982). The approach of Peterson (and Dekker) is to have two flags (`flag1` and `flag2`) that are manipulated by the process that 'owns' them and a `turn` variable that is only used if there is contention for entry to the critical sections:

```
process P1;
  loop
    flag1:= up;       (* announce intent to enter *)
    turn:= 2;         (* give priority to other process *)
    while flag2 = up and turn = 2 do
      null
    end;
    <critical section>
    flag1:= down;
```

```
    <non-critical section>
  end
end P1;



process P2;
  loop
    flag2:= up;      (* announce intent to enter *)
    turn:= 1;        (* give priority to other process *)
    while flag1 = up and turn = 1 do
      null
    end;
    <critical section>
    flag2:= down;
    <non-critical section>
  end
end P2;
```

If only one process wishes to enter its critical section then the other process's flag will be down and entry will be immediate. However, if both flags have been raised then the value of turn becomes significant. Let us say that it has the initial value 1; then there are four possible interleavings, depending on the order in which each process assigns a value to turn and then checks its value in the while statement:

```
First Possibility -- P1 first then P2
P1 sets turn to 2
P1 checks turn and enters busy loop
P2 sets turn to 1 (turn will now stay with that value)
P2 checks turn and enters busy loop
P1 loops around rechecks turn and enters critical section


Second Possibility -- P2 first then P1
P2 sets turn to 1
P2 checks turn and enters busy loop
P1 sets turn to 2 (turn will now stay with that value)
P1 checks turn and enters busy loop
P2 loops around rechecks turn and enters critical section


Third Possibility -- interleaved P1 and P2
P1 sets turn to 2
P2 sets turn to 1 (turn will stay with this value)
P2 enters busy loop
P1 enters critical section


Fourth Possibility -- interleaved P2 and P1
P2 sets turn to 1
P1 sets turn to 2 (turn will stay with this value)
P1 enters busy loop
P2 enters critical section
```

All four possibilities lead to one process in its critical section and one process in a busy loop.

In general, although a single interleaving can only illustrate the failure of a system to meet its specification, it is not possible to show easily that all possible interleavings lead to compliance with the specification. Normally, proof methods (including model checking) are needed to show such compliance.

Interestingly, the above algorithm is fair in the sense that if there is contention for access (to their critical sections) and, say, P1 was successful (via either the first or third possible interleaving) then P2 is bound to enter next. When P1 exits its critical section, it lowers flag1. This could let P2 into its critical section, but even if it does not (because P2 was not actually executing at that time) then P1 would proceed, enter and leave its non-critical section, raise flag1, set turn to 2 and then be placed in a busy loop. There it would remain until P2 had entered and left its critical section and reset flag2 as its exit protocol.

In terms of reliability, the failure of a process in its non-critical section will not affect the other process. This is not the case with failure in the protocols or critical section. Here, premature termination of a process would lead to livelock difficulties for the remaining program.

This discussion has been given at length to illustrate the difficulties of implementing synchronization between processes with only shared variables and no additional primitives other than those found in sequential languages. These difficulties can be summarized as follows:

- Protocols that use busy loops are difficult to design, understand and prove correct. (The reader might like to consider generalizing Peterson's algorithm for n processes.)

- Testing programs may not examine rare interleavings that break mutual exclusion or lead to livelock.

- Busy-wait loops are inefficient.

- An unreliable (rogue) task that misuses shared variables will corrupt the entire system.

No concurrent programming language relies entirely on busy waiting and shared variables; other methods and primitives have been introduced. For shared-variable systems, semaphores and monitors are the most significant constructs and are described in Sections 8.4 and 8.6.

8.3   Suspend and resume

One of the problems with busy-wait loops is that they waste valuable processor time. An alternative approach is to suspend (that is, remove from the set of runnable processes) the calling process if the condition for which it is waiting does not hold. Consider, for example, simple condition synchronization using a flag. One process sets the flag,

and another process waits until the flag is set and then clears it. A simple suspend and
resume mechanism could be used as follows:

```
process P1;  (* waiting process *)
  ...
  if flag = down do
    suspend;
  end;
  flag := down;
  ...
end P1;
process P2;  (* signalling process *)
  ...
  flag := up;
  resume P1; (* has no effect, if P1 is not suspended *)
  ...
end P2;
```

An early version of the Java Thread class provided the following methods in support
of this approach:

```
public final void suspend();
                  // throws SecurityException;
public final void resume();
                  // throws SecurityException;
```

Thus the above example would be represented in Java:

```
boolean flag;
final boolean up = true;
final boolean down = false;

class FirstThread extends Thread {

  public void run() {
    ...
    if(flag == down) {
      suspend();
    };
    flag = down;
    ...
  }
};

class SecondThread extends Thread { // T2

  FirstThread T1;

  public SecondThread(FirstThread T) {
    super();
    T1 = T;
  }
```

```
public void run() {
    ...
    flag = up;
    T1.resume();
    ...
  }
}
```

Unfortunately, this approach suffers from what is called a **race condition**. Thread T1 could test the flag, and then the underlying run-time support system (or operating system) could decide to preempt it and run T2. T2 sets the flag and resumes T1. T1 is, of course, not suspended, so the resume has no effect. Now, when T1 next runs, it thinks the flag is down and therefore suspends itself.

The reason for this problem, which was present with the examples given in the previous section, is that the flag is a shared resource which is being tested and an action is being taken which depends on its status (the process is suspending itself). This testing and suspending is not an atomic operation, and therefore interference can occur from other processes. It is for this reason that the most recent version of Java has made these methods obsolete.

There are several well-known solutions to this race condition problem, all of which provide a form of **two-stage suspend** operation. P1 essentially has to announce that it is planning to suspend in the near future; any resume operation which finds that P1 is not suspended will have a deferred effect. When P1 does suspend, it will immediately be resumed; that is, the suspend operation itself will have no effect.

Although suspend and resume is a low-level facility, which can be error-prone in its use, it is an efficient mechanism which can be used to construct higher-level synchronization primitives. For this reason, Ada provides, as part of its Real-Time Annex, a safe version of this mechanism. It is based around the concept of a **suspension** object, which can hold the value True or False. Program 8.1 gives the package specification.

All four subprograms defined by the package are atomic with respect to each other. On return from the Suspend_Until_True procedure, the referenced suspension object is reset to False.

Program 8.1 Synchronous task control.

```
package Ada.Synchronous_Task_Control is
  type Suspension_Object is limited private;
  procedure Set_True(S : in out Suspension_Object);
  procedure Set_False(S : in out Suspension_Object);
  function Current_State(S : Suspension_Object) return Boolean;
  procedure Suspend_Until_True(S: in out Suspension_Object);
    -- raises Program_Error if more than one task tries
    -- to suspend on S at once.
private
  -- not specified by the language
end Ada.Synchronous_Task_Control;
```

The simple condition synchronization problem, given earlier in this section, can, therefore, be easily solved.

```
with Ada.Synchronous_Task_Control;
use  Ada.Synchronous_Task_Control;

...
Flag : Suspension_Object;
...
task body P1 is
begin
   ...
   Suspend_Until_True(Flag);
   ...
end P1;

task body P2 is
begin
   ...
   Set_True(Flag);
   ...
end P1;
```

Suspension objects behave in much the same way as binary semaphores, which are discussed in the Section 8.4.4.

Although suspend and resume are useful low-level primitives, no operating system or language relies solely on these mechanisms for mutual exclusion and condition synchronization. If present, they clearly introduce a new state into the state transition diagram introduced in Chapter 7. The general state diagram for a process, therefore, is extended in Figure 8.1.

8.4 Semaphores

Semaphores are a simple mechanism for programming mutual exclusion and condition synchronization. They were originally designed by Dijkstra (1968a) and have the two following benefits:

(1) They simplify the protocols for synchronization.
(2) They remove the need for busy-wait loops.

A **semaphore** is a non-negative integer variable that, apart from initialization, can only be acted upon by two procedures. These procedures were called P and V by Dijkstra, but will be referred to as wait and signal in this book. The semantics of wait and signal are as follows:

(1) wait(S) If the value of the semaphore, S, is greater than zero then decrement its value by one; otherwise delay the process until S is greater than zero (and then decrement its value).

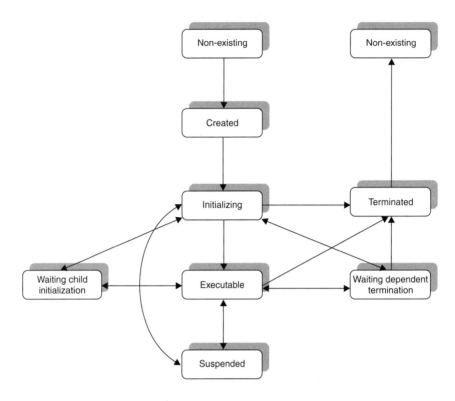

Figure 8.1   State diagram for a process.

(2) `signal(S)` Increment the value of the semaphore, `S`, by one.

General semaphores are often called **counting semaphores**, as their operations increment and decrement an integer count. The additional important property of `wait` and
`signal` is that their actions are atomic (indivisible). Two processes, both executing
`wait` operations on the same semaphore, cannot interfere with each other. Moreover,
a process cannot fail during the execution of a semaphore operation.

Condition synchronization and mutual exclusion can be programmed easily with
semaphores. First, consider condition synchronization:

```
(* condition synchronization *)
var consyn : semaphore; (* initially 0 *)
process P1; (* waiting process *)
   ...
   wait (consyn);
   ...
end P1;
```

```
process P2; (* signalling process *)
   ...
   signal (consyn);
   ...
end P2;
```

When P1 executes the wait on a 0 semaphore, it will be delayed until P2 executes the signal. This will set consyn to 1 and hence the wait can now succeed; P1 will continue and consyn will be decremented to 0. Note that if P2 executes the signal first, the semaphore will be set to 1, so P1 will not be delayed by the action of the wait.

Mutual exclusion is similarly straightforward:

```
(* mutual exclusion *)
var mutex : semaphore; (* initially 1 *)
process P1;
   loop
      wait (mutex);
         <critical section>
      signal (mutex);
      <non-critical section>
   end
end P1;
```

```
process P2;
   loop
      wait (mutex);
         <critical section>
      signal (mutex);
      <non-critical section>
   end
end P2;
```

If P1 and P2 are in contention then they will execute their wait statements simultaneously. However, as wait is atomic, one process will complete execution of this statement before the other begins. One process will execute a wait (mutex) with mutex=1, which will allow the process to proceed into its critical section and set mutex to 0; the other process will execute wait (mutex) with mutex=0, and be delayed. Once the first process has exited its critical section, it will signal (mutex). This will cause the semaphore to become 1 again and allow the second process to enter its critical section (and set mutex to 0 again).

With a wait/signal bracket around a section of code, the initial value of the semaphore will restrict the maximum amount of concurrent execution of the code. If the initial value is 0, no process will ever enter; if it is 1 then a single process may enter (that is, mutual exclusion); for values greater than one, the given number of concurrent executions of the code are allowed.

8.4.1 Suspended processes

In the definition of `wait` it is clear that if the semaphore is zero then the calling process is delayed. One method of delay (busy waiting) has already been introduced and criticized. A more efficient mechanism, that of suspending the process, was introduced in Section 8.3. In fact, all synchronization primitives deal with delay by some form of suspension; the process is removed from the set of executable processes.

When a process executes a `wait` on a zero semaphore, the RTSS (run-time support system) is invoked, the process is removed from the processor, and placed in a queue of suspended processes (that is a queue of processes suspended on that particular semaphore). The RTSS must then select another process to run. Eventually, if the program is correct, another process will execute a signal on that semaphore. As a result, the RTSS will pick out one of the suspended processes awaiting a signal on that semaphore and make it executable again.

From these considerations, a slightly different definition of `wait` and `signal` can be given. This definition is closer to what an implementation would do:

```
wait(S) :-
if S > 0 then
   S:= S-1
else
   number_suspended:= number_suspended + 1
   suspend calling process

signal(S) :-
if number_suspended > 0 then
   number_suspended:= number_suspended - 1
   make one suspended process executable again
else
   S:= S+1
```

With this definition, the increment of a semaphore immediately followed by its decrement is avoided.

Note that the above algorithm does not define the order in which processes are released from the suspended state. Usually, they are released in a FIFO order, although arguably with a true concurrent language, the programmer should assume a non-deterministic order (see Section 9.4.3). However, for a real-time programming language, the priority of the processes has an important role to play (see Chapter 13).

8.4.2 Implementation

The above algorithm for implementing a semaphore is quite straightforward, although it involves the support of a queue mechanism. Where difficulty could arise is in the requirement for indivisibility in the execution of the `wait` and `signal` operations. Indivisibility means that once a process has started to execute one of these procedures it will continue to execute until the operation has been completed. With the aid of the RTSS, this is easily achieved; the scheduler is programmed so that it does not swap out a process while it is executing a `wait` or a `signal`; they are **non-preemptible** operations.

Unfortunately, the RTSS is not always in full control of scheduling events. Although all internal actions are under its influence, external actions happen asynchronously and could disturb the atomicity of the semaphore operations. To prohibit this, the RTSS will disable interrupts for the duration of the execution of the indivisible sequence of statements. In this way, no external events can interfere.

This disabling of interrupts is adequate for a single processor system but not for a multiprocessor one. With a shared-memory system, two parallel processes may be executing a `wait` or `signal` (on the same semaphore) and the RTSS is powerless to prevent it. In these circumstances, a 'lock' mechanism is need to protect access to the operations. Two such mechanisms are used.

On some processors, a 'test and set' instruction is provided. This allows a process to access a bit in the following way.

(1) If the bit is zero then set it to one and return zero.

(2) If the bit is one return one.

These actions are themselves indivisible. Two parallel processes, both wishing to operate a `wait` (for example), will do a test and set operation on the same lock bit (which is initially zero). One process will succeed and set the bit to one; the other process will have returned a one and will, therefore, have to loop round and retest the lock. When the first process has completed the wait operation, it will assign the bit to zero (that is, unlock the semaphore) and the other process will proceed to execute its `wait` operation.

If no test and set instruction is available then a similar effect can be obtained by a swap instruction. Again, the lock is associated with a bit that is initially zero. A process wishing to execute a semaphore operation will swap a one with the lock bit. If it gets a zero back from the lock then it can proceed; if it gets back a one then some other process is active with the semaphore and it must retest.

As was indicated in Section 8.1, a software primitive such as a semaphore cannot conjure up mutual exclusion out of 'fresh air'. It is necessary for memory locations to exhibit the essence of mutual exclusion in order for higher-level structures to be built. Similarly, although busy-wait loops are removed from the programmer's domain by the use of semaphores, it may be necessary to use busy waits (as above) to implement the wait and signal operations. *It should be noted, however, that the latter use of busy waits is only short-lived (the time it takes to execute a wait or signal operation), whereas their use for delaying access to the program's critical sections could involve many seconds of looping.*

8.4.3 Liveness provision

In Section 8.2, the error condition livelock was illustrated. Unfortunately (but inevitably), the use of synchronization primitives introduces other error conditions. **Deadlock** is the most serious such condition and entails a set of processes being in a state from which it is impossible for any of them to proceed. This is similar to livelock but the processes are suspended. To illustrate this condition, consider two processes P1 and P2 wishing to gain access to two non-concurrent resources (that is, resources that can only be accessed by one process at a time) that are protected by two semaphores S1 and S2. If both processes access the resource in the same order then no problem arises:

```
P1                              P2
wait (S1);                      wait (S1);
   wait (S2);                      wait (S2);
   .                               .
   .                               .
   .                               .
   signal (S2);                    signal (S2);
signal (S1);                    signal (S1);
```

The first process to execute the wait on S1 successfully will also successfully undertake the wait on S2 and subsequently signal the two semaphores and allow the other process in. A problem occurs, however, if one of the processes wishes to use the resources in the reverse order, for example:

```
P1                              P2
wait (S1);                      wait (S2);
   wait (S2);                      wait (S1);
   .                               .
   .                               .
   .                               .
   signal (S2);                    signal (S1);
signal (S1);                    signal (S2);
```

In this case, an interleaving could allow P1 and P2 to execute successfully the wait on S1 and S2, respectively, but then inevitably both processes will be suspended waiting on the other semaphore which is now zero.

It is in the nature of an interdependent concurrent program that usually once a subset of the processes becomes deadlocked all the other processes will eventually become part of the deadlocked set.

The testing of software rarely removes other than the most obvious deadlocks; they can occur infrequently but with devastating results. This error is not isolated to the use of semaphores and is possible in all concurrent programming languages. The design of languages that prohibit the programming of deadlocks is a desirable, but not yet attainable, goal. Issues relating to deadlock avoidance, detection and recovery will be considered in Chapters 11 and 13.

Indefinite postponement (sometimes called **lockout** or **starvation**) is a less severe error condition whereby a process that wishes to gain access to a resource, via a critical section, is never allowed to do so because there are always other processes gaining access before it. With a semaphore system, a process may remain indefinitely suspended (that is, queued on the semaphore) due to the way the RTSS picks processes from this queue when a signal arrives. Even if the delay is not in fact indefinite, but merely open ended (indeterminate), this may give rise to an error in a real-time system.

If a process is free from livelocks, deadlocks and indefinite postponements then it is said to possess **liveness**. Informally, the liveness property implies that if a process wishes to perform some action then it will, eventually, be allowed to do so. In particular, if a process requests access to a critical section it will gain access within a finite time.

8.4.4 Binary and quantity semaphores

The definition of a (general) semaphore is a non-negative integer; by implication its actual value can rise to any supported positive number. But in all the examples given so far in this chapter (that is, for condition synchronization and mutual exclusion), only the values 0 and 1 have been used. A simple form of semaphore, known as a **binary semaphore**, can be implemented that takes only these values; that is, the signalling of a semaphore which has the value 1 has no effect – the semaphore retains the value 1. The construction of a general semaphore from two binary semaphores and an integer can then be achieved, if the general form is required.

Another variation on the normal definition of a semaphore is the **quantity semaphore**. With this structure, the amount to be decremented by the wait (and incremented by the signal) is not fixed as 1, but is given as a parameter to the procedures:

```
wait (S, i) :-    if S >= i then
                      S:= S-i
                  else
                      delay
                      S:= S-i
signal (S, i) :- S:= S+i
```

An example of the use of a quantity semaphore is given later in Section 8.6.2.

8.4.5 Example semaphore programs in Ada

Algol-68 was the first language to introduce semaphores. It provided a type sema that was manipulated by the operators up and down. To illustrate some simple programs that use semaphores, an abstract data type for semaphores, in Ada, will be used.

```
package Semaphore_Package is
   type Semaphore(Initial : Natural := 1) is limited private;
   procedure Wait (S : in out Semaphore);
   procedure Signal (S : in out Semaphore);
private
   type Semaphore is ...
end Semaphore_Package;
```

Ada does not directly support semaphores, but the Wait and Signal procedures can, however, be constructed from the Ada synchronization primitives; these have not yet been discussed, so the full definition of the type semaphore and the body of the package will not be given here (see Section 8.7). The essence of abstract data types is, however, that they can be used without knowledge of their implementation.

The first example is the producer/consumer system that uses a bounded buffer to pass integers between the two tasks:

```
procedure Main is
  package Buffer is
    procedure Append (I : Integer);
    procedure Take (I : out Integer);
  end Buffer;
  task Producer;
  task Consumer;

  package body Buffer is separate; -- see next page
  use Buffer;

  task body Producer is
    Item : Integer;
  begin
    loop
      -- produce item
      Append (Item);
    end loop;
  end Producer;

  task body Consumer is
    Item : Integer;
  begin
    loop
      Take (Item);
      -- consume item
    end loop;
  end Consumer;
begin
  null;
end Main;
```

The buffer itself must protect against concurrent access, appending to a full buffer and taking from an empty one. This it does by the use of three semaphores:

```
with Semaphore_Package; use Semaphore_Package;
separate (Main)
package body Buffer is
  Size : constant Natural := 32;
  type Buffer_Range is mod Size;
  Buf : array (Buffer_Range) of Integer;
  Top, Base : Buffer_Range := 0;

  Mutex : Semaphore; -- default is 1
  Item_Available : Semaphore(0);
  Space_Available : Semaphore(Initial => Size);

  procedure Append (I : Integer) is
  begin
    Wait(Space_Available);
    Wait(Mutex);
```

```
      Buf(Top) := I;
       Top := Top+1;
    Signal(Mutex);
    Signal(Item_Available);
  end Append;

  procedure Take (I : out Integer) is
  begin
    Wait(Item_Available);
    Wait(Mutex);
      I := Buf(Base);
      Base := Base+1;
    Signal(Mutex);
    Signal(Space_Available);
  end Take;
end Buffer;
```

The initial values of the three semaphores are different. `Mutex` is an ordinary mutual exclusion semaphore and is given the default initial value of 1; `Item_Available` protects against taking from an empty buffer and has the initial value 0; and `Space_Available` (initially `Size`) is used to prevent `Append` operations to a full buffer.

When the program starts, any consumer task that calls `Take` will be suspended on `Wait(Item_Available)`; only after a producer task has called `Append`, and in doing so `Signal(Item_Available)`, will the consumer task continue.

8.4.6   Semaphore programming using C and POSIX

Although few modern programming languages support semaphores directly, many operating systems do. POSIX, for example, provides counting semaphores to enable processes running in separate address spaces (or threads within the same address space) to synchronize and communicate using shared memory. Note, however, that it is more efficient to use mutexes and condition variables to synchronize and communicate in the same address space – see Section 8.6.3. Program 8.2 defines the POSIX C interface for semaphores (functions for naming a semaphore by a character string are also provided but have been omitted here). The standard semaphore operations *initialize*, *wait* and *signal* are called `sem_init`, `sem_wait` and `sem_post` in POSIX. A non-blocking wait (`sem_trywait`) and a timed-version (`sem_timedwait`) are also provided, as is a routine to determine the current value of a semaphore (`sem_getvalue`).

Consider an example of a resource controller which appears in many forms in real-time programs. For simplicity, the example will use threads rather than processes. Two functions are provided: `allocate` and `deallocate`; each take a parameter which indicates a priority level associated with the request. It is assumed that the calling thread deallocates the resource at the same priority with which it requested allocation. For ease of presentation, the example does not consider how the resource itself is transferred. Moreover, the solution does not protect itself against race conditions (see Exercise 8.27).

Program 8.2   A C POSIX interface to semaphores.

```
#include <time.h> typedef ... sem_t;

int sem_init(sem_t *sem_location, int pshared, unsigned int value);
  /* initializes the semaphore at location sem_location to value */
  /* if pshared is 1, the semaphore can be used between processes */
  /*    or threads */
  /* if pshared is 0, the semaphore can only be used between threads */
  /* of the same process */

int sem_destroy(sem_t *sem_location);
  /* remove the unnamed semaphore at location sem_location */

int sem_wait(sem_t *sem_location);
  /* a standard wait operation on a semaphore */

int sem_trywait(sem_t *sem_location);
 /* attempts to decrement the semaphore */
 /* returns -1 if the call might block the calling process */

int sem_timedwait(sem_t *sem, const struct timespec *abstime);
 /* returns -1 if the semaphore could not be locked */
 /* by abstime */

int sem_post(sem_t *sem_location);
 /* a standard signal operation on a semaphore */

int sem_getvalue(sem_t *sem_location, int *value);
 /* gets the current value of the semaphore to a location */
 /* pointed at by value; negative value indicates the number */
 /* of threads waiting */


/* All the above function return 0 if successful, otherwise -1. */
/* When an error condition is returned by any of the above */
/* functions, a shared variable errno contains the reason for */
/* the error */
```

```
#include <semaphore.h>

typedef enum {high, medium, low} priority_t;
typedef enum {false, true} boolean;

sem_t mutex;    /* used for mutual exclusive
                  access to waiting and busy */
sem_t cond[3]; /* used for condition synchronization */
int waiting;    /* count of number of threads
                  waiting at a priority level */
int busy; /* indicates whether the resource is in use*/
```

```
void allocate(priority_t P)
{
  SEM_WAIT(&mutex); /* lock mutex */
  if(busy) {
    SEM_POST(&mutex); /* release mutex */
    SEM_WAIT(&cond[P]); /* wait at correct priority level */
    /* resource has been allocated */
  }
  busy = true;
  SEM_POST(&mutex); /* release mutex */
}
```

A single semaphore, mutex, is used to ensure that all allocation and deallocation requests are handled in mutual exclusion. Three condition synchronization semaphores, cond[3], are used to queue the waiting threads at three priority levels (high, medium and low). The allocate function allocates the resource if it is not already in use (indicated by the busy flag).

The deallocation function simply signals the semaphore of the highest priority waiter.

```
int deallocate(priority_t P)
{

  SEM_WAIT(&mutex); /* lock mutex */
  if(busy) {
    busy = false;
    /* release highest priority waiting thread */
    SEM_GETVALUE(&cond[high],&waiting);
    if ( waiting < 0)  {
      SEM_POST(&cond[high]);
    }
    else {
      SEM_GETVALUE(&cond[medium],&waiting);
      if (waiting < 0)  {
        SEM_POST(&cond[medium]);
      }
      else {
        SEM_GETVALUE(&cond[low],&waiting);
        if (waiting < 0)  {
          SEM_POST(&cond[low]);
        }
        else SEM_POST(&mutex);
        /* no one waiting, release lock */
      }
    }
    /* resource and lock passed on to */
    /* highest priority waiting thread */
    return 0;
  }
  else return -1; /* error return */
}
```

An initialization routine sets the busy flag to false and creates the four semaphores used by allocate and deallocate.

```
void initialise() {
  priority_t i;

  busy = false;
  SEM_INIT(&mutex, 0, 1);
  for (i = high; i<= low; i++) {
    SEM_INIT(&cond[i], 0, 0) ;
  };
}
```

Remember that, as the C binding to POSIX uses non-zero return values to indicate an error has occurred, it is necessary to encapsulate every POSIX call in an if statement. This makes the code more difficult to understand (an Ada or C++ binding to POSIX would allow exceptions to be raised when errors occur). Consequently, as with the other C examples used in this book, SYS_CALL is used to represent a call to sys_call and any appropriate error recovery (see Section 6.1.1). For SEM_INIT this might include a retry.

A thread wishing to use the resource would make the following calls:

```
priority_t my_priority;

...
allocate(my_priority); /* wait for resource */
  /* use resource */
if(deallocate(my_priority) <= 0) {
    /* cannot deallocate resource, */
    /* undertake some recovery operation */
}
```

8.4.7 Criticisms of semaphores

Although the semaphore is an elegant low-level synchronization primitive, a real-time program built only upon the use of semaphores is again error-prone. It needs just one occurrence of a semaphore to be omitted or misplaced for the entire program to collapse at run-time. Mutual exclusion may not be assured and deadlock may appear just when the software is dealing with a rare but critical event. What is required is a more structured synchronization primitive.

What the semaphore provides is a means to program mutual exclusion over a critical section. A more structured approach would give mutual exclusion directly. This is precisely what is provided for by the constructs discussed in Sections 8.5 to 8.8.

The examples shown in Section 8.4.5 showed that an abstract data type for semaphores can be constructed in Ada. However, no high-level concurrent programming language relies entirely on semaphores. They are important historically but are arguably not adequate for the real-time domain.

8.5 Conditional critical regions

Conditional critical regions (CCRs) are an attempt to overcome some of the problems associated with semaphores. A critical region is a section of code that is guaranteed to be executed in mutual exclusion. This must be compared with the concept of a critical section that should be executed under mutual exclusion (but in error may not be). Clearly, the programming of a critical section as a critical region immediately meets the requirement for mutual exclusion.

Variables that must be protected from concurrent usage are grouped together into named regions and are tagged as being resources. Processes are prohibited from entering a region in which another process is already active. Condition synchronization is provided by guards on the regions. When a process wishes to enter a critical region, it evaluates the guard (under mutual exclusion); if the guard evaluates true, it may enter, but if it is false, the process is delayed. As with semaphores, the programmer should not assume any order of access if more than one process is delayed attempting to enter the same critical region (for whatever reason).

To illustrate the use of CCRs, an outline of the bounded buffer program is given below.

```
program buffer_eg;
   type buffer_t is record
      slots       : array(1..N) of character;
      size        : integer range 0..N;
      head, tail  : integer range 1..N;
   end record;

   buffer : buffer_t;

   resource buf : buffer;

   process producer;
     ...
     loop
       region buf when buffer.size < N do
          -- place char in buffer etc
       end region
       ...
     end loop;
   end

   process consumer;
     ...
     loop
       region buf when buffer.size > 0 do
          -- take char from buffer etc
       end region
       ...
     end loop;
   end
end
```

One potential performance problem with CCRs is that processes must re-evaluate their guards every time a CCR naming that resource is left. A suspended process must become executable again in order to test the guard; if it is still false, it must return to the suspended state.

A version of CCRs has been implemented in Edison (Brinch-Hansen, 1981), a language intended for embedded applications, implemented on multiprocessor systems. Each processor only executes a single process so that it may continually evaluate its guards if necessary. However, this may cause excess traffic on the network.

8.6 Monitors

The main problem with conditional regions is that they can be dispersed throughout the program. Monitors are intended to alleviate this problem by providing more structured control regions. They also use a form of condition synchronization that is more efficient to implement.

The intended critical regions are written as procedures and are encapsulated together into a single module called a monitor. As a module, all variables that must be accessed under mutual exclusion are hidden; additionally, as a monitor, all procedure calls into the module are guaranteed to execute with mutual exclusion.

Monitors appeared as a refinement of conditional critical regions; initial design and analysis of the structure was undertaken by Dijkstra (1968b), Brinch-Hansen (1973) and Hoare (1974). They can be found in numerous programming languages including Modula-1, Concurrent Pascal and Mesa .

To continue, for comparison, with the bounded buffer example, a buffer monitor would have the following structure:

```
monitor buffer;
   export append, take;
   var (* declaration of necessary variables *)

   procedure append (I : integer);
      ...
   end;

   procedure take (var I : integer);
      ...
   end;
begin
   (* initialization of monitor variables *)
end
```

With languages like Modula-2 and Ada, it is natural to program the buffer as a distinct module (package). This approach is also taken with a monitor. The only difference between a module and a monitor is that, in the latter case, concurrent calls to append and/or take (in the above example) are serialized – by definition. No mutual exclusion semaphore is needed.

Although providing for mutual exclusion, there is still a need for condition synchronization within the monitor. In theory, semaphores could still be used but normally a simpler synchronization primitive is introduced. In Hoare's monitors (Hoare, 1974), this primitive is called a **condition variable** and is acted upon by two operators which, because of similarities with the semaphore structure, will again be called wait and signal. When a process issues a wait operation, it is blocked (suspended) and placed on a queue associated with that condition variable (this can be compared with a wait on a semaphore with a value of zero; however, note that a wait on a condition variable *always* blocks unlike a wait on a semaphore). A blocked process then releases its mutually exclusive hold on the monitor, allowing another process to enter. When a process executes a signal operation, it will release one blocked process. If no process is blocked on the specified variable then the *signal has no effect*. (Again note the contrast with signal on a semaphore, which always has an effect on the semaphore. Indeed, wait and signal for monitors are more akin to suspend and resume in their semantics.) The bounded buffer example can now be given in full:

```
monitor buffer;
   export append, take;
   const size = 32;
   var buf : array[0...size-1] of integer;
       top, base : 0..size-1;
       SpaceAvailable, ItemAvailable : condition;
       NumberInBuffer : integer;

   procedure append (I : integer);
   begin
     if NumberInBuffer = size then
       wait(SpaceAvailable);
     buf[top] := I;
     NumberInBuffer := NumberInBuffer+1;
     top := (top+1) mod size;
     signal(ItemAvailable)
   end append;

   procedure take (var I : integer);
   begin
     if NumberInBuffer = 0 then
       wait(ItemAvailable);
     I := buf[base];
     base := (base+1) mod size;
     NumberInBuffer := NumberInBuffer-1;
     signal(SpaceAvailable)
   end take;

begin (* initialization *)
  NumberInBuffer := 0;
  top := 0;
  base := 0
end;
```

If a process calls (for example) take when there is nothing in the buffer, then it will become suspended on `ItemAvailable`. A process appending an item will, however, signal this suspended process when an item does become available.

The semantics for `wait` and `signal`, given above, are not complete; as they stand, two or more processes could become active within a monitor. This would occur following a signal operation in which a blocked process was freed. The freed process and the one that freed it are then both executing inside the monitor. To prohibit this clearly undesirable activity, the semantics of `signal` must be modified. Four different approaches are used in languages:

(1) A signal is allowed only as the last action of a process before it leaves the monitor (this is the case with the buffer example above).

(2) A signal operation has the side-effect of executing a return statement; that is, the process is forced to leave the monitor.

(3) A signal operation which unblocks another process has the effect of blocking itself; this process will only execute again when the monitor is free.

(4) A signal operation which unblocks another process does not block and the freed process must compete for access to the monitor once the signalling process exits.

In case (3), which was proposed by Hoare in his original paper on monitors, the processes that are blocked because of a signal action are placed on a 'ready queue' and are chosen, when the monitor is free, in preference to processes blocked on entry. In case (4), it is the freed process which is placed on the 'ready queue'.

Because of the importance of monitors, two languages that support this structure will be briefly described.

8.6.1   Modula-1

Modula-1 (as it must now be known) is the forerunner to Modula-2 and Modula-3 but has a quite different process model. It employs explicit process declaration (not coroutines) and monitors which are termed **interface modules**. Somewhat confusingly, the condition variables are called signals and are acted upon by three procedures.

(1) The procedure `wait(s,r)` delays the calling process until it receives the signal s. The process, when delayed, is given a priority (or delay rank r) where r must be a positive valued integer expression whose default is 1.

(2) The procedure `send(s)` sends the signal s to that process with the highest priority which has been waiting for s. If several waiting processes all have the same priority then the one which has been waiting the longest receives the signal. The process executing the send is suspended. If no process is waiting the call has no effect.

(3) The boolean function `awaited(s)` yields the value true if there is at least one process blocked on s; false otherwise.

The following is an example of a Modula-1 interface module. It accomplishes the resource control requirement that was programmed with semaphores earlier:

```
INTERFACE MODULE resource_control;

  DEFINE allocate, deallocate;  (* export list *)

  VAR busy : BOOLEAN;
      free : SIGNAL;

  PROCEDURE allocate;
  BEGIN
    IF busy THEN WAIT(free) END;
    busy := TRUE;
  END;

  PROCEDURE deallocate;
  BEGIN
    busy := FALSE;
    SEND(free)
  END;

BEGIN (* initialization of module *)
  busy := FALSE
END.
```

Note that in `deallocate`:

```
if AWAITED(free) then SEND(free)
```

could have been inserted, but as the effect of `SEND(free)` is null, when `AWAITED(free)` is false, there is nothing to be gained by doing the test.

8.6.2 Mesa

So far, it has been assumed that when a suspended process is unblocked, the condition that caused it to block no longer holds. For example, the process that is blocked waiting for the resource to be free (that is, not busy) can assume that it is free when it starts executing again. Similarly, a process delayed inside the bounded buffer monitor proceeds with its actions once executable again.

In Mesa (Lampson and Redell, 1980), a different approach is taken. There is a 'wait' operation, but processes cannot assume that, when woken, the condition that caused the block is removed. The 'notify' operation (comparable to a signal) merely indicates that the blocked process should re-evaluate the condition. Mesa also supports a 'broadcast' operation that notifies all processes waiting on a particular condition. (These processes are woken up one at a time to keep the monitor exclusive.) A process executing a notify or broadcast operation is not blocked.

There are three kinds of procedure allowed within a Mesa monitor: entry procedures, internal procedures and external procedures. Entry procedures operate with the monitor lock. Internal procedures can only be called from entry procedures. (In Modula-1 an internal procedure would simply be missing from the define list.) External procedures can be called without the monitor lock and are used to view the current state of the monitor. They cannot change variables, call internal procedures or use a condition variable. These restrictions are checked at compile time.

To give an example of a Mesa monitor, consider a refinement of the resource allocation problem. Rather than have a single resource which is either busy or free, the monitor must control access to N instances of the resource. An allocation request passes, as a parameter, the number of instances ($\leq N$) required. For simplicity this request parameter is not checked in the 'allocate' or 'deallocate' procedures. To obtain a secure structure, it would be necessary to check that a process returning a collection of resources actually had them to return. Secure resource control is considered again in Chapter 11. The Mesa code follows; procedure free_resources is included to illustrate an external procedure. The reader should be able to understand this module without further knowledge of Mesa (note that the assignment operator is < - in Mesa).

```
Resource_Control : monitor =
begin
  const N = 32;
  free : condition;
  resource_free : positive <- N;

  allocate : entry procedure[size : positive] =
    begin
      do
        if size <= resource_free then exit; -- exit from loop
        wait free;
      endloop;
      resource_free <- resource_free - size;
  end;

  deallocate : entry procedure[size : positive] =
  begin
    localfree[size];
    broadcast free;
  end;

  localfree : internal procedure[S : positive] =
  begin
    resource_free <- resource_free + S;
  end;

  free_resources : external procedure return[p : positive] =
  begin
    p <- resource_free;
  end;
end;
```

As a deallocation operation could free enough resources for a number of blocked allocate processes to proceed, a broadcast is made. All blocked processes (on free) will execute, in turn, and either obtain the resources, if size is now less than or equal to `resource_free`, or become blocked again.

If Mesa did not support a broadcast facility then the programmer would have to keep a count of the number of blocked processes and for each process to unblock the next one in the chain. This is due to the semantics of the notify operation, which does not block. In Modula-1, this is achieved implicitly because the send operation does cause a context switch to the awoken process.

```
PROCEDURE allocate(size : INTEGER);
BEGIN
  WHILE size > resource_free DO
    WAIT(free);
    SEND(free)
  END;
  resource_free := resource_free - size
END;

PROCEDURE deallocate(size : INTEGER);
BEGIN
  resource_free := resource_free + size;
  SEND(free)
END;
```

If a language supported quantity semaphores then the allocation and deallocation procedures would be very simple:

```
procedure allocate(size : integer);
begin
  wait(QS, size)
end;

procedure deallocate(size : integer);
begin
  signal(QS, size)
end;
```

where `QS` is a quantity semaphore initialized to the total number of resources in the system.

8.6.3   POSIX Mutexes and condition variables

In Section 8.4.6, POSIX semaphores were described as a mechanism for use between processes and between threads. If the threads extension to POSIX is supported then using semaphores for communication and synchronization between threads in the same address space is expensive as well as being unstructured. **Mutexes** and **condition variables**, when combined, provide the functionality of a monitor but with a procedural interface. Program 8.3 defines the basic C interface with the exception of the functions that manipulate attribute objects.

Each monitor has an associated (initialized) `mutex` variable, and all operations on the monitor (critical regions) are surrounded by calls to lock

Program 8.3   A C interface to POSIX mutexes and condition variables.

```
#include <time.h>

typedef ... pthread_mutex_t;
typedef ... pthread_mutexattr_t;
typedef ... pthread_cond_t;
typedef ... pthread_condattr_t;

int pthread_mutex_init(pthread_mutex_t *mutex,
                       const pthread_mutexattr_t *attr);
  /* initializes a mutex with certain attributes */
int pthread_mutex_destroy(pthread_mutex_t *mutex);
  /* destroys a mutex */
  /* undefined behaviour if the mutex is locked */

int pthread_mutex_lock(pthread_mutex_t *mutex);
  /* lock the mutex; if locked already suspend calling thread */
  /* the owner of the mutex is the thread which locked it */
int pthread_mutex_trylock(pthread_mutex_t *mutex);
  /* as for lock, but gives an error return if mutex is already locked */
int pthread_mutex_timedlock(pthread_mutex_t *mutex,
                            const struct timespec *abstime);
  /* as for lock, but return an error if the lock cannot */
  /* be obtained by the timeout */

int pthread_mutex_unlock(pthread_mutex_t *mutex);
  /* unlocks the mutex if called by the owning thread */
  /* undefined behaviour if the calling thread is not the owner */
  /* undefined behaviour if the mutex is not locked */
  /* when successful, results in a blocked thread being released */

int pthread_cond_init(pthread_cond_t *cond,
                      const pthread_condattr_t *attr);
  /* initializes a condition variable with certain attributes */
int pthread_cond_destroy(pthread_cond_t *cond);
  /* destroys a condition variable */
  /* undefined behaviour if threads are waiting on the condition */
  /* variable */

int pthread_cond_wait(pthread_cond_t *cond,
                      pthread_mutex_t *mutex);
  /* called by thread which owns a locked mutex */
  /* undefined behaviour if the mutex is not locked */
  /* atomically blocks the calling thread on the cond variable and */
  /* releases the lock on mutex */
  /* a successful return indicates that the mutex has been locked */
int pthread_cond_timedwait(pthread_cond_t *cond,
          pthread_mutex_t *mutex, const struct timespec *abstime);
  /* the same as pthread_cond_wait, except that a error is returned */
  /* if the timeout expires */
```

```
int pthread_cond_signal(pthread_cond_t *cond);
  /* unblocks at least one blocked thread */
  /* no effect if no threads are blocked */
  /* unblocked threads automatically contend for the associated mutex */
int pthread_cond_broadcast(pthread_cond_t *cond);
  /* unblocks all blocked threads */
  /* no effect if no threads are blocked */
  /* unblocked threads automatically contend for the associated mutex */

/* All the above functions return 0 if successful */
```

(pthread_mutex_lock) and unlock (pthread_mutex_unlock) the mutex. Condition synchronization is provided by associating condition variables with the mutex. Note that, when a thread waits on a condition variable (pthread_cond_wait, pthread_cond_timedwait), its lock on the associated mutex is released. Also, when it successfully returns from the conditional wait, it again holds the lock. However, because more than one thread could be released (even by pthread_cond_signal), the programmer must again test for the condition which caused it to wait initially.

Consider the following integer bounded buffer using mutexes and condition variables. The buffer consists of a mutex, two condition variables (buffer_not_full and buffer_not_empty), a count of the number of items in the buffer, the buffer itself, and the positions of the first and last item in the buffer. The append routine locks the buffer and while the buffer is full, waits on the condition variable buffer_not_full. When the buffer has space, the integer data item is placed in the buffer, the mutex is unlocked and the buffer_not_empty signal sent. The take routine is similar in structure.

```
#include <pthreads.h>

#define BUFF_SIZE 10

typedef struct {
  pthread_mutex_t mutex;
  pthread_cond_t buffer_not_full;
  pthread_cond_t buffer_not_empty;
  int count, first, last;
  int buf[BUFF_SIZE];
  } buffer;

int append(int item, buffer *B ) {
  PTHREAD_MUTEX_LOCK(&B->mutex);
  while(B->count == BUFF_SIZE)
    PTHREAD_COND_WAIT(&B->buffer_not_full, &B->mutex);
  /* put data in the buffer and update count and last */
  PTHREAD_COND_SIGNAL(&B->buffer_not_empty);
  PTHREAD_MUTEX_UNLOCK(&B->mutex);
  return 0;
}
```

```
int take(int *item, buffer *B ) {
  PTHREAD_MUTEX_LOCK(&B->mutex);
  while(B->count == 0)
    PTHREAD_COND_WAIT(&B->buffer_not_empty, &B->mutex);
  /* get data from the buffer and update count and first */
  PTHREAD_COND_SIGNAL(&B->buffer_not_full);
  PTHREAD_MUTEX_UNLOCK(&B->mutex);
  return 0;
}

/* an initialize() function is also required */
```

Although mutexes and condition variables act as a type of monitor, their semantics do differ when a thread is released from a conditional wait and other threads are trying to gain access to the critical region. With POSIX, it is unspecified which thread succeeds unless priority-based scheduling is being used (see Section 13.14.2). With most monitors, the released thread is given preference.

8.6.4 Nested monitor calls

There are many problems associated with the use of monitors, but the one that has received the most attention is the semantic implications of a monitor calling a procedure within another monitor.

> The controversy is over what (if anything) should be done if a process having made a nested monitor call is suspended in another monitor. The mutual exclusion in the last monitor call will be relinquished by the process, due to the semantics of the wait and equivalent operations. However, mutual exclusion will not be relinquished by processes in monitors from which the nested calls have been made. Processes that attempt to invoke procedures in these monitors will become blocked. This has performance implications, since blockage will decrease the amount of concurrency exhibited by the system. (Lampson and Redell, 1980)

Various approaches to the nested monitor problem have been suggested. The most popular one, adopted by Java, POSIX and Mesa, is to maintain the lock. Other approaches include prohibiting nested procedure calls altogether (as in Modula-1) and providing constructs which specify that certain monitor procedures may release their mutual exclusion lock during remote calls.

8.6.5 Criticisms of monitors

The monitor gives a structured and elegant solution to mutual exclusion problems such as the bounded buffer. It does not, however, deal well with condition synchronizations outside the monitor. In Modula-1, for example, signals are a general programming feature and are not restricted to use within a monitor. A language based on monitors, therefore, presents a mixture of high-level and low-level primitives. All the criticisms surrounding the use of semaphores apply equally (if not more so) to condition variables.

In addition, although monitors encapsulate all the entities concerned with a resource, and provide the important mutual exclusion, their internal structure may still be difficult to read due to the use of condition variables.

8.7 Protected objects

The criticism of monitors centres on their use of condition variables. By replacing this approach to synchronization by the use of guards, a more structured abstraction is obtained. This form of monitor will be termed a **protected object**. Ada is the only major language that provides this mechanism, and hence it will be described in terms of Ada.

A protected object in Ada encapsulates data items and allows access to them only via protected subprograms or protected entries. The language guarantees that these subprograms and entries will be executed in a manner that ensures that the data is updated under mutual exclusion. Condition synchronization is provided by having boolean expressions on entries (these are guards but are termed **barriers** in Ada) which must evaluate to true before a task is allowed entry. Consequently, protected objects are rather like monitors and conditional critical regions. They provide the structuring facility of monitors with the high-level synchronization mechanism of conditional critical regions.

A protected unit may be declared as a type or as a single instance; it has a specification and a body (hence it is declared in a similar way to a task). Its specification may contain functions, procedures and entries.

The following declaration illustrates how protected types can be used to provide simple mutual exclusion:

```
-- a simple integer
protected type Shared_Integer(Initial_Value : Integer) is
  function Read return  Integer;
  procedure Write(New_Value : Integer);
  procedure Increment(By : Integer);
private
  The_Data : Integer := Initial_Value;
end Shared_Integer;

My_Data : Shared_Integer(42);
```

The above protected type encapsulates a shared integer. The object declaration My_Data declares an instance of the protected type and passes the initial value for the encapsulated data. The encapsulated data can now only be accessed by the three subprograms: Read, Write and Increment.

A protected procedure provides mutually exclusive read/write access to the data encapsulated. In this case, concurrent calls to the procedure Write or Increment will be executed in mutual exclusion; that is, only one can be executing at any one time.

Protected functions provide concurrent read-only access to the encapsulated data.

In the above example, this means that many calls to Read can be executed simultaneously. However, calls to a protected function are still executed mutually exclusively with calls to a protected procedure. A Read call cannot be executed if there is a currently executing procedure call; a procedure call cannot be executed if there are one or more concurrently executing function calls.

The body of the Shared_Integer is simply

```
protected body Shared_Integer is
  function Read  return Integer is
  begin
    return The_Data;
  end Read;

  procedure Write(New_Value : Integer) is
  begin
    The_Data := New_Value;
  end Write;

  procedure Increment(By : Integer) is
  begin
    The_Data := The_Data + By;
  end Increment;
end Shared_Integer;
```

A protected entry is similar to a protected procedure in that it is guaranteed to execute in mutual exclusion and has read/write access to the encapsulated data. However, a protected entry is guarded by a boolean expression (the barrier) inside the body of the protected object; if this barrier evaluates to false when the entry call is made, the calling task is suspended until the barrier evaluates to true and no other tasks are currently active inside the protected object. Hence protected entry calls can be used to implement condition synchronization.

Consider a bounded buffer shared between several tasks. The specification of the buffer is

```
-- a bounded buffer

Buffer_Size : constant Integer := 10;
type Index is mod Buffer_Size ;
subtype Count is Natural range 0 .. Buffer_Size;
type Buffer is array (Index) of Data_Item;

protected type Bounded_Buffer is
  entry Get(Item: out Data_Item);
  entry Put(Item: in Data_Item);
private
  First : Index := Index'First;
  Last : Index := Index'Last;
  Number_In_Buffer : Count := 0;
  Buf : Buffer;
end Bounded_Buffer;

My_Buffer : Bounded_Buffer;
```

Two entries have been declared; these represent the public interface of the buffer. The data items declared in the private part are those items which must be accessed under mutual exclusion. In this case, the buffer is an array and is accessed via two indices; there is also a count indicating the number of items in the buffer.

The body of this protected type is given below:

```
protected body Bounded_Buffer is

  entry Get(Item: out Data_Item)
      when Number_In_Buffer /= 0 is
  begin
    Item := Buf(First);
    First := First + 1; -- mod types type around
    Number_In_Buffer := Number_In_Buffer - 1;
  end Get;

  entry Put(Item: in Data_Item)
      when Number_In_Buffer /= Buffer_Size is
  begin
    Last := Last + 1; -- mod types type around
    Buf(Last) := Item;
    Number_In_Buffer := Number_In_Buffer + 1;
   end Put;

end Bounded_Buffer;
```

The Get entry is guarded by the barrier 'when Number_In_Buffer /= 0"; only when this evaluates to true can a task execute the Get entry; similarly with the Put entry. Barriers define a precondition; only when they evaluate to true can the entry be accepted.

Although calls to a protected object can be delayed because the object is in use (that is, they cannot be executed with the requested read or read/write access), Ada does not view the call as being suspended. Calls which are delayed due to an entry barrier being false are, however, considered suspended and placed on a queue. The reason for this is:

- it is assumed that protected operations are short-lived

- once started a protected operation cannot suspend its execution – all calls which are potentially suspending are prohibitive and raise exceptions – it can only re-queue (see Section 11.4).

Hence a task should not be delayed for a significant period while attempting to access the protected object – other than for reasons associated with the order of scheduling. Once a procedure (or function) call has gained access it will immediately start to execute the subprogram; an entry call will evaluate the barrier and will, of course, be blocked if the barrier is false. In Section 13.14.1, the implementation strategy required by the Real-Time Systems Annex is considered which guarantees that a task is never delayed when trying to gain access to a protected object.

8.7.1   Entry calls and barriers

To issue a call to a protected object, a task simply names the object and the required subprogram or entry. For example, to place some data into the above bounded buffer requires the calling task to

```
My_Buffer.Put(Some_Item);
```

At any instant in time, a protected entry is either open or closed. It is open if, when checked, the boolean expression evaluates to true; otherwise it is closed. Generally, the protected entry barriers of a protected object are evaluated when:

(a) a task calls one of its protected entries and the associated barrier references a variable or an attribute which might have changed since the barrier was last evaluated;

(b) a task leaves a protected procedure or protected entry and there are tasks queued on entries whose barriers reference variables or attributes which might have changed since the barriers were last evaluated.

Barriers are not evaluated as a result of a protected function call. Note that it is not possible for two tasks to be active within a protected entry or procedure as the barriers are only evaluated when a task leaves the object.

When a task calls a protected entry or a protected subprogram, the protected object may already be locked: if one or more tasks are executing protected functions inside the protected object, the object is said to have an active **read lock**; if a task is executing a protected procedure or a protected entry, the object is said to have an active **read/write lock**.

If more than one task calls the same closed barrier then the calls are queued, by default, in a first-come, first-served fashion. However, this default can be changed (see Section 13.14.1).

Two more examples will now be given. Consider first the simple resource controller given earlier for other languages. When only a single resource is requested (and released) the code is straightforward:

```
protected Resource_Control is
   entry Allocate;
   procedure Deallocate;
private
   Free : Boolean := True;
end Resource_Control;

protected body Resource_Control is

   entry Allocate when Free is
   begin
     Free := False;
   end Allocate;
   procedure Deallocate is
```

```
begin
   Free := True;
end Deallocate;

end Resource_Control;
```

The resource is initially available and hence the `Free` flag is true. A call to `Allocate` changes the flag, and therefore closes the barrier; all subsequent calls to `Allocate` will be blocked. When `Deallocate` is called, the barrier is opened. This will allow one of the waiting tasks to proceed by executing the body of `Allocate`. The effect of this execution is to close the barrier again, and hence no further executions of the entry body will be possible (until there is a further call of `Deallocate`).

Interestingly, the general resource controller (where groups of resources are requested and released) is not easy to program using just guards. The reasons for this will be explained in Chapter 11, where resource control is considered in some detail.

Each entry queue has an attribute associated with it that indicates how many tasks are currently queued. This is used in the following example. Assume that a task wishes to broadcast a value (of type `Message`) to a number of waiting tasks. The waiting tasks will call a `Receive` entry which is only open when a new message has arrived. At that time, all waiting tasks are released.

Although all tasks can now proceed, they must pass through the protected object in strict sequence (as only one can ever be active in the object). The last task out must then raise the barrier again so that subsequent calls to `Receive` are blocked until a new message is broadcast. This explicit lowering and raising of the barriers can be compared with the use of condition variables which have no lasting effect (within the monitor) once all processes have exited. The code for the broadcast example is as follows (note that the attribute `Count` indicates the number of tasks queued on an entry):

```
protected type Broadcast is
   entry Receive(M : out Message);
   procedure Send(M : Message);
private
   New_Message : Message;
   Message_Arrived : Boolean := False;
end Broadcast;

protected body Broadcast is

   entry Receive(M : out Message) when Message_Arrived is
   begin
      M := New_Message;
      if Receive'Count = 0 then
         Message_Arrived := False;
      end if;
   end Receive;

   procedure Send(M : Message) is
   begin
      if Receive'Count > 0 then
```

```
      Message_Arrived := True;
      New_Message := M;
    end if;
  end Send;

end Broadcast;
```

As there may be no tasks waiting for the message, the send procedure has to check the count attribute. Only if it is greater than zero will it lower the barrier (and record the new message).

Finally, this section gives a full Ada implementation of the semaphore package given in Section 8.4.5. This shows that protected objects are not only an excellent structuring abstraction but have the same expressive power as semaphores.

```
package Semaphore_Package is
  type Semaphore(Initial : Natural := 1) is limited private;
  procedure Wait (S : in out Semaphore);
  procedure Signal (S : in out Semaphore);
private
  protected type Semaphore(Initial : Natural := 1) is
    entry Wait_Imp;
    procedure Signal_Imp;
  private
    Value : Natural := Initial;
  end Semaphore;
end Semaphore_Package;
```

```
package body Semaphore_Package is
  protected body Semaphore is
    entry Wait_Imp when Value > 0 is
    begin
      Value := Value - 1;
    end Wait_Imp;

    procedure Signal_Imp is
    begin
      Value := Value + 1;
    end Signal_Imp;
  end Semaphore;

  procedure Wait(S : in out Semaphore) is
  begin
    S.Wait_Imp;
  end Wait;

  procedure Signal(S : in out Semaphore) is
  begin
    S.Signal_Imp;
  end Signal;
end Semaphore_Package;
```

8.7.2 Protected objects and tagged types

Arguably, Ada does not fully integrate its models of concurrent and object-oriented programming. For example, neither tasks nor protected objects are extensible. It is beyond the scope of this book to address in detail how best to use the Ada features to get as much integration as possible – see Burns and Wellings (1998). Furthermore, see Wellings et al. (2000) for a comprehensive discussion on adding extensible protected types to Ada.

8.8 Synchronized methods

In many ways, Ada's protected objects are like objects in a class-based object-oriented programming language. The main difference, of course, is that they do not support an inheritance relationship. Java, having a fully integrated concurrency and object-oriented model, provides a mechanism by which monitors can be implemented in the context of classes and objects.

In Java, there is a lock associated with each object. This lock cannot be accessed directly by the application, but it is affected by:

- the method modifier `synchronized`, and
- block synchronization.

When a method is labelled with the `synchronized` modifier, access to the method can only proceed once the lock associated with the object has been obtained. Hence synchronized methods have mutually exclusive access to the data encapsulated by the object, if that data is only accessed by other synchronized methods. Non-synchronized methods do not require the lock, and can therefore be called at any time. Hence to obtain full mutual exclusion, every method has to be labelled synchronized. A simple shared integer is therefore represented by:

```
class SharedInteger
{
  private int theData;

  public SharedInteger(int initialValue)
  {
    theData = initialValue;
  }

  public synchronized int read()
  {
    return theData;
  };

  public synchronized void write(int newValue)
  {
    theData = newValue;
  };
```

```
public synchronized void incrementBy(int by)
  {
    theData = theData + by;
  };
}
```

```
SharedInteger myData = new SharedInteger(42);
```

Block synchronization provides a mechanism whereby a block can be labelled as synchronized. The `synchronized` keyword takes as a parameter an object whose lock it needs to obtain before it can continue. Hence synchronized methods are effectively implementable as

```
public int read()
  {
    synchronized(this) {
      return theData;
    }
  }
```

where **this** is the Java mechanism for obtaining the current object.

Used in its full generality, the synchronized block can undermine one of the advantages of monitor-like mechanisms: that of encapsulating synchronization constraints associate with an object into a single place in the program. This is because it is not possible to understand the synchronization associated with a particular object by just looking at the object itself when other objects can name that object in a synchronized statement. However, with careful use this facility augments the basic model and allows more expressive synchronization constraints to be programmed, as will be shown shortly.

Although synchronized methods or blocks allow mutually exclusive access to data in an object, this is not adequate if that data is *static*. Static data is shared between all objects created from the class. To obtain mutually exclusive access to this data requires **all** objects to be locked.

In Java, classes themselves are also objects and therefore there is a lock associated with the class. This lock may be accessed either by labelling a static method with the synchronized modifier or by identifying the class's object in a synchronized block statement. The latter can be obtained from the `Object` class associated with the object. Note, however, that this class-wide lock is not obtained when synchronizing on the object. Hence to obtain mutual exclusion over a static variable requires the following (for example):

```
class StaticSharedVariable
{
  private static int shared;
  ...

  public synchronized int Read()
  {
    synchronized(this.getClass())
    {
```

```
      return shared;
    };
  }

  public synchronized static void Write(int I)
  {
    shared = I;
  };
}
```

8.8.1 Waiting and notifying

To obtain conditional synchronization requires further support. This again comes from methods provided in the predefined object class:

```
public void wait();
             // throws IllegalMonitorStateException
public void notify();
             // throws IllegalMonitorStateException
public void notifyAll();
             // throws IllegalMonitorStateException
```

These methods are designed to be used only from within methods which hold the object lock (i.e. they are synchronized). If called without the lock, the exception `Illegal-MonitorStateException` is thrown.

The `wait` method always blocks the calling thread and releases the lock associated with the object. If the call is made from within a nested monitor then only the inner lock is associated with the `wait` and is released.

The `notify` method wakes up one waiting thread; the one woken is not defined by the Java language (however, it is defined by Real-Time Java; see Section 13.14.3). Note that `notify` does not release the lock, and hence the woken thread must still wait until it can obtain the lock before it can continue. To wake up **all** waiting threads requires use of the `notifyAll` method; again this does not release the lock and all the awoken threads must wait and contend for the lock when it becomes free. If no thread is waiting, then `notify` and `notifyAll` have no effect.

A waiting thread can also be awoken if it is interrupted by another thread. In this case the `InterruptedException` is thrown. The condition will be ignored in this chapter (the exception will be allowed to propagate), but discussed fully in Section 10.9.

Although it appears that Java provides the equivalent facilities to other languages supporting monitors, there is one important difference. There are no explicit condition variables. Hence, when a thread is awoken, it cannot necessarily assume that its 'condition' is true, as all threads are potentially awoken irrespective of what conditions they were waiting on. For many algorithms this limitation is not a problem, as the conditions under which tasks are waiting are mutually exclusive. For example, the bounded buffer traditionally has two condition variables: `WaitBufferNotFull` and `Wait-BufferNotEmpty`. However, if a thread is waiting for one condition, no other thread can be waiting for the other condition. Hence the thread can assume that when it wakes, the buffer is in the appropriate state.

```
public class BoundedBuffer
{
  private int buffer[];
  private int first;
  private int last;
  private int numberInBuffer = 0;
  private int size;

  public BoundedBuffer(int length)
  {
    size = length;
    buffer = new int[size];
    last = 0;
    first = 0;
  };

  public synchronized void put(int item) throws InterruptedException
  {
    if (numberInBuffer == size) {
      wait();
    };
    last = (last + 1) % size ; // % is modulus
    numberInBuffer++;
    buffer[last] = item;
    notify();
  };

  public synchronized int get() throws InterruptedException
  {
    if (numberInBuffer == 0) {
      wait();
    };
    first = (first + 1) % size ; // % is modulus
    numberInBuffer--;
    notify();
    return buffer[first];
  };
}
```

Of course, if notifyAll is used to wake up threads, then those threads must always re-evaluate their conditions before proceeding.

One of the standard concurrency control problems is the **readers–writers** problem. In this, many readers and many writers are attempting to access a large data structure. Readers can read concurrently, as they do not alter the data; however, writers require mutual exclusion over the data both from other writers and from readers. There are different variations on this scheme; the one considered here is where priority is always given to waiting writers. Hence, as soon as a writer is available, all new readers will be blocked until all writers have finished. Of course, in extreme situations this may lead to starvation of readers.

The solution to the readers–writers problem using standard monitors requires four monitor procedures `startRead`, `stopRead`, `startWrite` and `stopWrite`. The readers are structured:

```
startRead();
  // read data structure
stopRead();
```

Similarly, the writers are structured:

```
startWrite();
  // write data structure
stopWrite();
```

The code inside the monitor provides the necessary synchronization using two condition variables: `OkToRead` and `OkToWrite`. In Java, this cannot be directly expressed within a single monitor. Two approaches for solving this problem are now considered.

The first approach uses a single class:

```java
public class ReadersWriters
{

  private int readers = 0;
  private int waitingWriters = 0;
  private boolean writing = false;

  public synchronized void startWrite() throws InterruptedException
  {
    while(readers > 0 || writing)
    {
      waitingWriters++;
      wait();
      waitingWriters--;
    }
    writing = true;
  }

  public synchronized void stopWrite()
  {
    writing = false;
    notifyAll();
  }

  public synchronized void startRead() throws InterruptedException
  {
    while(writing || waitingWriters > 0) wait();
    readers++;
  }

  public synchronized void stopRead()
  {
```

```
    readers--;
    if(readers == 0) notifyAll();
  }
}
```

In this solution, on awaking after the wait request, the thread must re-evaluate the conditions under which it can proceed. Although this approach will allow multiple readers or a single writer, arguably it is inefficient, as all threads are woken up every time the data becomes available. Many of these threads, when they finally gain access to the monitor, will find that they still cannot continue and therefore will have to wait again.

An alternative solution, suggested by Lea (1997), is to use another class to implement a condition variable. Consider:

```
public class ConditionVariable {
  public boolean wantToSleep = false;
}
```

The general approach is to create instances of these variables inside another class and to use block synchronization. To avoid waiting in a nested monitor call, the flag wantToSleep is used to indicate whether the monitor wants to wait on the condition variable.

```
public class ReadersWriters
{
  private int readers = 0;
  private int waitingReaders = 0;
  private int waitingWriters = 0;
  private boolean writing = false;

  ConditionVariable OkToRead = new ConditionVariable();
  ConditionVariable OkToWrite = new ConditionVariable();

  public void startWrite() throws InterruptedException
  {
    synchronized(OkToWrite) // get lock on condition variable
    {
      synchronized(this) // get monitor lock
      {
        if(writing | readers > 0) {
          waitingWriters++;
          OkToWrite.wantToSleep = true;
        } else {
          writing = true;
          OkToWrite.wantToSleep = false;
        }
      } //give up monitor lock
      if(OkToWrite.wantToSleep) OkToWrite.wait();
    }
  }
```

```
public void stopWrite()
{
  synchronized(OkToRead)
  {
    synchronized(OkToWrite)
    {
      synchronized(this)
      {
        if(waitingWriters > 0) {
          waitingWriters--;
          OkToWrite.notify();
        } else {
          writing = false;
          OkToRead.notifyAll();
          readers = waitingReaders;
          waitingReaders = 0;
        }
      }
    }
  }
}

public synchronized void startRead() throws InterruptedException
{
  synchronized(OkToRead) {
    synchronized(this)
    {
      if(writing | waitingWriters > 0) {
        waitingReaders++;
        OkToRead.wantToSleep = true;
      } else {
        readers++;
        OkToRead.wantToSleep = false;
      }
    }
    if(OkToRead.wantToSleep) OkToRead.wait();
  }
}

public synchronized void stopRead()
{
  synchronized(OkToWrite)
  {
    synchronized(this)
    {
      readers--;
      if(readers == 0 & waitingWriters > 0) {
        waitingWriters--;
        writing = true;
        OkToWrite.notify();
      }
    }
  }
}
}
```

Every condition variable is represented by an instance of the `ConditionVariable` class declared inside the class which is acting as the monitor. Conditions are evaluated while holding the monitor lock and the lock on any condition variable which will be notified or waited on inside the monitor procedure. To ensure that no deadlock occurs, these locks should always be obtained in the same order.

8.8.2   Inheritance and synchronization

The combination of the object-oriented paradigm with mechanisms for concurrent programming may give rise to the so-called **inheritance anomaly** (Matsuoka and Yonezawa, 1993). An inheritance anomaly exists if the synchronization between operations of a class is not local but may depend on the whole set of operations present for the class. When a subclass adds new operations, it may become necessary to change the synchronization defined in the parent class to account for these new operations (Matsuoka and Yonezawa, 1993).

For example, consider the bounded buffer presented earlier in this section. With Java, the code that tests the conditions (`BufferNotFull` and `BufferNotEmpty`) is embedded in the methods. It will be shown in Chapter 11 that, in general, this approach has many advantages as it allows the methods to access the parameters to the method as well as the object attributes. However, it does cause some problems when inheritance is considered. Suppose that the bounded buffer is to be subclassed so that all access can be prohibited. Two new methods are added, `prohibitAccess` and `allowAccess`. A naive extension might include the following code

```
public class AccessError extends Exception{};
public class ControlledBoundedBuffer extends BoundedBuffer
{
  // Incorrect Code

  boolean prohibited;

  ControlledBoundedBuffer(int length)
  {
    super(length);
    prohibited = false;
  };

  public synchronized void prohibitAccess() throws InterruptedException
  {
    if (prohibited) wait();
    prohibited = true;
  }

  public synchronized void allowAccess() throws AccessError
  {
    if (!prohibited) throw new AccessError();
    prohibited = false;
    notify();
  }
}
```

The main problem with this extension is that it fails to take into account the fact that the superclass also issues `wait` and `notify` requests. Thus the `get` and `put` methods might wake up as a result of the notify request in the `allowAccess` method.

The problem is that the code in the superclass methods need to be modified to reflect the new synchronization conditions. This is the heart of the inheritance anomaly. Ideally, the code for `get` and `put` should be completely reusable. Of course, if it had been known when the bounded buffer was written that a controlled version was going to be produced, then a different design might have been chosen to facilitate the extension. However, it is not possible to anticipate all extensions.

One approach that can be taken is to **always** encapsulate condition tests in `while` loops irrespective of whether they appear necessary, and to always use `notifyAll`. Hence if the buffer is written as follows

```
public class BoundedBuffer
{
  private int buffer[];
  private int first;
  private int last;
  private int numberInBuffer = 0;
  private int size;

  public BoundedBuffer(int length)
  {
    size = length;
    buffer = new int[size];
    last = size - 1;
    first = size - 1;
  };

  public synchronized void put(int item) throws InterruptedException
  {
      while (numberInBuffer == size) {
        wait();
      };
      last = (last + 1) % size ;
      numberInBuffer++;
      buffer[last] = item;
      notifyAll();
  };


  public synchronized int get() throws InterruptedException
  {
      while (numberInBuffer == 0) {
        wait();
      };
      first = (first + 1) % size ;
      numberInBuffer--;
      notifyAll();
      return buffer[first];
  };
}
```

then the subclass could be written as:

```
public class LockableBoundedBuffer extends BoundedBuffer
{
  boolean prohibited ;

  // Incorrect Code

  LockableBoundedBuffer(int length)
  {
    super(length);
    prohibited = false;
  };

  public synchronized void prohibitAccess() throws InterruptedException
  {
    while (prohibited) wait();
    prohibited = true;
  }

  public synchronized void allowAccess() throws AccessError
  {
    if (!prohibited) throw new AccessError();
    prohibited = false;
    notifyAll();
  }

  public synchronized void put(int item) throws InterruptedException
  {
    while(prohibited) wait();
    super.put(item);
  }

  public synchronized int get() throws InterruptedException
  {
    while(prohibited) wait();
    return(super.get());
  }
}
```

Unfortunately, there is a subtle bug with this approach. Consider the case where a producer is attempting to put data into a full buffer. Access to the buffer is not prohibited so `super.put(item)` is invoked where the call is blocked waiting for the `Buffer-NotEmpty` condition. Now access to the buffer is prohibited. Any further calls to get and put are held in the overridden subclass methods, as will further calls to the `prohibitAccess` method. Now a call to the `allowAccess` method is made; this results in all waiting threads being released. Suppose the order in which the released threads acquire the monitor lock is: the consumer thread, the thread attempting to prohibit access to the buffer, the producer thread. The consumer finds that access to the buffer is not prohibited and takes data from the buffer. It issues a `notifyAll` request, but no threads are now currently waiting. The next thread which runs now prohibits access to the buffer. The producer thread runs next and places an item into the buffer although access is prohibited!

Although this example might seem contrived, it does illustrate the subtle bugs that can occur due to the inheritance anomaly.

Summary

Process interactions require operating systems and concurrent programming languages to support synchronization and interprocess communication. Communication can be based on either shared variables or message passing. This chapter has been concerned with shared variables, the multiple update difficulties they present and the mutual exclusion synchronizations needed to counter these difficulties. In this discussion, the following terms were introduced:

- critical section – code that must be executed under mutual exclusion;
- producer–consumer system – two or more processes exchanging data via a finite buffer;
- busy waiting – a process continually checking a condition to see if it is now able to proceed;
- livelock – an error condition in which one or more processes are prohibited from progressing whilst using up processing cycles.

Examples were used to show how difficult it is to program mutual exclusion using only shared variables. Semaphores were introduced to simplify these algorithms and to remove busy waiting. A semaphore is a non-negative integer that can only be acted upon by `wait` and `signal` procedures. The executions of these procedures are atomic.

The provision of a semaphore primitive has the consequence of introducing a new state for a process; namely, suspended. It also introduces two new error conditions:

- deadlock – a collection of suspended processes that cannot proceed;
- indefinite postponement – a process being unable to proceed as resources are not made available for it (also called lockout or starvation).

Semaphores can be criticized as being too low-level and error-prone in use. Following their development, four more structured primitives were introduced:

- conditional critical regions
- monitors
- protected objects
- synchronized methods.

Monitors are an important language feature, and are used in Modula-1, Concurrent Pascal and Mesa. They consist of a module, entry to which is assured (by definition) to be under mutual exclusion. Within the body of a monitor, a process can suspend itself if the conditions are not appropriate for it to proceed. This suspension is achieved using a condition variable. When a suspended process is awoken (by a `signal` operation on the condition variable), it is imperative that this does not result in two processes being active in the module at the same time. To make sure this does not happen, a language must prescribe one of the following:

(1) The `signal` operation can only be executed as the last action of a process in a monitor.

(2) The `signal` operation has the side-effect of forcing the signalling process to exit the monitor.

(3) The signalling process is itself suspended if it results in another process becoming active in the monitor.

(4) The signalling process is not suspended and the free processes must compete for access to the monitor once the signalling process exits.

A form of monitor can be implemented using a procedural interface. Such a facility is provided by mutexes and condition variables in POSIX.

Although monitors provide a high-level structure for mutual exclusion, other synchronizations must be programmed using very low-level condition variables. This gives an unfortunate mix of primitives in the language design. Ada's protected objects give the structuring advantages of monitors and the high-level synchronization mechanisms of conditional critical regions.

Integrating concurrency and OOP is fraught with difficulties. Ada tries to avoid the problem by providing separate facilities for OOP and protected types. Java, however, addresses the problem by providing synchronized member methods for classes. Using this facility (along with the synchronized statement and wait and notify primitives) provides a flexible object-oriented based monitor-like facility. Unfortunately, the inheritance anomaly is present with this approach.

The next chapter considers message-based synchronization and communication primitives. Languages that use these have, in effect, elevated the monitor to an active process in its own right. As a process can only be doing one thing at a time, mutual exclusion is assured. Processes no longer communicate with shared variables but directly. It is therefore possible to construct a single high-level primitive that combines communication and synchronization. This concept was first considered by Conway (1963) and has been employed in high-level real-time programming languages. It forms the basis of the rendezvous in both Ada and occam2.

Further reading

Andrews, G. A. (1991) *Concurrent Programming Principles and Practice.* Redwood City, CA: Benjamin/Cummings.

Ben-Ari, M. (1990) *Principles of Concurrent and Distributed Programming.* New York: Prentice Hall.

Burns, A. and Davies, G. (1993) *Concurrent Programming.* Reading: Addison-Wesley.

Burns, A. and Wellings, A. J. (1995) *Concurrency in Ada.* Cambridge: Cambridge University Press.

Butenhof, D. R. (1997) *Programming With POSIX Threads.* Reading, MA: Addison-Wesley.

Hyde, P. (1999) *Java Thread Programming.* Indianapolis, IN: Sams Publishing.

Lea, D. (1999) *Concurrent Programming in Java: Design Principles and Patterns.* Reading, MA: Addison-Wesley.

Oaks, A. and Wong, H. (1997) *Java Threads.* Sebastopol, CA: O'Reilly.

Nichols, B., Buttlar, D. and Farrell, J. (1996) *POSIX Threads Programming.* Sebastopol, CA: O'Reilly.

Silberschatz, A. and Galvin, P. A. (1998) *Operating System Concepts.* New York: John Wiley & Sons.

Wirth, N. (1977) Modula: a Language for Modular Multiprogramming. *Software Practice and Experience,* 7(1), 3–84.

Exercises

8.1 Show how Peterson's algorithm given in Section 8.2 can be modified to allow a high-priority process to be given preference over a low-priority one when busy waiting.

8.2 Consider a data item which is to be shared between a single producer and a single consumer. The producer is a periodic task which reads a sensor and writes the value to the shared data item. The consumer is a sporadic task which wishes to take the latest value placed in the shared data item by the producer.

The following package claims to provide a generic algorithm with which the producer and consumer can communicate safely, *without* the need for mutual exclusion or busy waiting.

```
generic
  type Data is private;
  Initialvalue : Data;
package Simpsonsalgorithm is
  procedure Write(Item: Data); -- non-blocking
  procedure Read (Item : out Data); -- non-blocking
end Simpsonsalgorithm;
```

```
package body Simpsonsalgorithm is

  type Slot is (First, Second);

  Fourslot : array (Slot, Slot) of Data :=
               (First => (Initialvalue, Initialvalue),
                Second => (Initialvalue, Initialvalue));

  Nextslot : array (Slot) of Slot := (First, First);

  Latest : Slot := First;
  Reading : Slot := First;

  procedure Write(Item : Data) is
    Pair, Index : Slot;
  begin
    if Reading = First then
      Pair := Second;
    else
      Pair := First;
    end if;
    if Latest = First then
      Index := Second;
    else
      Index := First;
    end if;

    Fourslot(Pair, Index) := Item;
    Nextslot(Pair) := Index;
    Latest := Pair;
  end Write;

  procedure Read(Item : out Data) is
    Pair, Index : Slot;
  begin
    Pair := Latest;
    Reading := Pair;
    Index := Nextslot(Pair);
    Item := Fourslot(Pair, Index);
  end Read;
end Simpsonsalgorithm;
```

Describe carefully how this algorithm works by explaining what happens when:

(1) a Write is followed by a Read
(2) a Read is preempted by a Write
(3) a Write is preempted by a Read
(4) a Read is preempted by more than one Write
(1) a Write is preempted by more than one Read

Comment how the algorithm trades off safe communication against data freshness.

Many compilers optimize code so that frequently accessed variables are held in registers local to a task. In this context, comment on whether the above algorithm's claim of safe communication is justifiable. Are there any changes to the algorithm needed to make it work for all implementations of Ada 95?

8.3   Consider a shared data structure that can be both read from and written to. Show how semaphores can be used to allow many concurrent readers or a single writer, but not both.

8.4   Show how Hoare's Conditional Critical Region can be implemented using semaphores.

8.5   Show how Hoare's (or Mesa's or Modula-1's) monitors can be implemented using semaphores.

8.6   Show how binary semaphores can be implemented using a single Modula-1 interface module. How would the solution be modified to cope with a general semaphore?

8.7   Consider the scheduling of a queue of requests to transfer data to/from a disk. In order to minimize the disk head movement, all the requests for a particular cylinder are serviced in one go. The scheduler sweeps up and down the disk servicing requests for each cylinder in turn. Write a Modula-1 interface module which provides the necessary synchronization. Assume that there are two interface procedures: one for requesting access to a particular cylinder, the other for releasing the cylinder. User processes call procedures in the following disk driver module:

```
module disk_driver;

    define read, write;

    procedure read(var data:data_t; addr:disk_address);
    begin
        (* work out cylinder address *)
        diskheadscheduler.request(cylinder);
        (* read data *)
        diskheadscheduler.release(cylinder);
    end read;

    (* similarly for write *)

end disk_driver;
```

8.8   Write a Modula-1 interface module to control the read/write access of a file in a database. In order to maintain the integrity of the file, only one process may update it at once; however, any number of processes may read the file as long as it is not in the process of being updated. Furthermore, requests to update the file should only be allowed when there are no current readers. However, once a request to update the file has been received all subsequent requests to read the file should be blocked until there are no more updates.

The interface module should define four procedures: startread, endread, startwrite and endwrite. Assume the interface module will be used in the following way.

```
module file_access;
  define readfile, writefile;
  use startread, endread, startwrite, endwrite;

  procedure readfile;
  begin
     startread;
      read the file
     endread;
  end readfile;

  procedure writefile;
  begin
     startwrite;
      write the file
     endwrite;
  end writefile;
end file_access.
```

8.9   A computer system is being used to control the flow of traffic through a *one-way* road tunnel. For safety reasons, there must never be more than *approximately N* vehicles in the tunnel at one time. Traffic lights at the entrance control the entry of traffic and vehicle detectors at entrance and exit are used to measure the traffic flow.

Sketch the structure of *two* Modula-1 PROCESSes and an INTERFACE MODULE which between them control the traffic flow. The first process monitors the exit vehicle detector and the second monitors the entrance detector. The INTERFACE module controls the traffic lights themselves. You may assume that the following functions have already been written and are in scope:

```
procedure CARS_EXITED: NATURAL;
begin
  (* returns the number of cars which have left *)
  (* the tunnel since the function was last called. *)
end CARS_EXITED;

procedure CARS_ENTERED : NATURAL;
begin
  (* returns the number of cars which have entered *)
  (* the tunnel since the function was last called. *)
end CARS_ENTERED;

procedure SET_LIGHTS( COL : COLOUR);
begin
  (* set the traffic lights to COL. *)
  (* COLOUR is an enumeration type in scope defined as *)
  (* type COLOUR = (RED, GREEN); *)
end SET_LIGHTS;
```

```
procedure DELAY_10_SECONDS;
begin
    (* delay the calling process 10 seconds *)
end DELAY_10_SECONDS;
```

Your solution should read the sensors (via the CARS_EXITED and CARS_ENTERED functions) every 10 seconds until the tunnel is full or empty. When the tunnel is full (and therefore the lights are set to red) the entrance monitoring task should *not* continually call the CARS_ENTERED function. Similarly, when the tunnel is empty the exit monitoring task should *not* continually call the CARS_EXITED function. Furthermore, the tasks should not busy wait. You should make *no* assumptions about the Modula-1 run-time task scheduler.

8.10 One of the criticisms of monitors is that condition synchronization is too low-level and unstructured. Explain what is meant by this statement. A higher level monitor synchronization primitive might take the form

```
WaitUntil boolean_expression;
```

where the process is delayed until the boolean expression evaluates to true. For example:

```
WaitUntil x < y +5;
```

would delay the process until $x < y + 5$.

Although this form of condition synchronization is more structured it is not found in most languages which support monitors. Explain why this in the case. Under what circumstances would the objections to the above high level synchronization facility be invalid? Show how the bounded buffer problem can be solved using the **WaitUntil** synchronization primitive inside a monitor.

8.11 Consider a system of three cigarette smoker processes and one agent process. Each smoker continuously makes a cigarette and smokes it. To make a cigarette three ingredients are needed: tobacco, paper and matches. One of the processes has paper, another tobacco and the third has matches. The agent has an infinite supply of all three ingredients. The agent places two ingredients, chosen randomly, on a table. The smoker who has the remaining ingredient can then make and smoke a cigarette. Once it has finished smoking the smoker signals the agent who then puts another two of the three ingredients on the table, and the cycle repeats.

Sketch the structure of a monitor which will synchronize the agent and all three smokers.

8.12 Contrast the internal facilities provided by the Unix Kernel (Bach, 1986) for mutual exclusion and condition synchronization with the corresponding facilities provided by semaphores.

8.13 Show how the internal facilities provided by Unix (Bach, 1986) can be used to control access to a shared data structure. Assume that there will be many readers and many writers. However, although many readers should be allowed to access the data structure concurrently, only a single writer is allowed access at any one time. Furthermore, a mixture of readers and writers is not allowed. The solution should also give priority to readers.

8.14 Show how the operations on a semaphore can be implemented in the nucleus of an operating system for a single processor system **without** busy waiting. What hardware facility does your solution require?

8.15 Show how POSIX mutexes and condition variables can be used to implement a shared data structure that can be both read from and written to. Allow many concurrent readers or a single writer but not both.

8.16 Show how POSIX mutexes and condition variables can be used to implement a resource controller.

8.17 Complete Exercise 7.8 using Ada's protected objects for process synchronization.

8.18 Compare and contrast the facilities provided by the POSIX mutexes and condition variables with those provided by Ada's protected objects.

8.19 Redo Exercise 7.11 using protected objects.

8.20 Implement quantity semaphores using protected objects.

8.21 Show how one or more protected objects can be used to implement Hoare's monitors.

8.22 Explain the synchronization imposed by the following Ada protected object.

```
protected type Barrier(Needed : Positive) is
    entry Wait;
private
    Releasing : Boolean := False;
end Barrier;

protected body Barrier is

    entry Wait when Wait'Count = Needed or Releasing is
    begin
        if Wait'Count = 0 then
            Releasing = False;
        else
            Releasing := True;
        end if;
    end Wait;
end Barrier;
```

The following package provides a simplified Ada binding to POSIX Mutexes and Condition Variables. All Mutexes and Condition Variables are initialized with default attributes.

```
package Pthreads is
    type Mutex_T is limited private;
    type Cond_T is limited private;

    procedure Mutex_Initialise (M: in out Mutex_T);
```

```
    procedure Mutex_Lock(M: in out Mutex_T);
    procedure Mutex_Trylock(M: in out Mutex_T);
    procedure Mutex_Unlock(M: in out Mutex_T);

    procedure Cond_Initialise(C: in out Cond_T);
    procedure Cond_Wait(C: in out Cond_T;
                          M : in out Mutex_T);

    procedure Cond_Signal(C: in out Cond_T);
    procedure Cond_Broadcast(C: in out Cond_T);
  private
    ...
  end Pthreads;
```

Show how Barriers, as defined above, can be implemented using this package. Do *not* use any of Ada's communication and synchronization facilities in the solution.

8.23 Using the Ada `Pthreads` package given in the previous question, redo the answer to Exercise 8.7 using Ada. Do not use the Ada synchronization facilities. Assume that there are two interface procedures: one for requesting access to a particular cylinder, the other for releasing the cylinder.

```
package Disk_Head_Scheduler is
  Size_Of_Disk : constant := ...;
  type Disk_Address is range 1 .. Size_Of_Disk;
  type Cylinder_Address is mod 1 .. 20;
  procedure Request(Dest: Cylinder_Address);
  procedure Release(Dest: Cylinder_Address);
end Disk_Head_Scheduler
```

Users call procedures in the following disk driver package:

```
with Disk_Head_Scheduler; use Disk_Head_Scheduler;
package Disk_Driver is
  procedure Read(Data: out  Data_T; Addr : Disk_Address);
  procedure Write(Data: in  Data_T; Addr : Disk_Address);
end Disk_Driver;

package body Disk_Driver is

  procedure Read(Data: out  Data_T; Addr : Disk_Address) is
     Cylinder : Cylinder_Address;
  begin
     -- work out cylinder address
     Disk_Head_Scheduler.Request(Cylinder);
     -- read data
     Disk_Head_Scheduler.Release(Cylinder);
  end Read;

  -- similarly for Write

end  Disk_Driver;
```

The solution should not contain any tasks or POSIX processes/threads.

8.24 The following package defines an Ada semaphore abstraction.

```
generic
  Initial : Natural:= 1; -- default initial value of semaphore
package Semaphore_Package is
  type Semaphore is limited private;
  procedure Wait (S : Semaphore);
  procedure Signal (S : Semaphore);
private
  type Semaphore is ...; -- not needed for this question
end Semaphore_Package;
```

Using the `Semaphore_Package`, show how the following communication paradigm (and their associated package specification) can be implemented.
A Multicast is where one task is able to send the same data to several waiting tasks. A package specification for the `Multicast` abstraction is given below.

```
package Multicast is

  procedure Send(I : Integer);
  procedure Receive(I : out Integer);

end Multicast;
```

The receiver tasks indicate their willingness to receive data by calling the procedure `Receive` defined in the package given above (in this example the data is of type `Integer`). The tasks are blocked by this call. A sender task indicates that it wishes to multicast data by calling the `Send` procedure. All tasks which are currently blocked on the receive are released when the sender invokes the `Send` procedure. The data passed by the sender is given to all waiting tasks. Once the `Send` procedure has finished, any new calls to `Receive` must wait for the next sender.
Show how the body of the `Multicast` package can be implemented using semaphores.

8.25 A Broadcast is similar to a multicast except that ALL intended recipients must receive the data. A package specification for the `Broadcast` abstraction is given below.

```
package Broadcast is

  -- for 10 tasks

  procedure Send(I : Integer);
  procedure Receive(I : out Integer);

end Broadcast;
```

Consider, for example, a system with 10 recipient tasks. These tasks all call the

Receive procedure when they are ready to receive the broadcast. The tasks are blocked by this call. A sender task indicates that it wishes to broadcast data by calling the Send procedure. The Send procedure waits until *all* ten tasks are ready to receive the broadcast before releasing the recipients and passing the data. If more than one call to Send occurs, then they are queued.

Show how the body of the Broadcast package can be implemented using the semaphore package given in Exercise 8.24.

8.26 It has been suggested that York should put a limit on the number of motorists that can enter the city at any one time. One proposal is to establish monitoring checkpoints at each of the city's Bars (entrances through the City's walls) and, when the city is full, to turn the traffic lights to red for incoming traffic. To indicate to the motorists that the city is full, the red light is set to flashing.

In order to achieve this goal, pressure sensors are placed in the road at the Bars' entry and exit points. Every time a car enters the city, a signal is set to a Bar-Controller task (as a task entry call); similarly when a car exits:

```
Max_Cars_In_City_For_Red_Light : constant Positive := N;
Min_Cars_In_City_For_Green_Light : constant Positive := N - 10;

type Bar is (Walmgate, Goodramgate, Micklegate,
             Bootham, Barbican);

task type Bar_Controller(G : Bar) is
  entry Car_Entered;
  entry Car_Exited;
end Bar_Controller;

Walmgate_Bar_Controller : Bar_Controller(Walmgate);
Goodramgate_Bar_Controller : Bar_Controller(Goodramgate);
Micklegate_Bar_Controller : Bar_Controller(Micklegate);
Bootham_Bar_Controller : Bar_Controller(Bootham);
Barbican_Bar_Controller : Bar_Controller(Barbican);
```

Show how the body of these tasks can be coordinated so that ONE of them calls the CityTrafficLightController (with the following task specification) to indicate whether more cars are to be allowed in or not.

```
task City_Traffic_Lights_Controller is
  entry City_Is_Full;
  entry City_Has_Space;
end City_Traffic_Lights_Controller;

task body Traffic_Lights_Controller is separate;
--  body of no interest in this question
```

8.27 Explain why the resource controller given in Section 8.4.6 suffers from a race condition. How can the algorithm be modified to remove this condition.

8.28 Show how the reader/writers problem can be implemented in Java where priority is given to readers and where writers are guaranteed to be serviced in a FIFO order.

8.29 Show how Java can be used to implement a resource controller.

8.30 Implement quantity semaphores using Java.

8.31 Redo the bounded buffer example in Java using two instances of the class `Con-ditionVariable` one for the `BufferNotFull` and one for the `Buffer-NotEmpty` conditions.

8.32 Extend the above solution to the bounded buffer problem to produce a buffer whose access can be prohibited. Does this approach solve the inheritance anomaly identified in Section 8.8.2?

8.33 Consider the following Java class

```
public class Event
{
  public synchronized void highPriorityWait();
  public synchronized void lowPriorityWait();
  public synchronized void signalEvent();
}
```

Show how this class be implemented so that `signalEvent` releases one high-priority waiting thread if one is waiting. If there is no high-priority waiting thread, release one low-priority waiting thread. If no thread is waiting, the `signalEvent` has no effect.

Now consider the case where an Id can be associated with the methods. How can the algorithm be modified so that the `signalEvent` wakes up the appropriate blocked thread.

Chapter 9

Message-based synchronization and communication

The alternative to shared variable synchronization and communication is based on message passing. The approach is typified by the use of a single construct for both synchronization and communication. Within this broad category, however, a wide variety of language models exist. This variety in the semantics of message passing arises from, and is dominated by, three issues:

(1) the model of synchronization,

(2) the method of process naming,

(3) the message structure.

Each of these issues is considered in turn. Following this, the message passing models of various languages, including Ada and occam2, are discussed along with the Real-time POSIX model. Java does not explicitly support a message-passing model, although classes could be produced which implement this model. However, as no new language features are introduced, Java will not be discussed in this chapter.

9.1   Process synchronization

With all message-based systems, there is the implicit synchronization that a receiver process cannot obtain a message before that message has been sent. Although this is quite obvious, it must be compared with the use of a shared variable; in this case, a receiver process can read a variable and not know whether it has been written to by the sender process. If a process executes an unconditional message receive when no message is available, then it will become suspended until the message arrives.

Variations in the process synchronization model arise from the semantics of the send operation, which can be broadly classified as follows:

- **Asynchronous** (or **no-wait**): the sender proceeds immediately, regardless of whether the message is received or not. The asynchronous send is found in CONIC (Sloman et al., 1984) and several operating systems including POSIX.

- **Synchronous**: the sender proceeds only when the message has been received. The synchronous send is used in CSP (Hoare, 1985), and occam2.

- **Remote invocation**: the sender proceeds only when a reply has been returned from the receiver. Remote invocation send models the request–response paradigm of communication, and is found in Ada, SR (Andrews and Olsson, 1993), CONIC(Sloman et al., 1984) and various operating systems.

To appreciate the difference between these approaches, consider the following analogy. The posting of a letter is an asynchronous send – once the letter has been put into the letter box the sender proceeds with his or her life; only by the return of another letter can the sender ever know that the first letter actually arrived. From the receiver's point of view, a letter can only inform the reader about an out-of-date event; it says nothing about the current position of the sender. (Everyone has received sun-drenched postcards from people they know have been back at work for at least two weeks!)

A telephone is a better analogy for synchronous communication. The sender now waits until contact is made and the identity of the receiver verified before the message is sent. If the receiver can reply immediately (that is, during the same call), the synchronization is remote invocation. Because the sender and receiver 'come together' for a synchronized communication it is often called a **rendezvous**. The remote invocation form is known as an **extended rendezvous**, as arbitrary computations can be undertaken before the reply is sent (that is, during the rendezvous).

Clearly, there is a relationship between these three forms of send. Two asynchronous events can essentially constitute a synchronous relationship if an acknowledgement message is always sent (and waited for):

```
        P1                              P2
asyn_send (message)             wait (message)
wait (acknowledgement)          asyn_send (acknowledgement)
```

Moreover, two synchronous communications can be used to construct a remote invocation:

```
        P1                              P2
syn_send (message)              wait (message)
wait (reply)                       . . .
                                construct reply
                                   . . .
                                syn_send (reply)
```

As an asynchronous send can be used to construct the other two, it could be argued that this model gives the greatest flexibility and should be the one that languages and operating systems adopt. However, there are a number of drawbacks to using this model:

(1) Potentially infinite buffers are needed to store messages that have not been read yet (perhaps because the receiver has terminated).

(2) Because asynchronous communication is out-of-date, most sends are programmed to expect an acknowledgement (that is, synchronous communication).

(3) More communications are needed with the asynchronous model, hence programs are more complex.

(4) It is more difficult to prove the correctness of the complete system.

Note that where asynchronous communication is desired in a synchronized message passing language, buffer processes can easily be constructed. However, the implementation of a process is not without cost; therefore, having too many buffer processes might have a detrimental affect on the overall performance of the system.

9.2   Process naming and message structure

Process naming involves two distinct sub-issues: direction versus indirection, and symmetry. In a direct naming scheme, the sender of a message explicitly names the receiver:

```
send <message> to <process-name>
```

With an indirect naming scheme, the sender names some intermediate entity (known variously as a channel, mailbox, link or pipe):

```
send <message> to <mailbox>
```

Note that, even with a mailbox, the message passing can still be synchronous (that is, the sender will wait until the message is read). Direct naming has the advantage of simplicity, while indirect naming aids the decomposition of the software; a mailbox can be seen as an interface between distinct parts of the program.

A naming scheme is symmetric if both sender and receiver name each other (directly or indirectly):

```
send <message> to <process-name>
wait <message> from <process-name>

send <message> to <mailbox>
wait <message> from <mailbox>
```

It is asymmetric if the receiver names no specific source but accepts messages from any process (or mailbox):

```
wait <message>
```

Asymmetric naming fits the client–server paradigm in which 'server' processes provide services in response to messages from any of a number of 'client' processes. An implementation, therefore, must be able to support a queue of processes waiting for the server.

If the naming is indirect then there are further issues to consider. The intermediary could have:

- a many-to-one structure (that is, any number of processes could write to it but only one process can read from it); this again fits the client–server paradigm
- a many-to-many structure (that is, many clients and many servers)
- a one-to-one structure (that is, one client and one server); note that with this structure no queues need to be maintained by the run-time support system.
- a one-to-many structure; this situation is useful when a process wishes to send a request to a group of worker processes and it does not care which process services the request.

9.2.1   Message structure

Ideally a language should allow any data object of any defined type (predefined or user) to be transmitted in a message. Living up to this ideal is difficult, particularly if data objects have different representations at the sender and receiver, and even more so if the representation includes pointers (Herlihy and Liskov, 1982). Because of these difficulties, some languages (for example, occam-1) have restricted message content to unstructured, fixed sized objects of system defined type. More modern languages have removed these restrictions; however, modern operating systems still require data to be converted into bytes before transmission.

9.3   Message-passing semantics of Ada and occam2

Both Ada and occam2 allow communication and synchronization to be based on message passing. With occam2, this is the only method available; with Ada, as seen in the last chapter, communication is also possible through shared variables and protected types. There are, however, important differences between the message-based schemes that the two languages incorporate. In short, Ada uses direct asymmetric remote invocation, while occam2 incorporates indirect symmetric synchronous message passing. Both languages allow messages to have a flexible structure. The two languages will now be described; occam2 first, as it has the simpler semantics.

9.3.1   The occam2 model

Occam2 processes are not named, and therefore it is necessary during communication to use indirect naming via a **channel**. Each channel can only be used by a single writer and a single reader process. Both processes name the channel; the syntax is somewhat terse:

```
ch ! X    -- write value of expression X
          -- onto channel ch

ch ? Y    -- read from channel ch
          -- into variable Y
```

In the above, the variable Y and the expression X will be of the same type. The communication is synchronous; therefore whichever process accesses the channel first will be suspended. When the other process arrives, data will pass from X to Y (this can be viewed as the distributed assignment Y := X). The two processes will then continue their executions concurrently and independently. To illustrate this communication, consider two processes that are passing 1000 integers between them:

```
CHAN OF INT ch:
PAR
   INT V:
   SEQ i = 0 FOR 1000          --- process 1
     SEQ
        -- generate value V
        ch ! V
   INT C:
   SEQ i = 0 FOR 1000          --- process 2
     SEQ
        ch ? C
        -- use C
```

With each iteration of the two loops, a rendezvous between the two processes occurs.

Channels in occam2 are typed and can be defined to pass objects of any valid type including structured types. Arrays of channels can also be defined.

It is important to appreciate that the input and output operations on channels are considered to be fundamental language primitives. They constitute two of the five primitive processes in occam2. The others being SKIP, STOP and assignment (see Chapter 3). By comparison, communication and synchronization do not have such a central role in Ada.

9.3.2   The Ada model

The semantics of remote invocation have many superficial similarities with a procedure call. Data passes to a receiver, the receiver executes and then data is returned. Because of this similarity, Ada supports the definition of a program's messages in a way that is compatible with the definition of procedures, protected subprograms and entries. In particular, the parameter-passing models are identical (that is, there is only one model that is used in all situations).

In order for a task to receive a message, it must define an **entry**. As before, any number of parameters, of any mode and of any type are allowed. For example:

```
task type Screen_Output(Id : Screen_Identifier) is
  -- a task type definition
  entry Call (Value : Character; X_Coordinate,
              Y_Coordinate: Integer);
end Screen_Output;

Display: Screen_Output(Tty1);
-- where Tty1 is of type Screen_Identifier

task Time_Server is -- a single task definition
  entry Read_Time (Now : out Time);
  entry Set_Time (New_Time : Time);
end Time_Server;
```

Entries may be defined as private; this means that they can only be called by tasks local to the task's body. For example, consider the following Telephone_Operator task type. It provides three services: an enquiry entry requiring the name and address of a subscriber, an alternative enquiry entry requiring the name and postal code of a subscriber and a fault-reporting service requiring the number of the faulty line. The task also has a private entry for use by its internal tasks:

```
task type Telephone_Operator is
  entry Directory_Enquiry(Person : in  Name; Addr : in Address;
                          Num : out Number);

  entry Directory_Enquiry(Person : in  Name;
        Zip : in Postal_Code; Num : out Number);

  entry Report_Fault(Num : Number);
private
  entry Allocate_Repair_Worker(Num : out Number);
end Telephone_Operator;
```

Ada also provides a facility whereby an array of entries can, in effect, be defined – these are known as **entry families**. For instance, consider a multiplexor which has seven input channels. Rather than representing each of these as a separate entry, Ada allows them to be defined as a family[1].

```
type Channel_Number is new Integer range 1 .. 7;
task Multiplexor is
   entry Channels(Channel_Number)(Data: Input_Data);
end Multiplexor;
```

The above defines seven entries, all with the same parameter specification.

---

[1] Ada also allows families of protected entries and protected private entries.

To call a task (that is, send it a message) simply involves naming the receiver task and its entry (naming is direct); for example,

```
Display.Call(Char,10,20); -- where char is a character

Multiplexor.Channels(3)(D);
-- where 3 indicates the index into the entry family
-- and D is of type Input_Data

Time_Server.Read_Time(T);   -- where T is of type Time
```

Note that, in the last example, the only data being transferred is passing in the opposite direction to the message itself (via an 'out' parameter). This can lead to terminology confusion, and hence the term 'message passing' is not usually applied to Ada. The phrase 'extended rendezvous' is less ambiguous.

Ada's protected entries and task entries are identical from the calling task's perspective.

If an entry call is made on a task that is no longer active then the exception Tasking_Error is raised at the point of the call. This allows alternative action to be taken if, unexpectedly, a task has terminated prematurely, as illustrated below.

```
begin
  Display.Call(C,I,J);
exception
  when Tasking_Error => -- log error and continue
end;
```

Note that this is not equivalent to checking beforehand that the task is available:

```
if Display'Terminated then
  -- log error and continue
else
  Display.Call(C,I,J);
end if;
```

An interleaving could cause a task to terminate after the attribute has been evaluated but before the call is handled.

To receive a message involves accepting a call to the appropriate entry:

```
accept Call(C: Character; I,J : Integer) do
  Local_Array(I,J) : = C;
end Call;

accept Read_Time(Now : out Time) do
  Now := Clock;
end Read_Time;

accept Channels(3)(Data: Input_Data) do
  -- store data from the 3rd channel in the family
end Channels;
```

An `accept` statement must be in a task body (not a called procedure) but can be placed where any other statement is valid. It can even be placed within another accept statement (although not for the same entry). All entries (and family members) should have accepts associated with them. These accepts name the entry concerned but not the task from which a call is sought. Naming is thus asymmetric.

To give a simple example of two tasks interacting, consider, as with the occam2 example, two tasks that loop round and pass data between them. In the Ada code, the tasks will swap data:

```ada
procedure Test is

  Number_Of_Exchanges : constant Integer := 1000;

  task T1 is
    entry Exchange (I : Integer; J : out Integer);
  end T1;

  task T2;

  task body T1 is
    A,B : Integer;
  begin
    for K in 1 .. Number_Of_Exchanges loop
      -- produce A
      accept Exchange (I : Integer; J : out Integer) do
        J := A;
        B := I;
      end Exchange;
      -- consume B
    end loop;
  end T1;

  task body T2 is
    C,D : Integer;
  begin
    for K in 1 .. Number_Of_Exchanges loop
      -- produce C
      T1.Exchange (C,D);
      -- consume D
    end loop;
  end T2;

begin
  null;
end Test;
```

Although the relationship between the two tasks (T1 and T2) is essentially symmetric, the asymmetric naming in Ada requires them to have quite different forms. This should be compared with the occam2 code, which retains the symmetry.

9.3.3 Exception handling and the rendezvous

As any valid Ada code can be executed during a rendezvous, there is the possibility that an exception could be raised within the `accept` statement itself. If this occurs then either:

- there is a valid exception handler within the accept (either as part of the accept statement, or within a blocked nested within the accept statement); in which case the accept will terminate normally, or

- the raised exception is not handled within the accept and the accept is immediately terminated.

In this latter case, the named exception will be re-raised in both the called and calling tasks. The called task will have the exception raised immediately after the accept; the calling task will have it raised after the entry call. Scope problems may, however, cause the exception to be anonymous in the calling task.

To illustrate the interaction between the rendezvous and the exception models, consider a task that acts as a file server. One of its entries will allow a client task to open a file:

```
task File_Handler is
  entry Open(F : File_Type);
  ...
end File_Handler;

task body File_Handler is
  ...
begin
  loop
    begin
      ...
      accept Open(F : File_Type) do
        loop
          begin
            Device_Open(F);
            return;
          exception
            when Device_Off_Line =>
              Boot_Device;
          end;
        end loop;
      end Open;
      ...
    exception
      when File_Does_Not_Exist =>
        null;
    end;
  end loop;
end File_Handler;
```

In this code, the `File_Handler` calls a device driver to open the specified file. This request can either succeed or lead to one of two exceptions being raised: `Device_Off_Line` or `File_Does_Not_Exist`. The first exception is handled within the accept; an attempt is made to boot the device and then the open request is repeated. As the exception handler is within the accept, the client is unaware of this activity (although if the device refuses to boot, it will be indefinitely suspended). The second exception is due to a faulty request by the user task. It is therefore not handled within the accept and will propagate out to the calling task which will need to protect itself against the exception:

```
begin
   File_Handler.Open(New_File);
exception
   when File_Does_Not_Exist =>
      File_Handler.Create(New_File);
      File_Handler.Open(New_File);
end;
```

Note that the server task also protects itself against this exception by having a block defined within the outer loop construct.

9.4 Selective waiting

In all the forms of message passing that have so far been discussed, the receiver of a message must wait until the specified process, or channel, delivers the communication. This is, in general, too restrictive. A receiver process may actually wish to wait for any one of a number of processes to call it. Server processes receive request messages from a number of clients, the order in which the clients call being unknown to the servers. To facilitate this common program structure, receiver processes are allowed to wait selectively for a number of possible messages. But to understand selective waiting fully, Dijkstra's guarded commands (Dijkstra, 1975) must be explained first.

A guarded command is one which is executed only if its guard evaluates to TRUE. For example:

```
x < y -> m := x
```

this means that if x is less than y then assign the value of x to m. A guarded command is not a statement in itself, but is a component of a **guarded command set**, of which there are a number. Here, the concern is only with the choice, or alternative, construct:

```
if x <= y -> m := x
☐ x >= y -> m:= y
fi
```

The ☐ signifies choice. In the above example, the program's execution will either assign x to m or y to m. If both alternatives are possible, that is, both guards evaluate true (x =

y in this example), then an *arbitrary* choice is made. The programmer cannot determine which path will be taken, the construct is **non-deterministic**. A well-constructed program will be valid for all possible choices. When x = y, in this example, both paths will have the same effect.

It is important to note that this non-deterministic structure is quite distinct from the deterministic form that could have been constructed using the normal if statement:

```
if x <= y then m := x;
elsif x >= y then m := y;
end if;
```

Here, the values x = y would ensure that m was assigned the value x.

The general choice construct can have any number of guarded components. If more than one guard evaluates to TRUE, the choice is arbitrary. But if no guard evaluates to TRUE then this is viewed to be an error condition and the statement, along with the process that executed it, is aborted.

The guarded command is a general program structure. If, however, the command being guarded is a message operator (normally the receive operator, although in some languages also the send), then the statement is known as **selective waiting**. This was first introduced in CSP (Hoare, 1978) and is available in both Ada and occam2.

9.4.1   The occam2 ALT

Consider a process that reads integers down three channels (ch1, ch2 and ch3) and then outputs whatever integers it receives down a further channel (chout). If the integers arrived in sequence down the three channels then a simple loop construct would suffice.

```
WHILE TRUE
  SEQ
    ch1    ?  I          -- for some local integer I
    chout  !  I
    ch2    ?  I
    chout  !  I
    ch3    ?  I
    chout  !  I
```

However, if the order of arrival is unknown then each time the process loops a choice must be made between the three alternatives:

```
WHILE TRUE
  ALT
    ch1    ?  I
      chout    !  I
    ch2    ?  I
      chout    !  I
    ch3    ?  I
      chout    !  I
```

If there is an integer on ch1, ch2 or ch3, it will be read and the specified action taken, which in this case is always to output the newly acquired integer down the output channel chout. In a situation where more than one of the input channels is ready for communication, an arbitrary choice is made as to which one is read. Before considering the behaviour of the ALT statement when none of the channels are ready, the general structure of an ALT statement will be outlined. It consists of a collection of guarded processes:

```
ALT
   G1
      P1
   G2
      P2
   G3
      P3
      :
   Gn
      Pn
```

The processes themselves are not restricted – they are any occam2 process. The guards (which are also processes) can have one of three forms (a fourth possibility involving the specification of a time delay is considered in Chapter 12).

```
<boolean_expression> & channel_input_operation
```

```
channel_input_operation
```

```
<boolean_expression> & SKIP
```

The most general form is therefore a boolean expression and a channel read, for example:

```
NOT BufferFull & ch ? BUFFER[TOP]
```

If the boolean expression is simply TRUE then it can be omitted altogether (as in the earlier example). The SKIP form of guard is used to specify some alternative action to be taken when other alternatives are precluded; for example:

```
ALT
   NOT BufferFull & ch ?  BUFFER[TOP]
      SEQ
         TOP := ...
   BufferFull & SKIP
      SEQ
         -- swap buffers
```

On execution of the ALT statement, the boolean expressions are evaluated. If none evaluate to TRUE (and there are no default TRUE alternatives) then the ALT process cannot proceed and it becomes equivalent to the STOP (error) process. Assuming a correct execution of the ALT, the channels are examined to see if there are processes waiting to write to them. One of the following possibilities could then ensue:

(1) There is only one ready alternative, that is one boolean expression evaluates to true (with a process waiting to write or a SKIP guard) – this alternative is chosen, the rendezvous takes place (if it is not a SKIP) and the associated subprocess is executed.

(2) There is more than one ready alternative – one is chosen arbitrarily, this could be the SKIP alternative if present and ready.

(3) There are no ready alternatives – the ALT is suspended until some other process writes to one of the open channels of the ALT.

The ALT will, therefore, become a STOP process if all the boolean expressions evaluate to FALSE, but will merely be suspended if there are no outstanding calls. Because of the non-shared variable model of occam2, it is not possible for any other process to change the value of any component of the boolean expression.

The ALT when combined with the SEQ, IF, WHILE, CASE and PAR furnishes the complete set of occam2 program constructs. A replicator can be attached to an ALT in the same way that it has been used with other constructs. For example, consider a concentrator process that can read from 20 processes (rather than three as before); however, rather than use 20 distinct channels, the server process uses an array of channels as follows:

```
WHILE TRUE
  ALT j = 0 FOR 20
    ch[j]  ?  I
      chout  !  I
```

Finally, it should be noted that occam2 provides a variant of the ALT construct which is not arbitrary in its selection of ready alternatives. If the programmer wishes to give preference to a particular channel then it should be placed as the first component of a PRI ALT. The semantics of PRI ALT dictate that the textually first ready alternative is chosen. The following are examples of PRI ALT statements.

```
PRI ALT
  VeryImportantChannel ? message
    -- action
  ImportantChannel ? message
    -- action
  LessImportantChannel ? message
    -- action

WHILE TRUE
  PRI ALT j = 0 FOR 20   -- ch[0] is given highest preference
    ch[j]  ?  I
      chout  !  I
```

An example of the use of PRI ALT is given in Section 11.3.1.

The bounded buffer

Occam2 provides no shared variable communication primitives and, therefore, resource controllers such as buffers have to be implemented as server processes (see Section 7.2.1). To implement a single reader and single writer buffer, requires the use of two channels that link the buffer process to the client processes (to cater for more readers and writers would require arrays of channels):

```
CHAN OF Data Take, Append:
```

Unfortunately, the natural form for this buffer would be:

```
VAL INT Size IS 32:
INT Top, Base, NumberInBuffer:
[Size]Data Buffer:
SEQ
  NumberInBuffer := 0
  Top := 0
  Base := 0
  WHILE TRUE
    ALT
      NumberInBuffer < Size & Append ? Buffer[Top]
        SEQ
          NumberInBuffer := NumberInBuffer + 1
          Top := (Top + 1) REM Size
      NumberInBuffer > 0 & Take ! Buffer[Base]   -- not legal occam
        SEQ
          NumberInBuffer := NumberInBuffer - 1
          Base := (Base + 1) REM Size
```

Output operations in this context are not allowed in occam2. Only input operations can form part of an ALT guard. The reason for this restriction is implementational efficiency on a distributed system. The essence of the problem is that the provision of symmetric guards could lead to a channel being accessed by an ALT at both ends. The arbitrary decision of one ALT would therefore be dependent on the decision of the other (and vice versa). If the ALTs are on different processors then the agreement on a collective decision would involve the passing of a number of low-level protocol messages.

To circumvent the restriction on guards, occam2 forces the Take operation to be programmed as a double interaction. First the client process must indicate that it wishes to TAKE, and then it must Take; a third channel is thus needed:

```
CHAN OF Data Take, Append, Request:
```

The client must make the following calls

```
SEQ
  Request ! ANY        -- ANY is an arbitrary token
  Take ? D             -- D is of type DATA
```

The buffer process itself has the form:

```
VAL INT size IS 32:
INT Top, Base, NumberInBuffer:
[Size]Data Buffer:
SEQ
  NumberInBuffer := 0
  Top := 0
  Base := 0
  Data ANY:
  WHILE TRUE
    ALT
      NumberInBuffer < Size & Append ? Buffer[Top]
        SEQ
          NumberInBuffer := NumberInBuffer + 1
          Top := (Top + 1) REM Size
      NumberInBuffer > 0 & Request ? ANY
        SEQ
          Take ! Buffer[Base]
          NumberInBuffer := NumberInBuffer - 1
          Base := (Base + 1) REM Size
```

The correct functioning of the buffer is thus dependent on correct usage by the client processes. This dependence is a reflection of poor modularity. Although the Ada select is also asymmetric (that is, you cannot select between accepts and entry calls), the fact that data can pass in the opposite direction to the call removes the difficulty that manifests itself in occam2.

9.4.2   The Ada select statement

Ada's many-to-one message-passing relationship can deal easily with a number of clients by having them all call the same entry. However, where a server must deal with possible calls to two or more different entries, an ALT type structure is again required; in Ada this is called a **select statement**. Consider, for illustration, a server task which offers two services, via entries S1 and S2. The following structure is often sufficient (that is, a loop containing a select statement which offers both services):

```
task Server is
  entry S1(...);
  entry S2(...);
end Server;

task body Server is
  ...
begin
  loop
    -- prepare for service
    select
      accept S1(...) do
        -- code for this service
      end S1;
    or
```

```
      accept S2(...) do
         -- code for this service
      end S2;
    end select;
    -- do any housekeeping
  end loop;
end Server;
```

On each execution of the loop, one of the accept statements will be executed.

As with the first occam2 example, this Ada program does not illustrate the use of boolean expressions in guards. The general form of the Ada select is

```
select
  when <Boolean-Expression> =>
    accept <entry> do
      ..
    end <entry>;
    -- any sequence of statements
  or
    -- similar
  ...
end select;
```

There can be any number of alternatives. Apart from accept alternatives (of which there must be at least one) there are three further forms (which cannot be mixed in the same statement):

(1) a terminate alternative

(2) an else alternative

(3) a delay alternative

The delay alternative is considered, with the occam2 equivalent, in Chapter 12. The else alternative is defined to be executed when (and only when) no other alternative is *immediately* executable. This can only occur when there are no outstanding calls on entries which have boolean expression that evaluate True (or no boolean expressions at all).

The terminate alternative has no equivalent in occam2, but is an important primitive. It has the following properties:

(1) If it is chosen, the task that executed the select is finalized and terminated.

(2) It can only be chosen if there are no longer any tasks that can call the select.

To be more precise, a task will terminate if all tasks that are dependent on the same master have already terminated or are similarly waiting on select statements with terminate alternatives. The effect of this alternative is to allow server tasks to be constructed that need not concern themselves with termination, but will nevertheless terminate when they are no longer needed. The lack of this provision in occam2 leads to complex termination conditions with associated deadlock problems (Burns, 1988).

The execution of the select follows a similar sequence to that of the ALT. First the boolean expressions are evaluated; those that produce a false value, lead to that alternative being closed for that execution of the select. Following this phase, a collection of possible alternatives is derived. If this collection is empty, the exception Program_Error is raised immediately after the select. For normal execution, one alternative is chosen. The choice is arbitrary if there is more than one alternative with an outstanding call. If there are no outstanding calls on eligible alternatives, either:

- the else alternative is executed, if there is one,

- the task is suspended waiting for a call to be made (or a timeout to expire – see Chapter 12),

- the task is terminated if there is a terminate option *and* there are no other tasks that could call it (as described above).

Note that shared variables can be contained in guards but this is not recommended as changes to them will not be noticed until the guard is re-evaluated. Also, the Real-Time Systems Annex allows priority to be given to the arms of the select according to the textual ordering. Thus, this gives the same functionality as occam2's PRI ALT. As a final example of the Ada select statement, consider the body of the Telephone_Operator task given in Section 9.3.2.

```
task body Telephone_Operator is
  Workers : constant Integer := 10;
  Failed : Number;
  task type Repair_Worker;
  Work_Force : array (1 .. Workers) of Repair_Worker;
  task body Repair_Worker is ...;
    ...
begin
  loop
    -- prepare to accept next request
    select
      accept Directory_Enquiry(Person : in  Name;
             Addr : in Address; Num : out Number) do
        -- look up telephone number and
        -- assign the value to Num
      end Directory_Enquiry;
    or
      accept Directory_Enquiry(Person : in  Name;
             Zip : in Postal_Code; Num : out Number) do
        -- look up telephone number and
        -- assign the value to Num
      end Directory_Enquiry;
    or
      accept Report_Fault(Num : Number) do
        Failed := Num;
      end Report_Fault;
      -- store failed number
    or
```

```
      when Unallocated_Faults =>
        accept Allocate_Repair_Worker(Num : out Number) do
          -- get next failed number
          Num := ...;
        end Allocate_Repair_Worker;
        -- update record of failed unallocated numbers
    or
      terminate;
    end select;
    ...
  end loop;
end Telephone_Operator;
```

A local task type `Repair_Worker` is responsible for repairing line faults when
they are logged. They communicate with the `Telephone_Operator` via the
`Allocate_Repair_Worker` private entry. To ensure that the worker tasks do not
continually communicate with the `Telephone_Operator`, the accepted statement is
guarded. Note also, the `Telephone_Operator` carries out as much work as possible
outside the rendezvous to enable the client tasks to continue as quickly as possible.

   An Ada select statement can also be used by a client task (see Section 12.4.2) and
to handle asynchronous events (see Section 10.8).

9.4.3 Non-determinism, selective waiting and synchronization primitives

In the above discussion, it was noted that when there is more than one ready alternative
in a selective waiting construct, the choice between them is arbitrary. The rationale
behind making the select arbitrary is that concurrent languages usually make few assumptions about the order in which processes are executed. The scheduler is assumed
to schedule processes non-deterministically. (Although individual schedulers will have
deterministic behaviour.)

   To illustrate this relationship, consider a process P that will execute a selective
wait construct upon which processes S and T could call. If the scheduler's behaviour
is assumed to be non-deterministic then there are a number of possible interleavings or
'histories' for this program:

(1) P runs first; it is blocked on the select statement. S (or T) then runs and ren-
    dezvous with P.

(2) S (or T) runs first and blocks on the call to P; P now runs and executes the select
    statement with the result that a rendezvous takes place with S (or T).

(3) S (or T) runs first and blocks on the call to P; T (or S) now runs and is also
    blocked on P. Finally P runs and executes the select statement on which T and S
    are waiting.

These three possible and legal interleavings lead to P having either none, one or two
calls outstanding on the selective wait. The select is defined to be arbitrary precisely

because the scheduler is assumed to be non-deterministic. If P, S and T can execute in any order then, in case (3), P should be able to choose to rendezvous with S or T – it will not affect the program's correctness.

A similar argument applies to any queue that a synchronization primitive defines. Non-deterministic scheduling implies that all such queues should release processes in a non-deterministic order. Although semaphore queues are often defined in this way, entry queues and monitor queues are usually specified to be FIFO. The rationale here is that FIFO queues prohibit starvation. This argument is, however, spurious; if the scheduler is non-deterministic then starvation can occur (a process may never be given a processor). It is inappropriate for the synchronization primitive to attempt to prevent starvation. It is arguable that entry queues should also be non-deterministic.

The scheduling of processes which have priorities assigned is considered in detail in Chapter 13.

9.5 POSIX messages

POSIX supports asynchronous, indirect message passing through the notion of message queues. A message queue can have many readers and many writers. Priority may be associated with each message (see Section 13.14.2).

Message queues are really intended for communication between (potentially distributed) processes. However, there is nothing to stop their use between threads in the same process, although it is more efficient to use shared memory and mutexes for this purpose (see Section 8.6.3).

All message queues have attributes which indicate the maximum size of the queue, the maximum size of each message in the queue, the number of messages currently queued and so on. An attribute object is used to set the queue attributes when it is created. The attributes of a queue are manipulated by the mq_getattr and mq_setattr functions (these functions manipulate the attributes themselves, not an attribute object; this is different from the thread or mutex attributes).

Message queues are given a name when they are created (similar to a file name but not necessarily represented in the file system). To gain access to the queue, simply requires the user process to mq_open the associated name. As with all Unix-like file systems, mq_open is used to both create and open an already existing queue. (There are also corresponding mq_close and mq_unlink routines.)

Sending and receiving messages is done via the mq_send and mq_receive routines. The data is read/written from/to a character buffer. If the buffer is full or empty, the sending/receiving process is blocked unless the attribute O_NONBLOCK has been set for the queue (in which case an error return is given). If senders and receivers are waiting when a message queue becomes unblocked, it is not specified which one is woken up unless the priority scheduling option is specified. If the process is multithreaded, each thread is considered to be a potential sender/receiver in its own right.

A process can also indicate that a signal (see Section 10.6) should be sent to it when an empty queue receives a message and there are no waiting receivers. In this way, a process can continue executing while waiting for messages to arrive on one or

Program 9.1   A C interface to POSIX message queues.

```c
typedef ... mqd_t;
typedef ... mode_t;
typedef ... size_t;
typedef ... ssize_t;

struct mq_attr {
  ...
  long mq_flags;
  long mq_maxmsg;
  long mq_msgsize;
  long mq_curmsg;
  ...
};

#define O_CREAT ...
#define O_EXCL ...
#define O_RDONLY ...

int mq_getattr(mqd_t mq, struct mq_attr *attrbuf);
  /* get the current attributes associated with mq */
int mq_setattr(mqd_t mq, const struct mq_attr *new_attrs,
               struct mq_attr *old_attrs);
  /* set the current attributes associated with mq */

mqd_t mq_open(const char *mq_name, int oflags, mode_t mode,
              struct mq_attr *mq_attr);
  /* open/create the named message queue */

int mq_close(mqd_t mq);
  /* close the message queue */

int mq_unlink(const char *mq_name);

ssize_t mq_receive(mqd_t mq, char *msq_buffer,
                   size_t buflen, unsigned int *msgprio);
  /* get the next message in the queue and store it in the */
  /* area pointed at by msq_buffer; */
  /* the actual size of the message is returned */
ssize_t mq_receive(mqd_t mq, char *msq_buffer,
                   size_t buflen, unsigned int *msgprio,
                   const struct timespec *abs_timeout);
  /* as for mq_receive but with a timeout */
  /* returns ETIMEDOUT if the timeout expires */

int mq_send(mqd_t mq, const char *msq,
            size_t msglen, unsigned int msgprio);
  /* send the message pointed at by msq */

int mq_timedsend(mqd_t mq, const char *msq,
                 size_t msglen, unsigned int msgprio,
                 const struct timespec *abs_timeout);
```

```
/* send the message pointed at by msq  with a timeout*/
/* returns ETIMEDOUT if the timeout expires */


int mq_notify(mqd_t mq, const struct sigevent *notification);
  /* request that a signal be sent to the calling process */
  /* if a message arrives on an empty mq and there are no */
  /* waiting receivers */

/* All the above integer functions return 0 if successful, else -1. */
/* When an error condition is returned by any of the above functions, */
/* a shared variable errno contains the reason for the error */
```

---

more message queues. It is also possible for a process to wait for a signal to arrive. This allows the equivalent of selective waiting to be implemented.

Program 9.1 summarizes a typical C interface to the POSIX message-passing facility.

To illustrate the use of message queues, the simple robot arm discussed in Chapters 7 and 8 is sketched with a parent process forking three controllers. This time, the parent communicates with the controllers to pass them the new position of the arm. First the controller code is given. Here, MQ_OPEN and FORK are assumed to be functions which test the error return from the mq_open and fork system calls and only return if the calls are successful.

```
typedef enum {xplane, yplane, zplane} dimension;

void move_arm(dimension D, int P);

#define DEFAULT_NBYTES 4
/* assume that the coordinate can be represented as 4 characters */
int nbytes = DEFAULT_NBYTES;


#define MQ_XPLANE  "/mq_xplane" /* message queue name */
#define MQ_YPLANE  "/mq_yplane" /* message queue name */
#define MQ_ZPLANE  "/mq_zplane" /* message queue name */
#define MODE ...                /* mode information for mq_open */
/* names of message queues */

void controller(dimension dim)
{
  int position, setting;
  mqd_t my_queue;
  struct mq_attr ma;
  char buf[DEFAULT_NBYTES];
  ssize_t len;

  position = 0;
  switch(dim) { /* open appropriate message queue */
    case xplane:
      my_queue = MQ_OPEN(MQ_XPLANE, O_RDONLY, MODE, &ma);
```

```
      break;
    case yplane:
      my_queue = MQ_OPEN(MQ_YPLANE, O_RDONLY, MODE, &ma);
      break;
    case zplane:
      my_queue = MQ_OPEN(MQ_ZPLANE, O_RDONLY, MODE, &ma);
      break;
    default:
      return;
    };

  while (1) {
    /* read message */
    len = MQ_RECEIVE(my_queue, &buf[0], nbytes, NULL);
    setting = *((int *) (&buf[0]));
    position = position + setting;
    move_arm(dim, position);
  };
}
```

Now the main program which creates the controller processes and passes the appropriate coordinates to them can be given:

```
int main(int argc, char **argv) {
  mqd_t mq_xplane, mq_yplane, mq_zplane;
    /* one queue for each process */
  struct mq_attr ma; /* queue attributes */
  int xpid, ypid, zpid;
  char buf[DEFAULT_NBYTES];

    /* set the required message queue attributes */
    ma.mq_flags = 0;    /* No special behaviour */
    ma.mq_maxmsg = 1;
    ma.mq_msgsize = nbytes;

    /* calls to set the actual attributes for the */
    /* three message queues */

    mq_xplane = MQ_OPEN(MQ_XPLANE, O_CREAT|O_EXCL, MODE, &ma);
    mq_yplane = MQ_OPEN(MQ_YPLANE, O_CREAT|O_EXCL, MODE, &ma);
    mq_zplane = MQ_OPEN(MQ_ZPLANE, O_CREAT|O_EXCL, MODE, &ma);

    /* Duplicate the process to get the three controllers */
    switch (xpid = FORK()) {
        case 0:      /* child */
              controller(xplane);
              exit(0);
        default:     /* parent */
            switch (ypid = FORK()) {
              case 0:      /* child */
                controller(yplane);
                exit(0);
              default:     /* parent */
                switch (zpid = FORK()) {
```

```
              case 0:        /* child */
                controller(yplane);
                exit(0);
              default:       /* parent */
                break;
          }
      }
  }


  while (1) {
    /* find new position and set up buffer to transmit each
       coordinate to the controllers, for example */
    MQ_SEND(mq_xplane, &buf[0], nbytes, 0);
  }
}
```

9.6   The CHILL language

In this section, a brief description is given of the concurrency model in CHILL. Other features of CHILL, such as its exception-handling model, have already been discussed.

The development of CHILL follows a similar path to that of Ada. Its intended application domain is, however, more restricted – telecommunications switching systems. Notwithstanding this restriction, such systems have all the characteristics of general real-time applications: they are large and complex, have specified time constraints and have high reliability requirements. In the early 1970s, the CCITT (Comité Consultatif International Télégraphique et Téléphonique) recognized the need for a single high-level language that would make telecommunication systems more independent of the hardware manufacturers. By 1973, it was decided that no existing language met their requirements and a group was set up to bring forward a preliminary language proposal. This language was used on several trial implementations and, after a number of design iterations, a final language proposal was agreed in the autumn of 1979. The name CHILL is derived from the international telecommunications committee (Ccitt HIgh Level Language).

CHILL's concurrency model is of interest here because of its pragmatic design. Processes can only be declared at the outermost level and they can be passed parameters when they are started. Consider the simple robotics arm controller given earlier. A process type control has as a parameter the dimension of movement (that is, in the x, y or z plane). The action of the process is to read a new relative position for its plane of action and then cause the robot arm to move:

```
newmode dimension = set(xplane, yplane, zplane);
  /* enumeration type */

control = process(dim dimension);
  dcl position, setting int;   /* declare variables position */
                               /* and setting to be integers */
```

```
  position := 0;
  do for ever;
    new_setting(dim, setting);
    position := position + setting;
    move_arm(dim, position);
  od;
end control;
```

To indicate the execution of three control processes (one for each dimension), the start statement is used:

```
start control(xplane);
start control(yplane);
start control(zplane);
```

This will cause three anonymous processes to commence their executions. If it is desired to identify each instance of a process then unique names can be given as part of the start statement. (A name is a variable of type *instance*.)

```
dcl xinst, yinst, zinst instance;

start control(xplane) set xinst;
start control(yplane) set yinst;
start control(zplane) set zinst;
```

A process instance may terminate itself by executing a *stop* statement.

9.6.1   Communication in CHILL

It is in its communication and synchronization mechanism that CHILL can be described as being pragmatic. Rather than having a single model it supports three distinct approaches:

(1) regions – these provide mutual exclusion to shared variables (that is, they are monitors)

(2) buffers – these allow for asynchronous communication between processes

(3) signals – these are a form of channel and can be compared with the occam mechanism.

The motivation for having three separate structures seems to be a recognition that there is no single model that is universally agreed to be the best:

One communication mechanism may not be able to function optimally in both distributed and common memory architectures (Smedema et al., 1983).

A region explicitly grants access to its procedures; within the region events can be used to delay processes. Events are acted upon by delay and continue. These have similar semantics to the wait and signal operations of Modula-1. The following implements a simple resource controller:

```
resource : region
  grant allocate, deallocate;
  syn max = 10;                     /* declare constant */
  decl used int := 0;
  no_resources event;

  allocate : proc;
    if used < max then
      used := used + 1;
    else
      delay(no_resource);
    fi;
  end allocate;

  deallocate : proc
    used := used - 1;
    continue(no_resource)
  end deallocate;

end resource;
```

Buffers are predefined to have send (put) and receive (get) operators:

```
syn size = 32;
dcl buf buffer(size) int;        /* declare integer buffer */
...

  send buf(I);                   /* I is an int */
...

  receive case
    (buf in J) :                 /* statements */
  esac
```

The receive is placed within a case statement, for, in general, a process may attempt to read from more than one buffer. If all such buffers are empty the process is delayed. It is also possible for a process reading from a buffer to know the name (instance) of the process that placed that data in the buffer. This is particularly important in telecommunication systems where links have to be made between consumer and producer processes.

Signals are defined in terms of the type of data they communicate and the destination process (type):

```
signal channel = (int) to consumer;
```

Here, consumer is a process type. To transmit data (I) via this signal, the send statement is used again:

```
send channel(I) to con;
```

where `con` is a process instance of type `consumer`. The receive operation uses the case statement thereby providing selective waiting (without guards).

It is interesting to consider the naming convention applied to CHILL signals. The send operation names the signal and the process instance; the receive mentions only the signal, but it can find out the identity of the associated process.

9.7   Remote procedure call

This chapter has so far concentrated on how processes can communicate and synchronize their activities. Discussions on the implications of this when processes reside on different machines connected by a network are postponed until Chapter 14. However, for completeness the concept of a **remote procedure call** (RPC) is introduced here as it is a common method of transferring control in a distributed environment.

In a single-processor system, processes execute procedures in order to transfer control from one section of code to another; only when they need to communicate and synchronize with another process do they require interprocess communication. Remote procedure calls extend this idea to enable a single process to execute code which resides on more than one machine. They allow a process currently executing on one processor to execute a procedure on another; whether this should be done transparently to the application programmer is arguable and will be discussed in Chapter 14. The execution of the procedure may involve communication with processes which reside on the remote machine; this is achieved either by shared variable methods (for example, monitors) or by message passing (for example, rendezvous).

It is worth noting that remote invocation message passing can be made to appear syntactically like a procedure call, with the message encoded in the input parameters and the reply encoded in the output parameters (see, for example, Ada entries and accepts). However, this syntactic convenience can be misleading, since the semantics of remote invocation message passing are quite different from those of a procedure call. In particular, remote invocation relies on the active cooperation of the receiver process in executing an explicit receive operation. A procedure call, on the other hand, is not a form of interprocess communication, but a transfer of control to a passive piece of code. When the procedure is local (on the same machine as the caller), its body can be executed by the calling process; in the case of a remote procedure call, the body may have to be executed on behalf of the caller by an anonymous surrogate process on the remote machine. The involvement of another process in this case is a matter of implementation, not of semantics. For a remote procedure call to have the same semantics as a (re-entrant) local one, the implementation must allow an arbitrary number of calls to be handled concurrently. This requires a process/thread to be created for each call, or the existence of a pool of processes/threads large enough to handle the maximum number of concurrent calls. The cost of process creation or maintenance may sometimes dictate that the degree of concurrency be limited.

Summary

Ada and POSIX provide a message-passing facility; they also support alternative communication paradigms. In occam2, however, the sole method by which processes can communicate is message passing.

The semantics of message-based communication are defined by three issues:

- the model of synchronization
- the method of process naming, and
- the message structure.

Variations in the process synchronization model arise from the semantics of the send operation. Three broad classifications exist:

- asynchronous – sender process does not wait
- synchronous – sender process waits for message to be read
- remote invocation – sender process waits for message to be read, acted upon and a reply generated.

Remote invocation can be made to appear syntactically similar to a procedure call. This can cause confusion when remote procedure calls (RPCs) are used in a distributed system. RPCs are, however, an implementation strategy; remote invocation defines the semantics of a particular message-passing model. The two processes involved in this communication may be on the same processor, or they may be distributed; the semantics are the same.

Process naming involves two distinct issues; direct or indirect, and symmetry. Ada uses remote invocation with direct asymmetric naming. Occam2, by comparison, contains a synchronous indirect symmetric scheme. Messages can take the form of any system or user-defined type. POSIX supports an asynchronous symmetrical scheme.

For two processes to communicate in occam2 requires the definition of a channel (of appropriate type protocol) and the use of the two channel operators ? and !. Communication in Ada requires one task to define an entry and then, within its body, accept any incoming call. A rendezvous occurs when one task calls an entry in another and it is accepted. In POSIX, communication is via message queues with send/receive primitives. Occam2 supports a one-to-one communication mechanism, Ada a many-to-one mechanism, and POSIX a many-to-many mechanism.

In order to increase the expressive power of message-based concurrent programming languages, it is necessary to allow a process to choose between alternative communications. The language primitive that supports this facility is known as *selective waiting*. Here, a process can choose between different alternatives; on any particular execution some of these alternatives can be closed off by using a boolean guard. Occam2's construct, which is known as ALT, allows a process to choose between an arbitrary number of guarded *receive* operations. Ada supports a similar language feature (the select statement). It has two extra facilities, however:

(1) A select statement may have an else part which is executed if there are no outstanding calls on open alternatives.

(2) A select statement may have a terminate alternative which will cause the process executing the select to terminate if none of the other tasks that could call it are still executable.

In POSIX, a process or thread can indicate that it is not prepared to block when the message queue is full or empty. A notification mechanism is used to allow the operating system to send a signal when a process can continue. This mechanism can be used to wait for a message on one or more message queues.

An important feature of Ada's extended rendezvous is its interaction with the exception-handling model. If an exception is raised but not handled during a rendezvous then it is propagated to both the calling and called tasks. A calling task must, therefore, protect itself against possibly anonymous exceptions being generated as a result of making a message-passing call.

In order to give a further example of a language design, an overview of CHILL was given. CHILL has an unusually pragmatic design, incorporating:

- initialization data for processes
- process names
- monitors (called regions)
- buffers (allow asynchronous communication)
- signals (a synchronous channel mechanism).

Further reading

Andrews, G. A. (1991) *Concurrent Programming Principles and Practice.* Redwood City, CA: Benjamin/Cummings.

Burns, A. (1988) *Programming in occam2.* Reading, Addison-Wesley.

Burns, A. and Davies, G. (1993) *Concurrent Programming.* Reading: Addison-Wesley.

Burns, A. and Wellings, A. J. (1995) *Concurrency in Ada.* Cambridge: Cambridge University Press.

Hoare, C. A. R. (1985) *Communicating Sequential Processes.* Englewood Cliffs, NJ: Prentice Hall.

Galletly, J. (1990) *Occam2.* London: Pitman.

Silberschatz, A. and Galvin, P. A. (1998) *Operating System Concepts.* New York: John Wiley & Sons.

Exercises

9.1 Given that Ada supports protected objects, should the Ada rendezvous facilities be removed from the language?

9.2 If an Ada task has two entry points, is it possible for it to accept the entry of the calling task which has been waiting for the longest period of time?

9.3 Show how to implement a binary semaphore using an Ada task and a rendezvous. What happens if a task issuing a `Wait` is aborted before it can issue a `Signal`?

9.4 Discuss the advantages and disadvantages of implementing semaphores with a rendezvous rather than a protected object.

9.5 Show how an Ada task and the rendezvous can be used to implement Hoare's monitors.

9.6 Figure 9.1 represents a process in occam2.

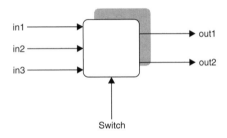

Figure 9.1   A process in occam2.

Integers are read down channels in1, in2, in3. The process takes these integers as they arrive. Initially, all input integers are output to channel out1. If there is any input down channel switch then output is moved to channel out2. Subsequent inputs down switch will change the output channel. Write an occam2 PROC that implements this process.

9.7 To what extent can an Ada rendezvous be considered a Remote Procedure Call? Discuss the following code which purports to implement a particular remote procedure. Consider both the called procedure and the implications for the calling task.

```
task type Rpc_Implementation is
    entry Rpc(Param1:Type1; Param2:Type2);
end Rpc_Implementation;
```

```
task body Rpc_Implementation is
begin
    accept Rpc(Param1:Type1; Param2:Type2) do
        -- body of procedure
    end Rpc;
end Rpc_Implementation;

-- declare an array of 1000 rpc_implementation tasks
Concurrent_Rpc : array(1 .. 1000) of Rpc_Implementation;
```

9.8 Complete Exercise 7.8 using (a) the Ada tasks and the rendezvous and (b) the occam2 channel for process synchronization.

9.9 Using POSIX message queues, redo the answer to Exercise 9.6.

9.10 Consider an Ada system of three cigarette smoker tasks and one agent task. Each smoker continually makes cigarettes and smokes them. To make a cigarette, three ingredients are required: tobacco, paper and matches. One of the smoker tasks has an infinite supply of paper, another has an infinite supply of tobacco and the third has an infinite supply of matches. The agent task has an infinite supply of all three ingredients. Each smoker task must communicate with the agent task to obtain the two ingredients it is missing.
The agent task has the following specification

```
task Agent is
    entry Give_Matches(...);
    entry Give_Paper(...);
    entry Give_Tobacco(...);
    entry Cigarette_Finished;
end Agent;
```

The body of the agent task chooses two ingredients randomly, and then accepts communication on the associated entries to pass the ingredients to the smokers. Once both ingredients have been passed, it waits for communication on the `Cigarette_Finished` entry before repeating the process indefinitely. A smoker, having received the required ingredients, makes and smokes a cigarette, indicates completion by calling the `Cigarette_Finished` entry and then requests new ingredients.
Sketch the specification and body of the three smoker tasks and the body of the agent task. If necessary, add parameters to the entry specifications of the `Agent` task. The solution should be deadlock-free.

9.11 A server task has the following Ada specification:

```
task Server is
    entry Service_A;
    entry Service_B;
    entry Service_C;
end Server;
```

Write the body of the `Server` task so that it performs all of the following operations.

- If client tasks are waiting on all the entries, the task should service the clients in a cyclic order; that is, accept first a `Service_A` entry, and then a `Service_B` entry, and then a `Service_C` entry, and then a `Service_A` entry and so on.
- If not all entries have a client task waiting, the `Server` should service the other entries in a cyclic order. The `Server` tasks should not be blocked if there are clients still waiting for a service.
- If the `Server` task has no waiting clients then it should NOT busy-wait; it should block waiting for a client's request to be made.
- If all the possible clients have terminated, the `Server` should terminate.

Assume that client tasks are not aborted and issue simple entry calls only.

9.12 A server process in occam2 receives synchronization messages on the following channels.

```
CHAN OF INT serviceA, serviceB, serviceC:
```

Write the body of the server process so that it performs all of the following operations.

- If client processes are waiting on all the channels, the server should service the clients in a cyclic order, that is, first a `serviceA` request, and then a `serviceB` request, and then a `serviceC` request, and then a `serviceA` request and so on.
- If not all channels have a client process waiting, the server should service the other channels in a cyclic order. The server should not be blocked if there are clients still waiting for a service.
- If the server process has no waiting clients then it should *not* busy-wait; it should block waiting for a client's request to be made.

9.13 The following Ada package provides a service. During the provision of this service the exceptions A, B, C, and D can be raised.

```
package Server is
  A, B, C, D : exception;
  procedure Service; -- can raise A, B, C or D
end Server;
```

In the following procedure two tasks are created; task One rendezvous with task Two. During the rendezvous task Two calls the `Service` provided by the server package.

```
with Server; use Server;
with Ada.Text_Io; use Ada.Text_Io;
procedure Main is
```

```
task One;

task Two is
  entry Sync;
end Two;

task body One is
begin
  One.Sync;
exception
  when A =>
    Put_Line("A trapped in one ");
    raise;
  when B =>
    Put_Line("B trapped in one");
    raise C;
  when C =>
    Put_Line("C trapped in one");
  when D =>
    Put_Line("D trapped in one");
end;



task body Two is
begin -- block X
  begin -- block Y
    begin -- block Z
      accept Sync do
        begin
          Service;
        exception
          when A =>
            Put_Line("A trapped in sync");
          when B =>
            Put_Line("B trapped in sync");
            raise;
          when C =>
            Put_Line("C trapped in sync");
            raise D;
        end;
      end Sync;
    exception
      when A =>
        Put_Line("A trapped in block Z");
      when B =>
        Put_Line("B trapped in block Z");
        raise C;
      when others =>
        Put_Line("others trapped in Z");
        raise C;
    end; -- block Z
  exception
    when C =>
      Put_Line("C trapped in Y");
```

```
   when others =>
      Put_Line("others trapped in Y");
      raise C;
   end; -- block Y
exception
  when A  =>
   Put_Line("A trapped in X");
  when others =>
    Put_Line("others trapped in X");
end; -- block X and task TWO


begin    -- procedure main
  null;


exception
  when A =>
     Put_Line("A trapped in main");
  when B =>
     Put_Line("B trapped in main");
  when C =>
     Put_Line("C trapped in main");
  when D =>
     Put_Line("D trapped in main");


end Main;
```

The procedure Put_Line is declared in the package Text_Io, and when called it prints its argument on the terminal.

What output would appear if the Service procedure

    (1) raised exception A?
    (2) raised exception B?
    (3) raised exception C?
    (4) raised exception D?

Assume that output does not become intermingled by concurrent calls to Put_Line.

9.14 Consider the following occam2 program fragment.

```
INT Number.Of.Procs is 10:
-- other declarations, if needed

PROC Controller
   -- code for Controller procedure
:

PROC Stop.Go(VAL INT Id)
   -- code for procedure
:

PAR
  PAR i = 0 FOR Number.Of.Procs
    SEQ
```

```
    -- Part A code for user process
    Stop.Go(i);
    -- Part B code for user process
Controller
```

This produces 10 user processes (which all execute their Part A code, then call the Stop.Go procedure, and then execute their Part B code) and a Controller process. The goal of the Stop.Go and Controller procedures is to ensure that *at least* six of the user processes execute their Part A before any execute their Part B.

Show how the Stop.Go and Controller procedures can be implemented. If necessary, introduce further declarations.

Chapter 10
Atomic actions, concurrent processes and reliability

Chapter 5 considered how reliable software could be produced in the presence of a variety of errors. Modular decomposition and atomic actions were identified as two techniques essential for damage confinement and assessment. Also, the notions of forward and backward error recovery were introduced as approaches to dynamic error recovery. It was shown that where processes communicate and synchronize their activities, backward error recovery may lead to the domino effect. In Chapter 6, exception handling was discussed as a mechanism for providing both forward and backward error recovery in sequential processes. Chapters 7, 8 and 9 then considered the facilities provided by operating systems and real-time languages for concurrent programming. This chapter brings together exception handling and concurrency in order to show how processes can interact reliably in the presence of other processes and in the presence of faults. The notion of an atomic action is explored in more detail and the concepts of asynchronous events and asynchronous transfers of control are introduced.

Cooperating and competing processes

In Chapter 7, the interaction of processes was described in terms of three types of behaviour:

- independence

318   ATOMIC ACTIONS, CONCURRENT PROCESSES AND RELIABILITY

- cooperation
- competition.

Independent processes do not communicate or synchronize with each other. Consequently, if an error occurs within one process, then recovery procedures can be initiated by that process in isolation from the rest of the system. Recovery blocks and exception handling can be used as described in Chapters 5 and 6.

Cooperating processes, by comparison, regularly communicate and synchronize their activities in order to perform some common operation. If any error condition occurs, it is necessary for all processes involved to perform error recovery. The programming of such error recovery is the topic of this chapter.

Competing processes communicate and synchronize in order to obtain resources; they are, however, essentially, independent. An error in one should have no effect on the others. Unfortunately, this is not always the case, particularly if the error occurred while a process was in the act of being allocated a resource. Reliable resource allocation is considered in Chapter 11.

Where cooperating processes communicate and synchronize through shared resources, recovery may involve the resource itself. This aspect of resource allocation will also be considered in Chapter 11.

10.1   Atomic actions

One of the main motivations for introducing concurrent processes into a language is that they enable parallelism in the real world to be reflected in application programs. This enables such programs to be expressed in a more natural way and leads to the production of more reliable and maintainable systems. Disappointingly, however, concurrent processes create many new problems which did not exist in the purely sequential program. Consequently, the last few chapters have been dedicated to discussing some of the solutions to these problems: in particular, communication and synchronization between processes using shared variables (correctly) and message passing. This was undertaken in a fairly isolated manner and no consideration has yet been given to the way in which groups of concurrent processes should be structured in order to coordinate their activities.

The interaction between two processes has, so far, been expressed in terms of a single communication. In reality, this is not always the case. For example, withdrawal from a bank account may involve a ledger process and a payment process in a sequence of communications to authenticate the drawer, check the balance and pay the money. Furthermore, it may be necessary for more than two processes to interact in this way to perform the required action. In all such situations, it is imperative that the processes involved see a consistent system state. With concurrent processes, it is all too easy for groups of processes to interfere with one other.

What is required is for each group of processes to execute their joint activity as an **indivisible** or **atomic action**. Of course, a single process may also want to protect itself from the interference of other processes (for example, during resource allocation).

It follows that an atomic action may involve one or more processes. Atomic actions have also been called *multiparty* interactions (Evangelist et al., 1989; Yuh-Jzer and Smolka, 1996).

There are several almost equivalent ways of expressing the properties of an atomic action (Lomet, 1977; Randell et al., 1978).

(1) An action is atomic if the processes performing it are not aware of the existence of any other active process, and no other active process is aware of the activity of the processes during the time the processes are performing the action.

(2) An action is atomic if the processes performing it do not communicate with other processes while the action is being performed.

(3) An action is atomic if the processes performing it can detect no state change except those performed by themselves and if they do not reveal their state changes until the action is complete.

(4) Actions are atomic if they can be considered, so far as other processes are concerned, to be indivisible and instantaneous, such that the effects on the system are as if they were interleaved as opposed to concurrent.

These are not quite all equivalent. For example, consider the second expression: an action is atomic if the processes performing it communicate only among themselves and not with other processes in the system. Unlike the other three, this does not really define the true nature of an atomic action. While it will guarantee that the action is indivisible, it is too strong a constraint on the processes. Interactions between an atomic action and the rest of the system can be allowed as long as they have no impact on the activity of the atomic action and do not provide the rest of the system with any information concerning the progress of the action (Anderson and Lee, 1990). In general, in order to allow such interactions requires detailed knowledge of the atomic action's function and its interface to the rest of the system. As this cannot be supported by a general language implementation, it is tempting, following Anderson and Lee (1990), to adopt the more restrictive (second) definition. This can only be done, however, if the resources necessary to complete an atomic action are acquired by the underlying implementation, not by instructions given in the program. If resources are to be acquired and released when the programmer desires, processes within atomic actions will have to communicate with general-purpose resource managers.

Although an atomic action is viewed as being indivisible, it can have an internal structure. To allow modular decomposition of atomic actions, the notion of a **nested atomic action** is introduced. The processes involved in a nested action must be a subset of those involved in the outer level of the action. If this were not the case, a nested action could smuggle information concerning the outer level action to an external process. The outer level action would then no longer be indivisible.

10.1.1   Two-phase atomic actions

Ideally, all processes involved in an atomic action should obtain the resources they require (for the duration of the action) prior to its commencement. These resources could then be released after the atomic action had terminated. If these rules were followed, there would be no need for an atomic action to interact with any external entity and the stricter definition of atomic action could be adopted.

Unfortunately, this ideal can lead to poor resource utilization, and hence a more pragmatic approach is needed. Firstly, it is necessary to allow an atomic action to start without its full complement of resources. At some point, a process within the action will request a resource allocation; the atomic action must then communicate with the resource manager. This manager may be a server process. If a strict definition of atomic action is adhered to, this server would have to form part of the atomic action, with the effect of serializing all actions involving the server. Clearly, this is undesirable, and hence an atomic action is allowed to communicate externally with resource servers.

Within this context, a resource server is defined to be a custodian of non-sharable system utilities. It protects these utilities against inappropriate access, but does not, itself, perform any actions upon them.

A further improvement in resource allocation can be made if a process is allowed to release a resource prior to completion of the associated atomic action. In order for this premature release to make sense, the state of the resource must be identical to that which would appertain if the resource was retained until completion of the atomic action. Its early release will, however, enhance the concurrency of the whole system.

If resources are to be obtained late and released early it could be possible for an external state change to be affected by a released resource and observed by the acquisition of a new resource. This would break the definition of atomic action. It follows that the only safe policy for resource usage is one that has two distinct phases. In the first 'growing' phase, resources can be requested (only); in the following 'shrinking' phase, resources can be released (but no new allocations can be made). With such a structure, the integrity of the atomic action is assured. However, it should be noted that if resources are released early then it will be more difficult to provide recovery if the atomic action fails. This is because the resource has been updated and another process may have observed the new state of the resource. Any attempt to invoke recovery in the other process may lead to the domino effect (see Section 5.5.3).

In all the following discussions, atomic actions are assumed to be two-phased; recoverable actions do not release any resources until the action successfully completes.

10.1.2   Atomic transactions

Within the theories of operating systems and databases, the term **atomic transaction** is often used. An atomic transaction has all the properties of an atomic action plus the added feature that its execution is allowed either to succeed or fail. By failure, it is meant that an error has occurred from which the transaction cannot recover; for example, a processor failure. If an atomic action fails then the components of the system, which are being manipulated by the action, may be left in an inconsistent state. With an atomic transaction, this cannot happen because the components are returned to their original state (that is, the state they were *before* the transaction commenced). Atomic transactions are sometimes called **recoverable actions** and, unfortunately, the terms **atomic action** and **atomic transaction** are often interchanged.

The two distinctive properties of atomic transactions are:

- failure atomicity; meaning that the transaction must either complete successfully or (in the case of failure) have no effect;

- synchronization atomicity (or isolation); meaning that the transaction is indivisible in the sense that its partial execution cannot be observed by any concurrently executing transaction.

Although atomic transactions are useful for those applications which involve the manipulation of databases, they are not suitable for programming fault-tolerant systems *per se*. This is because they imply that some form of recovery mechanism will be supplied by the system. Such a mechanism would be fixed, with the programmer having no control over its operation. Although atomic transactions provide a form of backward error recovery, they do not allow recovery procedures to be performed. Notwithstanding these points, atomic transactions do have a role in protecting the integrity of a real-time database system.

Atomic transactions are considered again in Chapter 14 in the context of distributed systems and processor failures.

10.1.3 Requirements for atomic actions

If a real-time programming language is to be capable of supporting atomic actions, it must be possible to express the requirements necessary for their implementation. These requirements are independent of the notion of a process and the form of interprocess communication provided by a language. They are:

- **Well-defined boundaries**

  Each atomic action should have a start, an end and a side boundary. The start boundary is the location in each process involved in the atomic action where the action is deemed to start. The end boundary is the location in each process involved in the atomic action where the action is deemed to end. The side boundary separates those processes involved in the atomic action from those in the rest of the system.

- **Indivisibility (Isolation)**

  An atomic action must not allow the exchange of any information between the processes active inside the action and those outside (resource managers excluded). If two atomic actions do share data then the value of that data after the atomic actions is determined by the strict sequencing of the two actions in some order. There is no implied synchronization at the start of an atomic action. Processes can enter at different times. However, there is an implied synchronization at the

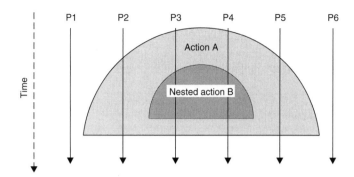

Figure 10.1   Nested atomic actions.

end of an atomic action; processes are not allowed to leave the atomic action until all processes are willing and able to leave.

- **Nesting**
  Atomic actions may be nested as long as they do not overlap with other atomic actions. Consequently, in general, only strict nesting is allowed (two structures are strictly nested if one is completely contained within the other).

- **Concurrency**
  It should be possible to execute different atomic actions concurrently. One way to enforce indivisibility is to run atomic actions sequentially. However, this could seriously impair the performance of the overall system and therefore should be avoided. Nevertheless, the overall effect of running a collection of atomic actions concurrently must be the same as that which would be obtained from serializing their executions.

- As it is the intention that atomic actions should form the basis of damage confinement, they must allow recovery procedures to be programmed.

Figure 10.1 diagrammatically represents the boundaries of a nested atomic action in a system of 6 processes. Action B involves only processes P3 and P4, whereas action A also includes P2 and P5. The other processes (P1 and P6) are outside the boundaries of both atomic actions.

It, perhaps, should be noted at this point, that some definitions of atomic actions require that all processes be synchronized on *both* entry and exit of the action.

10.2   Atomic actions in concurrent languages

Atomic actions provide structuring support for the software of large embedded systems. To get the full benefit of this aid requires the support of the real-time language. Unfortunately, such support is not directly provided by any of the major languages. This section considers the suitability of the various communication and synchronization primitives, discussed in Chapters 8 and 9, for programming atomic actions. Following this, a possible language framework is given, and then this framework is extended to provide forward and backward error recovery.

The problem of resource allocation is postponed until Chapter 11. For now, it is assumed that resources have two modes of use: sharable and non-sharable, with some resources being amenable to both sharable and non-sharable modes. Furthermore, it is assumed that all actions are two-phased, and that the resource manager will ensure that appropriate usage is made of the resources. Also processes within an action synchronize their own access to the resource to avoid any interference.

10.2.1   Semaphores

An atomic action performed by a single process can be implemented by simple mutual exclusion using a binary semaphore.

```
wait(mutual_exclusion_semaphore);
  atomic_action;
signal(mutual_exclusion_semaphore);
```

This 'semaphore' solution is, however, complicated when more than one process is involved in the atomic action. For example, consider a non-sharable resource which needs to be manipulated by two processes. The following code illustrates how processes P1 and P2 can achieve this resource manipulation whilst avoiding any interference from other processes. The semaphores `atomic_action_begin1` and `atomic_action_begin2` allow only two processes into the action. Any other process is blocked. Two further semaphores, `atomic_action_end1` and `atomic_action_end2`, ensure that neither process can leave the action until the other is ready to leave. It should be noted that other semaphores are also needed to control access to the shared resource (and to allocate the resource in the first place).

```
atomic_action_begin1, atomic_action_begin2 : semaphore := 1;
atomic_action_end1, atomic_action_end2 : semaphore := 0;

procedure code_for_first_process is
begin
    -- start atomic action
    wait(atomic_action_begin1);
        -- get resource in non-sharable mode
        -- update resource

        -- signal second process that it is ok
        -- for it to access resource

        -- any final processing

    wait(atomic_action_end2);
```

```
        -- return resource
    signal(atomic_action_end1);
    signal(atomic_action_begin1);
end code_for_first_process;


procedure code_for_second_process is
begin
    -- start atomic action
    wait(atomic_action_begin2);
        -- initial processing

        -- wait for first process to signal
        -- that it is ok to access resource

        -- access resource

    signal(atomic_action_end2);
    wait(atomic_action_end1);
    signal(atomic_action_begin2);
end code_for_second_process;
```

This structure provides the necessary protection, and again illustrates that semaphores can be used to program most synchronization problems; unfortunately, there are several drawbacks with the approach. Firstly, although only two processes have been allowed into the atomic action there is no guarantee that they are the correct two. Secondly, semaphores were criticized in earlier chapters as being error prone; a single access without protection (that is, leaving out the wait-signal structure) would break the atomicity. Finally, to extend the solution to N processes becomes much more complicated and hence even more error prone.

10.2.2 Monitors

By encapsulating the atomic action in a monitor, it is much easier to ensure that partial executions are not observed. The above example implemented as a monitor is shown below. The if statement at the start of each procedure ensures that only one process has access. The condition variables then provide the correct synchronizations within the action.

There are, however, two problems with this solution. It is not possible for the two processes to be active inside the monitor simultaneously. This is often more restrictive than necessary. Furthermore the implementation of nested actions, and resource allocation, will require nested monitor calls. The difficulties associated with nested monitor calls were discussed in Section 8.6.4. Maintaining the monitor lock while executing a nested monitor call could unnecessarily delay processes trying to execute within the outer action.

```
monitor atomic_action
    export code_for_first_process, code_for_second_process;

    first_process_active : boolean := false;
    second_process_active : boolean := false;
    first_process_finished : boolean := false;
    second_process_finished : boolean := false;
    no_first_process, no_second_process : condition;
    atomic_action_ends1, atomic_action_ends2 : condition;

procedure code_for_first_process
begin
    if first_process_active then
      wait(no_first_process);
    first_process_active := true;
        -- get resource in non-sharable mode
        -- update resource

        -- signal second process that it is ok
        -- for it to access resource

        -- any final processing
     if not second_process_finished then
       wait(atomic_action_end2);
     first_process_finished := true;
     -- release resource
     signal(atomic_action_end1);
     first_process_active := false;
     signal(no_first_process);
end;

procedure code_for_second_process
begin
    if second_process_active then
      wait(no_second_process);
    second_process_active := true;
        -- initial processing

        -- wait for first process to signal
        -- that it is ok to access resource

        -- access resource

     signal(atomic_action_end2);
     second_process_finished := true;
     if not first_process_finished then
       wait(atomic_action_end1);
     second_process_active := false;
     signal(no_second_process);
end;
```

Many of the limitations of the above solution can be removed by using the monitor as an 'action controller', and to perform the action themselves outside the monitor. This is the approach adopted in the Ada model given next.

10.2.3   Atomic actions in Ada

With languages whose communication and synchronization primitives are based solely on message passing, all single process actions are atomic if there are no shared variables and the process itself does not communicate during the action. For example, the extended rendezvous in Ada is designed to enable a common form of atomic action to be programmed. This is where a task communicates with another task to request some computation; the called task undertakes this execution and then replies via the out parameters of the rendezvous. The atomic action takes the form of an **accept** statement; it possesses synchronization atomicity as long as;

- it does not update any variable that another task can access, and
- it does not rendezvous with any other task.

An atomic action in Ada for three tasks could be programmed with a nested rendezvous; however, this would not allow any parallelism within the action.

An alternative model is to create an action controller and to program the required synchronization. This is the approach taken below using a protected object for the controller.

```ada
package Action_X is
  procedure Code_For_First_Task(--params);
  procedure Code_For_Second_Task(--params);
  procedure Code_For_Third_Task(--params);
end Action_X;


package body Action_X is
  protected Action_Controller is
    entry First;
    entry Second;
    entry Third;
    entry Finished;
  private
    First_Here : Boolean := False;
    Second_Here : Boolean := False;
    Third_Here : Boolean := False;
    Release : Boolean := False;
  end Action_Controller;

  protected body Action_Controller is
    entry First when not First_Here is
    begin
      First_Here := True;
    end First;

    entry Second when not Second_Here is
    begin
      Second_Here := True;
    end Second;
```

```
  entry Third when not Third_Here is
  begin
    Third_Here := True;
  end Third;

  entry Finished when Release or Finished'Count = 3 is
  begin
    if Finished'Count = 0 then
      Release := False;
      First_Here := False;
      Second_Here := False;
      Third_Here := False;
    else
      Release := True;
    end if;
  end Finished;
end Action_Controller;

procedure Code_For_First_Task(--params) is
begin
  Action_Controller.First;
  -- acquire resources
  -- the action itself, communicates with tasks executing
  -- inside the action via resources
  Action_Controller.Finished;
  -- release resources
end Code_For_First_Task;

-- similar for second and third task
begin
  -- any initialization of local resources
end Action_X;
```

In the above example, the action is synchronized by the `Action_Controller` protected object. This ensures that only three tasks can be active in the action at any one time and that they are synchronized on exit. The boolean `Release` is used to program the required release conditions on `Finished`. The first two calls on `Finished` will be blocked as both parts of the barrier expression are false. When the third call comes, the `Count` attribute will become three; the barrier becomes open and one task will execute the entry body. The `Release` variable ensures that the other two tasks are both released. The last task to exit must ensure that the barrier is closed again.

More details on how to program atomic actions in Ada can be found in Wellings and Burns (1997).

10.2.4 Atomic actions in Java

The previous section has illustrated the basic structure for programming atomic action. The Java approach could follow a similar structure. However, this section takes the opportunity to expand on this approach so that the Java support can easily be extended using inheritance.

First, an interface can be defined for a three-way atomic action:

```
public interface ThreeWayAtomicAction
{
  public void role1();
  public void role2();
  public void role3();
}
```

Using this interface, it is possible to provide several action controllers that implement a variety of models. Applications can then choose the appropriate controller without having to change their code.

The following action controller implements the same semantics as that given previously for semaphores, monitors and Ada. The algorithm is very similar to the Ada version. A synchronized `Controller` class implements the required entry and exit synchronization protocols. The `finished` method is, however, a little more complex than its Ada counterpart. This is due to the semantics of `wait` and `notifyAll`. In particular, it is necessary to count the processes as they leave the action (using `toExit`) in order to know when to reset the internal data structures for the next action. In Ada this was achieved via the `Count` attribute.

```
public class AtomicActionControl implements ThreeWayAtomicAction
{
  protected Controller Control;
  public AtomicActionControl()  // constructor
  {
    Control = new Controller();
  }

  class Controller
  {
    protected boolean firstHere, secondHere, thirdHere;
    protected int allDone;
    protected int toExit;
    protected int numberOfParticipants;

    Controller()
    {
      firstHere = false;
      secondHere = false;
      thirdHere = false;
      allDone = 0;
      numberOfParticipants = 3;
      toExit = numberOfParticipants;
    }

    synchronized void first() throws InterruptedException
    {
      while(firstHere) wait();
      firstHere = true;
    }
```

```
  synchronized void second() throws InterruptedException
  {
    while(secondHere) wait();
    secondHere = true;
  }

  synchronized void third() throws InterruptedException
  {
    while(thirdHere) wait();
    thirdHere = true;
  }

  synchronized void finished() throws InterruptedException
  {
    allDone++;
    if(allDone == numberOfParticipants) {
      notifyAll();
    } else while(allDone != numberOfParticipants) {
        wait();
    }
    toExit--;
    if(toExit == 0) {
      firstHere = false;
      secondHere = false;
      thirdHere = false;
      allDone = 0;
      toExit = numberOfParticipants;
      notifyAll(); // release process waiting for the next action
    }
  }
}

public void role1()
{
  boolean done = false;
  while(!done) {
    try {
      Control.first();
      done = true;
    } catch (InterruptedException e) {
      // ignore
    }
  }

  // .... perform action

  done = false;
  while(!done) {
    try {
      Control.finished();
      done = true;
    } catch (InterruptedException e) {
      // ignore
    }
  }
};
```

```java
public void role2()
{
  // similar to role1
}

public void role3()
{
  // similar to role1
}
}
```

Given the above framework, it is now possible to extend this to produce, say, a four-way action:

```java
public interface FourWayAtomicAction extends ThreeWayAtomicAction {
  public void role4();
}
```

and then

```java
public class NewAtomicActionControl extends AtomicActionControl
            implements FourWayAtomicAction
{
  public NewAtomicActionControl()
  {
    Control = new RevisedController();
  }

  class RevisedController extends Controller
  {
    protected boolean fourthHere;

    RevisedController() {
      super();
      fourthHere = false;
      numberOfParticipants = 4;
      toExit = numberOfParticipants;
    }

    synchronized void fourth() throws InterruptedException
    {
      while(fourthHere) wait();
      fourthHere = true;
    }

    synchronized void finished() throws InterruptedException
    {
      super.finished();
      if(allDone == 0) {
        fourthHere = false;
        notifyAll();
      }
    }
  }
}
```

```
public void role4()
{
  boolean done = false;
  while(!done) {
    try {
      // As Control is of type Controller, it must first
      // be converted to a RevisedController in order
      // to call the fourth method
      ((RevisedController)Control).fourth();
      done = true;
    } catch (InterruptedException e) {
      // ignore
    }
  }

  // .... perform action

  done = false;
  while(!done) {
    try {
      Control.finished();
      done = true;
    } catch (InterruptedException e) {
      // ignore
    }
  }
}
}
```

Note that it has been necessary to override the finished method. Care must be taken here because of Java's automatic run-time dispatching of method calls. All calls to finished in the original code will dispatch to the overridden method.

10.2.5 Atomic actions in occam2

Where a language supports only message passing, the action controller itself is also a process. Each component of the action sends a message to the controller at the beginning and end of its atomic operation. As the occam2 rendezvous is not extended, a double interaction with the controller is required at the end of the action. Also, as occam2 channels have only a single reader and a single writer, it is necessary for the action controller to have an array of channels for each component of the action. Potential processes are allocated a channel from this array.

```
VAL INT max IS 20:   -- maximum number of client processes
                     -- in any of the three groups

[max]CHAN OF INT First, Second, Third:
CHAN OF INT First.Finished, Second.Finished, Third.Finished:
CHAN OF INT First.Continue, Second.Continue, Third.Continue:
```

```
-- all the above channels are used for synchronization only
-- they are defined to be of protocol INT as a default

PROC Action.Controller
  BOOL First.Here, Second.Here, Third.Here:
  INT Any:
  WHILE TRUE
    SEQ
      First.Here := FALSE
      Second.Here := FALSE
      Third.Here := FALSE
      WHILE NOT (First.Here AND Second.Here AND Third.Here)
        ALT
          ALT i = 0 FOR max
            NOT First.Here & First[i]?Any
              First.Here := TRUE
          ALT i = 0 FOR max
            NOT Second.Here & Second[i]?Any
              Second.Here := TRUE
          ALT i = 0 FOR max
            NOT Third.Here & Third[i]?Any
              Third.Here := TRUE
      First.Finished?Any
      Second.Finished?Any
      Third.Finished?Any
      PAR
        First.Continue!Any
        Second.Continue!Any
        Third.Continue!Any
:

PROC action.1(CHAN OF INT first.client)
  INT Any:
  SEQ
    first.client!Any

    -- the action itself

    First.Finished!Any
    First.Continue?Any
:
-- similarly for action.2 and action.3

PAR
    -- all processes in the system including
    Action.Controller
```

10.2.6   A language framework for atomic actions

Although the various language models described above have enabled a simple atomic action to be expressed, they all rely on programmer discipline to ensure that no interactions with external processes occur (apart from with resource allocators). Moreover, they assume that no process within an atomic action is aborted; if the real-time language supports an abort facility then a process could be asynchronously removed from the action leaving the action in an inconsistent state.

In general, none of the mainstream languages or operating systems directly support backward or forward error recovery facilities in the context of atomic actions. (However, Ada, Java and POSIX do provide asynchronous notification mechanisms which can be used to help program recovery – see Sections 10.6, 10.8 and 10.9.) Language mechanisms have been proposed in research-oriented systems. In order to discuss these mechanisms, a simple language framework for atomic actions is introduced. The proposed recovery mechanisms are then discussed in the context of this framework.

To simplify the framework, only static processes will be considered. Also it will be assumed that all the processes taking part in an atomic action are known at compile time. Each process involved in an action declares an action statement which specifies: the action name, the other processes taking part in the action, and the code to be executed by the declaring process on entry to the action. For example a process P_1 which wishes to enter into an atomic action A with processes P_2 and P_3 would declare the following action:

```
action A with (P₂, P₃) do
    -- acquire resources
    -- communicate with P₂ and P₃
    -- release resources
end A;
```

It is assumed that resource allocators are known and that communication inside the action is restricted to the three P processes (together with external calls to the resource allocators). These restrictions are checked at compile time. All other processes declare similar actions, and nested actions are allowed as long as strict nesting is observed. Note that if the processes are not known at compile time, then any communication with a process will be allowed only if both processes are active in the same atomic action.

The imposed synchronization on the action is as follows. Processes entering the action are not blocked. A process is blocked inside the action only if it has to wait for a resource to be allocated, or if it attempts to communicate with another process inside the action and that process is either active in the action, but not in a position to accept the communication, or is not as yet active in the action.

Processes may leave the action only when all processes active in the action wish to leave. This was not the case in the examples given earlier for semaphore, monitors, Ada and occam2. There it was assumed that all processes must enter the action before any could leave. Here it is possible for a subset of the named processes to enter the action and subsequently leave (without recourse to any interactions with the missing processes). This facility is deemed to be essential in a real-time system where deadlines are important. It solves the **deserter** problem where all processes are held in an action because one process has not arrived. This will be considered along with error recovery in the next two sections.

10.3   Atomic actions and backward error recovery

In the last section, the notion of an atomic action was considered. Atomic actions are important because they constrain the flow of information around the system to well-defined boundaries and therefore can provide the basis for both damage confinement and error recovery. In this section, two approaches to backward error recovery between concurrent processes are described. Discussion of backward error recovery in the context of processor failure is deferred until Chapter 14.

In Chapter 5, it was shown that when backward error recovery is applied to groups of communicating processes, it is possible for all the processes to be rolled back to the start of their execution. This was the so-called *domino effect*. The problem occurred because there was no consistent set of recovery points or a recovery line. An atomic action provides that recovery line automatically. If an error occurs inside an atomic action then the processes involved can be rolled back to the start of the action and alternative algorithms executed; the atomic action ensures that processes have not passed any erroneous values through communication with processes outside the action. When atomic actions are used in this way they are called **conversations** (Randell, 1975).

10.3.1   Conversations

With conversations each action statement contains a recovery block. For example:

```
action A with (P₂, P₃) do
   ensure <acceptance test>
   by
      -- primary module
   else by
      -- alternative module
   else by
      -- alternative module
   else error
end A;
```

Other processes involved in the conversation declare their part in the action similarly. The basic semantics of a conversation can be summarized as follows:

- On entry to the conversation, the state of a process is saved. The set of entry points forms the recovery line.

- While inside the conversation, a process is allowed only to communicate with other processes active in the conversation and general resource managers. As conversations are built from atomic actions, this property is inherited.

- In order to leave the conversation, all processes active in the conversation must have passed their acceptance test. If this is the case, then the conversation is finished and all recovery points are discarded.

- *If any process fails its acceptance test, all processes have their state restored to that saved at the start of the conversation and they execute their alternative modules*. It is, therefore, assumed that any error recovery to be performed inside a conversation *must* be performed by *all* processes taking part in the conversation.

- Conversations can be nested, but only strict nesting is allowed.
- If all alternatives in the conversation fail then recovery must be performed at a higher level.

It should be noted that in conversations, as defined by Randell (1975), all processes taking part in the conversation must have entered the conversation before any of the other processes can leave. This differs from the semantics described here. If a process does not enter into a conversation, either because of tardiness or because it has failed, then as long as the other processes active in the conversation do not wish to communicate with it, the conversation can complete successfully. If a process does attempt to communicate with a missing process then either it can block and wait for the process to arrive or it can continue. Adopting this approach has two benefits (Gregory and Knight, 1985):

- It allows conversations to be specified where participation is not compulsory.
- It allows processes with deadlines to leave the conversation, continue and if necessary take some alternative action.

Although conversations allow groups of processes to coordinate their recovery, they have been criticized. One important point is that when a conversation fails, all the processes are restored and all enter their alternative modules. This forces the same processes to communicate again to achieve the desired effect; a process cannot break out of the conversation. This may be not what is required. Gregory and Knight (1985) point out that in practice when one process fails to achieve its goal in a primary module through communication with one group of processes, it may wish to communicate with a completely new group of processes in its secondary module. Furthermore, the acceptance test for this secondary module may be quite different. There is no way to express these requirements using conversations.

10.3.2   Dialogs and colloquys

To overcome some of the problems associated with conversations, Gregory and Knight (1985) have proposed an alternative approach to backward error recovery between concurrent processes. In their scheme, a group of processes, which wish to take part in a backward recoverable atomic action, indicate their desire to do so by executing a **dialog** statement. The dialog statement has three functions: it identifies the atomic action, declares a global acceptance test for the atomic action, and specifies the variables which are to be used in the action. The dialog statement takes the form:

```
DIALOG name_and_acceptance_test SHARES (variables)
```

Note that the dialog's name is the same name as that of the function defining the acceptance test.

Each process which wishes to participate in the action defines a **discuss** statement naming the action. The format of the discuss statement is:

```
DISCUSS dialog_name BY
    -- sequence of statements
TO ARRANGE boolean_expression;
```

The `boolean_expression` is the process's local acceptance test for the action.

The discuss statement is a component of the atomic action and therefore has all the properties defined above. The group of discuss statements which together form the complete action defines the recovery line. The state of every process which enters into the dialog is therefore saved. No process can leave the dialog unless all the active processes have successfully passed their local acceptance tests and the global acceptance test has also been passed. If any of these acceptance tests fail then the dialog is deemed to have failed and the processes are restored to their state on entry to the atomic action.

This ends the operation of the discuss statement. There are no alternative modules which are executed; instead discuss statements can be combined using another statement called a **dialog sequence**. By analogy, if the discuss statement is equivalent to an Ada accept statement then the dialog sequence is equivalent to the Ada select statement. Syntactically it can be represented as below:

```
SELECT
    dialog_1
OR
    dialog_2
OR
    dialog_3
ELSE
    -- sequence of statements
END SELECT;
```

On execution, the process first attempts `dialog_1`; if this succeeds then control is passed to the statement following the select statement. If `dialog_1` fails then `dialog_2` is attempted and so on. It is important to note that `dialog_2` may involve a completely different set of processes to that involved in `dialog_1`. It is the combined execution of associated select statements that is called a **colloquy**.

If all attempted dialogs fail then the statements following the `ELSE` are executed. This gives the programmer a last chance to salvage the situation. If this fails then any surrounding colloquy fails. Note that a process can explicitly fail a dialog or colloquy by executing the fail statement.

To enable the colloquy concept to be used in real-time systems, it is possible to associate a timeout with the select. This is discussed in Section 12.8.2.

10.4   Atomic actions and forward error recovery

It was pointed out in Chapter 5, that although backward error recovery enables recovery from unanticipated errors, it is difficult to undo any operation that may have been performed in the environment in which the embedded system operates. Consequently forward error recovery and exception handling must be considered. In this section, exception handling between the concurrent processes involved in an atomic action is discussed.

With backward error recovery, when an error occurs all processes involved in the atomic action participate in recovery. The same is true with exception handling and forward error recovery. If an exception occurs in one of the processes active in an atomic action then that exception is raised in *all* processes active in the action. The exception is said to be **asynchronous** as it originates from another process. The following is a possible Ada-like syntax for an atomic action supporting exception handling.

```
action A with (P₂, P₃) do
   -- the action
exception
   when exception_a =>
       -- sequence of statements
   when exception_b =>
       -- sequence of statements
   when others =>
     raise atomic_action_failure;
end A;
```

With the termination model of exception handling, if all processes active in the action have a handler and all handle the exception without raising any further exception, then the atomic action completes normally. If a resumption model is used, when the exception has been handled, the processes active in the atomic action resume their execution at the point where the exception was raised.

With either model, if there is no exception handler *in any one of the processes active in the action* or one of the handlers fails then *the atomic action fails* with a standard exception *atomic_action_failure*. This exception is raised in all the involved processes.

There are two issues which must be considered when exception handling is added to atomic actions: resolution of concurrently raised exceptions and exceptions in nested actions (Campbell and Randell, 1986). These are now briefly reviewed.

10.4.1   Resolution of concurrently raised exceptions

It is possibly for more than one process active in an atomic action to raise different exceptions at the same time. As Campbell and Randell (1986) point out, this event is likely if the errors resulting from some fault cannot be uniquely identified by the error detection facility provided by each component of the atomic action. If two exceptions are simultaneously raised in an atomic action, there may be two separate exception handlers in each process. It may be difficult to decide which one should be chosen. Furthermore, the two exceptions in conjunction constitute a third exception which is the exception that indicates that both the other two exceptional conditions have occurred.

In order to resolve concurrently raised exceptions, Campbell and Randell propose the use of an **exception tree**. If several exceptions are raised concurrently then the ex-

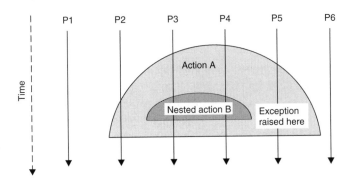

Figure 10.2   An exception in a nested atomic actions.

ception used to identify the handler is that at the root of the smallest subtree that contains all the exceptions (although it is not clear how to combine any parameters associated with this exception). Each atomic action component can declare its own exception tree; the different processes involved in an atomic action may well have different exception trees.

10.4.2   Exceptions and internal atomic actions

Where atomic actions are nested, it is possible for one process active in an action to raise an exception when other processes in the same action are involved in a nested action. Figure 10.2 illustrates the problem.

When the exception is raised, all processes involved must participate in the recovery action. Unfortunately, the internal action, by definition, is indivisible. To raise the exception in that action would potentially compromise that indivisibility. Furthermore, the internal action may have no knowledge of the possible exceptions that can be raised.

Campbell and Randell (1986) have discussed two possible solutions to this problem. The first solution is to hold back the raising of the exception until the internal action has finished. This they reject because:

- In a real-time system, the exception being raised may be associated with the missing of a deadline. To hold back the recovery procedure may seriously place in jeopardy the action's timely response.
- The error condition detected may indicate that the internal action may never terminate because some deadlock condition has arisen.

For these reasons, Campbell and Randell allow internal actions to have a predefined abortion exception. This exception is raised to indicate to the action that an exception has been raised in a surrounding action and that the pre-conditions under which the action was invoked are no longer valid. If such an exception is raised, the internal action should invoke fault-tolerant measures to abort itself. Once the action has been aborted, the containing action can handle the original exception.

If the internal action cannot abort itself then it must signal an atomic action failure exception. This then may be combined with the outstanding exception so as to affect the choice of recovery performed by the surrounding action. If no abortion exception is defined, the surrounding action must wait for the internal action to complete. Alternatively, a default handler could be provided which would raise the atomic action failure exception.

10.5   Asynchronous notification

Although forward and backward error recovery have been discussed separately, in reality they may need to be combined in many real-time systems. Backward error recovery is needed to recover from unanticipated errors, and forward error recovery is needed to undo or ameliorate any interaction with the environment. Indeed, forward error handling can be used to implement a backward error recovery scheme – see Section 10.8.2.

As discussed in Section 10.2, none of the major real-time languages support atomic actions, and it is necessary to use more primitive language facilities to achieve the same effect. The same is true for recoverable actions. One of the main requirements for a recoverable action is to be able to gain the attention of a process involved in an action and notify it that an error has occurred in another process. Most languages and operating systems support some form of asynchronous notification mechanism. As with exceptions, there are two basic models: resumption and termination.

The resumption model of asynchronous notification handling (often called **event handling**) behaves like a software interrupt. A process indicates which events it is willing to handle; when the event is signalled, the process is interrupted (unless it has temporally inhibited the event from being delivered) and an event handler is executed. The handler responds to the asynchronous event and then the process continues with its execution from the point at which it was interrupted. This, of course, sounds very similar to the resumption model of exception handling given in Section 6.2.4. The main difference is that the event is usually *not* signalled by the affected process (or because of an operation the affected process is performing), but is signalled asynchronously. However, many operating systems do not provide a special exception handling facility for synchronous exception handling, but use the asynchronous events mechanisms instead. The POSIX signal facility is an example of an asynchronous event model with resumption.

Note that, with the resumption model, the flow of control of a process is only temporarily changed; after the event has been handled the process is resumed. In a multithreaded process, it is possible to associate a distinct thread with the event and to schedule the thread when the event is signalled. Real-Time Java provides support for this model.

With the termination model of asynchronous notification, each process specifies a domain of execution during which it is prepared to receive an asynchronous notification which will cause the domain to be terminated. This form is often called **asynchronous transfer of control** or ATC. If an ATC request occurs outside this domain, it may be ignored or queued. After the ATC has been handled, control is returned to the interrupted process at a location different to that where the ATC was delivered. This, of course, is very similar to the termination model of exception handling. The Ada and Real-Time Java languages support asynchronous transfer of control mechanisms.

The inclusion of an asynchronous notification mechanism into a language (or operating system) is controversial, as it complicates the language's semantics and increases the complexity of the run-time support system. This section thus first considers the application requirements which justify the inclusion of such a facility. The POSIX and Real-Time Java models of asynchronous event handling are then discussed followed by consideration of the asynchronous transfer of control mechanisms in Ada and Real-Time Java.

10.5.1   The user need for asynchronous notification

The fundamental requirement for an asynchronous notification facility is to enable a process to respond *quickly* to a condition which has been detected by another process. The emphasis here is on a quick response; clearly a process can always respond to an event by simply polling or waiting for that event. The notification of the event could be mapped onto the process's communication and synchronization mechanism. The handling process, when it is ready to receive the event, simply issues the appropriate request.

Unfortunately, there are occasions when polling for events or waiting for the event to occur is inadequate. These include the following:

- **Error recovery**
  This chapter has already emphasized that when groups of processes undertake atomic actions, an error detected in one process requires all other process to participate in the recovery. For example, a hardware fault may mean that the process will never finish its planned execution because the preconditions under which it started no longer hold; the process may never reach its polling point. Also, a timing fault might have occurred, which means that the process will no longer meet the deadline for the delivery of its service. In both these situations, the process must be informed that an error has been detected and that it must undertake some error recovery as quickly as possible.

- **Mode changes**
  A real-time system often has several modes of operation. For example, a fly-by-wire civil aircraft may have a take-off mode, a cruising mode and a landing mode. On many occasions, changes between modes can be carefully managed and will occur at well-defined points in the system's execution, as in a normal flight plan for a civil aircraft. Unfortunately, in some application areas, mode changes are expected but cannot be planned. For example, a fault may lead to an aircraft abandoning its take-off and entering an emergency mode of operation; or

an accident in a manufacturing process may require an immediate mode change to ensure an orderly shutdown of the plant. In these situations, processes must be quickly and safely informed that the mode in which they are operating has changed, and that they now need to undertake a different set of actions.

- **Scheduling using partial/imprecise computations**
  There are many algorithms where the accuracy of the results depends on how much time can be allocated to their calculation. For example, numerical computations, statistical estimations and heuristic searches may all produce an initial estimation of the required result, and then refine that result to a greater accuracy. At run-time, a certain amount of time can be allocated to an algorithm, and then, when that time has been used, the process must be interrupted to stop further refinement of the result.

- **User interrupts**
  In a general interactive computing environment, users often wish to stop the current processing because they have detected an error condition and wish to start again.

One approach to asynchronous notification handling is to abort the process and allow another process to perform some recovery. All operating systems and most concurrent programming languages provide such a facility. However, aborting a process can be expensive and is often an extreme response to many error conditions. Consequently, some form of asynchronous notification mechanism is also required.

10.6   POSIX signals

POSIX provides an asynchronous event-handling mechanism called a **signal**, which is also used for a class of environment-detected synchronous errors (such as divide by zero, illegal pointer and so on). Signals were defined before threads, and there has been some difficulty in extending the model to a multithreaded environment. For single-threaded processes the model is quite simple (see Program 10.1 for the specification of a C interface to the POSIX signal interface). There are a number of pre-defined signals, each of which is allocated an integer value. There are also an implementation-defined number of signals which are available for application use. Each signal has a default handler, which usually terminates the receiving process. Example signals are: SIGABRT for abnormal termination, SIGALARM for alarm clock expiry, SIGILL for illegal instruction exception, SIGRTMIN for the identifier of the first real-time application-definable exception, and SIGRTMAX for the identifier of the last real-time application-definable exception. Only those signals whose numbers lie between SIGRTMIN and SIGRTMAX are considered to be real-time by POSIX. A real-time signal is one which can have extra information passed to the handler by the process which generated it; in addition, they are queued.

There are three ways in which a process can deal with a signal:

Program 10.1   A C interface to POSIX signals.

```
union sigval {
  int sival_int;
  void *sival_ptr;
};

struct sigevent {
  /* used for message queue notification and timers */
  int sigev_notify; /* notification: SIGEV_SIGNAL, */
                    /* SIGEV_THREAD or SIGEV_NONE */
  int sigev_signo;  /* signal to be generated */
  union sigval sigev_value; /* value to be queued */
  void (*)sigev_notify_function(union sigval s);
  /* function to be treated as thread */
  pthread_attr_t *sigev_notify_attributes;
  /* thread attributes */
}

typedef struct {
  int si_signo;
  int si_code;
  union sigval si_value;
} siginfo_t;

typedef ... sigset_t;

struct sigaction {
  void (*sa_handler) (int signum); /* non real-time handler */
  void (*sa_sigaction) (int signum, siginfo_t *data,
                        void *extra); /*real-time handler */
  sigset_t sa_mask; /* signals to mask during handler */
  int sa_flags; /*indicates if signal is to be queued */
};

int sigaction(int sig, const struct sigaction *reaction,
              struct sigaction *old_reaction);
/* sets up a signal handler, reaction, for sig */

/* the following functions allow a  */
/* process to wait for a signal */
int sigsuspend(const sigset_t *sigmask);
int sigwaitinfo(const sigset_t *set, siginfo_t *info);
int sigtimedwait(const sigset_t *set, siginfo_t *info,
                 const struct timespec *timeout);

int sigprocmask(int how, const sigset_t *set, sigset_t *oset);
/* manipulates a signal mask according to the value of how     */
/* how = SIG_BLOCK -> the set is added to the current set       */
/* how = SIG_UNBLOCK -> the set is subtracted from the current set */
/* how = SIG_SETMASK -> the given set becomes the mask          */

/* the following routines allow a signal */
```

```
/* set to be created and manipulated */
int sigemptyset(sigset_t *s); /* initialize a set to empty */
int sigfillset(sigset_t *s); /* initialize a set to full */
int sigaddset(sigset_t *s, int signum); /* add a signal */
int sigdelset(sigset_t *s, int signum); /* remove a signal */
int sigismember(const sigset_t *s, int signum);
   /* returns 1 if a member */

int kill (pid_t pid, int sig);
   /* send the signal sig to the process pid */
int sigqueue(pid_t pid, int sig, const union sigval value);
   /* send signal and data */

/* All the above functions return -1 when errors have occurred. */
/* A shared variable errno contains the reason for the error */
```

- it can **block** the signal and either handle it later or accept it;
- it can **handle** the signal by setting a function to be called whenever it occurs;
- it can **ignore** the signal altogether (in which case the signal is simply lost).

A signal which is not blocked and not ignored is **delivered** as soon as it is **generated**. A signal which is blocked is **pending** delivery, or may be **accepted** by calling one of the sigwait() functions.

10.6.1 Blocking a signal

POSIX maintains the set of signals that have been currently masked by a process. The function sigprocmask is used to manipulate this set. The how parameter is set to: SIG_BLOCK to add signals to the set, SIG_UNBLOCK to subtract signals from the set, or SIG_SETMASK to replace the set.[1] The other two parameters contain pointers to the set of signals to be added/subtracted/replaced (set) and the returned value of the old set (oset). Various functions (sigemptyset, sigfillset, sigaddset, sigdelset, and sigismember) allow a set of signals to be manipulated.

When a signal is blocked, it remains pending until it is unblocked or accepted. When it is unblocked, it is then delivered. Some signals *cannot* be blocked.

10.6.2 Handling a signal

A signal handler can be set up using the function sigaction. The sig parameter indicates which signal is to be handled, reaction is a pointer to a structure containing information about the handler, and old_reaction points to information

---

[1] SIG_BLOCK, SIG_UNBLOCK and SIG_SETMASK are compile-time constants.

about the previous handler. Essentially, the information about a handler contains a pointer to the handler function (sa_handler if the signal is a non-real-time signal, or sa_sigaction if the signal is a real-time one), the set of signals to be masked during the handler's execution (sa_mask), and whether the signalled is to be queued (indicated by setting sa_flags to the symbolic constant SA_SIGINFO – only signals whose value lies between SIGRTMIN and SIGRTMAX can be queued). The sa_handler member indicates the action associated with the signal and can be:

- SIG_DFL – default action (usually to terminate the process);

- SIG_IGN – ignore the signal;

- pointer to a function – to be called when the signal is delivered.

For non-real-time signals, only an integer parameter can be passed to the handler when the signal is generated. The value of this parameter normally indicates the signal itself (the same handler can be used for more than one signal). However, for the real-time signals, more data can be passed via a pointer to the siginfo_t structure. This structure contains the signal number (again), a code which indicates the cause of the signal (for example, a timer signal) and an integer or pointer value.

If more than one *real-time* signal is queued, the one with the lowest value is delivered first (that is, SIGRTMIN is delivered before SIGRTMIN + 1 and so on).

A process can also wait for a signal to arrive using the functions sigsuspend, sigwaitinfo or sigtimedwait. The function sigsuspend replaces the mask with that given by the parameter to the call and suspends the process until:

(1) a non-blocked signal is delivered and

(2) the associated handler is executed.

If the handler terminates the process, the sigsuspend function never returns; otherwise it returns with the signal mask reset to the state that existed *prior* to the call of sigsuspend.

The sigwaitinfo function also suspends the calling process until the signal arrives. However, this time the signal must be blocked, and thus the handler is not called. Instead, the function returns the selected signal number and stores the information about the delivered signal in the info argument. The function sigtimedwait has the same semantics as sigwaitinfo, but allows a timeout to be specified for the suspension. If no signals are delivered by the timeout, sigwaitinfo returns with –1 and errno set to EAGAIN.

Care must clearly be taken when using signals for condition synchronization. There is a potential race condition between checking to see whether a signal has already arrived and issuing a request which causes suspension. The appropriate protocol is to block the signal first, then test to see if it has occurred and, if not, suspend and unblock the signal using one of the above functions.

10.6.3 Ignoring a signal

A signal can be ignored by simply setting the value of sa_handler to SIG_IGN in a call to the function sigaction.

10.6.4 Generating a signal

There are two ways in which a process can generate a signal to be sent to another process. The first is via the kill function and the second is via the sigqueue function. The latter can only send real-time signals.

Note, however, that a process can also request that a signal be sent to itself: when a timer expires (for example, SIGALRM – see Section 12.8.1), when asynchronous I/O completes, by the arrival of a message on an empty message queue (see Section 9.5), or by using the C raise statement.

For timers, asynchronous I/O and message arrival, the POSIX interface allows a value of struct sigevent to be passed. This defines what should happen when notification of the event has been received. There are three options

- SIGEV_NONE – no notification should be delivered
- SIGEV_SIGNAL – generate a signal in the usual way
- SIGEV_THREAD – call the sigev_notify function as if it were the start routine of a newly created thread which has sigev_notify_attributes. A null attribute indicates that the thread should be treated as if it has been detached.

10.6.5 A simple example of POSIX signals

As an illustration of POSIX signals, consider the program fragment below. A process performs some computation periodically. The actual computation to be performed depends on a system-wide mode of operation. A mode change is propagated to all processes via an application-defined real-time signal MODE_CHANGE. The signal handler change_mode simply changes a global variable mode. The processes access mode at the beginning of each iteration. To ensure that the mode does not change while it is accessing it, the MODE_CHANGE signal is blocked.

```
#include <signal.h>

#define MODE_A 1
#define MODE_B 2
#define MODE_CHANGE SIGRTMIN +1

int mode = MODE_A;

void change_mode(int signum, siginfo_t *data, void *extra) {
  /* signal handler */
  mode = data -> si_value.sival_int;;
}
```

```c
int main() {

  sigset_t mask, omask;
  struct sigaction s, os;
  int local_mode;

  SIGEMPTYSET(&mask);
  SIGADDSET(&mask, MODE_CHANGE);

  s.sa_flags = SA_SIGINFO;
  s.sa_mask = mask;
  s.sa_sigaction = &change_mode;
  s.sa_handler = &change_mode;

  SIGACTION(MODE_CHANGE, &s, &os); /* assign handler */

  while(1) {

    SIGPROCMASK(SIG_BLOCK, &mask, &omask);
      local_mode = mode;
    SIGPROCMASK(SIG_UNBLOCK, &mask, &omask);

    /* periodic operation using mode*/
    switch(local_mode) {
      case MODE_A:
        . . .
        break;
      case MODE_B:
        . . .
        break;
      default:
        . . .
    }
  }
  . . .
}
```

10.6.6 Signals and threads

The original POSIX signal model came from Unix and was extended to make it more appropriate for real-time when the Real-Time Extensions to POSIX were specified. With the POSIX Thread Extensions, the model has become more complex and is a compromise between a per process model and a per thread model. The following points should be noted:

- Signals which are generated as a result of a synchronous error condition, such as memory violation, are delivered only to the thread that caused the signal.

- Other signals may be sent to the process as a whole; however, each one is only delivered to a single thread in the process.

- The `sigaction` function sets the handler for *all* threads in the process.
- The functions `kill` and `sigqueue` still apply to processes. A new function `pthread_kill`

```
int pthread_kill(pthread_t thread, int sig);
```

allows a process to send a signal to an individual thread.

- Threads can also be terminated using the function `pthread_cancel`.

```
int pthread_cancel(pthread_t thread);
```

The effect of a cancellation request can be disabled using the function `pthread_setcancelstate` or deferred using the function `pthread_setcanceltype`.

```
int pthread_setcancelstate(int state, int *oldstate);
int pthread_setcanceltype(int type, int *oldtype);
```

- If more than one thread is eligible to have a signal delivered to it, it is not defined which thread is chosen.
- If the action specified by a handler for the signal is for termination, *the whole process is terminated*, not just the thread.
- Signals can be blocked on a per thread basis using a function `pthread_sigmask` which has the same set of parameters as `sigprocmask`. The use of the function `sigprocmask` is not specified for a multithreaded process.
- The functions `sigsuspend`, `sigwaitinfo` or `sigtimedwait` operate on the calling thread not the calling process.
- A new function `sigwait`

```
int sigwait(const sigset_t *set, int *sig);
```

allows a thread to wait for one of several blocked signals to occur. It behaves the same as `sigwaitinfo()` except that the information associated with the signal is not returned. The signals are specified in the location referenced `set`. The function returns zero when a successful wait has been performed and the location referenced by `sig` contains the received signal.

If one of the signals is already pending when the function is called, the function returns immediately. If more than one is pending, it is not defined which one is chosen unless only real-time signals are pending. In this case, the one with the lowest value is chosen.

- If a signal action is set by a thread to 'ignore', it is unspecified whether the signal is discarded immediately it is generated or remains pending.

Although POSIX allows a thread or a process to handle an asynchronous event, care must be taken because some of the POSIX system calls are termed **async-signal unsafe** and **async-cancel unsafe**. It is undefined what happens if a signal interrupts an async-unsafe function that was called from a signal-catching function. For example, it is not safe to use the function `pthread_cond_signal` in a signal handler because of the race condition it introduces with the function `pthread_cond_wait`.

10.6.7   POSIX and atomic actions

Given the close interaction between activities in an atomic action, it is more appropriate to consider the action to take place between POSIX threads rather than POSIX processes. There are at least two approaches to implementing an atomic action-like structure between threads:

(1) Use a combination of signals and `setjmp` and `longjmp` to program the required coordination. Unfortunately, `longjmp` and all the thread system calls are async-signal unsafe. This means they cannot be called from a signal handler.

(2) Use thread creation and cancelling to program the required recovery. As POSIX threads are designed to be cheap, this approach does not have the same performance penalty that would be associated with a more heavyweight process structure.

The need for these approaches comes from the use of the resumption model. A more straightforward structure is obtainable if a termination model is supported. This is discussed in the context of Ada in Section 10.8 and Real-Time Java in Section 10.9.

10.7   Asynchronous event handling in Real-Time Java

The equivalent of a POSIX signal in Real-Time Java is an asynchronous event. Indeed, there is even a class `POSIXSignalHandler` which allows POSIX signals to be mapped onto Real-Time Java events for the occasion when Real-Time Java is being implemented on top of a POSIX-compliant operating system (see Section 15.5.2).

Program 10.2 shows the three main classes associated with asynchronous events in Real-Time Java. Each `AsyncEvent` can have one or more `AsyncEventHandlers`. When the event occurs (indicated by a call to the `fire` method), all the handlers associated with the event are scheduled for execution according to their `SchedulingParameters` – see Section 13.14.3. Note that the firing of an event can also be associated with the occurrence of an implementation-dependent external action by using the `bindTo` method.

Each handler is scheduled once for each outstanding event firing. Note, however, that the handler can modify the number of outstanding events by the methods in the `AsyncEventHandler` class.

Although an event handler is a schedulable entity, the goal is that it will not suffer the same overhead as an application thread. Consequently, it cannot be assumed

Program 10.2   The AsyncEvent, AsyncEventHandler and BoundAsync-
EventHandler classes.

```java
public class AsyncEvent
{
  public AsyncEvent();

  public synchronized void addHandler(AsyncEventHandler handler);
  public synchronized void removeHandler(AsyncEventHandler handler);
  public void setHandler(AsyncEventHandler handler);
  // Associate a new handler with this event,
  // removing all existing handlers.

  public void bindTo(java.lang.String happening);
  // bind to external event

  public ReleaseParameters createReleaseParameters();
  // creates a ReleaseParameters object representing the
  // characteristics of this event

  public synchronized void fire();
  // Execute the run() methods of the set of handlers for this event.
  public boolean handledBy(AsyncEventHandler target);
  // Returns true if this event is handled by this handler.
}

public abstract class AsyncEventHandler implements Schedulable
{
  public AsyncEventHandler();
  // parameters are inherited from the current thread

  public AsyncEventHandler(SchedulingParameters scheduling,
          ReleaseParameters release, MemoryParameters memory,
          MemoryArea area, ProcessingGroupParameters group);
  ... // other constructors available

  // methods which implement the Schedulable interface,
  // see Chapter 13

  protected final synchronized int getAndClearPendingFireCount();
  // Atomically set to zero the number of pending executions
  // of this handler and returns the value from before
  // it was cleared.
  protected synchronized int getAndDecrementPendingFireCount();
  protected synchronized int getAndIncrementPendingFireCount();

  public abstract void handleAsyncEvent();
  // Override this method to define the action to be
  // taken by this handler

  public final void run();
}
```

```
public abstract class BoundAsyncEventHandler extends AsyncEventHandler
{
  public BoundAsyncEventHandler();
  // other constructors
}
```

that there is a separate implementation thread for each handler, as more than one handler may be associated with a particular implementation thread. If a dedicated thread is required, the `BoundAsyncEventHandler` should be used.

10.8   Asynchronous transfer of control in Ada

In POSIX, it is possible to set up domains for signal handlers by blocking the signal and unblocking the signal at appropriate points in the program. However, without language support, this becomes unstructured and error-prone. Ada provides a more structured form of asynchronous notification handling called **asynchronous transfer of control** (ATC). Furthermore, to emphasize that ATC is a form of communication and synchronization, it builds the mechanism on top of the inter-task communication facility.

The Ada `select` statement was introduced in Chapter 9. It has the following forms:

- a selective accept (to support the server side of the rendezvous) – this was discussed in Section 9.4.2,

- a timed and a conditional entry call (to either a task or a protected entry) – this is discussed in Section 12.4.2,

- an asynchronous select – discussed here.

The asynchronous select statement provides an asynchronous notification mechanism with termination semantics.

The execution of the asynchronous select begins with the issuing of the triggering entry call or the issuing of the triggering delay. If the triggering statement is an entry call, the parameters are evaluated as normal and the call issued. If the call is queued, then a sequence of statements in an abortable part is executed.

If the triggering statement completes before the execution of the abortable part completes, the abortable part is aborted. When these activities have finished, the optional sequence of statements following the triggering statement is executed.

If the abortable part completes before the completion of the entry call, an attempt is made to cancel the entry call and, if successful, the execution of the asynchronous select statement is finished. The following illustrates the syntax:

```
select
  Trigger.Event;
  -- optional sequence of statements to be
  -- executed after the event has been received
```

```
then abort
  -- abortable sequence of statements
end select;
```

Note that the triggering statement can be a delay statement and, therefore a timeout can be associated with the abortable part (see Section 12.4.3).

If the cancellation of the triggering event fails because the protected action or rendezvous has started, then the asynchronous select statement waits for the triggering statement to complete before executing the optional sequence of statements following the triggering statement.

Clearly, it is possible for the triggering event to occur even before the abortable part has started its execution. In this case the abortable part is not executed and therefore not aborted.

Consider the following example:

```
task Server is
    entry Atc_Event;
end Server;

task To_Be_Interrupted;

task body Server is
begin
  . . .
  accept Atc_Event do
    Seq2;
  end Atc_Event;
  . . .
end Server;

task body To_Be_Interrupted is
begin
  . . .
  select   -- ATC statement
    Server.Atc_Event;
    Seq3;
  then abort
    Seq1;
  end select;
  Seq4;
  . . .
end To_Be_Interrupted;
```

When the above ATC statement is executed, the statements which are executed will depend on the order of events that occur:

```
if the rendezvous is available immediately then
   Server.Atc_Event is issued
   Seq2 is executed
   Seq3 is executed
   Seq4 is executed ( Seq1 is never started)
```

```
elsif no rendezvous starts before  Seq1 finishes then
   Server.Atc_Event is issued
   Seq1 is executed
   Server.Atc_Event is cancelled
   Seq4 is executed
elsif the rendezvous finishes before  Seq1 finishes then
   Server.Atc_Event is issued
   partial execution of  Seq1 occurs concurrently with  Seq2
   Seq1 is aborted and finalised
   Seq3 is executed
   Seq4 is executed
else (the rendezvous finishes after  Seq1 finishes)
   Server.Atc_Event is issued
   Seq1 is executed concurrently with partial execution of  Seq2
   Server.Atc_Event cancellation is attempted but is unsuccessful
   execution of  Seq2 completes
   Seq3 is executed
   Seq4 is executed
end if
```

Note that there is a race condition between Seq1 finishing and the rendezvous finishing. The situation could occur where Seq1 does finish but is nevertheless aborted.

Ada allows some operations to be **abort deferred**. If Seq1 contains an abort-deferred operation, then its cancellation will not occur until the operation is completed. An example of such an operation is a call on a protected object.

The above discussion has concentrated on the concurrent behaviour of Seq1 and the triggering rendezvous. Indeed, on a multiprocessor implementation it could be the case that Seq1 and Seq2 are executing in parallel. However, on a single-processor system, the triggering event will only ever occur if the action that causes it has a higher priority than Seq1. The normal behaviour will thus be the preemption of Seq1 by Seq2. When Seq2 (the triggering rendezvous) completes, Seq1 will be aborted before it can execute again. And hence the ATC is 'immediate' (unless an abort-deferred operation is in progress).

10.8.1 Exceptions and ATC

With the asynchronous select statement, potentially two activities occur concurrently: the abortable part may execute concurrently with the triggering action (when the action is an entry call). In either one of these activities, exceptions may be raised and unhandled. Therefore, at first sight it may appear that potentially two exceptions can be propagated simultaneously from the select statement. However, this is not the case: one of the exceptions is deemed to be lost (that raised in the abortable part when it is aborted), and hence only one exception is propagated.

10.8.2   Ada and atomic actions

It was shown in Section 6.5 that backward error recovery in a sequential system could be implemented by exception handling. In this section, the Ada ATC facility and exception handling is used to implement backward and forward error recovery. It is assumed that the underlying Ada implementation and run-time are fault free, and therefore the strong typing provided by Ada will ensure that the Ada program itself remains viable.

Backward error recovery

The following package is a generic version of the one was given in Section 6.5 for saving and restoring a task's state.

```
generic
  type Data is private;
package Recovery_Cache is
  procedure Save(D : in Data);
  procedure Restore(D : out Data);
end Recovery_Cache;
```

Consider three Ada tasks which wish to enter into a recoverable atomic action. Each will call their appropriate procedure in the package given below.

```
package Conversation is

  procedure T1(Params : Param); -- called by task 1
  procedure T2(Params : Param); -- called by task 2
  procedure T3(Params : Param); -- called by task 3

  Atomic_Action_Failure : exception;

end Conversation;
```

The body of the package encapsulates the action and ensures that only communication between the three tasks is allowed during the conversation.[2] The `Controller` protected object is responsible for propagating any error condition noticed in one task to all tasks, saving and restoring any persistent data in the recovery cache, and ensuring that all tasks leave the action at the same time. It contains three protected entries and a protected procedure.

- The `Wait_Abort` entry represents the asynchronous event on which the tasks will wait while performing their part of the action.

---

[2] In practice, this might be difficult to ensure because of Ada's scope rules. One way of increasing the security would be to require that the `Conversation` package is at the library level and its body only references pure (state-free) packages. The solution presented here assumes that the tasks are well behaved. It also assumes, for simplicity, that the correct tasks call `T1`, `T2` and `T3` at the correct times.

- Each task calls Done if it has finished its component of the action without error. Only when all three tasks have called Done will they be allowed to leave.
- Similarly, each task calls Cleanup if it has had to perform any recovery.
- If any task recognizes an error condition (either because of a raised exception or the failure of the acceptance test), it will call Signal_Abort. This will set the flag Killed to true, indicating that the tasks must be recovered.

Note that, as backward error recovery will be performed, the tasks are not concerned with the actual cause of the error. When Killed becomes true, all tasks in the action receive the asynchronous event. Once the event has been handled, all tasks must wait on the Cleanup entry so that they can all terminate the conversation module together.

```
with Recovery_Cache;
package body Conversation is

  Primary_Failure, Secondary_Failure,
          Tertiary_Failure: exception;
  type Module is (Primary, Secondary, Tertiary);

  protected Controller is
    entry Wait_Abort;
    entry Done;
    entry Cleanup;
    procedure Signal_Abort;
  private
    Killed : Boolean := False;
    Releasing_Done : Boolean := False;
    Releasing_Cleanup : Boolean := False;
    Informed : Integer := 0;
  end Controller;

  -- any local protected objects for communication between actions


  protected body Controller is
    entry Wait_Abort when Killed is
    begin
      Informed := Informed + 1;
      if Informed = 3 then
        Killed := False;
        Informed := 0;
      end if;
    end Wait_Abort;

    procedure Signal_Abort is
    begin
      Killed := True;
    end Signal_Abort;

    entry Done when Done'Count = 3 or Releasing_Done is
    begin
      if Done'Count > 0 then
```

```
      Releasing_Done := True;
    else
      Releasing_Done := False;
    end if;
  end Done;

  entry Cleanup when Cleanup'Count = 3 or Releasing_Cleanup is
  begin
    if Cleanup'Count > 0 then
      Releasing_Cleanup := True;
    else
      Releasing_Cleanup := False;
    end if;
  end Cleanup;
end Controller;

procedure T1(Params : Param) is separate;
procedure T2(Params : Param) is separate;
procedure T3(Params : Param) is separate;

end Conversation;
```

The code for each task is contained within a single procedure: e.g. T1. Within such a procedure, three attempts are made to perform the action. If all attempts fail, the exception Atomic_Action_Failure is raised. Each attempt is surrounded by a call that saves the state and restores the state (if the attempt fails). Each attempt is encapsulated in a separate local procedure (T1_Primary etc), which contains a single 'select and then abort' statement to perform the required protocol with the controller. The recovery cache is used by each task to save its local data.

```
separate(Conversation)
procedure T1(Params : Param) is
  procedure T1_Primary is
  begin
    select
      Controller.Wait_Abort; -- triggering event
      Controller.Cleanup; -- wait for all to finish
      raise Primary_Failure;
    then abort
      begin
        -- code to implement atomic action,
        -- the acceptance test might raise an exception
        if Accept_Test = Failed then
          Controller.Signal_Abort;
        else
          Controller.Done; --signal completion
        end if;
      exception
        when others =>
          Controller.Signal_Abort;
      end;
    end select;
  end T1_Primary;
```

```
    procedure T1_Secondary is ... ;
    procedure T1_Tertiary is ... ;

    package My_Cache is new Recovery_Cache(..); -- for local data

begin
  My_Cache.Save(..);
  for Try in Module loop
    begin
      case Try is
        when Primary => T1_Primary; return;
        when Secondary => T1_Secondary; return;
        when Tertiary => T1_Tertiary;
      end case;
    exception
      when Primary_Failure =>
        My_Cache.Restore(..);
      when Secondary_Failure =>
        My_Cache.Restore(..);
      when Tertiary_Failure =>
        My_Cache.Restore(..);
        raise Atomic_Action_Failure;
      when others =>
        My_Cache.Restore(..);
        raise Atomic_Action_Failure;
    end;
  end loop;
end T1;

-- similarly for T2 and T3
```

Figure 10.3 illustrates a simple state transition diagram for a participating task in a conversation.

Forward error recovery

Ada's ATC facility can be used with exceptions to implement atomic actions with forward error recovery between concurrently executing tasks. Consider again the following package for implementing an atomic action between three tasks.

```
package Action is

  procedure T1(Params : Param); -- called by task 1
  procedure T2(Params : Param); -- called by task 2
  procedure T3(Params : Param); -- called by task 3

  Atomic_Action_Failure : exception;

end Action;
```

As with backward error recovery, the body of the package encapsulates the action

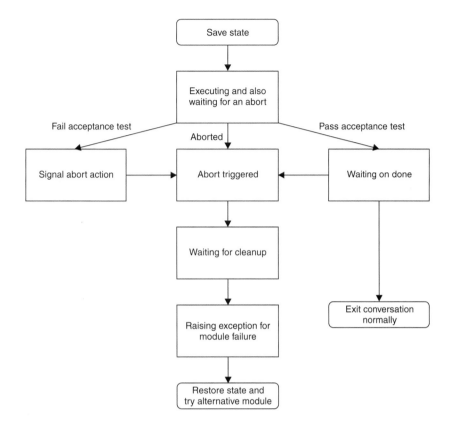

Figure 10.3   Simple state transition diagram for a conversation.

and ensures that only communications between the three tasks are allowed. The `Con-troller` protected object is responsible for propagating any exception raised in one task to all tasks, and for ensuring that all tasks leave the action at the same time.

```
with Ada.Exceptions;
use Ada.Exceptions;
package body Action is

  type Vote_T is (Commit, Aborted);
  protected Controller is
    entry Wait_Abort(E: out Exception_Id);
    entry Done;
    procedure Cleanup (Vote: Vote_T);
    entry Wait_Cleanup(Result : out Vote_T);
    procedure Signal_Abort(E: Exception_Id);
  private
    Killed : Boolean := False;
```

```
      Releasing_Cleanup : Boolean := False;
      Releasing_Done : Boolean := False;
      Reason : Exception_Id;
      Final_Result : Vote_T := Commit;
      Informed : Integer := 0;
   end Controller;

-- any local protected objects for communication between actions

   protected body Controller is
      entry Wait_Abort(E: out Exception_Id) when Killed is
      begin
        E := Reason;
        Informed := Informed + 1;
        if Informed = 3 then
          Killed := False;
          Informed := 0;
        end if;
      end Wait_Abort;

      entry Done when Done'Count = 3 or Releasing_Done is
      begin
        if Done'Count > 0 then
          Releasing_Done := True;
        else
          Releasing_Done := False;
        end if;
      end Done;

      procedure Cleanup (Vote: Vote_T) is
      begin
        if Vote = Aborted then
          Final_Result := Aborted;
        end if;
      end Cleanup;

      procedure Signal_Abort(E: Exception_Id) is
      begin
        Killed := True;
        Reason := E;
      end Signal_Abort;

      entry Wait_Cleanup (Result: out Vote_T)
            when Wait_Cleanup'Count = 3 or Releasing_Cleanup is
      begin
        Result := Final_Result;
        if Wait_Cleanup'Count > 0 then
          Releasing_Cleanup := True;
        else
          Releasing_Cleanup := False;
          Final_Result := Commit;
        end if;
      end Wait_Cleanup;
   end Controller;
```

```ada
procedure T1(Params: Param) is
  X : Exception_Id;
  Decision : Vote_T;
begin
  select
    Controller.Wait_Abort(X); -- triggering event
    Raise_Exception(X); -- raise common exception
  then abort
    begin
      -- code to implement atomic action
      Controller.Done; --signal completion
    exception
      when E: others =>
        Controller.Signal_Abort(Exception_Identity(E));
    end;
  end select;
exception
    -- if any exception is raised during the action
    -- all tasks must participate in the recovery
  when E: others =>
    -- Exception_Identity(E) has been raised in all tasks

    -- handle exception
    if Handled_Ok then
      Controller.Cleanup(Commit);
    else
      Controller.Cleanup(Aborted);
    end if;
    Controller.Wait_Cleanup(Decision);
    if Decision = Aborted then
      raise Atomic_Action_Failure;
    end if;
end T1;

procedure T2(Params : Param) is ...;

procedure T3(Params : Param) is ...;

end Action;
```

Each component of the action (T1, T2, and T3) has identical structure. The component executes a select statement with an abortable part. The triggering event is signalled by the Controller protected object if any component indicates that an exception has been raised and not handled locally in one of the components. The abortable part contains the actual code of the component. If this code executes without incident, the Controller is informed that this component is ready to commit the action. If any exceptions are raised during the abortable part, the Controller is informed and the identity of the exception passed. Note that, unlike backward error recovery (given in the previous section), here the cause of the error must be communicated.

If the Controller has received notification of an unhandled exception, it releases all tasks waiting on the Wait_Abort triggering event (any task late in arriving will receive the event immediately it tries to enter into its select statement). The tasks

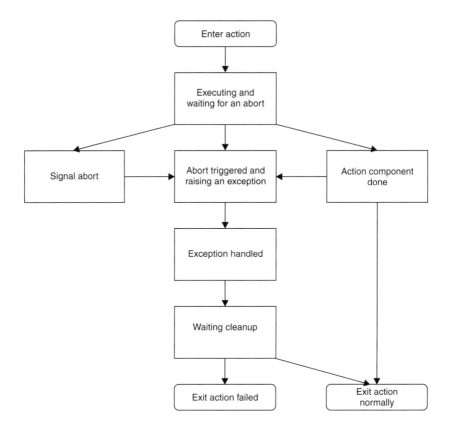

Figure 10.4   Simple state transition diagram illustrating forward error recovery.

have their abortable parts aborted (if started), and the exception is raised in each task by the statement after the entry call to the controller. If the exception is successfully handled by the component, the task indicates that it is prepared to commit the action. If not, then it indicates that the action must be aborted. If any task indicates that the action is to be aborted, then all tasks will raise the exception `Atomic_Action_Failure`. Figure 10.4 shows the approach using a simply state transition diagram.

The above example illustrates that it is possible to program atomic actions with forward error recovery in Ada. However, there are two points to note about this example:

- Only the first exception to be passed to the `Controller` will be raised in all tasks. It is not possible to get concurrent raising of exceptions, as any exception raised in an abortable part when it is aborted is lost.

- The approach does not deal with the deserter problem. If one of the participants in the action does not arrive, the others are left waiting at the end of the action.

To cope with this situation, it is necessary for each task to log its arrival with the action controller (see Exercise 10.10).

10.9   Asynchronous transfer of control in Real-Time Java

Early versions of Java allowed one thread to asynchronously affect another thread through the following methods.

```
public final void suspend() throws SecurityException;
public final void resume() throws SecurityException;

public final void stop() throws SecurityException;
public final void stop(Throwable except) throws SecurityException;
```

The `suspend` and `resume` methods have been discussed in Section 7.3.7. The `stop` method causes the thread to stop its current activity and throw a `ThreadDeath` exception, and similarly with the `stop(Throwable except)` method, only this time the exception passed as a parameter is thrown.

All of the above methods are now obsolete and therefore should not be used. Standard Java now only supports the following:

```
public void interrupt() throws SecurityException;
public boolean isInterrupted();
public void destroy();
```

One thread can signal an interrupt to another thread by calling the `interrupt` method. The result of this depends on the current status of the interrupted thread.

- If the interrupted thread is blocked in the `wait`, `sleep` or `join` methods, it is made runnable and the `InterruptedException` is thrown.

- If the interrupted thread is executing, a flag is set indicating that an interrupt is outstanding. *There is no immediate effect on the interrupted thread.* Instead, the called thread must periodically test to see if it has been 'interrupted' using the `isInterrupted` method.

By itself, this does not meet the user needs outlined in Section 10.5.1.

The `destroy` method is similar to the Ada abort facility and destroys the thread without any cleanup.

Real-Time Java provides an alternative approach for interrupting a thread, based on asynchronous transfer of control (ATC). The Real-Time Java ATC model is similar to the Ada one in that it is necessary to indicate which regions of code can receive the ATC request. However, the Real-Time Java model is different in two important respects.

(1) The Real-Time Java model is integrated with the Java exception-handling facility, whereas the Ada model is integrated into the select statement and entry-handling mechanisms.

(2) The Real-Time Java model requires each method to indicate that it is prepared to allow the ATC to occur. ATC is deferred until the thread is executing within such a method. In contrast, Ada's default is to allow the ATC if a subprogram has been called from within the select-then-abort statement; a deferred response must be explicitly handled.

Both languages defer the ATC during interaction with other threads/tasks (for example synchronized statements/methods in Java and protected actions and rendezvous in Ada) or within constructors and finalization (finally) clauses.

The Real-Time Java ATC model brings together the Java exception-handling model and an extension of thread interruption. The model is best explained in two stages. The first is the low-level support and overall approach; the second is the use of the high-level support to provide a structured means for handling ATC. Use of the basic ATC facilities requires three activities:

(1) declaring an `AsynchronouslyInterruptedException` (AIE)

(2) identifying methods which can be interrupted

(3) signalling an `AsynchronouslyInterruptedException` to a thread.

Program 10.3 shows the specification of the `AsynchronouslyInterrupted-Exception` class. The methods will be explained in due course, but for now all that is required is to know that for each thread there is an associated generic AIE.

An AIE may be placed in the `throws` list associated with a method. For example, consider the following class which provides an interruptible service using a package which declares non-interruptible services (that is, ones which do not have `throws` lists containing `AsynchronouslyInterruptedExceptions`).

```
import nonInterruptibleServices.*;

public class InterruptibleService
{
  public AsynchronouslyInterruptedException stopNow =
       AsynchronouslyInterruptedException.getGeneric();

  public boolean Service() throws AsynchronouslyInterruptedException
  {
    //code interspersed with calls to NonInterruptibleServices
  }
}
```

Now assume that a real-time thread t has called an instance of this class to provide the `Service`:

```
public InterruptibleService IS = new InterruptibleService();

// code of thread, t
if(IS.Service()) { ... }
else { ... };
```

Program 10.3 The Real-Time Java `AsynchronouslyInterruptedException` class.

```
public class AsynchronouslyInterruptedException extends
                java.lang.InterruptedException
{
  public  AsynchronouslyInterruptedException();

  public synchronized boolean disable();
  // only valid within a doInterruptible, returns true if successful
  public boolean doInterruptible (Interruptible logic);
  // Only one specific Interruptible can be running per thread
  // at any one time.
  // Returns True, if the Interruptible is executed, false if one
  // is already in progress for this thread.

  public synchronized boolean enable();
  public synchronized boolean fire();

  public boolean happened (boolean propagate);

  public static AsynchronouslyInterruptedException getGeneric();
  // returns the AsynchronouslyInterruptedException which
  // is generated when RealtimeThread.interrupt() is invoked

  public boolean isEnabled();

  public void propagate();
}
```

and that another thread interrupts `t`:

```
t.interrupt;
```

The consequences of this call depend on the current state of `t` when the call is made.

- If at any point `t` is executing within an ATC-deferred section, the `AsynchronouslyInterruptedException` is marked as pending. The exception is thrown as soon as `t` leaves the ATC-deferred region and is executing in a method with an `AsynchronouslyInterruptedException` declared in its `throws` list.

- If `t` is executing in a method which has **no** `AsynchronouslyInterruptedException` declared in its `throws` list (such as those in the package `nonInterruptibleServices`), then the exception is marked as pending. The exception is thrown as soon as `t` returns to (or calls) a method with an `AsynchronouslyInterruptedException` declared in its `throws` list.

- If t is executing within a try block within a method which has declared an AsynchronouslyInterruptedException in its throws list, then the try block is terminated and control is transferred to the first statement of the catch clause. If no appropriate catch clause is found, the Asynchronously-InterruptedException is propagated to the calling method. Otherwise, the appropriate handler is executed, and processing of the Asynchronously-InterruptedException is completed (unless the AIE is propagated from within the handler).

- If t is executing outside a try block within a method which has declared an AsynchronouslyInterruptedException in its throws list, the method is terminated and the AsynchronouslyInterruptedException is thrown immediately in the calling method.

- If t is blocked inside a wait, sleep or join method called from within a method which has declared an AsynchronouslyInterrupted-Exception in its throws list, t is rescheduled and the Asynchronously-InterruptedException is thrown.

- If t is blocked inside a wait, sleep or join methods called from within a method which has *no* AsynchronouslyInterruptedException declared in its throws list, t is rescheduled and the Asynchronously-InterruptedException is marked as pending. The exception is thrown as soon as t returns to a method with an AsynchronouslyInterrupted-Exception declared in its throws list.

Once an ATC has been thrown and control is passed to an appropriate exception handler, it is necessary to ascertain whether the caught ATC is the one expected by the interrupted thread. If it is, the exception can be handled. If it is not, the exception should be propagated to the calling method. The happened method defined in the class AsynchronouslyInterruptedException is used for this purpose. Consider the following:

```
import NonInterruptibleServices.*;
public class InterruptibleService
{
  public AsynchronouslyInterruptedException stopNow =
          new AsynchronouslyInterruptedException;

  public boolean Service() throws AsynchronouslyInterruptedException
  {
    try {
      //code interdispersed with calls to NonInterruptibleServices
    }
    catch AsynchronouslyInterruptedException AIE {
      if(stopNow.happened(true)) {
        //handle the ATC
      }
      // no else clause, the true parameter indicates that
      // if the current exception is not stopNow,
```

```
            // it is to be immediately propagated
            // to the calling method
        }
    }
}
```

Here, when the AIE is thrown, control is passed to the catch clause at the end of the try block. A handler is found for AsynchronouslyInterruptedExceptions. In order to determine whether the current AsynchronouslyInterrupted-Exception is stopNow, a call is made to the stopNow.happened method. This returns true if stopNow is the current exception. If it is not the current exception then, as the parameter to happened is true, the exception is propagated. If the parameter were false, control would return to the catch statement with a false value. Now the thread might do some cleanup routines before propagating the exception using the propagate method: :

```
catch AsynchronouslyInterruptedException AIE {
    if(stopNow.happened(false)) {
        //handle the ATC
    } else {
        //cleanup
        AIE.propagate();
    }
}
```

The Interruptible **Interface**

The above discussion illustrates the basic mechanisms provided by Real-Time Java for handling ATCs. To facilitate their structured use, the language also provides an interface called Interruptible – see Program 10.4 .

An object which wishes to provide an interruptible method does so by implementing the Interruptible interface. The run method is the method that is interruptible; the interruptAction method is called by the system if the run method is interrupted.

Once this interface is implemented, the implementation can be passed as a parameter to the doInterruptible method in the Asynchronously-InterruptedException class. The method can then be interrupted by calling the fire method in the AsynchronouslyInterruptedException class. Further control over AsynchronouslyInterruptedException is given by the disable, enable and isEnabled methods. A disabled Asynchronously-InterruptedException is deferred until it is enabled. An example of this latter use will be given in Section 10.9.1.

Note that only one doInterruptible method for a particular AsynchronouslyInterruptedException can be active at one time. If a call is outstanding, the method returns immediately with a false value.

Program 10.4 The Real-Time Java Interruptible interface.

```
public interface Interruptible
{

  public void interruptAction (
          AsynchronouslyInterruptedException exception);

  public void run (AsynchronouslyInterruptedException exception)
        throws AsynchronouslyInterruptedException;

}
```

Multiple AsynchronouslyInterruptedExceptions

Given that AsynchronouslyInterruptedException can be deferred, it is possible for multiple ATCs to be deferred. This can happen when the run method of one class (which implements the Interruptible interface) calls a doInterruptible on an AIE. The associated run method may also call another doInterruptible. Hence it is possible for a thread to be executing nested doInterruptibles. Consider the following example:

```
import javax.realtime.*;

public class NestedATC
{
  AsynchronouslyInterruptedException AIE1 = new
          AsynchronouslyInterruptedException();
  AsynchronouslyInterruptedException AIE2 = new
          AsynchronouslyInterruptedException();
  AsynchronouslyInterruptedException AIE3 = new
          AsynchronouslyInterruptedException();

  public void method1()
  {
    // ATC-deferred region
  }

  public void method2() throws AsynchronouslyInterruptedException
  {
    AIE1.doInterruptible
      (new Interruptible()
        {
            public void run(AsynchronouslyInterruptedException e)
                throws AsynchronouslyInterruptedException
            {
              method1();
            }
```

```
      public void interruptAction(
          AsynchronouslyInterruptedException e)
      {
        if(AIE1.happened(false)) {
         // recovery here
        } else {
         // cleanup
         e.propagate();
        }
      }
     }
    );
}

public void method3() throws AsynchronouslyInterruptedException
{
   AIE2.doInterruptible
      (new Interruptible()
        {
          public void run(AsynchronouslyInterruptedException e)
              throws AsynchronouslyInterruptedException
          {
            method2();
          }
          public void interruptAction(
              AsynchronouslyInterruptedException e)
          {
            if(AIE2.happened(false)) {
             // recovery here
            } else {
             // cleanup
             e.propagate();
            }
          }
        }
      );
}

public void method4() throws AsynchronouslyInterruptedException
{
   AIE3.doInterruptible
      (new Interruptible()
        {
          public void run(AsynchronouslyInterruptedException e)
              throws AsynchronouslyInterruptedException
          {
            method3();
          }
          public void interruptAction(
              AsynchronouslyInterruptedException e)
          {
            if(AIE3.happened(false)) {
             // recovery here
            } else {
             // cleanup
```

```
                    e.propagate();
                }
            }
        }
    );
}

}
```

Now suppose that a thread `t` has created an instance of `NestedATC` and has called `method4`, which has called `method3`, which has called `method2`, which has called `method1` which is an ATC-deferred region.. Assume that the thread is interrupted by a call to `AIE2.fire()`. This is held pending. If `AIE3` now comes in then `AIE2` is discarded as `AIE3` is at a higher level in the nesting. If `AIE1` comes in then `AIE1` is discarded (because it is at a lower level). Once `method1` has returned, the currently pending AIE is thrown.

10.9.1   Real-Time Java and atomic actions

This section illustrates how Real-Time Java's ATC facilities can be used to implement atomic actions with forward error recovery.

First, an `AtomicActionException AsynchronouslyInterrupted-Exception` is defined along with an `AtomicActionFailure` exception.

```
import javax.realtime.AsynchronouslyInterruptedException;

public class AtomicActionException extends
            AsynchronouslyInterruptedException
{
  public static Exception cause;
  public static boolean wasInterrupted;
}

public class AtomicActionFailure extends Exception;
```

Using a `ThreeWayRecoverableAtomicAction` similar to that defined earlier:

```
public interface ThreeWayRecoverableAtomicAction {
  public void role1() throws AtomicActionFailure;
  public void role2() throws AtomicActionFailure;
  public void role3() throws AtomicActionFailure;
}
```

a `RecoverableAction` class can be implemented with a similar structure to that given for Ada.

```java
import javax.realtime.*;

public class RecoverableAction
            implements ThreeWayRecoverableAtomicAction
{
  protected RecoverableController Control;
  private final boolean abort = false;
  private final boolean commit = true;

  private AtomicActionException aae1, aae2, aae3;

  public RecoverableAction()  // constructor
  {
    Control = new RecoverableController();
      // for recovery
      aae1 = new AtomicActionException();
      aae2 = new AtomicActionException();
      aae3 = new AtomicActionException();
  }

  class RecoverableController {
    protected boolean firstHere, secondHere, thirdHere;
    protected int allDone;
    protected int toExit, needed;
    protected int numberOfParticipants;
    private boolean committed = commit;

    RecoverableController()
    {
      // for synchronization
      firstHere = false;
      secondHere = false;
      thirdHere = false;
      allDone = 0;
      numberOfParticipants = 3;
      toExit = numberOfParticipants;
      needed = numberOfParticipants;
    }

    synchronized void first() throws InterruptedException
    {
      while(firstHere) wait();
      firstHere = true;
    }

    synchronized void second() throws InterruptedException
    {
      while(secondHere) wait();
      secondHere = true;
    }

    synchronized void third() throws InterruptedException
    {
      while(thirdHere) wait();
      thirdHere = true;
    }
```

```java
synchronized void signalAbort(Exception e)
{
 allDone = 0;
 AtomicActionException.cause = e;
 AtomicActionException.wasInterrupted = true;
 // raise an AsynchronouslyInterruptedException
 // in all participants
 aae1.fire();
 aae2.fire();
 aae3.fire();
}

private void reset()
{
  firstHere = false;
  secondHere = false;
  thirdHere = false;
  allDone = 0;
  toExit = numberOfParticipants;
  needed = numberOfParticipants;
  notifyAll();
}

synchronized void done() throws InterruptedException
{
  allDone++;
  if(allDone == needed) {
    notifyAll();
  } else while(allDone != needed) {
      wait();
  }
  toExit--;
  if(toExit == 0) {
    reset();
  }
}

synchronized void cleanup(boolean abort)
{
  if(abort) { committed = false; };
}

synchronized boolean waitCleanup() throws InterruptedException
{
  allDone++;
  if(allDone == needed) {
    notifyAll();
  } else while(allDone != needed) {
      wait();
  }
  toExit--;
  if(toExit == 0) {
    reset();
  }
  return committed;
```

```
  };
};

public void role1() throws AtomicActionFailure,
                           AsynchronouslyInterruptedException
{
  boolean Ok;
  // entry protocol
  // no AIE until inside the atomic action
  boolean done = false;
  while(!done) {
    try {
      Control.first();
      done = true;
    } catch (InterruptedException e) {
    // ignore
    }
  }

  // the following defines an interruptible
  // section of code, and a routine to be called
  // if the code is interrupted
  Ok = aae1.doInterruptible
      (new Interruptible()
        {
          public void run(AsynchronouslyInterruptedException e)
              throws AsynchronouslyInterruptedException
          {
            try {

              // perform action
              // if necessary call e.disable() and e.enable() to
              // defer AIE
              Control.done();
            }
            catch(Exception x) {
              if(x.getClass().getName() ==
                "AsynchronouslyInterruptedException")
                ((AsynchronouslyInterruptedException) x).propagate();
              else
                Control.signalAbort(x);
            }
          }

          public void interruptAction(
              AsynchronouslyInterruptedException e)
          {
            // no action required
          }
        }
      );
  if(!Ok) throw new AtomicActionFailure();
```

```
    if(aae1.wasInterrupted) {
      try {
        // try to recover
        Control.cleanup(commit);
        if(Control.waitCleanup() != commit) {
          throw new AtomicActionFailure();
        };
      }
      catch(Exception x) {
        throw new AtomicActionFailure();
      }
    };
}

public void role2() throws AtomicActionFailure,
                  AsynchronouslyInterruptedException
{// similar to role1 };

public void role3() throws AtomicActionFailure,
                  AsynchronouslyInterruptedException
{// similar to role1  };

}
```

Summary

Reliable execution of processes is essential if real-time embedded systems are to be used in critical applications. When processes interact, it is necessary to constrain their interprocess communication so that recovery procedures can be programmed, if required. Atomic actions have been discussed in this chapter as a mechanism by which programs, consisting of many tasks, can be structured to facilitate damage confinement and error recovery.

Actions are atomic if they can be considered, so far as other processes are concerned, to be indivisible and instantaneous, such that the effects on the system are as if they are interleaved as opposed to concurrent. An atomic action has well-defined boundaries and can be nested. Resources used in an atomic action are allocated during an initial *growing phase*, and released either as part of a subsequent *shrinking phase* or at the end of the action (if the action is to be recoverable).

The syntax of an atomic action can be expressed by an action statement. The following statement executed within process P_1 indicates that P_1 wishes to enter into an atomic action with P_2 and P_3.

```
action A with (P2, P3) do
    -- sequence of statements
end A;
```

P_2 and P_3 must execute similar statements.

A *conversation* is an atomic action with backward error recovery facilities (in the form of recovery blocks).

```
action A with (P₂, P₃) do
   ensure <acceptance test>
   by
      -- primary module
   else by
      -- alternative module
   else error
end A;
```

On entry to the conversation, the state of the process is saved. While inside the conversation, a process is only allowed to communicate with other processes active in the conversation and general resource managers. In order to leave the conversation, all processes active in the conversation must have passed their acceptance test. If any process fails its acceptance test, all processes have their state restored to that saved at the start of the conversation and they execute their alternative modules. Conversations can be nested and if all alternatives in an inner conversation fail then recovery must be performed at an outer level.

Conversations are limited because when a conversation fails all the processes are restored and all enter their alternative modules. This forces the same processes to communicate again to achieve the desired affect; a process cannot break out of the conversation. Often when one process fails to achieve its goal in a primary module through communication with one group of processes, it may wish to communicate with a completely new group of processes in its secondary module. Dialogs and colloquys remove the limitations of conversations.

Forward error recovery via exception handlers can also be added to atomic actions. If an exception is raised by one process then all processes active in the action must handle the exception.

```
action A with (P₂, P₃) do
   -- the action
exception
   when exception_a =>
      -- sequence of statements
   when others =>
      raise atomic_action_failure;
end A;
```

Two issues that must be addressed when using this approach are the resolution of concurrently raised exceptions and exceptions in internal actions.

Few mainstream languages or operating systems directly support the notion of an atomic action or a recoverable atomic action. However, most communication and synchronization primitives allow the isolation property of an action to be programmed. To implement a recoverable action requires an asynchronous notification mechanism. This can either have resumption semantics (in which case it is called an asynchronous event handling mechanism) or it can have termination semantics (in which case it is called asynchronous transfer of control). POSIX supports asynchronous events using signals and a thread cancelling mechanism. A signal can be handled, blocked or ignored. Real-Time Java also supports asynchronous events.

Both Ada and Real-Time Java provide the termination model of asynchronous transfer of control. The Ada mechanism is built on top of the select statement. Real-Time Java's ATC, in contrast, is integrated into its exception and thread interrupt mechanisms. These termination approaches, in combination with exceptions, allow for an elegant implementation of a recoverable action.

Further reading

Anderson, T. and Lee, P. A. (1990) *Fault Tolerance Principles and Practice*, 2nd edn. Englewood Cliffs, NJ: Prentice Hall.

Bollella, G., Brosgol, B., Dibble, P., Furr, S., Gosling, J., Hardin, D. and Turnbull, M. (2000) *The Real-Time Specification for Java*. Reading, MA: Addison-Wesley.

Lynch, N. A. (ed.) (1993). *Atomic Transactions*. San Mateo, CA: Morgan Kaufmann.

Lea, D. (1999) *Concurrent Programming in Java: Design Principles and Patterns*. Reading: Addison-Wesley.

Northcutt, J. D. (1987) *Mechanisms for Reliable Distributed Real-time Operating Systems: The Alpha Kernel*. New York: Academic Press.

Shrivastava, S. K., Mancini, L. and Randell, B. (1987) *On the Duality of Fault Tolerant Structures*, Lecture Notes in Computer Science, Volume 309, pp. 19–37. Berlin: Springer-Verlag.

Exercises

10.1 Distinguish between an atomic *action* and an atomic *transaction*. What is the relationship between an atomic transaction and a conversation?

10.2 Extend the semaphore implementation of an atomic action, given in Section 10.2.1, from a two-process interaction to a three-process interaction.

10.3 Rewrite the monitor implementation of an atomic action, given in Section 10.2.2, to allow both the processes to be active in the action simultaneously.

10.4 Rewrite the `Action_X` Ada package given in Section 10.2.3 so that it becomes a general purpose package for controlling a three-task conversation. (Hint: use generics).

10.5 Can your solution to Exercise 10.4 be extended to cope with an arbitrary number of tasks participating in the atomic action?

10.6 What would be the implications of extending Ada to enable one task to raise an exception in another?

10.7 Compare and contrast asynchronous notification and exception handling.

10.8 The following code illustrates a simple conversation between two processes. Show how this can be constructed as a Colloquy.

```
x,y,z : INTEGER;

PROCESS B;

PROCESS A;
BEGIN
  ...
  ACTION conversation (B) do
    ENSURE A_acceptance_test
    BY
       -- A_primary
       -- uses x,y
    ELSE BY
       -- A_secondary
       -- uses y,z
    ELSE
       ERROR
  END conversation;
  ...
END A;

PROCESS B;
BEGIN
  ...
  ACTION conversation (A) do
    ENSURE B_acceptance_test
    BY
       -- B_primary
       -- uses x,y
    ELSE BY
       -- B_secondary
       -- uses y,z
    ELSE
       ERROR
  END conversation;
  ...
END B;
```

10.9 In Section 10.8.2, backward and forward error recovery is shown between three Ada tasks. Show how they can be combined into a single solution that gives both forward and backward error recovery between the same three tasks.

10.10 Update the solution given in Section 10.8 to deal with the deserter problem.

10.11 Consider the following four fragments of code.

```
-- Fragment 1
select
    T.Call; -- an entry call to task T
    Flag := A;
```

```
or
      delay 10.0;
      Flag := B;
      -- code taking 2 seconds to execute
end select;

-- Fragment 2
select
      T.Call; -- an entry call to task T
      Flag := A;
else
      delay 10.0;
      Flag := B;
      -- code taking 2 seconds to execute
end select;

-- Fragment 3
select
      T.Call; -- an entry call to task T
      Flag := A;
then abort
      delay 10.0;
      Flag := B;
      -- code taking 2 seconds to execute
end select;

-- Fragment 4
select
      delay 10.0;
      Flag := A;
then abort
      T.Call; -- an entry call to task T
      Flag := B;
      -- code taking 2 seconds to execute
end select;
```

A rendezvous with T.Call takes 5 seconds to execute. What is the value of the Flag variable after the execution of each of the four fragments in each of the following cases. You may assume a Flag assignment statement takes zero execution time.

(1) T.Call is available when the select is executed.
(2) T.Call is NOT available when the select is executed and does not become available in the next 14 seconds.
(3) T.Call is NOT available when the select is executed, but does become available after 2 seconds.
(4) T.Call is NOT available when the select is executed but does become available after 8 seconds.

10.12 Consider the following package specification which provides a procedure to search part of a large character array for a *unique* fixed-length string. The procedure returns the position of the start of the string if it is found.

```
package Search_Support is
  type Array_Bounds is range 1 .. 1_000_000_000;
  type Large_Array is array(Array_Bounds) of Character;
  type Pointer is access Large_Array;

  type Search_String is new String(1..10);

  procedure Search(Pt: Pointer;
              Lower, Upper: Array_Bounds;
              Looking_For : Search_String;
              Found : out Boolean;
              At_Location : out Array_Bounds);
end Search_Support;
```

Three tasks wish to perform a concurrent search of the array for the same string; they are derived from a common task type:

```
task type Searcher(Search_Array: Pointer;
                   Lower, Upper: Array_Bounds) is
  entry Find(Looking_For : Search_String);
  entry Get_Result(At_Location : out Array_Bounds);
end Searcher;
```

The string to be found is passed via an initial rendezvous with the tasks.

Sketch the body of the task type (and any other objects you might need) so that when one task finds the string, all other tasks are *immediately* informed of the string's location so that further fruitless search is avoided. Assume that the SearchString will be found by one of the three tasks. Furthermore, all tasks must be prepared to pass back the result via the GetResult entry.

10.13 Consider the following Ada code fragment:

```
Error_1, Error_2 : exception;
task Watch;
task Signaller;

protected Atc is
  entry Go;
  procedure Signal;
private
  Flag : Boolean := False;
end Atc;

protected body Atc is
  entry Go when Flag is
  begin
    raise Error_1;
  end Go;

  procedure Signal is
  begin
    Flag := True;
  end Signal;
end Atc;
```

```
task body Watch is
begin
  . . .
  select
    Atc.Go;
  then abort
    -- code taking 100 millisecond
    raise Error_2;
  end select;
  . . .
exception
  when Error_1 =>
    Put_Line("Error_1 Caught");
  when Error_2 =>
    Put_Line("Error_2 Caught");
  when others =>
    Put_Line("Other Errors Caught");
end Watch;


task body Signaller is
begin
  . . .
  Atc.Signal;
  . . .
end Signaller;
```

Describe carefully the possible executions of this program fragment assuming that context switches between tasks can happen at any time.

10.14 A particular POSIX-based application consists of several periodic processes and has two modes of operation: MODE A and MODE B. The application has one process which only operates in MODE A. Sketch the design of this process assuming that when the system wishes to undertake a mode change, it sends a signal to all processes indicating the current mode of operation. Assume also the existence of a routine called WAITNEXTPERIOD, which will suspend the process until its next period of execution is due. Note that a mode change should only affect the process at the beginning of each period.

10.15 Illustrate how Ada's OOP model can be used to produce extensible atomic actions.

10.16 Compare and contrast the Ada and Java models for asynchronous transfer of control.

10.17 To what extent can standard Java be used to implement atomic actions?

10.18 Why have the Java routines resume(), stop() and suspend() been made obsolete?

10.19 Redo Exercise 10.14 for Real-Time Java.

10.20 Show how Ada's termination model of exception handling can be implemented in response to the receipt of a POSIX signal.

Chapter 11
Resource control

Chapter 10 considered the problem of achieving reliable process cooperation. It was pointed out that coordination between processes is also required if they are to share access to scarce resources such as external devices, files, shared data fields, buffers and encoded algorithms. These processes were termed **competing** processes. Much of the logical (that is, non-temporal) behaviour of real-time software is concerned with the allocation of resources between competing processes. Although the processes do not communicate directly with each other to pass information concerning their own activities, they may communicate to coordinate access to the shared resources. A few resources are amenable to unlimited concurrent access, however, most are in some way restricted in their usage.

As noted in Chapter 7, the implementation of resource entities requires some form of control agent. If the control agent is passive then the resource is said to be **protected** (or **synchronized**). Alternatively, if an active agent is required to program the correct level of control, the resource controller is called a **server**.

This chapter discusses the problem of reliable resource control. The general allocation of resources between competing processes is considered. Although such processes are independent of each other, the act of resource allocation has implications for reliability. In particular, failure of a process could result in an allocated resource becoming unavailable to other processes. Processes may be starved of resources if other processes are allowed to monopolize them. Furthermore, processes can become deadlocked by holding resources that other processes require while at the same time requesting more resources.

11.1 Resource control and atomic actions

Although processes need to communicate and synchronize to perform resource allocation, this need not be in the form of an atomic action. This is because the only information exchanged is that necessary to achieve harmonious resource sharing; it is not possible to exchange arbitrary information (Shrivastava and Banatre, 1978). As a result of this, the resource controller, be it in the form of a protected resource or a server, is able to ensure the global acceptability of any change to its local data. If this were *not* the case, then when a process (which had been allocated a resource) failed, it would be necessary to inform all processes, which had recently communicated with the resource controller, of its failure. However, the code necessary for a particular process to communicate with the controller should be an atomic action; thus no other process in the system can disrupt the process when it is being allocated, or is freeing, a resource. Furthermore, a resource manager and client process may use forward and backward error recovery to cope with any anticipated or unanticipated error conditions.

Although in the last chapter it was shown that in general no real-time language directly supported atomic actions, the indivisibility effect can be achieved by careful use of the available communication and synchronization primitives.

11.2 Resource management

Concerns of modularity (in particular information hiding) dictate that resources must be encapsulated and be accessed only through a high-level procedural interface; for example, in Ada, a package should, wherever possible, be used:

```
package Resource_Control is

   type Resource is limited private;
   function Allocate return Resource;
   procedure Free(This_Resource : Resource);

private
   type Resource is   ...

end Resource_Control;
```

If the resource manager is a server, then the body of Resource_Control will contain a task (or an access object to a task type). A protected resource will use a protected object within the package body.

In occam2, the only form for a resource manager is a server process (that is, all resource controllers must be programmed as active servers). Such a server should be instantiated from a procedure (PROC) with channel parameters:

```
PROC resource.manager([] CHAN OF Any request,
                      [] CHAN OF resource allocate,
                      [] CHAN OF resource free)
  ...
:
```

With monitor-based synchronization, such as POSIX with condition variables and mutexes or Java's synchronized classes, protected resources are naturally encapsulated within a monitor. For example, in Java:

```
public class ResourceManager
{
  public synchronized Resource allocate();
  public synchronized void free(Resource r);
}
```

Other forms of synchronization, such as busy waiting and semaphores, do not give the appropriate level of encapsulation, and will therefore not be considered further is this chapter. Conditional critical regions (CCRs) are also not explicitly evaluated, as protected objects are essentially a modern form of CCR.

The next section is concerned with a discussion of the expressive power and ease of use (usability) of various approaches to resource management. After this discussion, a further section on security will look at how a resource controller can protect itself against misuse.

11.3   Expressive power and ease of use

Bloom (1979) has suggested criteria for evaluating synchronization primitives in the context of resource management. This analysis forms the basis of this section, which looks at the expressive power and ease of use of synchronization primitives for resource control. The primitives to be evaluated are monitors/synchronized methods (with their use of condition synchronization), servers (with a message-based interface) and protected resources (implemented as protected objects). The latter two both use guards for synchronization, and hence one aspect of this analysis is a comparison between **condition synchronization** and **avoidance synchronization**.

Bloom uses the term 'expressive power' to mean the ability of a language to express required constraints on synchronization. Ease of use of a synchronization primitive encompasses:

- the ease with which it expresses each of these synchronization constraints,
- the ease with which it allows the constraints to be combined to achieve more complex synchronization schemes.

In the context of resource control, the information needed to express these constraints can be categorized (following Bloom) as follows:

- the type of service request;
- the order in which requests arrive;
- the state of the server and any objects it manages;
- the parameters of a request.

Bloom's original set of constraints included 'the history of the object' (that is, the sequence of all previous service requests). It is assumed here that the state of the object can be extended to include whatever historical information is needed. An addition to the list is however made, as Bloom did not include:

- the priority of the client.

A full discussion of process priority is given in Chapter 13. For the purpose of this chapter, the priority of a process is taken to be a measure of the process's importance.

As indicated above, there are in general two linguistic approaches to constraining access to a service (Liskov et al., 1986). The first is the **conditional wait**: all requests are accepted, but any process whose request cannot currently be met is suspended on a queue. The conventional monitor typifies this approach: a process whose request cannot be met is queued on a condition variable, and resumed when the request can be serviced. The second approach is **avoidance**: requests are not accepted unless they can be met. The conditions under which a request can safely be accepted are expressed as a guard on the action of acceptance.

Each of the five criteria, introduced above, for assessing synchronization approaches will now be considered.

11.3.1 Request type

Information about the type of operation requested can be used to give preference to one type of request over another (for example, read requests over write requests to a real-time database). With monitor-based synchronization and synchronized methods, the read and write operations could be programmed as distinct procedures, but the semantics of a monitor usually imply that outstanding calls on these monitor procedures are handled in an arbitrary, priority or FIFO way. It is not possible, therefore, to deal with read requests first; nor is it feasible to know how many outstanding calls there are to monitor procedures.

In Ada, different request types can readily be represented by different entries in the server task or protected object. Before gaining access to the entity (in order to queue on an entry), there is again no way of being giving preference over other calls. However, a natural way of giving preference to particular requests once they are queued is through guards which use the 'count' attribute of entries. The following shows a case in which Update requests are intended to have priority over Modify requests:

```
protected Resource_Manager is
  entry Update(...);
  entry Modify(...);
  procedure Lock;
  procedure Unlock;
private
  Manager_Locked : Boolean := False;
  ...
end Resource_Manager;

protected body Resource_Manager is

  entry Update(...) when not Manager_Locked is
  begin
    ...
  end Update;

  entry Modify(...) when not Manager_Locked and
                    Update'Count = 0 is
  begin
    ...
  end Modify;

  procedure Lock is
  begin
    Manager_Locked := True;
  end Lock;


  procedure Unlock is
  begin
    Manager_Locked := False;
  end Unlock;

end Resource_Manager;
```

With protected objects, only entries can have guards; procedures, once they gain access to the object, will execute immediately and hence preference to particular request types cannot be given using procedures.

In the occam2 language, each request type is associated with a different channel group. To choose between alternative actions, a server process must use a selective wait construct; fortunately occam2 provides a form of selective waiting that gives each alternative a different priority. The update–modify server is thus easily structured:

```
WHILE TRUE
  PRI ALT
    ALT i = 0 FOR max
      update[i] ? object
        -- update resource
    ALT j = 0 FOR max
      modify[j] ? object
        -- modify resource
```

Remember that if any of the operations require information to pass back to the caller, a double interaction is needed:

```
WHILE TRUE
  PRI ALT
    ALT i = 0 FOR max
      update[i] ? object
    ALT j = 0 FOR max
      read[j] ? Any
        -- extract appropriate component from resource
        output[j] ! object
```

with the caller making the following calls:

```
SEQ
  read[MyChannelToServer] ! Any
  output[MyChannelToServer] ? Result
```

The use of `PRI ALT` gives a static deterministic select. An equivalent form of select statement is available in Ada if one of the pragmas (`Queuing_Policy`) defined in the Real-Time Annex is used. This pragma defines the queuing policy for entries and select statements. It allows a deterministic select to be programmed (again using textual order to indicate priority), but requires all calling tasks to have the same priority (if they do not, then the priority of the calling task is given preference over the static ordering of the select alternatives).

11.3.2 Request order

Certain synchronization constraints may be formulated in terms of the order in which requests are received (to ensure fairness, for example, or to avoid starvation of a client). As has already been observed, monitors usually deal with requests in FIFO order, and therefore immediately meet this requirement. In Ada, outstanding requests of the same type (calls to the same entry) can also be serviced in a FIFO manner if the appropriate queuing policy is chosen. Outstanding requests of different types (for example, calls to different entries within a select statement) are, unfortunately, serviced in an arbitrary order with this policy. It is outside the programmer's control. Thus, there is no way of servicing requests of different types according to order of arrival unless a FIFO policy is used and all clients first call a common 'register' entry:

```
Server.Register;
Server.Action(...);
```

But this double call is not without difficulty (as will be explained in Section 11.3.4). With occam2's one-to-one naming structure, it is impossible for outstanding requests to a single `ALT` construct to be dealt with in the order of their arrival. A process may have a number of service channels to choose from, but cannot detect which channel has had a process waiting for the longest time. It should also be noted here that an occam2 server process must know the number of possible clients it has; each must be allocated a separate channel. Ada's model is much more amenable to the client–server paradigm as any number of clients can call an entry and each entry can be dealt with in a FIFO order. This is true for the server's task and protected resources (objects).

11.3.3 Server state

Some operations may be permissible only when the server and the objects it administers are in a particular state. For example, a resource can be allocated only if it is free, and an item can be placed in a buffer only if there is an empty slot. With avoidance synchronization, constraints based on state are expressed as guards and, with servers, on the positioning of accept statements (or message receive operators). Monitors are similarly quite adequate – with condition variables being used to implement constraints.

11.3.4 Request parameters

The order of operations of a server may be constrained by information contained in the parameters of requests. Such information typically relates to the identity or (in the case of quantifiable resources like memory) to the size of the request. A straightforward monitor structure (in Java) for a general resource controller follows. A request for a set of resources contains a parameter that indicates the size of the set required. If not enough resources are available then the caller is suspended; when any resources are released, all suspended clients are woken up to see if their request can now be met.

```
public class ResourceManager
{

  private final int maxResources = ...;
  private int resourcesFree;

  public ResourceManager()
  {
    resourcesFree = maxResources;
  }

  public synchronized void allocate(int size) throws
                    IntegerConstraintError, InterruptedException
    // see  Section 6.3.2 for definition of IntegerConstraintError
  {
    if(size > maxResources) throw new
                    IntegerConstraintError(1, maxResources, size);
    while(size < resourcesFree) wait();
    resourcesFree = resourcesFree - size;
  }

  public synchronized void free(int size)
  {
    resourcesFree = resourcesFree + size;
```

```
    notifyAll();
  }
}
```

With simple avoidance synchronization, the guards only have access to variables local to the server (or protected object); the data being carried with the call cannot be accessed until the call has been accepted. It is therefore necessary to construct a request as a double interaction. The following discusses how a resource allocator that will cater for this problem can be constructed as a server in Ada. The associated structures for a protected object (in Ada) and a server in occam2 are left as exercises for the reader (see Exercise 11.3 and 11.4). This Ada example is an adaptation of one given by Burns et al. (1987).

Resource allocation and Ada – an example

A way of tackling the problem in Ada is to associate an entry family with each type of request. Each permissible parameter value is mapped onto a unique index of the family so that requests with different parameters are directed to different entries. Obviously, this is only appropriate if the parameter is of discrete type.

 The approach is illustrated in the following package, which shows how lack of expressive power leads to a complex program structure (that is, poor ease of use). Again, consider an example of resource allocation in which the size of the request is given as a parameter of the request. As indicated above, the standard approach is to map the request parameters onto the indices of a family of entries, so that requests of different sizes are directed to different entries. For small ranges, the technique described earlier for 'request type' can be used, with the select statements enumerating the individual entries of the family. However, for larger ranges a more complicated solution is needed.

```
package Resource_Manager is
  Max_Resources : constant Integer := ...;
  type Resource_Range is new Integer range 1..Max_Resources;
  subtype Instances_Of_Resource is Resource_Range range 1.. ...;
  procedure Allocate(Size : Instances_Of_Resource);
  procedure Free(Size : Instances_Of_Resource);
end Resource_Manager;

package body Resource_Manager is

  task Manager is
    entry Sign_In(Size : Instances_Of_Resource);
    entry Allocate(Instances_Of_Resource); -- entry family
    entry Free(Size : Instances_Of_Resource);
  end Manager;

  procedure Allocate(Size : Instances_Of_Resource) is
  begin
    Manager.Sign_In(Size);  -- size is a parameter
    Manager.Allocate(Size); -- size is an index into a family
  end Allocate;
```

```
  procedure Free(Size : Instances_Of_Resource) is
  begin
    Manager.Free(Size);
  end Free;

  task body Manager is
     Pending : array(Instances_Of_Resource) of
       Natural := (others => 0);
     Resource_Free : Resource_Range := Resource_Range'Last;
     Allocated : Boolean;
  begin
    loop
      select
        accept Sign_In(Size : Instances_Of_Resource) do
          Pending(Size) := Pending(Size) + 1;
        end Sign_In;
      or
        accept Free(Size : Instances_Of_Resource) do
          Resource_Free := Resource_Free + Size;
        end Free;
      end select;
      loop -- main loop
        loop -- accept any pending Sign-In or Frees, do not wait
          select
            accept Sign_In(Size : Instances_Of_Resource) do
              Pending(Size) := Pending(Size) + 1;
            end Sign_In;
          or
            accept Free(Size : Instances_Of_Resource) do
              Resource_Free := Resource_Free + Size;
            end Free;
          else
            exit;
          end select;
        end loop;
        Allocated := False;

        for Request in reverse Instances_Of_Resource loop
          if Pending(Request) > 0 and Resource_Free >= Request then
            accept Allocate(Request);
            Pending(Request) := Pending(Request) - 1;
            Resource_Free := Resource_Free - Request;
            Allocated := True;
            exit; --loop to accept new Sign-Ins
          end if;
        end loop;
        exit when not Allocated;
      end loop;
    end loop;
  end Manager;
end Resource_Manager;
```

The manager gives priority to large requests. In order to acquire resources, a two-stage
interaction with the manager is required: a 'sign-in' request and an 'allocate' request.

This double interaction is hidden from the user of the resource by encapsulating the manager in a package and providing a single procedure (Allocate) to handle the request.

When there are no outstanding calls, the manager waits for a sign-in request or a free request (to release resources). When a sign-in arrives, its size is noted in the array of pending requests. A loop is then entered to record all sign-in and free requests that may be outstanding. This loop terminates as soon as there are no more requests.

A for loop is then used to scan through the pending array, and the request with the greatest size that can be accommodated is accepted. The main loop is then repeated in case a greater size request has attempted to sign-in. If no request can be services, the main loop is exited and the manager waits for new requests.

The solution is complicated by the need for the double rendezvous transaction. It is also expensive, as an entry is required for every possible size.

A much simpler system is to be found in the language SR (Andrews and Olsson, 1993). Here guards are allowed to access (that is, refer to) 'in' parameters. A resource request is, therefore, only accepted when the server or protected resource knows that it is in a state in which the request can be accommodated. The double call is not needed. For example (using Ada-like code, but not valid Ada, for a protected resource):

```
protected Resource_Control is    -- NOT VALID ADA
   entry Allocate(Size : Instances_Of_Resource);
   procedure Free(Size : Instances_Of_Resource);
private
   Resource_Free : Resource_Range := Max_Resources;
end Resource_Control;

protected body Resource_Control is

   entry Allocate(Size : Instances_Of_Resource)
      when Resources_Free >= Size is    -- NOT VALID ADA
   begin
      Resource_Free := Resource_Free - Size;
   end Allocate;

   procedure Free(Size : Instances_Of_Resource) is
   begin
      Resource_Free := Resource_Free + Size;
   end Free;

end Resource_Control;
```

Although syntactically simple, this type of solution has the disadvantage that it is not clear under what circumstances the guards or barriers need to be reevaluated. This can lead to inefficient implementations. An alternative approach is to keep the guards simple but to increase the expressive power of the communication mechanism by adding a **requeue** facility. This will be explained in detail in Section 11.4; however, in essence, it allowed a call that has been accepted (that is, it has passed a guard evaluation) to be requeued on a new (or indeed the same) entry where it must again pass a guard. The following also motivates the need for a requeue facility.

Double interactions and atomic actions

In the above discussions, examples in both Ada and occam2 were given that require the client process to make a double call on the server. One of the main factors that necessitates this double interaction is the lack of expressive power in simple avoidance synchronization. To program reliable resource control procedures, this structure must, therefore, be implemented as an atomic action. In occam2, the double call:

```
SEQ
  read[MyChannelToServer] ! Object
  output[MyChannelToServer] ? Result
```

does form an atomic action as the client is guaranteed to read the object having sent the request (similarly, the server is guaranteed to send the data). Unfortunately, with Ada this guarantee cannot be made (Wellings et al., 1984). Between the two calls; that is, after 'sign-in' but before 'allocate', an intermediate state of the client is observable from outside the 'atomic action':

```
begin
  Manager.Sign_In(Size);
  Manager.Allocate(Size);
end;
```

This state is observable in the sense that another task can abort the client between the two calls and leave the server in some difficulty:

- If the server assumes the client will make the second call, the abort will leave the server waiting for the call (that is, deadlocked).

- If the server protects itself against the abort of a client (by not waiting indefinitely for the second call), it may assume the client has been aborted when in fact it is merely slow in making the call; hence the client is blocked erroneously.

In the context of real-time software, three approaches have been advocated for dealing with the abort problem:

- Define the abort primitive to apply to an atomic action rather than a process; forward or backward error recovery can then be used when communicating with the server.

- Assume that abort is only used in extreme situations where the breaking of the atomic action is of no consequence.

- Try to protect the server from the effect of client abort.

The third approach, in Ada, involves removing the need for the double call by requeuing the first call (rather than have the client make the second call). As indicated above, this will be explained in more detail in Section 11.4 after the final assessment criteria has been dealt with.

11.3.5 Requester priority

The final criterion for evaluating synchronization primitives for resource management involves the use of client priority. If a collection of processes are runnable then the dispatcher can order their executions according to priority. The dispatcher cannot, however, have any control over processes suspended waiting for resources. It is therefore necessary for the order of operations of the resource manager also to be constrained by the relative priorities of the client processes.

In Ada, Real-Time Java and POSIX it is possible to define a queuing policy that is priority ordered, but in general concurrent programming languages, processes are released from primitives such as semaphores or condition variables in either an arbitrary or FIFO manner; monitors are often FIFO on entry; selective waits are often arbitrary or have a static textual priority ordering. In this latter case, it is possible to program clients so that they access the resource via a different interface (that is, entry or channel). For a small priority range, this is now equivalent to the *Request Type* constraint. For large priority ranges, it becomes equal to using *Request Parameters*, and hence the earlier approaches can be used.

Although monitors are often described as having a FIFO queue discipline, this is not really a fundamental property. Priority ordered monitors are clearly possible. Indeed, the POSIX and Real-Time Java implementations of monitors not only allow priority queues but also (conceptually) merge the external queue (of processes waiting to enter the monitor) and the internal one (of processes released by the signalling of a condition variable) to give a single priority-ordered queue. Hence, a higher priority process waiting to gain access to the monitor will be given preference over a process that is released internally.

11.3.6 Summary so far

In the above discussions, five requirements have been used to judge the appropriateness of current language structures for dealing with general resource control. Monitors, with their condition synchronization, deal well with request parameters; avoidance-based primitives needed to be augmented to deal with parameters but have the edge on request type.

It should, however, be noted that the requirements themselves are not mutually consistent. There may well be conflict between the priority of the client and the order of arrival of the requests; or between the operation requested and the priority of the requester. For example, in occam2 (with its deterministic selective wait) an update request was given priority over a modify by:

```
WHILE TRUE
  PRI ALT
    ALT i = 0 FOR max
      update[i] ? object
        -- update resource
```

```
ALT j = 0 FOR max
  modify[j] ? object
    -- modify resource
```

Arguably, if a caller to `modify` has a higher priority than a caller to `update` then the `modify` operation should take place first. These objectives cannot both be satisfied, and there is a need for synchronization primitives to be developed that will allow the programmer to deal with this conflict in a structured way.

It has been shown that it is necessary to construct the client's interaction with a resource manager as an atomic action. The absence of direct language primitives to support atomic actions and the existence of abort and asynchronous transfer of control (ATC) makes this difficult; processes can be asynchronously removed from monitors or terminated between two related calls to a server process. Abort is used to eliminate erroneous or redundant processes. If a monitor is constructed correctly then it can be assumed that a rogue process can do no damage while in a monitor (given that the knowledge that it is rogue was only available after it entered). Similarly a rogue client can do no damage if it is just waiting to make a second synchronous call.

It follows that there are well-specified situations in which a process should not be aborted (to be accurate, the effect of the abort will still occur but is postponed). This leads to the notion of **abort-deferred regions**.

Java has the notion of an ATC-deferred region. However, the Java `destroy` method does cause problems for resource controllers, and therefore should not be used. Similar arguments apply to the obsolete methods in the Java `Thread` class.

Ada defines the execution of a protected object (and a rendezvous) to be an abort-deferred region. However, interactions with resource controllers are usually potentially suspending and such calls are not allowed from within a protected object. For example, a double call on a server task could *not* be encapsulated within a protected object. However, as indicated earlier, the requeue solves many of these resource control problems; it is described in the next section.

11.4   The requeue facility

The discussion of Bloom's criteria has shown that avoidance synchronization leads to a more structured way of programming resource managers, but lacks expressive power when compared with lower-level condition synchronization. One means of enhancing the usability of avoidance synchronization is to add a requeue facility. The Ada language has such a facility, and hence the following discussion will focus on that language's model.

The key notion behind requeue is to move the task (which has been through one guard or barrier) to 'beyond' another guard. For an analogy, consider a person (task) waiting to enter a room (protected object) which has one or more doors (guarded entries) giving access to the room. Once inside, the person can be ejected (requeued) from the room and once again be placed behind a (potentially closed) door.

Ada allows requeues between task entries and protected object entries. A requeue can be to the same entry, to another entry in the same unit, or to another unit altogether.

Requeues from task entries to protected object entries (and vice versa) are allowed. However, the main use of requeue is to send the calling task to a different entry of the same unit from which the requeue was executed.

In Section 10.8.2, code was given that implemented forward error recovery and used a double interaction with Controller (that is, a call to Cleanup followed by a call to Wait_Cleanup). This could have been coded as a single call on Cleanup by requeuing onto Wait_Cleanup from within the protected entry (the Wait_Cleanup would then become a private entry):

```
entry Cleanup (Vote: Vote_T; Result : out Vote_T) when True is
begin
   if Vote = Aborted then
      Final_Result := Aborted;
   end if;
   requeue Wait_Cleanup with abort;
end Cleanup;
```

The 'with abort' facility will be described later. The effect of the call is to move the calling task onto the Wait_Cleanup entry (just as if the call had been made from outside). The execution of the requeue statement terminates the execution of the originally called entry.

The resource control problem provides another illustrative example of the application of requeue. In the following algorithm, an unsuccessful request is requeued on to a private entry (called Assign) of the protected object. The caller of this protected object now makes a single call on Request. Whenever resources are released, a note is taken of how many tasks are on the Assign entry. This number of tasks can then retry and either obtain their allocations or be requeued back onto the same Assign entry. The last task to retry opens the barrier:

```
type Request_Range is range 1..Max;

protected Resource_Controller is
   entry Request(R : out Resource; Amount : Request_Range);
   procedure Free(R : Resource; Amount : Request_Range);
private
   entry Assign(R : out Resource; Amount : Request_Range);
   Freed : Request_Range := Request_Range'Last;
   New_Resources_Released : Boolean := False;
   To_Try : Natural := 0;
   ...
end Resource_Controller;


protected body Resource_Controller is
   entry Request(R : out Resource; Amount : Request_Range)
         when Freed > 0 is
   begin
     if Amount <= Freed then
        Freed := Freed - Amount;
        -- allocate
```

```
      else
        requeue Assign;
      end if;
  end Request;



  entry Assign(R : out Resource; Amount : Request_Range)
      when New_Resources_Released is
  begin
    To_Try := To_Try - 1;
    if To_Try = 0 then
      New_Resources_Released := False;
    end if;
    if Amount <= Freed then
      Freed := Freed - Amount;
      -- allocate
    else
      requeue Assign;
    end if;
  end Assign;



  procedure Free(R : Resource; Amount : Request_Range) is
  begin
    Freed := Freed + Amount;
    -- free resources
    if Assign'Count > 0 then
      To_Try := Assign'Count;
      New_Resources_Released := True;
    end if;
  end Free;
end Resource_Controller;
```

Note that this will only work if the Assign entry queuing discipline is FIFO. It is left
as an exercise for the reader (Exercise 11.5) to develop a priority-based algorithm.

It should be observed that a more efficient algorithm can be derived if the protected
object records the smallest outstanding request. The barrier should then only be opened
in Free (or remain opened in Assign) if Freed >= Smallest.

Even with this style of solution, however, it is difficult to give priority to certain
requests other than in FIFO or task priority order. As indicated earlier, to program
this level of control requires a family of entries. However, with requeue, an improved
structure can be given; that is rather than

```
procedure Allocate(Size : Instances_Of_Resource) is
begin
  Manager.Sign_In(Size);   -- size is a parameter
  Manager.Allocate(Size); -- size is a family index
end Allocate;
```

with the server task having:

```
accept Sign_In(Size : Instances_Of_Resource) do
   Pending(Size) := Pending(Size) + 1;
end Sign_In;
```

the double call can be made atomic by using:

```
procedure Allocate(Size : Instances_Of_Resource) is
begin
  Manager.Sign_In(Size);   -- size is a parameter
end Allocate;
```

and

```
accept Sign_In(Size : Instances_Of_Resource) do
   Pending(Size) := Pending(Size) + 1;
   requeue Allocate(Size);
end Sign_In;
```

The server task can then be made more secure by having its Allocate entry private:

```
task Manager is
  entry Sign_In(Size : Instances_Of_Resource);
  entry Free(Size : Instances_Of_Resource);
private
  entry Allocate(Instances_Of_Resource)
                (Size : Instances_Of_Resource);
end Manager;
```

This algorithm is not only more straightforward than the one given earlier, but it also has the advantage that it is resilient to a task removing itself from an entry queue (after the count attribute has acknowledged its presence). Once a task has been requeued it cannot be aborted or subject to a time out on the entry call – see following discussion.

11.4.1 Semantics of requeue

It is important to appreciate that requeue is not a simple call. If procedure P calls procedure Q, then, after Q has finished, control is passed back to P. But if entry X requeues on entry Y, control is not passed back to X. After Y has completed, control passes back to the object that called X. Hence, when an entry or accept body executes a requeue, that body is completed.

One consequence of this is that when a requeue is from one protected object to another then mutual exclusion on the original object is given up once the task is queued. Other tasks waiting to enter the first object will be able to do so. However, a requeue to the same protected object will retain the mutual exclusion lock (if the target entry is open).

The entry named in a requeue statement (called the **target** entry) must either have no parameters or have a parameter profile that is equivalent (that is, type conformant)

with that of the entry (or accept) statement from which the requeue is made. For example, in the resource control program, the parameters of Assign are identical to those of
Allocate. Because of this rule, it is not necessary to give the actual parameters with
the call; indeed, it is forbidden to do so (in case the programmer tries to change them).
Hence if the target entry has no parameters, no information is passed; if it has parameters, then the corresponding parameters in the entity that is executing the requeue are
mapped across. Because of this rule, the algorithm given earlier to get FIFO ordering
over a number of different entries – that is, using a single register entry:

```
Server.Register;
Server.Action(...);
```

– cannot be programmed as a single call using requeue (as the parameters to all the
different actions may not be identical).

An optional 'with abort' clause can be used with the requeue statement. Usually
when a task is on an entry queue, it will remain there until serviced unless it made
a timed entry call (see Section 12.4.2) or is removed due to the use of asynchronous
transfer of control or abort. Once the task has been accepted (or starts to execute the
entry of a protected object), the timeout is cancelled and the effect of any abort attempt
is postponed until the task comes out of the entry. There is, however, a question as to
what should happen with requeue. Consider the abort issue; clearly two views can be
taken:

- As the first call has been accepted, the abort should now remain postponed so that
  the task or protected object can be assured that the second call is there.

- If the requeue puts the calling task back onto an entry queue, then abort should
  again be possible.

A similar argument can be made with timeouts. The requeue statement allows
both views to be programmed; the default does not allow further timeouts or aborts, the
addition of the 'with abort' clause enables the task to be removed from the second entry.
These semantics are needed, for example, with the forward error recovery algorithm
given at the beginning of this section.

The real issue (in deciding whether to use 'with abort' or not) is whether the
protected object (or server task) having requeued the client task expects it to be there
when the guard/barrier is opened. If the correct behaviour of the object requires the
task's presence, then 'with abort' should *not* be used.

11.4.2 Requeuing to other entries

Although requeuing to the same entity represents the normal use of requeue, there are
situations in which the full generality of this language feature is useful.

Consider the situation in which resources are controlled by a hierarchy of objects.
For example, a network router might have a choice of three communication lines on
which to forward messages: Line_A is the preferred route, but if it becomes overloaded

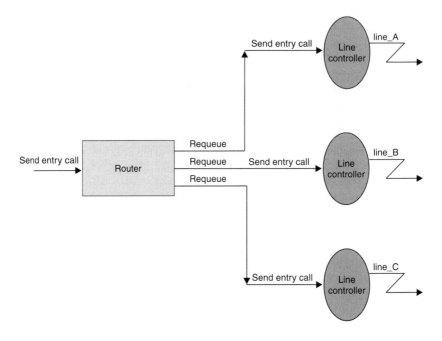

Figure 11.1   A network router.

Line_B can be used; if this also becomes overloaded Line_C can be used. Each line
is controlled by a server task; it is an active entity as it has housekeeping operations to
perform. A protected unit acts as an interface to the router: it decides which of the three
channels should be used and then uses requeue to pass the request to the appropriate
server. The structure of the solution is illustrated in Figure 11.1, and the program is
given below:

```
type Line_Id is (Line_A, Line_B, Line_C);
type Line_Status is array (Line_Id) of Boolean;

task type Line_Controller(Id : Line_Id) is
   entry Request(...);
end Line_Controller;

protected Router is
   entry Send(...);    --   same parameter profile as Request
   procedure Overloaded(Line : Line_Id);
   procedure Clear(Line : Line_Id);
private
   Ok : Line_Status := (others => True);
end Router;
```

```
La : Line_Controller(Line_A);
Lb : Line_Controller(Line_B);
Lc : Line_Controller(Line_C);


task body Line_Controller is
  ...
begin
  loop
    select
      accept Request(...) do
        -- service request
      end Request;
    or
      terminate;
    end select;
    -- housekeeping including possibly
    Router.Overloaded(Id);
    -- or
    Router.Clear(Id);
  end loop;
end Line_Controller;


protected body Router is

  entry Send(...) when Ok(Line_A) or Ok(Line_B) or Ok(Line_C) is
  begin
    if Ok(Line_A) then
      requeue La.Request with abort;
    elsif Ok(Line_B) then
      requeue Lb.Request with abort;
    else
      requeue Lc.Request with abort;
    end if;
  end Send;

  procedure Overloaded(Line : Line_Id) is
  begin
    Ok(Line) := False;
  end Overloaded;

  procedure Clear(Line : Line_Id) is
  begin
    Ok(Line) := True;
  end Clear;

end Router;
```

11.5 Asymmetric naming and security

In languages that have direct symmetric naming, a server process (or protected resource) always knows the identity of the client process with which it is dealing. This is also the case with indirect naming schemes based on a one-to-one intermediary (such as an occam2 channel). Asymmetric naming, however, results in the server being unaware of the identity of the client. It was noted earlier that this has the advantage that general-purpose servers can be written but it can lead to poor security on the use of resources. In particular, a server process may wish to know the identity of the calling client so that

- a request can be refused on the grounds of deadlock prevention (see Section 11.7) or fairness (that is, to grant the request would be unfair to other clients)

- it can be guaranteed that resources are released only by the process that earlier obtained them.

In CHILL, processes can have an **instance** or name associated with them (see Section 9.6) which enables a resource controller (a **region** in CHILL) to know the identity of calling processes. A similar facility can be programmed in Ada using task identification (see Section 7.3.6) or in Java using `Thread.currentThread`. Consider the simple resource controller, in Ada, that only manages one resource.

```
protected Controller is
   entry Allocate;
   procedure Free;
private
   Allocated : Boolean := False;
   Current_Owner : Task_Id := Null_Task_Id;
end Controller;


protected body Controller is

   entry Allocate when not Allocated is
   begin
     Allocated := True;
     Current_Owner := Allocated'Caller;
   end Allocate;

   procedure Free is
   begin
     if Current_Task /= Current_Owner then
       raise Invalid_Caller; -- an appropriate exception
     end if;
     Allocated := False;
     Current_Owner := Null_Task_Id;
   end Free;

end Controller;
```

Note that with this Ada facility, the caller of an entry is identified by the `Caller` attribute, whereas the caller of a procedure is obtained from the function `Current_Task`. The reasons for this difference are not important here (see Burns and Wellings (1998) for the rationale).

11.6   Resource usage

When competing or cooperating processes require resources, the normal mode of operation is for them to: `request` the resource (waiting if necessary), `use` the resource, and then `release` it. A resource is normally requested for use in one of two modes of access. These are shared access or exclusive access. Shared access is where the resource can be used concurrently by more than one process: for example a read-only file. Exclusive access requires that only one process is allowed access to the resource at any one time: for example a physical resource like a line printer. Some resources can be used in either mode. In this case, if a process requests access to the resource in sharable mode while it is being accessed in exclusive mode, then that process must wait. If the resource was already being accessed in sharable mode then the process can continue. Similarly, if exclusive access to a resource is requested then the process making the request must wait for the processes currently accessing the resource in sharable mode to finish.

As processes may be blocked when requesting resources, it is imperative that they do not request resources until they need them. Furthermore, once allocated they should release them as soon as possible. If this is not done then the performance of the system can drop dramatically as processes continually wait for their share of a scarce resource. Unfortunately, if processes release resources too soon and then fail, they may have passed on erroneous information through the resource. For this reason, the *two-phased* resource usage, introduced in Section 10.1.1, must be modified so that resources are not released until the action is completed. Any recovery procedure within the action must either release the resources, if successful recovery is performed, or undo any effects on the resource. The latter is required if recovery cannot be achieved and the system must be restored to a safe state. With forward error recovery, these operations can be performed by exception handlers. With backward error recovery, it is not possible to perform these operations without some additional language support (Shrivastava, 1979).

11.7   Deadlock

With many processes competing for a finite number of resources, a situation may occur where one process, P_1, has sole access to a resource, R_1, while waiting for access to another resource, R_2. If process P_2 already has sole access to R_2 and is waiting for access to R_1, then **deadlock** has occurred because both processes are waiting for each other to release a resource. With deadlock, all affected processes are suspended indefinitely. A similar acute condition is where a collection of processes are inhibited from proceeding but are still executing. This situation is known as **livelock**. A typical example would be a collection of interacting processes stuck in loops from which they cannot proceed but in which they are doing no useful work.

Another possible problem occurs when several processes are continually attempting to gain sole access to the same resource; if the resource allocation policy is not fair, one process may never get its turn to access the resource. This is called **indefinite postponement** or **starvation** or **lockout** (see Chapter 8). In concurrent systems, **liveness** means that if something is supposed to happen, it eventually will. Breaches of liveness result from deadlock, livelock or starvation. Note that liveness is not as strong a condition as fairness. It is, however, difficult to give a single precise definition of fairness.

The remainder of this section concentrates on deadlock and how it can be prevented, avoided, detected and recovered from.

11.7.1   Necessary conditions for deadlock to occur

There are four necessary conditions that must hold if deadlock is to occur:

- **mutual exclusion** – only one process can use a resource at once (that is, the resource is non-sharable or at least limited in its concurrent access);
- **hold and wait** – there must exist processes which are holding resources while waiting for others;
- **no preemption** – a resource can only be released voluntarily by a process; and
- **circular wait** – a circular chain of processes must exist such that each process holds resources which are being requested by the next process in the chain.

11.7.2   Methods of handling deadlock

If a real-time system is to be reliable, it must address the issue of deadlock. There are three possible approaches:

- deadlock prevention
- deadlock avoidance
- deadlock detection and recovery.

These are now briefly discussed. For a more comprehensive discussion the reader is referred to any book on operating systems.

Deadlock prevention

Deadlock can be prevented by ensuring that at least one of the four conditions required for deadlock never occurs.

Mutual exclusion: If resources are sharable they cannot be involved in a deadlock. Unfortunately, although a few resources are amenable to concurrent access most are, in some way, restricted in their usage.

Hold and wait: One very simple way in which deadlock can be avoided is to require that processes either request resources before they begin their execution or at stages in their execution when they have no resources allocated. Unfortunately, this tends to be inefficient in its use of resources and can lead to starvation.

No preemption: If the constraint that resources should not be preempted from processes is relaxed then deadlock can be prevented. There are several approaches, including releasing all the resources of a process if it tries to allocate a further resource and fails; and stealing a resource if a process requests a resource which is allocated to another process which is blocked (waiting for another resource). The blocked process is now waiting for one extra resource. The disadvantage of this approach is that it requires the state of the resource to be saved and restored; in many cases this may not be possible.

Circular waits: To avoid circular waits, a linear ordering on all resource types can be imposed. Each resource type can then be allocated a number according to this ordering. Suppose R is the set of resource types thus

$$R = \langle R_1, R_2, ...R_n \rangle \ the \ set \ of \ all \ resources$$

and the function F takes a resource type and returns its position in the linear order. If a process has resource R_J and it requests resource R_K, the request will only be considered if

$$F(R_J) < F(R_K)$$

Alternatively, a process requesting a resource R_J must first release all resources R_I where

$$F(R_I) < F(R_J).$$

Note that the function F should be derived according to the usage of the resource.

Another approach to prevention is to analyze the program formally so that it is possible to verify that circular waits are not possible. The ease with which programs can be so analyzed is very dependent upon the concurrency model employed. Low-level synchronization primitives are extremely difficult to examine in this way; message-based structures are, by comparison, much more amenable to the application of formal proof rules. Occam2 is particularly well designed for this purpose. Its semantics have been formally specified and much of the theory of deadlock-free programs that has been developed for CSP is equally applicable to occam2 (Hoare, 1985).

Deadlock avoidance

If more information on the pattern of resource usage is known then it is possible to construct an algorithm which will allow all the four conditions necessary for deadlock

Process	Has	Needs
P_0	5	10
P_1	2	4
P_2	2	9

Total allocated = 9
Tape units available = 3

Table 11.1   Safe state.

to occur but which will also ensure that the system never enters a deadlock state. A deadlock avoidance algorithm will examine dynamically the resource allocation state and take action to ensure that the system can never enter into deadlock. However, it is not sufficient merely to ask whether the next new state is deadlock, for if it is, it may not be possible to take any alternative action that would avoid this condition. Rather, it is necessary to ask if the system remains in a safe state. The resource allocation state is given by:

```
state = number of resources available, number allocated and
            maximum demand on resources of each process
```

The system is **safe** if the system can allocate resources to each process (up to the maximum they require) in some order and still avoid deadlock. For example, consider a data acquisition system which requires access to bulk secondary storage. It has 12 magnetic tape units and consists of three processes: P_0, which requires a maximum of 10 tape units, P_1, which requires 4, and P_2, which requires 9. Suppose at a time T_i that P_0 has 5, P_1 has 2 and P_2 has 2 (3 tape units are therefore available) as illustrated in Table 11.1.

This is a safe state because there exists a sequence $\langle P_1, P_0, P_2 \rangle$ which will allow all the processes to terminate. If at time $T_i + 1$, P_2 requests 1 tape unit and it is allocated, the state becomes: P_0 has 5, P_1 has 2 and P_2 has 3 and there are 2 available, as shown in Table 11.2.

Process	Has	Needs
P_0	5	10
P_1	2	4
P_2	3	9

Total allocated = 10
Tape units available = 2

Table 11.2   Unsafe state.

This is no longer a safe state; with the available tape units only P_1 can terminate, leaving: P_0 with 5, P_2 with 3 but only 4 available. Neither P_0 nor P_2 can, therefore, be satisfied so the system may enter a deadlock situation. The request from P_2 at $T_i + 1$ should be blocked by the system.

Obviously, deadlock is an unsafe state. A system which is unsafe may lead to deadlock, but *it may not*. However, if the system remains safe it will *not deadlock*. With more than one resource type, the avoidance algorithm becomes more complicated. A common one in use is the **Banker's** algorithm. A discussion of this can be found in most operating system texts.

Deadlock detection and recovery

In many general-purpose concurrent systems, the resource allocation usage is *a priori* unknown. Even if it is known, the cost of deadlock avoidance is often prohibitive. Consequently many of these systems will ignore the problems of deadlock until they enter a deadlock state. They then take some corrective action. Unfortunately, if there are many processes, it may be quite difficult to detect deadlock. One approach is to use **resource allocation graphs** (sometimes called **resource dependency graphs**).

To detect whether a group of processes are deadlocked requires the resource allocation system to be aware of which resources have already been allocated to which processes, and which processes are blocked waiting for resources that have already been allocated. If it has this information, it can construct a resource allocation graph.

Using the graph, the system can determine whether deadlock exists. It does this by first examining those processes that are not blocked. It then reduces the graph by removing those processes, the assumption being that if the processes continue to run they will eventually terminate.

In general, if no cycles appear in a resource allocation graph, no deadlock has occurred. However, if there is a cycle the system may *or may not* be in deadlock, depending on other processes in the graph. Therefore resource allocation graphs can be used to prevent deadlock. Every time a resource is requested, the graph is updated. If a cycle exists then potentially deadlock may occur, and the request must therefore be refused.

If deadlock can be detected then recovery can take place by breaking mutual exclusion on one or more resources, aborting one or more processes, or preempting some resources from one or more deadlocked processes. Breaking mutual exclusion, although easy to achieve, could leave the system in an inconsistent state; if a resource was sharable then it should be made sharable. Aborting one or more processes is a very drastic measure to take, and again may leave the system in an inconsistent state. If either of these options is adopted, account must be taken of the cost of the action which may include considerations of process priority, how long a process has been executing, how many more resources it needs, and so on.

Preemption requires that one or more victims be selected. Selection should include consideration of the priority of the processes, whether the resources are simple to preempt, and how near the processes are to completion. Once selected, the course of action will depend on what form of error recovery is used. With backward error recovery, the process is restarted at a recovery point prior to the allocation of the resource. With forward error recovery, an appropriate exception is raised in the victim, which must then take some corrective action.

Clearly, care must be taken to ensure that the same process is not continually rolled back and therefore starved of resources. The most common solution to this problem is to include, as part of a cost factor, the number of times a process gets preempted.

This section has briefly reviewed the possible approaches that a system can adopt to avoid or cope with deadlock. The majority of these are very expensive to implement and may well be prohibitive in a real-time system. This is particularly true if the system is distributed. Consequently, some systems use simple timeouts on resource allocation requests. If the timeout expires then processes can assume potential deadlock and take some alternative course of action. In Chapter 13, an approach to resource sharing based upon priority scheduling is introduced. It has the distinctly useful property that it is deadlock free – at least on single processor systems.

Summary

In every computer system, there are many processes competing for a limited set of resources. Algorithms are required which both manage the resource al- location/deallocation procedures (the mechanism of resource allocation) and which guarantee that resources are allocated to processes according to a pre- defined behaviour (the policy of resource allocation). These algorithms are also responsible for ensuring that processes cannot deadlock while waiting for re- source allocation requests to be fulfilled.

Sharing resources between processes requires those processes to com- municate and synchronize. Therefore it is essential that the synchronization facilities provided by a real-time language have sufficient expressive power to allow a wide range of synchronization constraints to be specified. These con- straints can be categorized as follows: resource scheduling must take account of

- the type of service request;
- the order in which requests arrive;
- the state of the server and any objects it manages;
- the parameters of a request;
- the priority of the client.

Monitors (with condition synchronization) deal well with request parame- ters; avoidance synchronization in message-based servers or protected objects cope adequately with request types.

Where there is insufficient expressive power, processes are often forced into a double interaction with a resource manager. This must be performed as an atomic action; otherwise it is possible for the client process to be aborted after the first interaction but before the second. If this possibility does exist then it is very difficult to program reliable resource managers. One means of extending the expressive power of guards is to allow requeuing. This facility enables avoidance synchronization to be as effective as condition synchronization.

A key requirement of resource management is the provision of deadlock-free usage. There are four necessary conditions that must hold if deadlock is to occur:

- mutual exclusion
- hold and wait
- no preemption
- circular wait.

If a real-time system is to be reliable it must address the issue of deadlock. There are three possible approaches:

- deadlock prevention – preventing deadlock by ensuring that at least one of the above four conditions never occurs;
- deadlock avoidance – using information on the pattern of resource usage to construct an algorithm which will allow all the four conditions to occur, but which will also ensure that the systems never enters a deadlock state;
- deadlock detection and recovery – allowing deadlock to occur (and be detected) and then recovering by: breaking mutual exclusion on one or more resources, aborting one or more processes, or by preempting some resources from one or more deadlocked processes.

Further reading

Bloom, T. (1979) Evaluating Synchronization Mechanisms. *Proceedings of the Seventh Symposium on Operating Systems Principles*, ACM, pp. 24–32.

Silberschatz, A. and Galvin, P. A. (1998) *Operating System Concepts*. New York: John Wiley & Sons.

Exercises

11.1 The following resource controller attempts to associate priorities with request.

```
type Level is (Urgent, Medium, Low);

task Controller is
    entry Request(Level) (D:Data);
end Controller;
```

```
task body Controller is
  . . .
begin
  loop
    . . .
    select
      accept Request(Urgent)(D:Data) do
        . . .
      end;
    or
      when Request(Urgent)'Count = 0 =>
        accept Request(Medium)(D:Data) do
          . . .
        end;
    or
      when Request(Urgent)'Count = 0  and
           Request(Medium)'Count = 0 =>
        accept Request(Low)(D:Data) do
          . . .
        end;
    end select
    . . .
  end loop;
end Controller;
```

Explain this solution and indicate under what conditions it will fail. Why would it not be advisable to extend the above solution to cope with a numeric priority which falls in the range 0 to 1000? Sketch an alternative solution which will cope with larger priority ranges. You may assume that the calling tasks issue simple entry calls and are not aborted.

11.2 Show how the resource manager given in Section 11.3.1 can be programmed in Java (which does not have a requeue facility).

11.3 Show how the Ada resource manager given in Section 11.3.4 can be programmed using protected objects.

11.4 Show how the Ada resource manager given in Section 11.3.4 can be programmed in occam2.

11.5 Show how the Ada resource manager given in Section 11.4 can be updated to allow high priority clients to be given preference over low priority clients.

11.6 Show how POSIX mutexes and condition variables can be used to implement a resource controller where several identical resources can be allocated and freed. Clients can request and free one or more resources using the following interface:

```
typedef struct {
    ... /* fill in */
  } resource;

void allocate(int size, resource *R);
void deallocate(int size, resource *R);

void initialize(resource *R);
```

11.7 Consider a system which has five processes (P_1, P_2 .. P_5) and 7 resource types (R_1, R_2 .. R_7) There is one instance of resources 2, 5 and 7 and two instances of resources 1, 3, 4 and 6. Process 1 has been allocated an instance of R_1 and requires an instance of R_7. Process 2 has been allocated an instance of R_1, R_2 and R_3 and requires R_5. Process 3 has been allocated an instance of R_3 and R_4 and requires R_1. Process 4 has been allocated R_4 and R_5 and requires R_2. Process 5 has been allocated R_7.

Is this system in deadlock? Give your reasons.

11.8 A system is in a state described in Table 11.3: Is this system in a safe or an unsafe state? Give your reasons.

	Current load	Maximum need
Process 1	2	12
Process 2	4	10
Process 3	2	5
Process 4	0	5
Process 5	2	4
Process 6	1	2
Process 7	5	13
Units available = 1		

Table 11.3   A system's state for Exercise 11.8.

11.9 A system that is in an unsafe state will not necessarily deadlock. Explain why this is true. Give an example of an unsafe state and show how the processes could complete without deadlock occurring.

11.10 Show how the network router example given in Section 11.4.2 can be programmed in Java.

Chapter 12
Real-time facilities

In Chapter 1, it was noted that a language for programming embedded systems requires facilities for real-time control. Indeed, the term 'real-time' has been used as a synonym for this class of system. Given the importance of time in many embedded systems, it may appear strange that consideration of this topic has been postponed until Chapter 12. Facilities for real-time control are, however, generally built upon the concurrency model within the language, and it is therefore necessary to have covered this area first.

The introduction of the notion of time into a programming language can best be described in terms of three largely independent topics:

(1) Interfacing with 'Time'; for example, accessing clocks so that the passage of time can be measured, delaying processes until some future time, and programming timeouts so that the non-occurrence of some event can be recognized and dealt with.

(2) Representing timing requirements; for example, specifying rates of execution and deadlines.

(3) Satisfying timing requirements.

This chapter is largely concerned with the first two of these topics, although it will commence with some discussion of the notion of time itself. Chapter 13 considers ways of implementing systems such that the worst-case temporal behaviour can be predicted, and hence timing requirements ratified.

12.1   The notion of time

Our everyday experiences are so intrinsically linked to notions of past, present and future that it is surprising that the question 'What is time?' is still largely unresolved. Philosophers, mathematicians, physicists and, more recently, engineers have all studied 'time' in minute detail, but there is still no consensus on a definitive theory of time. As St Augustine stated:

> What, then, is time? If no one asks me, I know what it is. If I wish to explain it to him who asks me, I do not know.

A key question in the philosophical discussions of time can be stated succinctly as 'do we exist in time, or is time part of our existence?'. The two mainstream schools of thought are Reductionism and Platonism. All agree that human (and biological) history is made up of events, and that these events are ordered. Platonists believe that time is a fundamental property of nature; it is continuous, non-ending and non-beginning, 'and possesses these properties as a matter of necessity'. Our notion of time is derived from a mapping of historical events onto this external time reference.

Reductionists, by comparison, do without this external reference. Historical time, as made up of historical events, is the only meaningful notion of time. By assuming that certain events are 'regular' (for example, sunrise, winter solstice, vibrations of atoms, and so on), they can invent a useful time reference that enables the passage of time to be measured. But this time reference is a construction, not a given.

A consequence of the Reductionists view is that time cannot progress without change occurring. If the universe started with a 'Big Bang' then this represents the very first historical event and hence time itself started with 'space' at this first epoch. For Platonists, the Big Bang is just one event on an unbounded time line.

Over large distances, Einstein showed that relativity effects impinge not only on time directly but also on the temporal ordering of events. Within the special theory of relativity, the observer of events imposes a frame of references. One observer may place event A before event B; another observer (in a different frame of reference) may reverse the order. Due to such difficulties with temporal ordering, Einstein introduced **causal ordering**. Event A can cause event B if all possible observers see event A occurring first. Another way of defining such causality is to postulate the existence of a signal that travels, at a speed no greater than the speed of light, from event A to event B.

These different themes of time are well illustrated by the notion of simultaneous events. To Platonists, the events are simultaneous if they occur 'at the same time'. For Reductionists, simultaneous events 'happen together'. With Special Relativity, simultaneous events are those for which a causal relationship does not exist.

From a mathematical point of view, there are many different topologies for time. The most common one comes from equating the passage of time with a 'real' line. Hence time is linear, transitive, irreflexive and dense:

- Linearity: $\forall x, y : x < y \ or \ y < x \ or \ x = y$
- Transitivity: $\forall x, y, z : (x < y \ and \ y < z) \Rightarrow x < z$
- Irreflexivity: $\forall x : not \ (x < x)$
- Density: $\forall x, y : x < y \Rightarrow \exists z : (x < z < y)$

The engineering perspective can largely ignore the philosopher's issue of time. An embedded real-time computer system needs to coordinate its execution with the 'time' of its environment. The term 'real' is used to draw a distinction with the computer's time. It is real because it is external. Whether this external frame of reference is a Reductionist's construction or an approximative for the Platonists' 'absolute' time frame is not significant. Moreover, for most applications, relativistic effects can also be ignored. In terms of the mathematical topology of real-time systems, there are conflicting opinions as to whether time should be viewed as dense or discrete. Because computers work in discrete time, there is some advantage in constructing computational models based upon discrete time. The significant experience that other branches of engineering have in using, to good effect, dense time models argues the other way. Attempts to integrate both approaches has merely led to a third approach – hybrid systems. If, by general consensus, a series of events is deemed to be regular then it is possible to define a standard measurement of time. Many such standards have existed in the past. Table 12.1 gives a brief description of some of the more significant ones. This description is taken from Hoogeboom and Halang (1992).

12.2   Access to a clock

If a program is going to interact in any meaningful way with the time frame of its environment then it must have access to some method of 'telling the time' or, at least, have some way of measuring the passage of time. This can be done in two distinct ways:

- by having direct access to the environment's time frame,
- by using an internal hardware clock that gives an adequate approximation to the passage of time in the environment.

The first approach is not common but can be achieved in a number of ways. The simplest is for the environment to supply a regular interrupt that is clocked internally. At the other extreme, the system (or indeed each node of a distributed system) can be fitted with radio receivers and use one of the international time signals. For example, in Germany, transmitters are provided for UTC and IAT signals. The worldwide navigation system (GPS) also provides a UTC service.

From the programmer's perspective, access to time can either be provided by a clock primitive in the language or via a device driver for the internal clock, external clock or radio receiver. The programming of device drivers is the topic of Chapter 15; the following subsections illustrate how occam, Ada, Java, and POSIX provide clock abstractions.

Name	Description	Note
True solar day	Time between two successive culminations (highest point of the Sun)	Varies through the year by 15 minutes (approx.)
Temporal hour	One-twelfth part of the time between sunrise and sunset	Varies considerably through the year
Universal Time (UT0)	Mean solar time at Greenwich meridian	Defined in 1884
Second (1)	1/86 400 of a mean solar day	
Second (2)	1/31 566 925.9747 of the tropical year for 1900	Ephemeris Time defined in 1955
UT1	Correction to UT0 because of polar motion	
UT2	Correction of UT1 because of variation in the speed of rotation of the Earth	
Second (3)	Duration of 9 192 631 770 periods of the radiation corresponding to the transition between two hyperfine levels of the ground state of the caesium 133 atom	Accuracy of current caesium atomic clocks deemed to be one part in 10^{13} (that is, one clock error per 300 000 years)
International Atomic Time (IAT)	Based upon caesium atomic clock	
Coordinated Universal Time (UTC)	An IAT clock synchronized to UT2 by the addition of occasional leap ticks	Maximum difference between UT2 (which is based on astronomical measurement) and UTC (which is based upon atomic measurement) is kept to below 0.5 seconds

Table 12.1   Time standards.

12.2.1 TIMERs in occam2

Any occam2 process can obtain a value of the 'local' clock by reading from a TIMER (there is no facility for accessing calendar time). To be consistent with the occam2 model of communication (which is one-to-one), each process must use a distinct TIMER. Reading from a TIMER follows the syntax of channel read, but the semantics are different in that a TIMER read cannot lead to suspension, that is, the clock is always ready to output.

```
TIMER clock:
INT Time:
SEQ
  clock ? Time     -- read time
```

The value produced by a TIMER is of type INT, but of implementation-dependent meaning: it gives a relative, not absolute, clock value. A single reading of a TIMER is, therefore, meaningless, but the subtraction of two readings will give a value for the passage of time between the two readings:

```
TIMER clock:
INT old, new, interval:
SEQ
  clock ? old
  -- other computations
  clock ? new
  interval := new MINUS old
```

The operator MINUS is used rather than '-' to take account of wrap-around. This occurs because the integer given by a TIMER is incremented by one for each unit of time; eventually the maximum integer is reached, so for the subsequent 'tick' the integer becomes the most negative one and then continues to be incremented. Users can be unaware of this action as long as they use the appropriate (language-defined) arithmetic operators, which are MINUS, PLUS, MULT and DIVIDE. In effect, each TIMER undertakes a 'PLUS 1' operation for each increment of the clock.

As the above illustrates, the facilities provided by occam2 are primitive (though arguably quite adequate). As only one integer is allocated for the clock there is clearly a trade-off between the granularity of the clock (that is, what interval of time each tick of the clock represents) and the range of times that can be accommodated. With a 32 bit integer, Table 12.2 gives typical values.

12.2.2 The clock packages in Ada

Access to a clock in Ada is provided by a predefined (compulsory) library package called Calendar and an optional real-time facility. The Calendar package (see Program 12.1) implements an abstract data type for Time. It provides a function Clock for reading the time and various subprograms for converting between Time and humanly

Program 12.1 The Ada `Calendar` package.

```
package Ada.Calendar is

   type Time is private;

   subtype Year_Number is Integer range 1901..2099;
   subtype Month_Number is Integer range 1..12;
   subtype Day_Number is Integer range 1..31;
   subtype Day_Duration is Duration range 0.0..86400.0;

   function Clock return Time;

   function Year(Date:Time) return Year_Number;
   function Month(Date:Time) return Month_Number;
   function Day(Date:Time) return Day_Number;
   function Seconds(Date:Time) return Day_Duration;

   procedure Split(Date:in Time; Year:out Year_Number;
                   Month:out Month_Number; Day:out Day_Number;
                   Seconds:out Day_Duration);

   function Time_Of(Year:Year_Number; Month:Month_Number;
                    Day:Day_Number; Seconds:Day_Duration := 0.0)
                    return Time;

   function "+"(Left:Time;Right:Duration) return Time;
   function "+"(Left:Duration;Right:Time) return Time;
   function "-"(Left:Time;Right:Duration) return Time;
   function "-"(Left:Time;Right:Time) return Duration;

   function "<"(Left,Right:Time) return Boolean;
   function "<="(Left,Right:Time) return Boolean;
   function ">"(Left,Right:Time) return Boolean;
   function ">="(Left,Right:Time) return Boolean;

   Time_Error:exception;
   -- Time_Error is raised by Time_Of, Split,"+",and "-"

private
   -- implementation dependent
end Ada.Calendar;
```

understandable units, such as `Years`, `Months`, `Days` and `Seconds`. The first three of these are given as integer subtypes. `Seconds` are, however, defined as a subtype of the primitive type `Duration`.

Type `Duration` is a predefined fixed-point real that represents an interval of time (relative time). Both its accuracy and its range are implementation-dependent, although its range must be at least $-86\,400.0 \ .. \ 86\,400.0$, which covers the number of seconds in a day. Its granularity must be no greater than 20 milliseconds. In essence,

Granularity	Range (approximately)
1 microsecond	71.6 minutes
100 microsecond	119 hours
1 millisecond	50 days
1 second	136 years

Table 12.2   TIMER granularities for a 32-bit integer.

a value of type Duration should be interpreted as a value in seconds. Note that in addition to the above subprograms, the Calendar package defines arithmetic operators for combinations of Duration and Time parameters and comparative operations for Time values.

The code required to measure the time taken to perform a computation is quite straightforward. Note the use of the "-" operator, which takes two Time values but returns a value of type Duration.

```
declare
  Old_Time, New_Time : Time;
  Interval : Duration;
begin
  Old_Time := Clock;
  -- other computations
  New_Time := Clock;
  Interval := New_Time - Old_Time;
end;
```

The other language clock is provided by the optional package Real_Time. This has a similar form to Calendar but is intended to give a finer granularity. The constant Time_Unit is the smallest amount of time representable by the Time type. The value of Tick must be no greater than one millisecond; the range of Time (from the epoch that represents the program's start-up) must be at least fifty years.

As well as providing a finer granularity, the Clock of Real_Time is defined to be monotonic. The Calendar clock is intended to provide an abstraction for a 'wall clock' and is, therefore, subject to leap years, leap seconds and other adjustments. The Real_Time package is outlined in Program 12.2.

12.2.3   Clocks in Real-Time Java

Standard Java supports the notion of a wall clock, and thus has facilities similar to Ada. The current time can be found in Java by calling the static method System.currentTimeMillis in the package java.lang. This returns the number of milliseconds since midnight, January 1, 1970 GMT. The class Date in java.util uses this method as a default when constructing date objects.

Program 12.2   The Ada real-time clock package.

```
package Ada.Real_Time is
  type Time is private;
  Time_First: constant Time;
  Time_Last: constant Time;
  Time_Unit: constant :=  -- implementation-defined-real-number;

  type Time_Span is private;
  Time_Span_First: constant Time_Span;
  Time_Span_Last: constant Time_Span;
  Time_Span_Zero: constant Time_Span;
  Time_Span_Unit: constant Time_Span;

  Tick: constant Time_Span;
  function Clock return Time;

  function "+" (Left: Time; Right: Time_Span) return Time;
  ...

  function "<" (Left, Right: Time) return Boolean;
  ...

  function "+" (Left, Right: Time_Span) return Time_Span;
  ...

  function "<" (Left, Right: Time_Span) return Boolean;
  ...

  function "abs"(Right : Time_Span) return Time_Span;

  function To_Duration (Ts : Time_Span) return Duration;
  function To_Time_Span (D : Duration) return Time_Span;

  function Nanoseconds  (Ns: Integer) return Time_Span;
  function Microseconds (Us: Integer) return Time_Span;
  function Milliseconds (Ms: Integer) return Time_Span;

  type Seconds_Count is range -- implementation-defined

  procedure Split(T : in Time; Sc: out Seconds_Count;
                  Ts : out Time_Span);
  function Time_Of(Sc: Seconds_Count; Ts: Time_Span) return Time;

private
  -- not specified by the language
end Ada.Real_Time;
```

Program 12.3   An extract of the Real-Time Java `HighResolutionTime` class.

```
public abstract class HighResolutionTime implements
        java.lang.Comparable
{
  public abstract AbsoluteTime absolute(Clock clock,
                                        AbsoluteTime destination);

  ...

  public boolean equals(HighResolutionTime time);

  public final long getMilliseconds();
  public final int getNanoseconds();

  public void set(HighResolutionTime time);
  public void set(long millis);
  public void set(long millis, int nanos);
}
```

Real-Time Java adds to these facilities real-time clocks with high-resolution time types. Program 12.3 shows a summary of the base definition of the high-resolution time class. There are methods to read, write and compare time values. This abstract class has three subclasses: one which represents absolute time, one which represents relative time (similar to Ada's `Duration` type), and one which represents rational time. These are given in Program 12.4. Absolute time is actually expressed as a time relative to 1 January 1970, GMT. Rational time is a relative time type which has an associated frequency. It is used to represent the rate at which certain events occur (for example, periodic thread execution).

The `HighResolutionTime`, `AbsoluteTime`, `RelativeTime` and `RationalTime` classes are all reasonably self-explanatory. However, the method `absolute` does need further discussion. Its role is to convert the encapsulated time (be it absolute, relative or rational) to an absolute time relative to some clock. If an `AbsoluteTime` object is passed as a parameter, the object is updated to reflect the encapsulated time value. Furthermore, the same object is also returned by the function. This is because if a null object is passed as a parameter, a new object is created and returned. In Java, the parameter is copied by value and, therefore, cannot be updated. Consequently, it is necessary for the function to create a new `AbsoluteTime` object and return it.

The Real-Time Java `Clock` class, given in Program 12.5, defines the abstract class from which all clocks are derived. The language allows many different types of clocks; for example, there could be an execution-time clock which measures the amount of execution time being consumed. There is always one real-time clock which advances in sync with the external world. The method `getRealtimeClock` allows this clock to be obtained.[1] Other methods are provided to get the resolution of a clock and, if the hardware permits, to set the resolution of a clock.

---

[1] Note that this is a static method, and therefore it can be called directly without knowledge of any subclasses.

Program 12.4   The Real-Time Java absolute, relative and rational time classes.

```
public class AbsoluteTime extends HighResolutionTime
{
  // various constructor methods including
  public AbsoluteTime(AbsoluteTime T);
  public AbsoluteTime(long millis, int nanos);

  public AbsoluteTime absolute(Clock clock, AbsoluteTime dest);

  public AbsoluteTime add(long millis, int nanos);
  public final AbsoluteTime add(RelativeTime time);
  ...
  public final RelativeTime subtract(AbsoluteTime time);
  public final AbsoluteTime subtract(RelativeTime time);

}

public class RelativeTime extends HighResolutionTime
{
  // various constructor methods including
  public RelativeTime(long millis, int nanos);
  public RelativeTime(RelativeTime time);

  public AbsoluteTime absolute(Clock clock, AbsoluteTime destination);

  public RelativeTime add(long millis, int nanos);
  public final RelativeTime add(RelativeTime time);

  public void addInterarrivalTo(AbsoluteTime destination);

  public final RelativeTime subtract(RelativeTime time);

  ...
}

public class RationalTime extends RelativeTime
{
  // various constructor methods including
public RationalTime(int frequency, RelativeTime interval)
      throws IllegalArgumentException;

public AbsoluteTime absolute(Clock clock, AbsoluteTime destination);

public void addInterarrivalTo(AbsoluteTime destination);
public int getFrequency();
public RelativeTime getInterarrivalTime(RelativeTime destination);
public void set(long millis, int nanos)
      throws IllegalArgumentException;
public void setFrequency(int frequency)
      throws ArithmeticException;
}
```

Program 12.5 The Real-Time Java `Clock` class.

```
public abstract class Clock
{
  public Clock();

  public static Clock getRealtimeClock();

  public abstract RelativeTime getResolution();

  public AbsoluteTime getTime();
  public abstract void getTime(AbsoluteTime time);

  public abstract void setResolution(RelativeTime resolution);

}
```

The code to measure the time taken to perform a computation is:

```
{
  AbsoluteTime oldTime, newTime;
  RelativeTime interval;
  Clock clock = Clock.getRealtimeClock();

  oldTime = clock.getTime();
  // other computations
  newTime = clock.getTime();

  interval = newTime.subtract(oldTime);

}
```

12.2.4 Clocks in C and POSIX

ANSI C has a standard library for interfacing to 'calendar' time. This defines a basic time type `time_t` and several routines for manipulating objects of type time; Program 12.6 defines some of these functions. POSIX allows many clocks to be supported by an implementation. Each clock has its own identifier (of type `clockid_t`), and the IEEE standard requires that at least one clock be supported (`CLOCK_REALTIME`). A typical C interface to POSIX clocks is illustrated by Program 12.7. The value returned by a clock (via `clock_gettime`) is given by the structure `timespec`; `tv_sec` represents the number of seconds expired since 1 January 1970 and `tv_nsec` the additional number of nanoseconds (although it is shown as a long integer, the value taken by `tv_nsec` must always be less than 1 000 000 000 and non-negative – C provides no subtyping mechanism). POSIX requires that the minimum resolution of `CLOCK_REALTIME` is 50 Hz (20 milliseconds); the function `clock_getres` allows the resolution of a clock to be determined.

Execution-time clocks will be discussed in Section 12.8.1.

Program 12.6 An interface to ANSI C dates and time.

```
typedef ... time_t;

struct tm {
  int tm_sec;      /* seconds after the minute - [0, 61] */
                   /* 61 allows for 2 leap seconds */
  int tm_min;      /* minutes after the hour - [0, 59] */
  int tm_hour;     /* hour since midnight - [0, 23] */
  int tm_mday;     /* day of the month - [1, 31] */
  int tm_mon;      /* months since January - [0, 11] */
  int tm_year;     /* years since 1900 */
  int tm_wday;     /* days since Sunday - [0, 6] */
  int tm_yday;     /* days since January 1 - [0, 365] */
  int tm_isdst;    /* flag for alternate daylight savings time */
};
double difftime(time_t time1, time_t time2);
  /* subtract two time values */
time_t mktime(struct tm *timeptr); /* compose a time value */
time_t time(time_t *timer);
  /* returns the current time and if timer is not null */
  /*it also places the time at that location */
```

Program 12.7 A C interface to POSIX clocks.

```
#define CLOCK_REALTIME ...;
#define CLOCK_PROCESS_CPUTIME_ID ...;
#defineCLOCK_THREAD_CPUTIME_ID ...;

struct timespec {
  time_t tv_sec;   /* number of seconds */
  long   tv_nsec;  /* number of nanoseconds */
};
typedef ... clockid_t;

int clock_gettime(clockid_t clock_id, struct timespec *tp);
int clock_settime(clockid_t clock_id, const struct timespec *tp);
int clock_getres(clockid_t clock_id, struct timespec *res);

int clock_getcpuclockid(pid_t pid, clockid_t *clock_id);
int clock_getcpuclockid(pthread_t_t thread_id, clockid_t *clock_id);

int nanosleep(const struct timespec *rqtp, struct timespec *rmtp);
/* Note, that a nanosleep return -1 if the sleep is interrupted */
/* by a signal. In this case, rmtp has the remaining sleep time */
```

12.3   Delaying a process

In addition to having access to a clock, processes must also be able to delay their execution either for a relative period of time or until some absolute time in the future.

12.3.1   Relative delays

A relative delay enables a process to queue on a future event rather than busy-wait on calls to the clock. For example, the following Ada code shows how a task can loop waiting for 10 seconds to pass:

```
Start := Clock; -- from calendar
loop
   exit when (Clock - Start) > 10.0;
end loop;
```

To eliminate the need for these busy-waits, most languages and operating systems provide some form of delay primitive. In Ada, this is a delay statement.

```
delay 10.0;
```

The value after **delay** (of type `Duration`) is relative (that is, the above statement means delay 10 seconds from the current time – a negative value is treated as zero).

In POSIX, a delay can be obtained by use of the 'sleep' system call if a coarse granularity is required (that is, a delay of 'seconds'), or 'nanosleep' if a finer granularity is required (see Program 12.7). The latter being measured in terms of the `CLOCK_REALTIME`. Java provides similar facilities to POSIX. The `sleep` method in the `Thread` class allows a thread to delay itself at the milliseconds granularity. The `RealtimeThread` class allows a high-resolution sleep relative to a clock.

It is important to appreciate that a 'delay' or 'sleep' only guarantees that the process is made runnable after the period has expired.[2] The actual delay before the task begins executing is, of course, dependent on the other processes which are competing for the processor. It should also be noted that the granularity of the delay and the granularity of the clock are not necessarily the same. For example, POSIX and Real-Time Java allow a granularity down to the nanoseconds; however, few current systems will support this. Moreover, the internal clock may be implemented using an interrupt which could be inhibited for short periods. Figure 12.1 illustrates the factors affecting the delay.

---

[2] In POSIX, the process can actually be woken early if it receives a signal. In this case an error indication is returned, and the `rmpt` parameter returns the delay time remaining. The situation in Java is similar. If a thread is interrupted then is awoken and the error object `InterruptedException` is thrown. In Ada, a delayed tasks is only woken early if it is within a select-then-abort statement.

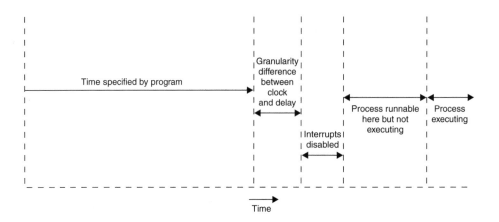

Figure 12.1   Delay times.

12.3.2 Absolute delays

The use of **delay** in Ada (and `sleep` in POSIX or Real-Time Java) supports a relative time period (for example, 10 seconds from now). If a delay to an absolute time is required, then either the programmer must calculate the period to delay or an additional primitive is required. For example, if an action should take place 10 seconds after the start of some other action, then the following Ada code could be used (with `Calendar`):

```
Start := Clock;
First_Action;
delay 10.0 - (Clock - Start);
Second_Action;
```

Unfortunately, this might not achieve the desired result. In order for this formulation to have the required behaviour, then

```
delay 10.0 - (Clock - Start);
```

would have to be an uninterruptible (atomic) action, which it is not. For example, if `First_Action` took two seconds to complete then

```
10.0 - (Clock - Start);
```

would equate to eight seconds. But after having calculated this value, if the task involved is preempted by some other task it could be three seconds (say) before it next executes. At that time it will delay for eight seconds rather than five. To solve this problem, Ada introduces the **delay until** statement:

```
Start := Clock;
First_Action;
delay until Start + 10.0;
Second_Action;
```

As with delay, **delay until** is accurate only in its lower bound. The task involved will not be released before the current time has reached that specified in the statement but it may be released later.

The time overrun associated with both relative and absolute delays is called the **local drift** and it it cannot be eliminated. It is possible, however, to eliminate the **cumulative drift** that could arise if local drifts were allowed to superimpose. The following code, in Ada, shows how the computation Action is programmed to be executed, on average, every 7 seconds. This code will compensate for any local drift. For example, if two consecutive calls to Action were actually 7.4 seconds apart then the subsequent delay would be for only 6.6 seconds (approximately).

```
declare
  Next : Time;
  Interval : constant Duration := 7.0;
begin
  Next := Clock + Interval;
  loop
    Action;
    delay until Next;
    Next := Next + Interval;
  end loop;
end;
```

In Real-Time Java, the sleep method (defined in the RealtimeThread class) can be used for both relative and absolute delays.

Occam2 only supports absolute delays. To emphasize its open-ended semantics, the keyword AFTER is used. If a process wishes to wait for 10 seconds, it must first read the TIMER clock, add 10 seconds and then delay until this time. The value 10 seconds is obtained via the constant G which is introduced (here) to give a measure of the granularity of the implementation (G is the number of TIMER updates per second):

```
SEQ
  clock ? now
  clock ? AFTER now PLUS (10 * G)
```

In occam2, the code for avoiding cumulative drift is:

```
INT next, now:
VAL interval IS 7*G:
SEQ
  clock ? now
  next := now PLUS interval
  WHILE TRUE
    SEQ
      ACTION
```

```
clock ? AFTER next
next := next PLUS interval
```

An absolute delay can also be constructed in POSIX by using an absolute timer and waiting for the signal generated when it expires (see Section 12.8.1).

12.4 Programming timeouts

Perhaps the simplest time constraint that an embedded system can have is the requirement to recognize, and act upon, the non-occurrence of some external event. For example, a temperature sensor may be required to log a new reading every second, the failure to give a reading within 10 seconds being defined as a fault. In general, a **timeout** is a restriction on the time a process is prepared to wait for a communication. Chapters 8 and 9 have discussed, in detail, interprocess communication facilities. Each one requires a timeout if it is to be used in a real-time environment.

As well as waiting for communication, timeouts are also required on the execution of actions. For example, a programmer might require that a section of code be executed within a certain time. If this does not happen at run-time, then some error recovery might be required.

12.4.1 Shared variable communication and timeouts

In Chapter 8, various communication and synchronization mechanisms based on shared variables were discussed. Both mutual exclusive access to a critical section and condition synchronization were seen as being important requirements. When a process attempts to gain access to a critical section, it is blocked if another process is already active in the section. This blocking, however, is bounded by the time taken to execute the code of the section and the number of other processes which also wish to execute the critical section. For this reason, it is not usually deemed necessary to have a timeout associated with attempting entry. (However, POSIX does provide such timeouts.) In Section 13.10, the issue of analyzing this blocking time is considered in detail.

In contrast, the blocking associated with condition synchronization is not so easily bounded and depends on the application. For example, a producer process attempting to place data in a full buffer must wait for a consumer process to take data out. The consume processes might not be prepared to do this for a significant period of time. For this reason, it is important to allow processes the option of timing out while waiting for condition synchronization.

The condition synchronization facilities considered in Chapter 8 included:

- semaphores
- conditional critical regions
- condition variables in monitors, mutexes or synchronized methods
- entries in protected objects.

Real-Time Euclid (Kligerman and Stoyenko, 1986) uses semaphores and extends the semantics of `wait` to include a time bound. The following statement illustrates how a process could suspend itself on the semaphore `CALL` with a timeout value of 10 seconds:

```
wait CALL noLongerThan 10 : 200
```

If the process is not signalled within 10 seconds, the exception 200 is raised (exceptions in Real-Time Euclid are numbered). Note, however, that there is no requirement for the process to be actually scheduled and executing within 10 seconds. The same is true for all timeout facilities. They merely indicate that the process should become runnable again.

POSIX supports an explicit timeout for waiting on a semaphore or on a condition variable (see Programs 8.2 and 8.3). The following statement illustrates how a process could suspend itself on the semaphore `call` with an absolute timeout value of `timeout`:

```
if(sem_timedwait(&call, &timeout) < 0) {
  if ( errno ==  ETIMEDOUT) {
    /* timeout occurred */
  }
  else {
    /* some other error */
  }
} else {
  /* semaphore locked */
};
```

If the semaphore could not be locked by the `timeout`, `errno` is set to the value `ETIMEDOUT`.

With Ada's protected objects, avoidance synchronization is used and, therefore, it is at the point of the protected entry call that the timeout must be applied. As Ada treats a protected entry call the same as a task entry call, an identical mechanism for timeout is used. This is described below in terms of message passing.

With Java, the `wait` method can be used with a timeout either at millisecond granularity or at nanosecond granularity.

12.4.2 Message-passing and timeouts

Chapter 9 has considered the various forms of message passing. All forms require synchronization. Even with asynchronous systems, a process may wish to wait for a message (or a sending process's message buffer might become full). With synchronous message passing, once a process has committed itself to a communication it must wait until such an event has occurred. For these reasons, timeouts are required. To illustrate the programming of timeouts consider, first, a controller task (in Ada) that is called by some other driver task and given a new temperature reading:

```
task Controller is
   entry Call(T : Temperature);
end Controller;

task body Controller is
   -- declarations
begin
   loop
      accept Call(T : Temperature) do
         New_Temp := T;
      end Call;
      -- other actions
   end loop;
end Controller;
```

It is now required that the controller be modified so that the lack of the entry call is acted upon. This requirement can be provided using the constructs already discussed. A second task is used that delays itself for the timeout period and then calls the controller. If the controller accepts this before the normal Call then a timeout has occurred:

```
task Controller is
   entry Call(T : Temperature);
private
   entry Timeout;
end Controller;

task body Controller is
   task Timer is
      entry Go(D : Duration);
   end Timer;
   -- other declarations
   task body Timer is
      Timeout_Value : Duration;
   begin
      accept Go(D : Duration) do
         Timeout_Value := D;
      end Go;
      delay Timeout_Value;
      Controller.Timeout;
   end Timer;
begin
   loop
      Timer.Go(10.0);
      select
         accept Call(T : Temperature) do
            New_Temp := T;
         end Call;
      or
         accept Timeout;
         -- action for timeout
      end select;
      -- other actions
   end loop;
end Controller;
```

Although this code will only deal with the first timeout period, it can be modified (non-trivially) to deal with continuous performance. Nevertheless, the need for a timeout is so common that a more concise way of expressing it is desirable. This is usually provided in a real-time language as a special form of alternative in a selective wait. The above example would, more appropriately, be coded as follows:

```
task Controller is
  entry Call(T : Temperature);
end Controller;

task body Controller is
  -- declarations
begin
  loop
    select
      accept Call(T : Temperature) do
        New_Temp := T;
      end Call;
    or
      delay 10.0;
      -- action for timeout
    end select;
    -- other actions
  end loop;
end Controller;
```

The delay alternative becomes ready when the time delay has expired. If this alternative is chosen (that is, a Call is not registered within 10 seconds) then the statements after the delay are executed.

The above example uses a relative delay, but absolute delays are also possible. Consider the following code that enables a task to accept registrations up to time Closing_Time:

```
task Ticket_Agent is
  entry Registration(...);
end Ticket_Agent;

task body Ticket_Agent is
  -- declarations
  Shop_Open : Boolean := True;
begin
  while Shop_Open loop
    select
      accept Registration(...) do
        -- log details
      end Registration;
    or
      delay until Closing_Time;
      Shop_Open := False;
    end select;
    -- process registrations
  end loop;
end Ticket_Agent;
```

Within the Ada model, it would not make sense to mix an else part, a terminate alternative and delay alternatives. These three structures are, therefore, mutually exclusive; a select statement can have, at most, only one of them. However, if it is a delay alternative, the select can have a number of delays but they must all be of the same kind (that is, all delays or all delay untils). The one with the shortest duration or earliest absolute time being the operative one on each occasion.

A timeout facility is common in message-based concurrent programming languages. Occam2, like Ada, uses the 'delay' primitive as part of a selective wait construct to indicate a timeout:

```
WHILE TRUE
  SEQ
    ALT
      call ? new_temp
        -- other actions
      clock ? AFTER (10 * G)
        -- action for timeout
```

where clock is a TIMER.

Both the occam2 and Ada examples show how a timeout on a message receive is programmed. Ada actually goes further and allows a timeout on a message send. To illustrate this, consider the device driver that is feeding temperatures to the controller in the above Ada code:

```
loop
  -- get new temperature T
  Controller.Call(T);
end loop;
```

As new temperature readings are available continuously (and there is no point in giving the controller an out-of-date value), the device driver may wish to be suspended waiting for the controller for only half a second before withdrawing the call. This is achieved by using a special form of the select statement which has a single entry call and a single delay alternative:

```
loop
  -- get new temperature T
  select
    Controller.Call(T);
  or
    delay 0.5;
    null;
  end select;
end loop;
```

The **null** is not strictly needed but shows that again the delay can have arbitrary statements following, that are executed if the delay expires before the entry call is accepted. This is a special form of the select. It cannot have more than one entry call and it cannot mix entry calls and accept statements. The action it invokes is called a **timed entry call**.

It must be emphasized that the time period specified in the call is a timeout value for the call being accepted; *it is not a timeout on the termination of the associated accept statement.*

If a task wishes only to make an entry call if the called task is immediately prepared to accept the call, then rather than make a timed entry call with time zero, a **conditional entry call** can be made:

```
select
   T.E   -- entry E in task T
else
   -- other actions
end select;
```

The 'other actions' are executed only if T is not prepared to accept E immediately. 'Immediately' means that either T is already suspended on **accept** E or on a select statement with such an open alternative (and it is chosen).

The above examples have used timeouts on interprocess communication; it is also possible, within Ada, to do timed (and conditional) entry call on protected objects:

```
select
   P.E ; -- E is an entry in Protected Object P
or
   delay 0.5;
end select;
```

12.4.3 Timeouts on actions

In Section 10.5, mechanisms were discussed which allowed processes to have their control flows altered by asynchronous notifications. A timeout can be considered such a notification, and therefore if asynchronous notifications are supported, timeouts can also be used. Both a resumption (asynchronous events) and a termination (asynchronous transfer of control) model can be augmented by timeouts. Although for timeouts on actions, it is the termination model that is needed.

For example, in Section 10.8, the Ada asynchronous transfer of control (ATC) facility was introduced. With this, an action can be aborted if a 'triggering event' occurs before the action has completed. One of the allowed triggering events is the passage of time. To illustrate this, consider a task that contains an action that must be completed within 100 milliseconds. The following code supports this requirement directly:

```
select
   delay 0.1;
then abort
   -- action
end select;
```

If the action takes too long, the triggering event will be taken and the action will be aborted. This is clearly an effective way of catching 'runaway code'.

Program 12.8   The Real-Time Java `Timed` class.

```
public class Timed extends AsynchronouslyInterruptedException
                                  implements java.io.Serializable
{
  public Timed(HighResolutionTime time) throws IllegalArgumentException;

  public boolean doInterruptible(Interruptible logic);

  public void resetTime(HighResolutionTime time);
}
```

Timeouts are usually associated with error conditions; if a communication has not occurred within X milliseconds then something unfortunate has happened and corrective action must be taken. This is, however, not their only use. Consider a task that has a compulsory component and an optional part. The compulsory computations produce (quickly) an adequate result that is assigned to a protected object. The task must complete by a fixed time; but if there is time available after the compulsory component has been completed, an optional algorithm can be used to incrementally improve the output value. To program this again requires a timeout on an action.

```
declare
  Precise_Result : Boolean;
begin
  Completion_Time := ...
  --  compulsory part
  Results.Write(...); -- call to procedure in
                      -- external protected object
  select
    delay until Completion_Time;
    Precise_Result := False;
  then abort
    while Can_Be_Improved loop
      -- improve result
      Results.Write(...);
    end loop;
    Precise_Result := True;
  end select;
end;
```

Note that if the timeout expires during the write to the protected object it will complete its write correctly, as a call to a protected object is an abort-deferred action (that is, the effect of the abort is postponed until the task leaves the protected object).

With Real-Time Java, timeouts on actions are provided by a subclass of `Asyn-chronouslyInterruptedException` called `Timed`. This class is defined in Program 12.8 (see Section 14.4.3 for information concerning `java.io. Serial-izable`).

The above Ada example would be written in Real-Time Java:

```java
public class PreciseResult
{
  public resultType value; // the result
  public boolean preciseResult; // indicates if it is imprecise
}

public class ImpreciseComputation
{
  private HighResolutionTime CompletionTime;
  private PreciseResult result = new PreciseResult();

  public ImpreciseComputation(HighResolutionTime T)
  {
    CompletionTime = T;   //can be absolute or relative
  }

  private resultType compulsoryPart()
  {
    // function which computes the compulsory part
  };

  public PreciseResult Service()  // public service
  {
    Interruptible I = new Interruptible()
    {
      public void run(AsynchronouslyInterruptedException exception)
                    throws AsynchronouslyInterruptedException
      {
        // this is the optional function which improves on the
        // compulsory part
        boolean canBeImproved = true;

        while(canBeImproved)
        {
          // improve result
          synchronized(this) {
            // write result --
            // the synchronized statement ensures
            // atomicity of the write operation
          }
        }
        result.preciseResult = true;
      }

      public void interruptAction(
             AsynchronouslyInterruptedException exception)
      {
        result.preciseResult = false;
      }
    };

    Timed t = new Timed(CompletionTime);

    result.value = compulsoryPart();  // compute the compulsory part
    if(t.doInterruptible(I))
```

```
        // execute the optional part with the timer
        return result;
    else   ... ;
  }
}
```

Timeouts are an important feature of real-time systems; they are, however, far from being the only time constraints of significance. The rest of this chapter, and the following one, deals with the more general topic of time deadlines and how to ensure that they are met.

12.5   Specifying timing requirements

For many important real-time systems, it is not sufficient for the software to be logically correct; the programs must also satisfy timing constraints determined by the underlying physical system. These constraints can go far beyond simple timeouts. Unfortunately, existing practices in the engineering of large real-time systems are, in general, still rather *ad hoc*. Often, a logically correct system is specified, designed and constructed (perhaps as a prototype) and then tested to see if it meets its timing requirements. If it does not, then various fine tunings and rewrites ensue. The result is a system that may be difficult to understand and expensive to maintain and upgrade. A more systematic treatment of time is required.

Work on a more rigorous approach to this aspect of real-time systems has followed two largely distinct paths. One direction of development has concerned the use of formally defined language semantics and timing requirements, together with notations and logics that enable temporal properties to be represented and analyzed. The other path has focused on the performance of real-time systems in terms of the feasibility of scheduling the required workload on the available resources (processors and so on).

In this book, attention is focused mainly on the latter work. The reasons for this are three-fold. Firstly, the formal techniques are not yet mature enough to reason about large complex real-time systems. Secondly, there is little reported experience of the use of these techniques in actual real-time systems. Finally, to include a full discussion of such methods would involve a substantial amount of material that is outside the scope of this book. This is not meant to imply that the area is irrelevant to real-time systems. The understanding of, for example, formal techniques based on CSP, temporal logics, real-time logics, model checking and specification techniques that incorporate notions of time, is becoming increasingly important. For example, RTL (Real-Time Logic) can be used to verify the temporal requirements of a system; thereby complementing the use of methods such as VDM and Z for analyzing the functional requirements.

The success of model checking in verifying functional properties has recently been extended into the real-time domain. A system is modelled as a Timed Automaton (that is, a finite state machine with clocks) and then model checking is used to 'prove' that undesirable states cannot be reached or that desirable states will be entered before some internal clock has reached a critical time (deadline). The latter property is known as *bounded liveliness*. Although the explorations undertaken by model checking are subject to state explosion, a number of tools are now available that can tackle problems of a reasonable size. The technique is likely to become standard industrial practice over the coming years.

The verification of a real-time system can usefully be interpreted as requiring a two-stage process:

(1) Verifying requirements/designs – given an infinitely fast reliable computer, are the temporal requirements coherent and consistent; that is, have they the potential to be satisfied?

(2) Verifying the implementation – with a finite set of (possible unreliable) hardware resources, can the temporal requirements be satisfied?

As indicated above, (1) may require formal reasoning (and/or model checking) to verify that necessary temporal (and causal) orderings are satisfied. For example, if event A must be completed before event B, but is dependent on some event C that occurs after B, then no matter how fast the processor it will never be possible to satisfy these requirements. Early recognition of this difficulty is therefore very useful. The second issue (implementation verification) is the topic of the following chapter. The remainder of this chapter will concentrate on how temporal requirements can actually be represented in languages.

12.6 Temporal scopes

To facilitate the specification of the various timing constraints found in real-time applications, it is useful to introduce the notion of **temporal scopes**. Such scopes identify a collection of statements with an associated timing constraint. The possible attributes of a temporal scope (TS) are illustrated in Figure 12.2, and include

(1) deadline – the time by which the execution of a TS must be finished;

(2) minimum delay – the minimum amount of time that must elapse before the start of execution of a TS;

(3) maximum delay – the maximum amount of time that can elapse before the start of execution of a TS;

(4) maximum execution time – of a TS;

(5) maximum elapse time – of a TS.

Temporal scopes with combinations of these attributes are also possible.

Temporal scopes can themselves be described as being either **periodic** or **aperiodic**. Typically, periodic temporal scopes sample data or execute a control loop and have explicit deadlines that must be met. Aperiodic, or **sporadic**, temporal scopes usually arise from asynchronous events outside the embedded computer. These scopes have specified response times associated with them.

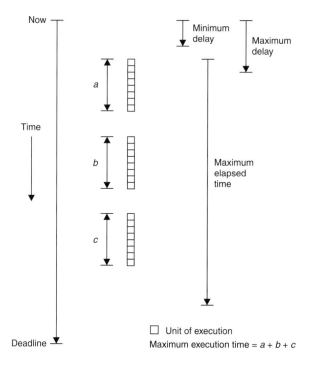

Figure 12.2   Temporal scopes.

In general, aperiodic temporal scopes are viewed as being activated randomly, following, for example, a Poisson distribution. Such a distribution allows for bursts of arrivals of external events, but does not preclude any possible concentration of aperiodic activity. It is therefore not possible to do worst-case analysis (there is a non-zero probability of any number of aperiodic events occurring within a given time). To allow worst-case calculations to be made, a minimum period between any two aperiodic events (from the same source) is often defined. If this is the case, the process involved is said to be **sporadic**. In this book, the term 'aperiodic' will be used for the general case and 'sporadic' will be reserved for situations where a minimum delay is needed.

In many real-time languages, temporal scopes are, in effect, associated with the processes that embody them. Processes can be described as either periodic, aperiodic or sporadic depending on the properties of their internal temporal scope. Most of the timing attributes given in the above list can thus be satisfied by:

(1) running periodic processes at the correct rate;
(2) completing all processes by their deadline.

The problem of satisfying timing constraints thus becomes one of scheduling processes to meet deadlines, or **deadline scheduling**. Note that the maximum delay requirement can be accommodated by splitting the scope into two precedence related processes. The first, which represents the early phase of the TS, can then have a deadline that will ensure that the maximum start delay is not violated. The application need for this type of structure comes from a computation that first reads a sensor and then produces an output. To get fine control over when the sensor is read, a tight deadline is needed for this initial action. The output can then be produced by a later deadline. The variation of when a sensor is read or an actuator value is output is called **input** and **output jitter**.

Although all computer systems strive to be efficient, and many are described as real-time, further classification is needed to deal adequately with the different levels of importance that time has within applications. As noted in the Introduction, a system is said to be **hard** real-time if it has deadlines that cannot be missed or else the system fails. By comparison, a system is **soft** if the application is tolerant of missed deadlines. A system is merely **interactive** if it does not have specified deadlines but strives for 'adequate response times'. To give a little more precision, a process with a soft deadline may still deliver its service late – the system will still draw some value from the tardy service. A non-hard process that has a fixed rigid deadline (that is, a tardy service is useless/valueless) is said to be **firm**.

The distinction between hard, firm and soft real-time becomes somewhat blurred in fault-tolerant systems. Nevertheless, it is usually appropriate to use the term 'hard' if a specific error recovery (or fail safe) routine is triggered by a missed deadline, and firm/soft if the nature of the application is tolerant of the occasional missed deadline or deadlines that are not missed by much. Finally, note that, many hard real-time systems will have some deadlines which are soft or firm.

12.6.1 Specifying processes and temporal scopes

In real-time systems, it is necessary to deal explicitly with timing requirements, five types of which were given earlier. A general scheme for a periodic process is thus as follows:

```
process periodic_P;
  ...
begin
  loop
    IDLE
    start of temporal scope
      ...
    end of temporal scope
  end;
end;
```

The time constraints take the form of maximum and/or minimum times for IDLE and the requirement that the end of the temporal scope be by some deadline. This deadline can itself be expressed in terms of either

- absolute time,
- execution time since the start of the temporal scope, or
- elapsed time since the start of the temporal scope.

If the process is sampling data then this would take place at the start of the temporal scope; the accuracy of the IDLE period is thus important. The temporal scope would contain the necessary processing (or simply buffering) of this data and the deadline at the end of the temporal scope is only to ensure that the process can loop round and be in time to take the next reading.

For a process sending out a regular control signal, the temporal scope incorporates whatever computations are needed to calculate the signal's value (this may include taking external readings). The signal itself is sent out at the end of the temporal scope, and hence deadlines are associated with this event.

Similar deadlines are necessary with aperiodic processes; here the temporal scope is triggered by an external event that will normally take the form of an interrupt:

```
process aperiodic_P;
  ...
begin
  loop
    wait for interrupt
    start of temporal scope
      ...
    end of temporal scope
  end;
end;
```

Clearly, a periodic process has a defined periodicity (that is, how often the process loop is executed); this measure may also be applied to an aperiodic process in which case it means the maximum rate at which this process will cycle (that is, the fastest rate for interrupt arrivals). As stated earlier, such aperiodic processes are known as sporadic.

In some real-time systems, the deadlines may be associated with some data that passes through a number of processes (this is often called a real-time transaction). In order to schedule these processes, it is necessary to partition the available time between the processes that manipulate the data. This partitioning may get quite complicated if the times in each process are dynamic (that is, data-dependent) or, even worse, if the path the data takes through the processes is also data-dependent. No real-time languages currently address this problem explicitly.

12.7   Language support for temporal scopes

In the following sections, a number of languages are described (in terms of their support for temporal scopes). The languages chosen represent a broad spectrum of the available engineering languages:

- Ada, occam2 and C/POSIX
- Real-Time Euclid and Pearl
- Real-Time Java
- DPS
- Esteral

12.7.1 Ada, occam2 and C/POSIX

In keeping with many real-time languages (notable exceptions are discussed below), Ada, occam2 and C/POSIX do not support the explicit specification of periodic or sporadic processes with deadlines; rather a delay primitive, timer and so on, must be used within a looping process (although POSIX does allow a periodic timer to be set).

For example, in Ada, a periodic task must take the following form:

```
task body Periodic_T is
  Next_Release : Time;
  Release_Interval : constant Duration := ...; -- or
  Release_Interval : constant Time_Span := Milliseconds(...);
begin
  -- read clock and calculate the next
  -- release time (Next_Release)
  loop
    -- sample data (for example) or
    -- calculate and send a control signal
    delay until Next_Release;
    Next_Release := Next_Release + Release_Interval;
  end loop;
end Periodic_T;
```

Compare this to the more verbose C/POSIX representation which requires the explicit use of a timer and signal handling.

```
#include <signal.h>
#include <time.h>
#include <pthread.h>
void periodic_thread() /* destined to be the thread */
{
  int signum;                /* signal caught */
  sigset_t set;              /* signals to be waited for */
  struct sigevent sig;       /* signal information */
  timer_t periodic_timer;         /* timer for a periodic thread */
  struct itimerspec required, old;  /* timer details */
  struct timespec first, period;    /* start and repetition */
  long Thread_Period = ....   /* actual period in nanoseconds */

  /* set up signal interface */
  sig.sigev_notify = SIGEV_SIGNAL;
  sig.sigev_signo = SIGRTMIN; /* for example */
  /* allow, for example, 1 sec from now for system initialization */
```

```
CLOCK_GETTIME(CLOCK_REALTIME, &first);     /* get current time */
first.tv_sec = first.tv_sec + 1;
period.tv_sec = 0;              /* set repetition value to period*/
period.tv_nsec = Thread_Period;
required.it_value = first;              /* initialise timer details */
required.it_interval = period;
TIMER_CREATE(CLOCK_REALTIME, &sig, &periodic_timer);
SIGEMPTYSET(&set);                      /* initialise signal set to null */
SIGADDSET(&set, SIGRTMIN);          /* only allow timer interrupts*/
TIMER_SETTIME(periodic_timer, 0, &required, &old);

/* enter periodic loop */
while(1) {
  SIGWAIT(&set, &signum);
  /* code to be executed each period here */
}
}


int init()
{
  pthread_attr_t attributes;     /* thread attributes */
  pthread_t PT;                  /* thread pointer */

  PTHREAD_ATTR_INIT(&attributes); /* default attributes */
  PTHREAD_CREATE(&PT, &attributes,
                 (void *) periodic_thread, (void *)0);
}
```

A sporadic Ada task that is triggered by an interrupt would contain no explicit time information but would, typically, use a protected object to handle the interrupt and release the task for execution:

```
protected Sporadic_Controller is
  procedure Interrupt; -- mapped onto interrupt
  entry Wait_For_Next_Interrupt;
private
    Call_Outstanding : Boolean := False;
end Sporadic_Controller;

protected body Sporadic_Controller is

  procedure Interrupt is
  begin
    Call_Outstanding := True;
  end Interrupt;

  entry Wait_For_Next_Interrupt when Call_Outstanding is
  begin
    Call_Outstanding := False;
  end Wait_For_Next_Interrupt;
end Sporadic_Controller;
```

```
task body Sporadic_T is
begin
  loop
    Sporadic_Controller.Wait_For_Next_Interrupt;
    -- action
  end loop;
end Sporadic_T;
```

What the above examples show is that in Ada (and many other so-called real-time languages), the only time constraint that can be guaranteed to be met is the minimum time before the start of a temporal scope. This is achieved with the delay primitive.

12.7.2   Real-Time Euclid and Pearl

The languages that do give support to deadline scheduling have appropriate timing primitives for deadline specification. In Real-Time Euclid (Kligerman and Stoyenko, 1986), processes are static and non-nested. Each process definition must contain activation information that pertains to its real-time behaviour (the term **frame** is used instead of temporal scope). This information takes one of two forms which relate to periodic and sporadic processes:

(1) periodic *frameInfo* first activation *timeOrEvent*

(2) atEvent *conditionId frameInfo*

The clause *frameInfo* defines the periodicity of the process (including the maximum rate for sporadic processes). The simplest form this can take is an expression in real-time units:

```
frame realTimeExpn
```

The value of these units is set at the beginning of the program.

A periodic process can be activated for the first time in two different ways. It can have a start time defined or it can wait for an interrupt to occur. Additionally, it can wait for either of these conditions. The syntax for *timeOrEvent* must, therefore, be one of the following

(1) atTime *realTimeExpn*

(2) atEvent *conditionId*

(3) atTime *realTimeExpn* or atEvent *conditionId*

conditionId is a condition variable associated with an interrupt. It is also used with sporadic processes.

To give an example of part of a Real-Time Euclid program, consider a cyclic temperature controller. Its periodicity is 60 units (that is, every minute if the time unit is set to 1 second) and it is to become active after 600 units (10 minutes) or when a *startMonitoring* interrupt arrives:

```
realTimeUnit := 1.0  % time unit = 1 seconds

var Reactor: module   % Euclid is module based
var startMonitoring : activation condition atLocation 16#A10D
% This defines a condition variable which is mapped
% onto an interrupt

  process TempController : periodic frame 60 first activation
                          atTime 600 or atEvent startMonitoring
  % import list
  %
  % execution part
  %
  end TempController
end Reactor
```

Note that there is no loop within this process. It is the scheduler that controls the required and specified periodic execution.

To illustrate how this code would need to be constructed in Ada, the process (task) part is given (a loop is needed here to force the task to cycle round):

```
task body Tempcontroller is
  -- definitions, including
  Next_Release : Duration;
begin
  select
    accept Startmonitoring;   -- or a timed entry call
                              -- onto a protected object
  or
    delay 600.0;
  end select;
  Next_Release := Clock + 60.0; -- take note of next release time
  loop
    -- execution part
    --
    delay until Next_Release;
    Next_Release := Next_Release + 60.0;
  end loop;
end Tempcontroller;
```

Not only is this more cumbersome, but the scheduler is not aware of the deadline associated with this task. Its correct execution will depend on the task becoming active again almost immediately the delay has expired.

Pearl

The language Pearl (Werum and Windauer, 1985) also provides explicit timing information concerning the start, frequency and termination of processes. A simple 10 second periodic task, T, is activated by:

```
EVERY 10 SEC ACTIVATE T
```

To activate at a particular point in time (say 12.00 noon each day):

```
AT 12:00:00 ACTIVATE LUNCH
```

A sporadic task, S, released by an interrupt, IRT, is defined by

```
WHEN IRT ACTIVATE S;
```

or if an initial delay of one second is required:

```
WHEN IRT AFTER 1 SEC ACTIVATE S;
```

Although the syntax is different, Pearl gives almost the same functionality as that described for Real-Time Euclid. The temperature controller example, however, illustrates one significant difference; a task in Pearl can be activated by a time schedule or an interrupt but *not* both. Therefore either of the following are admissible in Pearl:

```
AFTER 10 MIN ALL 60 SEC ACTIVATE TempController;
```

```
WHEN startMonitoring ALL 60 SEC ACTIVATE TempController;
```

The term ALL 60 SEC means repeat periodically, after the first execution, every 60 seconds.

12.7.3   Real-Time Java

Real-Time Java provides similar support to Real-Time Euclid and Pearl but from within an object-oriented framework. Objects which are to be scheduled must implement the Schedulable interface; this will be considered in the next chapter. Furthermore, objects must specify:

- their memory requirements via the class MemoryParameters – these will be considered in Chapter 15;
- their scheduling requirements via the class SchedulingParameters – these will be considered in Chapter 13;
- their timing requirements via the class ReleaseParameters.

The latter is achieved via the ReleaseParameters class hierarchy. The base abstract class, defined in Program 12.9, gives the general parameters that all schedulable objects need. A schedulable object can have a deadline and a cost associated with each time it is released for execution. The cost is the amount of execution time that a scheduler should give to the object. If the object is still executing when either its deadline or its cost expire, the associated event handlers are scheduled. It should be noted that Real-Time Java does not require an implementation to support execution time monitoring. However, it does require it to detect missed deadlines. It should perhaps also be noted

---

Program 12.9   The `ReleaseParameters` class.

```
public abstract class ReleaseParameters
{
  protected ReleaseParameters(RelativeTime cost, RelativeTime deadline,
                              AsyncEventHandler overrunHandler,
                              AsyncEventHandler missHandler);
  public RelativeTime getCost();
  public AsyncEventHandler getCostOverrunHandler();

  public RelativeTime getDeadline();
  public AsyncEventHandler getDeadlineMissHandler();

  public void setCost(RelativeTime cost);
  public void setCostOverrunHandler(AsyncEventHandler handler);

  public void setDeadline(RelativeTime deadline);
  public void setDeadlineMissHandler(AsyncEventHandler handler);
}
```

---

that the release events for sporadic and aperiodic threads are currently not well-defined. Consequently, it is difficult to see how an implementation can detect deadline overrun. Of course, a program can indicate that it is not concerned with a missed deadline by passing a null handler.

Subclasses of the `ReleaseParameters` class support periodic, aperiodic and sporadic release parameters – as shown in Program 12.10. All relative time values are relative to a point in time when an associated thread is started (released).

Using the above parameter classes, it is possible to express the timing properties of the following schedulable objects:

- `RealtimeThread`
- `NoHeapRealtimeThread` – considered in Section 13.14.3
- `AsyncEventHandler`

Real-Time threads

A Real-Time Java thread is an extension of the base language's thread. The class is defined in Program 12.11 (`ProcessingGroupParameters` are considered in Section 13.8.2). When creating a real-time thread, it is possible to create the thread without release parameters. In effect, these have no specified timing requirements.

Periodic threads are those real-time threads created with `PeriodicParameters`. The method `start` is called for the initial release of the thread; Once the thread has executed, it calls `waitForNextPeriod` to indicate to the scheduler that it should be made executable again when its next period is due. The following program

Program 12.10 `PeriodicParameters`, `AperiodicParameters` and `Spo-`
`radicParameters` classes.

```
public class PeriodicParameters extends ReleaseParameters
{
  public PeriodicParameters(HighResolutionTime start,
        RelativeTime period, RelativeTime cost,
        RelativeTime deadline, AsyncEventHandler overrunHandler,
        AsyncEventHandler missHandler);

  public RelativeTime getPeriod();
  public HighResolutionTime getStart();
  public void setPeriod(RelativeTime period);
  public void setStart(HighResolutionTime start);
}

public class AperiodicParameters extends ReleaseParameters
{
  public AperiodicParameters(RelativeTime cost,
        RelativeTime deadline, AsyncEventHandler overrunHandler,
        AsyncEventHandler missHandler);
}

public class SporadicParameters extends AperiodicParameters
{
  public SporadicParameters(RelativeTime minInterarrival,
        RelativeTime cost, RelativeTime deadline,
        AsyncEventHandler overrunHandler,
        AsyncEventHandler missHandler);

  public RelativeTime getMinimumInterarrival();
  public void setMinimumInterarrival(RelativeTime minimum);
}
```

fragment illustrates the structure of a 10 millisecond periodic thread with a 5 millisecond deadline, whose first execution is delayed until an absolute time A. The thread should consume no more than 1 millisecond of processor time.

```
public class Periodic extends RealtimeThread
{
  public Periodic( PriorityParameters PP, PeriodicParameters P)
  { ... };

  public void run()
  {
   while(true) {
     // code to be run each period
     ...
     waitForNextPeriod();
   }
  }
}
```

Program 12.11   A summary of the `RealtimeThread` class.

```
public class RealtimeThread extends java.lang.Thread
      implements Schedulable
{

  public RealtimeThread(SchedulingParameters s);
  public RealtimeThread(SchedulingParameters s, ReleaseParameters r);
  public RealtimeThread(SchedulingParameters s, ReleaseParameters rp,
        MemoryParameters m, ProcessingGroupParameters p,
        java.lang.Runnable r);

  // methods for the Schedulable interface
  public synchronized void addToFeasibility();
  public MemoryParameters getMemoryParameters();
  public ReleaseParameters getReleaseParameters();
  public Scheduler getScheduler();
  public SchedulingParameters getSchedulingParameters();
  public synchronized void removeFromFeasibility();
  public void setMemoryParameters(MemoryParameters  p);
  public void setReleaseParameters(ReleaseParameters p);
  public void setScheduler(Scheduler s)
        throws IllegalThreadStateException;
  public void setSchedulingParameters(SchedulingParameters s);

  public static RealtimeThread currentRealtimeThread();

  public synchronized void schedulePeriodic();
  // add the periodic thread to the list of schedulable objects
  public synchronized void deschedulePeriodic();
  // remove the periodic thread from the list of schedulable object
  // this only takes effect when the thread has issued a waitForNextPeriod
  public boolean waitForNextPeriod() throws IllegalThreadStateException;

  public MemoryArea getMemoryArea();
  public ProcessingGroupParameters getProcessingGroupParameters();
  public void setProcessingGroupParameters(ProcessingGroupParameters p);

  public synchronized void interrupt();
  // overrides java.lang.Thread.interrupt()
  public static void sleep(Clock c, HighResolutionTime time)
        throws InterruptedException;
  public static void sleep(HighResolutionTime time)
        throws InterruptedException;
}
```

```
{
  AbsoluteTime A = new AbsoluteTime(...);
  PeriodicParameters P = new PeriodicParameters(
        A, new RelativeTime(10,0),
        new RelativeTime(1,0), new RelativeTime(5,0),
        null,  null );
```

```
PriorityParameters PP = new PriorityParameters(...);

Periodic ourThread = new Periodic(PP, P); //create thread

ourThread.start(); // release it

}
```

Aperiodic and Sporadic threads can be created in a similar fashion. Here, however, the thread would wait for a release event and not call `waitForNextPeriod`. It has already been mentioned that the release event for sporadic and aperiodic threads are currently not well-defined.

In Section 10.5, asynchronous notification was discussed: both a termination model and a resumption model for event handling were introduced. It was pointed out that a resumption model for asynchronous notification handling in a multithreaded process was equivalent to executing an aperiodic/sporadic thread in response to the notification. This is the model adopted by Real-Time Java. However, the handler is not viewed as an explicit thread but as an object which supports the `Schedulable` interface. In practice, more than one handler may be bound to a single thread, and this binding is done dynamically when the event is fired. The class `BoundAsyncEventHandler` can be used to permanently bind the event handler to a thread (thereby allowing a quicker response to the event). Given that the handler for an asynchronous event is a schedulable class, it must be given appropriate release parameters. As an event handler has an explicit release, its deadline overrun may be easily detected.

12.7.4 DPS

Whereas Pearl, Real-Time Euclid and Java associate temporal scopes with processes (threads), and therefore necessitate the specification of timing constraints on the process itself, other languages such as DPS (Lee and Gehlot, 1985) provide local timing facilities that apply at the block level.

In general, a DPS temporal block (scope) may need to specify three distinct timing requirements (these are similar to the more global requirements discussed earlier):

- delay start by a known amount of time;
- complete execution by a known deadline;
- take no longer than a specified time to undertake a computation.

To illustrate these structures, consider the important real-time activity of making and drinking instant coffee:

```
get_cup
put_coffee_in_cup
boil_water
put_water_in_cup
```

```
drink_coffee
replace_cup
```

The act of making a cup of coffee should take no more than 10 minutes; drinking it is more complicated. A delay of 3 minutes should ensure that the mouth is not burnt; the cup itself should be emptied within 25 minutes (it would then be cold) or before 17:00 (that is, 5 o'clock and time to go home). Two temporal scopes are required:

```
start elapse 10 do
  get_cup
  put_coffee_in_cup
  boil_water
  put_water_in_cup
end
```

```
start after 3 elapse 25 by 17:00 do
  drink_coffee
  replace_cup
end
```

For a temporal scope that is executed repetitively, a time loop construct is useful; that is,

```
from <start> to <end> every <period>
```

For example, many software engineers require regular coffee throughout the working day:

```
from 9:00 to 16:15 every 45 do
  make_and_drink_coffee
```

where `make_and_drink_coffee` could be made up of the two temporal scopes given above (minus the 'by' constraint on the drinking block). Note that if this were done, the maximum elapsed time for each iteration of the loop would be 35 minutes; this is less than the period for the loop, and therefore requires a gap between drinking two cups of coffee.

Although block-level timing constraints can be specified in this way, they result in processes that experience different deadlines during their executions; at times they may even have no deadlines at all. By decomposing these processes into subprocesses where each subprocess is a single block, it is possible to represent all deadlines as process-level constraints. The run-time scheduler is thus easier to implement; for example, in some of the algorithms discussed in the next chapter, a static priority scheme is sufficient and the scheduler does not need to be explicitly aware of deadlines.

12.7.5 Esteral

Esteral (Boussinot and de Simone, 1991) is an example of a synchronous language; others include Signal (le Guernic et al., 1991) and Lustre (Halbwachs et al., 1991).

These languages attempt to support verification by making certain assumptions about the temporal behaviour of their programs. The fundamental assumption underpinning this computational model is the *ideal* (or *perfect*) **synchronous hypothesis** (Berry, 1989):

Ideal systems produce their outputs synchronously with their inputs.

Hence all computation and communication is assumed to take zero time (that is, all temporal scopes are executed instantaneously). Clearly, this is a very strong, and unrealistic, assumption. However, it enables the temporal ordering of events to be determined more easily. During implementation, the *ideal synchronous hypothesis* is interpreted to imply 'the system must execute fast enough for the effects of the synchronous hypothesis to hold'. What this means, in reality, is that following any input event, all associated outputs must occur before any new input could possibly happen. The system is then said to 'keep up' with its environment. An Esteral program is event-driven and uses signals for communication (which are broadcast). One signal, tick, is assumed to be regular (although its granularity is not defined). The following thus defines a repeating (every 10 ticks) periodic module:

```
module periodic;
input tick;
output result(integer);
var V : integer in
  loop
    await 10 tick;
    -- undertake required computation to set v
    emit result(v);
  end
end
```

A sporadic module has an identical form.

One consequence of the synchronous hypothesis is that all actions are atomic. Interactions between concurrent actions are impossible as actions themselves are instantaneous. In the above example, the result is signalled at the same instant as the awaited tick (and therefore the module does not suffer from local or cumulative drift). A sporadic module that is awaiting result will execute 'at the same time' as this periodic module. This behaviour significantly reduces non-determinism. Unfortunately it also leads to potential causality problems. Consider:

```
signal S in
  present S else emit S end
end
```

This program is incoherent. If S is absent then it is emitted; on the other hand if it were present it would not be emitted.

A formal definition of the behavioral semantics of Esterel helps to eliminate these problems (Boussinot and de Simone, 1991). A program can be checked for coherence. To implement a legal Esternal program is straightforward; with the synchronous hypothesis it is always possible to construct a finite state machine. Hence a program moves from an initial state (where it reads any inputs) to a final state (where it produces any outputs). As it moves between states, no other interactions with the environment take place. As indicated earlier, as long as the finite state machine (**automaton**) is implemented with sufficient speed, the atomicity assumption can be deemed to hold.

12.8 Fault tolerance

Throughout this book, it has been assumed that real-time systems have high reliability requirements. One method of achieving this reliability is to incorporate fault tolerance into the software. The inclusion of timing constraints introduces the possibility of these constraints being broken; for example, timeouts expiring or deadlines not being met.

With soft systems, a process may need to know if a deadline has been missed, even though it can accommodate this under normal execution. More importantly, in a hard system (or subsystem), where deadlines are critical, a missed deadline needs to trigger some error recovery routine. If the system has been shown to be schedulable under worst-case execution times then it is arguable that deadlines cannot be missed. However, the discussions of reliability in earlier chapters indicated strongly the need for a multifaceted approach to reliability; that is, prove that nothing can go wrong and include routines for adequately dealing with the problems that arise when they do. In this particular situation, a deadline could be missed in a 'proven' system if:

- worst-case execution time (WCET) calculations were inaccurate,
- assumptions made in the schedulability checker were not valid,
- the schedulability checker itself had an error,
- the scheduling algorithm could not cope with a load even though it is theoretically schedulable,
- the system is working outside its design parameters.

In this latter case (for instance, an information overflow manifesting itself as an unacceptable rate of interrupts), the system designers may still wish for fail-soft or fail-safe behaviour.

In summary, to be fault tolerant of timing failures, it is necessary to be able to detect:

- overrun of deadline
- overrun of worst-case execution time
- sporadic events occurring more often than predicted
- timeout on communications.

Of course the last three 'failures' in this list do not necessary indicate that deadlines will be missed; for example, an overrun of WCET in one process might be compensated by a sporadic event occurring less often than the maximum allowed. Hence, the damage confinement and assessment phase of providing fault tolerance (introduced in Section

5.5) must determine what actions to take. Both forward and backward recovery are possible. The following subsection will discuss the first three of these timing faults, communications timeout has already been discussed in Section 12.4.

12.8.1 Timing error detection and forward error recovery

If timing errors are to be handled, they have to be detected first. If the run-time environment or operating system is aware of the salient characteristics of a process (as it is in the Real-Time Java approach, for example), it will be able to detect problems and bring them to the attention of the application. Alternatively, it is necessary to provide primitive facilities which will allow the application to detect its own timing errors.

Deadline overrun detection

This chapter has already illustrated the facilities provided by languages and operating systems for the specification of periodic and sporadic processes along with temporal scopes.

The Ada run-time support system is unaware of the timing requirements of its application tasks, and therefore has to provide primitive mechanisms to detect deadline overrun. This is achieved using the asynchronous transfer of control facility discussed in Section 10.8. Hence to detect a deadline overrun of the periodic task given in Section 12.7.1 requires the main loop to be embedded in a 'select then abort' statement.

```ada
task body Periodic_T is
  Next_Release : Time;
  Next_Deadline : Time;
  Release_Interval : constant Duration := ...; -- or
  Release_Interval : constant Time_Span := Milliseconds(...);
  Deadline : constant Time_Span := Milliseconds(...);
begin
  -- read clock and calculate the next
  -- release time (Next_Release) and
  -- next deadline (Next_Deadline)
  loop
    select
      delay until Next_Deadline;
      -- deadline overrun detected here
      -- perform recovery
    then abort
      -- sample data (for example) or
      -- calculate and send a control signal
    end select;
    delay until Next_Release;
    Next_Release := Next_Release + Release_Interval;
    Next_Deadline := Next_Release + Deadline;
  end loop;
end Periodic_T;
```

A similar approach can be used to detect a deadline overrun in a sporadic task.

One of the problems with this approach is that it assumes that the recovery strategy requires the task to stop what it is doing. This is, clearly, one option, but there are other approaches; for example, allowing the task to continue its execution at a different priority. For these, a more appropriate response to detecting a deadline overrun is to raise an asynchronous event. In Real-Time Java, the virtual machine will signal an asynchronous event when a periodic thread is still executing when its deadline has passed. Sporadic event handlers in Real-Time Java have no explicit deadline overrun detection; they are assumed to be soft.

C/POSIX allows timers to be created and set which will generate user-defined signals (SIGALRM by default) when they expire. Hence this will allow the process to decide what is the correct course of action to pursue. Program 12.12 shows a typical C interface.

In Section 5.5.1, the watchdog timer approach to fault detection was presented. This can be easily programmed using POSIX signals. For example, consider the case where one thread (monitor) creates another thread (server) and wishes to monitor its progress to see if it meets a deadline. The deadline of the server is given by struct timespec deadline. The monitor thread creates a per process timer indicating a signal handler to be executed if the timer expires. It then creates the server thread and passes a pointer to the timer. The server thread performs its action and then deletes the timer. If the alarm goes off, the server is late.

```c
#include <signal.h>
#include <timer.h>
#include <pthread.h>

timer_t timer; /* timer shared between monitor and server */

struct timespec deadline = ...;
struct timespec zero = ...;

struct itimerspec alarm_time, old_alarm;

struct sigevent s;

void server(timer_t *watchdog)
{
  /* perform required service */
  TIMER_DELETE(*watchdog);
}

void watchdog_handler(int signum, siginfo_t *data, void *extra)
{
  /* SIGALRM handler */

  /* server is late: undertake recovery */
}
```

Program 12.12 A C interface to POSIX timers.

```
#define TIMER_ABSTIME ..

struct itimerspec {
  struct timespec it_value; /* first timer signal */
  struct timespec it_interval; /* subsequent intervals */
};
typedef ... timer_t;


int timer_create(clockid_t clock_id, struct sigevent *evp,
                 timer_t *timerid);
  /* Create a per-process timer using the specified clock as the */
  /* timing base. evp points to a structure which contains */
  /* all the information needed concerning the signal */
  /* to be generated. */

int timer_delete(timer_t timerid);
  /* delete a per-process timer */

int timer_settime(timer_t timerid, int flags,
                  const struct itimerspec *value,
                  struct itimerspec *ovalue);
  /* Set the next expiry time for the timer specified. */
  /* If flags is set to TIMER_ABSTIME, then */
  /* the timer will expire when the clock reaches the */
  /* absolute value specified by *value.it_value */
  /* if flags is NOT set to TIMER_ABSTIME, then the timer will */
  /* expire when the interval specified by value->it_value passes */
  /* if *value.it_interval is non-zero, then a periodic timer will */
  /* go off every value->it_interval after value->it_value has */
  /* expired */
  /* Any previous timer setting is returned in *ovalue. */


int timer_gettime(timer_t timerid, struct itimerspec *value);
  /* get the details of the current timer */

int timer_getoverrun(timer_t timerid);
  /* if real-time signals are supported, return the number of signals */
  /* that have been generated by this timer but not handled */


/* All the above functions, except timer_getoverrun, return 0 if  */
/* successful, otherwise -1. timer_getoverrun returns the number */
/* of overruns.  When an error condition is returned by any of */
/* the above functions, a shared variable errno contains the */
/* reason for the error */
```

```
void monitor()
{
  pthread_attr_t attributes;
  pthread_t serve;


  sigset_t mask, omask;
  struct sigaction sa, osa;
  int local_mode;

  SIGEMPTYSET(&mask);
  SIGADDSET(&mask, SIGALRM);

  sa.sa_flags = SA_SIGINFO;
  sa.sa_mask = mask;
  sa.sa_sigaction = &watchdog_handler;

  SIGACTION(SIGALRM, &sa, &osa); /* assign handler */


  alarm_time.it_value = deadline;
  alarm_time.it_interval = zero; /* one shot timer */

  s.sigev_notify = SIGEV_SIGNAL;
  s.sigev_signo = SIGALRM;

  TIMER_CREATE(CLOCK_REALTIME, &s, &timer);

  TIMER_SETTIME(timer, TIMER_ABSTIME, &alarm_time, &old_alarm);

  PTHREAD_ATTR_INIT(&attributes);
  PTHREAD_CREATE(&serve, &attributes, (void *)server, &timer);

}
```

However, as noted in Section 10.6.6, if the process is multithreaded, the signal is sent to the whole process, not an individual thread. In general, therefore, it is difficult to determine which thread has overrun its deadline.

Real-Time Java also supports timers. Programs 12.13 and 12.14 define the associated classes.

With local time structures in DPS, it is appropriate to associate timing errors with exceptions:

```
start <timing constraints> do
  -- statements
exception
  -- handlers
end
```

In addition to the necessary computations required for damage limitation, error recovery and so on, the handler may wish to extend the deadline period and continue execution of the original block. Thus a *resumption* rather than *termination* model may be more appropriate (see Chapter 6).

Program 12.13 The Real-Time Java `Timer` class.

```
public abstract class Timer extends AsyncEvent
{
  protected Timer(HighResolutionTimer time, Clock clock,
                  AsyncEventHandler handler);

  public ReleaseParameters createReleaseParameters();

  public AbsoluteTime getFireTime();
  // Get the time at which this event will fire.

  public void reschedule(HighResolutionTimer time);
  // Change the scheduled time for this event.

  public Clock getClock();

  public void disable();
  // Disable this timer, preventing it from firing. However,
  // a disabled timer continues to count while it is
  // disabled

  public void enable();
  // Re-enable this timer after it has been disabled.
  // The timer will immediately fire if its fire
  // time has passed.

  public void start(); // start the timer ticking
}
```

In a time-dependent system, it may also be necessary to give the deadline constraints of the handlers. Usually the execution time for the handler is taken from the temporal scope itself; for example, in the following, the statement sequence will be prematurely terminated after 19 time units:

```
start elapse 22 do
  -- statements
exception
  when elapse_error within 3 do
    -- handler
end
```

As with all exception models, if the handler itself gives rise to an exception this can only be dealt with at a higher level within the program hierarchy. If a timing error occurs within a handler at the process level then the process must be terminated (or at least the current iteration of the process). There might then be some system level handlers to deal with failed processes or it may be left to the application software to recognize and cope with such events.

Program 12.14   The Real-Time Java `OneShotTimer` and `PeriodicTimer` classes.

```
public class OneShotTimer extends Timer
{
  public OneShotTimer(HighResolutionTimer time,
                      AsyncEventHandler handler);
  // Create an instance of AsyncEvent that will execute its
  // fire method at the expiration of the given time.

  public OneShotTimer(HighResolutionTimer start, Clock clock,
                      AsyncEventHandler handler);
  // Create an instance of AsyncEvent, based on the given
  // clock, that will execute its fire method at the
  // expiration of the given time.
}

public class PeriodicTimer extends Timer
{
  public PeriodicTimer(HighResolutionTimer start, RelativeTime interval,
                       AsyncEventHandler handler);
  // create an instance of AsyncEvent that executes it fire
  // method periodically

  public PeriodicTimer(HighResolutionTimer start,
                       RelativeTime interval,
                       Clock clock, AsyncEventHandler handler);
  // Create an instance of AsyncEvent that executes it fire
  // method periodically from start based on a particular clock

  public ReleaseParameters createReleaseParameters();

  public void setInterval(RelativeTime interval);
  // Resets the interval of this Timer
  public RelativeTime getInterval();

  public void fire();
  // Overrides fire in class AsyncEvent
  public AbsoluteTime getFireTime();
}
```

If exception handlers are added to the coffee-making example given earlier, the code would have the following form (exceptions for logic errors such as 'no cups available' are not included). It is assumed that only `boil_water` and `drink_coffee` have any significant temporal properties; timing errors are, therefore, due to overrun on these activities.

```
from 9:00 to 16:15 every 45 do
  start elapse 11 do
    get_cup
    boil_water
```

```
      put_coffee_in_cup
      put_water_in_cup
    exception
      when elapse_error within 1 do
        turn_off_kettle   -- for safety
        report_fault
        get_new_cup
        put_orange_in_cup
        put_water_in_cup
      end
    end

    start after 3 elapse 26 do
      drink
    exception
      when elapse_error within 1 do
        empty_cup
      end
    end
    replace_cup
  exception
    when any_exception do
      null    -- go on to next iteration
    end
  end
```

Overrun of worst-case execution time

Good software engineering practices attempt to confine the consequences of an error to a well-defined region of the program. Facilities such as modules, packages and atomic actions help with this goal. However, if a process consumes more of the CPU resource than has been anticipated, then it may not be that process that misses its deadline. For example, it may be a high-priority process with a fair amount of slack time; the processes that will miss a deadline may be lower priority processes with less slack available. Ideally, it should be possible to catch the timing error in the process that caused it. This implies that it is necessary to be able to detect when a process overruns the worst-case execution time that the programmer has allowed for it. Of course, if a process is non preemptively scheduled (and does not block waiting for resources), its CPU execution time is equal to its elapse time and the same mechanisms that were used to detect deadline overrun can be used. However, processes are usually preemptively scheduled, and this makes measuring CPU time usage more difficult.

POSIX supports execution-time time monitoring using its clock and timer facilities. Two clocks are defined: `CLOCK_PROCESS_CPUTIME_ID` and `CLOCK_THREAD_CPUTIME_ID`. These can be used in the same way as `CLOCK_REALTIME`. Each process/thread has an associated execution-time clock; calls to:

```
clock_settime(CLOCK_PROCESS_CPUTIME_ID, &some_timespec_value);

clock_gettime(CLOCK_PROCESS_CPUTIME_ID, &some_timespec_value);

clock_getres(CLOCK_PROCESS_CPUTIME_ID, &some_timespec_value)
```

will set/get the execution-time or get the resolution of the execution time clock associated with the calling process (similarly for threads).

Two functions allow a process/thread to obtain and then access the clock of another process/thread.

```
int clock_getcpuclockid(pid_t pid, clockid_t *clock_id);

int pthread_getcpuclockid(pthread_t thread_id, clockid_t *clock_id);
```

The timers defined in Program 12.12 can be used to create timers which, in turn, can be used to generate process-signals when the execution time set has expired. It is implementation-defined what happens if a `timer_create` is used with a `clock_id` different from that of the calling process/thread. As the signal generated by the expiry of the timer is directed at the process, it is application-dependent which thread will get the signal if a thread's execution-time timer expires. An application can disallow the use of the timer for a thread (because of the overhead in supporting the facility).

As with all execution time monitoring, it is difficult to guarantee the accuracy of the execution-time clock in the presence of context switches and interrupts.

Real-Time Java allows a 'cost' value to be associated with the execution of a schedulable object. If supported by the implementation, this allows an asynchronous event to be fired if the cost is exceeded.

Overrun of sporadic events

A sporadic event firing more frequently than anticipated can have an enormous consequence for a system attempting to meet hard deadlines. It is therefore necessary either to ensure that this is prohibited or to detect it when it occurs and take some corrective action.

There are essentially two approaches to prohibiting sporadic event overrun. The first is where the event is triggered by a hardware interrupt. On most occasions, the interrupt can be inhibited from occurring by manipulating the associated device control registers.

An alternative approach is to use sporadic server technology; see Section 13.8.2. If sporadic servers are not used and interrupts cannot be prohibited, then it is necessary to detect when they are occurring too frequently. Most real-time languages and operating systems are woefully lacking in support for this.

12.8.2   Timing error detection and backward error recovery

As an alternative to using forward error recovery, a timing error could invoke backward error recovery. All backward error recovery techniques involve acceptance tests. It is therefore possible to include a temporal requirement in these tests. The run-time system can asynchronously fail an acceptance test if the deadline has been overrun. This is illustrated using a timeout facility incorporated within Dialogs and Colloquys (Gregory and Knight, 1985), which were discussed in Chapter 10. The dialog sequence now becomes:

```
SELECT
    dialog_1
OR
    dialog_2
OR
    dialog_3
TIMEOUT value
    -- sequence of statements
ELSE
    -- sequence of statements
END SELECT;
```

As before, on execution, the process first attempts `dialog_1`. If this succeeds control is passed to the statement following the select statement. If the dialog fails then `dialog_2` is attempted and so on. However, to enable the colloquy concept to handle missed deadlines it is possible to associate a timeout with the select. The timing constraint specifies an interval during which the process may execute as many dialog attempts as possible. Different processes involved in the dialogs may have different timeout values. If a timeout expires then the currently executing dialog fails, the process's state is restored to what it was on execution of the select statement, and the statements after the `TIMEOUT` clause are executed. The other processes involved in the dialog also fail, but their actions are determined by the options set in their select statements. They may try another dialog, timeout or fail altogether. As with the else clause, the statements after the `TIMEOUT` can be considered to be a last attempt to achieve the goal of the process. If it fails then the surrounding colloquy fails.

It is now possible to program a simple deadline mechanism using a dialog sequence consisting of a single dialog attempt and a timeout. For example, consider an Ada-like real-time language which does not explicitly support the specification of deadlines. A task could recover from a deadline error when communicating with many tasks as follows:

```
task body deadline_example is
begin
  loop
    ...
    time := calculated_time_to_deadline;
    slack := calculate_time_for_degraded_algorithm;
    restore := state_restoration_time;
    timeout_value := time - (slack + restore);
    ...
```

```
    SELECT
      dialog_1;
    TIMEOUT timeout_value
        -- sequence of statements to recover
        -- from missed deadline
    ELSE
        fail;
    END SELECT;
  end loop;
end deadline_example;
```

The task first calculates the time delay until the next deadline. It then subtracts from this the time estimated to recover from a missed deadline and the time taken for state restoration. The difference between these values is called the slack time. If the dialog has not been completed in this time due to a timing error or a design error then the recovery sequence is initiated.

12.8.3   Mode changes and event-based reconfiguration

In the above discussions, it has generally been assumed that a missed deadline can be dealt with by the process/thread that is actually responsible for the deadline. This is not always the case. Often the consequences of a timing error are that

- Other processes must alter their deadlines or even terminate what they are doing.
- New processes may need to be started.
- Critically important computation may require more processor time than is currently available; to obtain the extra time, other less significant processes may need to be 'suspended'.
- Processes may need to be 'interrupted' in order to undertake one of the following (typically):
  - immediately return the best result it has obtained so far;
  - change to a quicker (but presumably less accurate) algorithm;
  - forget what it is presently doing and become ready to take new instructions: 'restart without reload'.

These actions are sometimes known as **event-based reconfiguration**.

Some systems may additionally enter anticipated situations in which deadlines are liable to be missed. A good illustration of this is found in systems that experience **mode changes**. This is where some event in the environment occurs which results in certain computations that have already been initialized, no longer being required. If the system were to complete these computations then other deadlines would be missed; it is thus necessary to terminate prematurely the processes or temporal scopes that contain the computations.

To perform event-based reconfiguration and mode changes requires communication between the processes concerned. Due to the asynchronous nature of this communication, it is necessary to use the asynchronous notification mechanisms found in languages like Ada, Java and C/POSIX (see Section 10.5). These mechanisms are low level; arguably what is really required to to be able to tell the scheduler to stop invoking certain processes which are now not required and to begin to invoke other processes. Real-Time Java goes some way towards this by having methods associated with real-time threads which inform the scheduler that the thread is currently not required.

Real-Time Euclid is interesting in this respect because it ties its asynchronous event handling mechanism to its real-time abstractions. In Real-Time Euclid time constraints are associated with processes and numbered exceptions can be defined. Handlers must be provided in each process. For example, consider the following temperature controller process which defines three exceptions.

```
process TempController : periodic frame 60 first activation
                      atTime 600 or atEvent startMonitoring
  % import list
  handler (except_num)
    exceptions (200,201,304)   % for example
    imports (var consul, ...)
    var message : string(80), ...
    case except_num of
      label 200:  % very low temperature
        message := "reactor is shut down"
        consul := message
      label 201:  % very high temperature
        message := "meltdown has begun - evacuate"
        consul := message
        alarm := true   % activate alarm device
      label 304:  % timeout on sensor
                  % reboot sensor device
    end case
  end handler
  %
  % execution part
  %
end TempController
```

Real-Time Euclid allows a process to raise an exception in another process. Three different kinds of raise statement are supported: *except*, *deactivate* and *kill*; as their names imply they have increasing severity.

The *except* statement is essentially the same as the Ada raise, the difference being that once the handler has been executed, control is returned to where it left off (that is, resumption model). By comparison, the *deactivate* statement causes that iteration of the (periodic) process to be terminated. The victim process still executes the exception handler, but will then only become reactivated when its next period is due. To terminate a process, the *kill* statement is available; this explicitly removes a process (possibly itself) from the set of active processes. It differs from an unconditional abort in that the exception handler is executed before termination. This has the advantage that a process may perform some important 'last rites'. It has the disadvantage that an error in the handler could still cause the process to malfunction.

To illustrate the use of these exceptions, the temperature control process given earlier will have some detail added to its execution part. Note that, in this example, exceptions are raised and handled synchronously within the same process, and asynchronously in another process. First, the process waits on a condition variable; a timeout is specified and an exception number is given. (If this timeout occurs, the numbered exception is raised using *except*.) A temperature is then read and logged. Tests on the temperature value could lead to other exceptions being raised. A low value will result in an appropriate message and deactivation until the next period; a high value will result in an even more appropriate, if somewhat futile, message, an exception being raised in an alarm process, and the temperature controller terminating. All available processor time can now be dedicated to the alarm process.

```
process TempController : periodic frame 60 first activation
                        atTime 600 or atEvent startMonitoring
  % import list
  handler (except_num)
    exceptions (200,201,304)   % for example
    imports (var consul, ...)
    var message : string(80), ...
    case except_num of
      ... % as before
    end case
  end handler

  wait(temperature_available) noLongerThan 10 : 304
  currentTemperature := ...   % low-level i/o
  log := currentTemperature
  if currentTemperature < 100 then
    deactivate TempController : 200
  elseif currentTemperature > 10000 then
    kill TempController : 201
  end if
  %  other computations
end TempController
```

To perform this form of reconfiguration in Ada, two mechanisms are available:

- abort – similar to *kill*
- ATC – similar to *deactivate*

Ada allows 'last rites' to be programmed using a *controlled variable* (see Chapter 4). As indicated in Section 10.8, the ATC feature is a general one, and hence it can deal with *deactivate* and most other forms of event-based reconfiguration. See Real and Wellings (1999a) and Real and Wellings (1999b) for a discussion on mode changes in Ada.

Summary

The management of time presents a number of difficulties that set embedded systems apart from other computing applications. Current real-time languages are often inadequate in their provisions for this vital area.

The introduction of the notion of time into real-time programming languages has been described in terms of four requirements:

- access to a clock,
- delaying,
- timeouts,
- deadline specification and scheduling.

The sophistication of the means provided to measure the passage of time varies greatly between languages. Occam2 supports a TIMER facility which merely returns an integer of implementation-defined meaning. Ada and Real-Time Java go somewhat further in providing two abstract data types for time and a collection of time-related operators. C/POSIX provides a comprehensive set of facilities for clocks and timers including periodic timers.

If a process wishes to pause for a period of time, a delay (or sleep) primitive is needed to prevent the process having to busy wait. Such a primitive always guarantees to suspend the process for at least the designated time, but it cannot force the scheduler to run the process immediately the delay has expired. One cannot, therefore, avoid local drift, although it is possible to limit the cumulative drift that could arise from repeated execution of delays.

For many real-time systems, it is not sufficient for the software to be logically correct; the programs must also satisfy timing constraints. Unfortunately, existing practices in the engineering of large real-time systems are, in general, still rather *ad hoc*. To facilitate the specification of timing constraints and requirements, it is useful to introduce the notion of a 'temporal scope'. Possible attributes of temporal scopes include:

- deadline for completion of execution
- minimum delay before start of execution
- maximum delay before start of execution
- maximum execution time
- maximum elapse time

Consideration was given in this chapter as to how temporal scopes can be specified within programming languages.

The degree of importance of timing requirements is a useful way of characterizing real-time systems. Constraints that must be met are termed hard; those that can be missed occasionally, or by a small amount, are called firm or soft.

To be fault tolerant of timing failures, it is necessary to be able to detect:

- overrun of deadline
- overrun of worst-case execution time
- sporadic events occurring more often than predicted

- timeout on communications.

Following detection, event-based reconfiguration may need to be undertaken.

Further reading

Buttazzo, G. C. (1997) *Hard Real-Time Computing Systems: Predictable Scheduling Algorithms and Applications*. New York: Kluwer Academic.

Galton, A. (ed.) (19887) *Temporal Logics and their Application*. London: Academic Press.

Halang, W. A. and Stoyenko, A. D. (1991) *Constructing Predictable Real-Time Systems*. New York: Kluwer.

Joseph, M. (ed.) (1996) *Real-Time Systems: Specification, Verification and Analysis*. Englewood Cliffs, NJ: Prentice Hall.

Koptez, H. (1997) *Real-Time Systems*. New York: Kluwer Academic.

Turski, W. M. (1988) Time Considered Irrelevant For Real-time Systems. *BIT*, 28(3), 473–488.

Exercises

12.1 Explain how a system can be transformed so that all timing failures manifest themselves as value failures. Can the converse be achieved?

12.2 Should Ada's timed entry call specify a timeout on the *completion* of the rendezvous, rather than the start of the rendezvous? Give an example of when such an approach might be useful. How might the same effect be obtained?

12.3 In a real-time Ada-like language that uses exceptions for forward error recovery, two new predefined exceptions (potentially raised by the run-time system) are proposed:
DEADLINE_ERROR – raised when a block of code has not been completed in the required time interval (relative to the start of the block); and
WCET_ERROR – raised when a block has used more CPU time than specified (that is, it has overrun its Worst-Case Execution Time).
Discuss:

> (1) how these exceptions could be integrated into an Ada-like language, in particular how the required deadline and WCET values might be specified;
> (2) how these two exceptions could be implemented (in the run-time system);
> (3) how they might be used in an application.

12.4 Consider the following monitor interface to a simple (coarse) delay mechanism:

```
monitor TIME is
   procedure TICK;
   procedure DELAY (D : NATURAL);
end TIME;
```

A caller of DELAY wishes to be suspended for D ticks. The procedure TICK is called by some clock routine. Whenever it is caller each process blocked on DELAY wakes up, decrements some counter (which is initialized to D) and exits the monitor if the the counter has reached zero – otherwise it reblocks.

Show how the body of this monitor can be implemented. Use condition variables that have wait and signal operations defined on them. Indicate what semantics are assumed for signal.

12.5 Discuss how a package Time in Ada could provide the same delay mechanism as that given in Exercise 12.4 (Do *not* use the Ada delay statement).

12.6 Can the deadline overrun of a periodic thread in Real-Time Java be detected?

12.7 What is the role of deadline in the specification of a Real-Time Java event handler?

12.8 To what extent can event-based reconfiguration be performed in Real-Time Java?

Chapter 13
Scheduling

In a concurrent program, it is not necessary to specify the exact order in which processes execute. Synchronization primitives are used to enforce the local ordering constraints, such as mutual exclusion, but the general behaviour of the program exhibits significant non-determinism. If the program is correct then its functional outputs will be the same regardless of internal behaviour or implementation details. For example, five independent processes can be executed non-preemptively in 120 different ways on a single processor. With a multiprocessor system or preemptive behaviour, there are infinitely more interleavings.

While the program's outputs will be identical with all these possible interleavings, the timing behaviour will vary considerably. If one of the five processes has a tight deadline then perhaps only interleavings in which it is executed first will meet the program's temporal requirements. A real-time system needs to restrict the non-determinism found within concurrent systems. This process is known as scheduling. In general, a scheduling scheme provides two features:

- An algorithm for ordering the use of system resources (in particular the CPUs).
- A means of predicting the worst-case behaviour of the system when the scheduling algorithm is applied.

The predictions can then be used to confirm that the temporal requirements of the system are satisfied.

A scheduling scheme can be static (if the predictions are undertaken before execution) or dynamic (if run-time decisions are used). This chapter will concentrate mainly on static schemes. Most attention will be given to preemptive priority-based schemes. Here, processes are assigned priorities such that at all times the process with the highest priority is executing (if it is not delayed or otherwise suspended). A scheduling scheme will therefore involve a priority assignment algorithm and a schedulability test.

13.1   Simple process model

An arbitrarily complex concurrent program cannot easily be analyzed to predict its worst-case behaviour. Hence it is necessary to impose some restrictions on the structure of real-time concurrent programs. This section will present a very simple model in order to describe some standard scheduling schemes. The model is generalized in later sections of this chapter (and is further examined in Chapters 14 and 16). The basic model has the following characteristics:

- The application is assumed to consist of a fixed set of processes.
- All processes are periodic, with known periods.
- The processes are completely independent of each other.
- All system's overheads, context-switching times and so on are ignored (that is, assumed to have zero cost).
- All processes have deadlines equal to their periods (that is, each process must complete before it is next released).
- All processes have fixed worst-case execution times.

One consequence of the process's independence is that it can be assumed that at some point in time all processes will be released together. This represents the maximum load on the processor and is known as a **critical instant**.

Table 13.1 gives a standard set of notations for process characteristics.

13.2   The cyclic executive approach

With a fixed set of purely periodic processes, it is possible to lay out a complete schedule such that the repeated execution of this schedule will cause all processes to run at their

Notation	Description
B	Worst-case blocking time for the process (if applicable)
C	Worst-case computation time (WCET) of the process
D	Deadline of the process
I	The interference time of the process
J	Release jitter of the process
N	Number of processes in the system
P	Priority assigned to the process (if applicable)
R	Worst-case response time of the process
T	Minimum time between process releases (process period)
U	The utilization of each process (equal to C/T)
$a-z$	The name of a process

Table 13.1   Standard notation.

correct rate. The cyclic executive is, essentially, a table of procedure calls, where each procedure represents part of the code for a 'process'. The complete table is known as the **major cycle**; it typically consists of a number of **minor cycles** each of fixed duration. So, for example, four minor cycles of 25 ms duration would make up a 100 ms major cycle. During execution, a clock interrupt every 25 ms will enable the scheduler to loop through the four minor cycles. Table 13.2 provides a process set that must be implemented via a simple four-slot major cycle. A possible mapping onto the cyclic executive is shown in Figure 13.1 which illustrates the job that the processor is executing at any particular time. The code for such a system would have a simple form:

```
loop
  wait_for_interrupt;
  procedure_for_a;
  procedure_for_b;
  procedure_for_c;
  wait_for_interrupt;
  procedure_for_a;
  procedure_for_b;
  procedure_for_d;
  procedure_for_e;
  wait_for_interrupt;
  procedure_for_a;
  procedure_for_b;
  procedure_for_c;
  wait_for_interrupt;
  procedure_for_a;
  procedure_for_b;
  procedure_for_d;
end loop;
```

Even this simple example illustrates some important features of this approach:

Process	Period, T	Computation time, C
a	25	10
b	25	8
c	50	5
d	50	4
e	100	2

Table 13.2   Cyclic executive process set.

Figure 13.1   Time-line for process set.

- No actual processes exist at run-time; each minor cycle is just a sequence of procedure calls.
- The procedures share a common address space and can thus pass data between themselves. This data does not need to be protected (via a semaphore, for example) because concurrent access is not possible.
- All 'process' periods must be a multiple of the minor cycle time.

This final property represents one of the major drawbacks of the cyclic executive approach; others include (Locke, 1992):

- the difficulty of incorporating sporadic processes;
- the difficulty of incorporating processes with long periods; the major cycle time is the maximum period that can be accommodated without secondary schedules (that is, a procedure in a major cycle that will call a secondary procedure every N major cycles);
- the difficulty of actually constructing the cyclic executive;
- any 'process' with a sizable computation time will need to be split into a fixed number of fixed sized procedures (this may cut across the structure of the code from a software engineering perspective, and hence may be error-prone).

If it is possible to construct a cyclic executive then no further schedulability test is needed (the scheme is 'proof by construction'). However, for systems with high utilization, the building of the executive is problematic. An analogy with the classical bin packing problem can be made. With that problem, items of varying sizes (in just one dimension) have to be placed in the minimum number of bins such that no bin is over-full. The bin packing problem is known to be NP-hard and hence is computationally infeasible for sizable problems (a typical realistic system will contain perhaps 40 minor cycles and 400 entries). Heuristic sub-optimal schemes must therefore be used.

Although for simple periodic systems, the cyclic executive will remain an appropriate implementation strategy, a more flexible and accommodating approach is furnished by the process-based scheduling schemes. These approaches will therefore be the focus in the remainder of this chapter.

13.3 Process-based scheduling

With the cyclic executive approach, at run-time, only a sequence of procedure calls are executed. The notion of process (thread) is not preserved during execution. An alternative approach is to support process execution directly (as is the norm in general-purpose operating systems) and to determine which process should execute at any one time by the use of one or more scheduling attributes. With this approach, a process is deemed to be in one of a number of *states* (assuming no interprocess communication):

- runnable
- suspended waiting for a timing event – appropriate for periodic processes
- suspended waiting for a non-timing event – appropriate for sporadic processes

13.3.1 Scheduling approaches

There are, in general, a large number of different scheduling approaches. In this book we will consider three.

- Fixed-Priority Scheduling (FPS) – this is the most widely used approach and is the main focus of this chapter. Each process has a fixed, **static**, priority which is computed pre-run-time. The runnable processes are executed in the order determined by their priority. *In real-time systems, the 'priority' of a process is derived from its temporal requirements, not its importance to the correct functioning of the system or its integrity.*

- Earliest Deadline First (EDF) Scheduling. Here the runnable processes are executed in the order determined by the absolute deadlines of the processes; the next process to run being the one with the shortest (nearest) deadline. Although it is usual to know the relative deadlines of each process (e.g. 25 ms after release), the absolute deadlines are computed at run-time, and hence the scheme is described as **dynamic**.

- Value-Based Scheduling (VBS). If a system can become overloaded then the use of simple static priorities or deadlines is not sufficient; a more **adaptive** scheme is needed. This often takes the form of assigning a *value* to each process and employing an online value-based scheduling algorithm to decide which process to run next.

As indicated earlier, the bulk of this chapter is concerned with FPS as it is supported by various real-time languages and operating system standards. The use of EDF is also important and some consideration of its analytical basis is given in the following discussions. A short description of the use of VBS is given towards the end of the chapter in section 13.13.

13.3.2 Preemption and non-preemption

With priority-based scheduling, a high-priority process may be released during the execution of a lower priority one. In a **preemptive** scheme, there will be an immediate switch to the higher-priority process. Alternatively, with **non-preemption**, the lower-priority process will be allowed to complete before the other executes. In general, preemptive schemes enable higher-priority processes to be more reactive, and hence they are preferred. Between the extremes of preemption and non-preemption, there are alternative strategies that allow a lower priority process to continue to execute for a bounded time (but not necessarily to completion). These schemes are known as **deferred preemption** or **cooperative dispatching**. These will be considered again in Section 13.12.1. Before then, dispatching will be assumed to be preemptive. Schemes such as EDF and VBS can also take on a preemptive or non-preemptive form.

13.3.3 FPS and rate monotonic priority assignment

With the straightforward model outlined in Section 13.1, there exists a simple optimal priority assignment scheme known as **rate monotonic** priority assignment. Each process is assigned a (unique) priority based on its period: the shorter the period, the higher the priority (that is, for two processes i and j, $T_i < T_j \Rightarrow P_i > P_j$). This assignment is optimal in the sense that if any process set can be scheduled (using preemptive priority-based scheduling) with a fixed-priority assignment scheme, then the given process set can also be scheduled with a rate monotonic assignment scheme. Table 13.3 illustrates a five process set and shows what the relative priorities must be for optimal temporal behaviour. Note that priorities are represented by integers, and that the higher the integer, the greater the priority. Care must be taken when reading other books and papers on priority-based scheduling, as often priorities are ordered the other way; that is, priority 1 is the highest. In this book, *priority 1 is the lowest*, as this is the normal usage in most programming languages and operating systems.

Process	Period, T	Priority, P
a	25	5
b	60	3
c	42	4
d	105	1
e	75	2

Table 13.3   Example of priority assignment.

N	Utilization bound
1	100.0%
2	82.8%
3	78.0%
4	75.7%
5	74.3%
10	71.8%

Table 13.4   Utilization bounds.

13.4   Utilization-based schedulability tests

This section describes a very simple schedulability test for FPS which, although not exact, is attractive because of its simplicity.

Liu and Layland (1973) showed that by considering only the utilization of the process set, a test for schedulability can be obtained (when the rate monotonic priority ordering is used). If the following condition is true then all N processes will meet their deadlines (note that the summation calculates the total utilization of the process set):

$$\sum_{i=1}^{N} \left(\frac{C_i}{T_i} \right) \leq N(2^{1/N} - 1) \tag{13.1}$$

Table 13.4 shows the utilization bound (as a percentage) for small values of N. For large N, the bound asymptotically approaches 69.3%. Hence any process set with a combined utilization of less than 69.3% will always be schedulable by a preemptive priority-based scheduling scheme, with priorities assigned by the rate monotonic algorithm.

Three simple examples will now be given to illustrate the use of this test. In these examples, the units (absolute magnitudes) of the time values are not defined. As long as all the values (Ts, Cs and so on) are in the same units, the tests can be applied. So in these (and later examples), the unit of time is just considered to be a *tick* of some notional time base.

Process	Period, T	Computation time, C	Priority, P	Utilization, U
a	50	12	1	0.24
b	40	10	2	0.25
c	30	10	3	0.33

Table 13.5   Process set A.

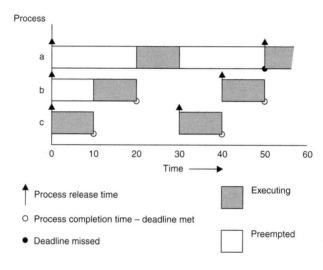

Figure 13.2   Time-line for process set A.

Table 13.5 contains three processes that have been allocated priorities via the rate monotonic algorithm (hence process c has the highest priority and process a the lowest). Their combined utilization is 0.82 (or 82%). This is above the threshold for three processes (0.78), and hence this process set fails the utilization test.

The actual behaviour of this process set can be illustrated by drawing out a **time-line**. Figure 13.2 shows how the three processes would execute if they all started their executions at time 0. Note that, at time 50, process a has consumed only 10 ticks of execution, whereas it needed 12, and hence it has missed its first deadline.

Time-lines are a useful way of illustrating execution patterns. For illustration, Figure 13.2 is drawn as a **Gantt chart** in Figure 13.3.

The second example is contained in Table 13.6. Now the combined utilization is 0.775, which is below the bound, and hence this process set is guaranteed to meet all its deadlines. If a time-line for this set is drawn, all deadlines would be satisfied.

Although cumbersome, time-lines can actually be used to test for schedulability. But how far must the line be drawn before one can conclude that the future holds no

Figure 13.3   Gantt chart for process set A.

Process	Period, T	Computation time, C	Priority, P	Utilization, U
a	80	32	1	0.400
b	40	5	2	0.125
c	16	4	3	0.250

Table 13.6   Process set B.

surprises? For process sets that share a common release time (that is, they share a *critical instant*), it can be shown that a time-line equal to the size of the longest period is sufficient (Liu and Layland, 1973). So if all processes meet their first deadline then they will meet all future ones.

A final example in given in Table 13.7. This is again a three-process system, but the combined utility is now 100%, so it clearly fails the test. At run-time however, the behaviour seems correct, all deadlines are met up to time 80 (see Figure 13.4). Hence the process set fails the test, but at run-time does not miss a deadline. Therefore, the test is said to be **sufficient** but not **necessary**. If a process set passes the test, it *will* meet all deadlines; if it fails the test, it *may* or *may not* fail at run-time. A final point to note about this utilization-based test is that it only supplies a simple yes/no answer. It does not give any indication of the actual response times of the processes. This is remedied in the response time approach described in Section 13.5.

Process	Period, T	Computation time, C	Priority, P	Utilization, U
a	80	40	1	0.50
b	40	10	2	0.25
c	20	5	3	0.25

Table 13.7   Process set C.

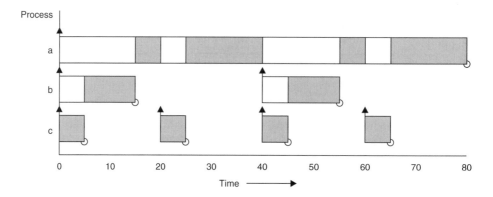

Figure 13.4   Time-line for process set C.

13.4.1 Utilization-based schedulability tests for EDF

Not only did the seminal paper of Liu and Layland (1973) introduce a utilization-based test for fixed priority scheduling but it also gave one for EDF:

$$\sum_{i=1}^{N} \left(\frac{C_i}{T_i} \right) \leq 1 \tag{13.2}$$

Clearly this is a much simpler test. As long as the utilization of the process set is less than the total capacity of the processor then all deadlines will be met (for the simple process model). In this sense EDF is superior to FPS; it can always schedule any process set that FPS can, but not all process sets that are passed by the EDF test can be scheduled using fixed priorities. Given this advantage it is reasonable to ask why EDF is not the preferred process-based scheduling method? The reason is that FPS has a number of advantages over EDF:

- FPS is easier to implement, as the scheduling attribute (*priority*) is static; EDF is dynamic and hence requires a more complex run-time system which will have higher overhead.

- It is easier to incorporate processes without deadlines into FPS (by merely assigning them a priority); giving a process an arbitrary deadline is more artificial.

- The deadline attribute is not the only parameter of importance; again it is easier to incorporate other factors into the notion of priority than it is into the notion of deadline.

- During overload situations (which may be a fault condition) the behaviour of FPS is more predictable (the lower priority processes are those that will miss their deadlines first); EDF is unpredictable under overload and can experience a domino effect in which a large number of processes miss deadlines. This is consider again in Section 13.13.

- The utilization-based test, for the simple model, is misleading as it is necessary and sufficient for EDF but only sufficient for FPS. Hence higher utilizations can, in general, be achieved for FPS.

Notwithstanding this final point, EDF does have an advantage over FPS because of its higher utilization, and hence it continues to be studied and used in some experimental systems.

13.5   Response time analysis for FPS

The utilization-based tests for FPS have two significant drawbacks: they are not exact, and they are not really applicable to a more general process model. This section provides a different form of test. The test is in two stages. First, an analytical approach is used to predict the worst-case response time of each process. These values are then compared, trivially, with the process deadlines. This requires each process to be analyzed individually.

For the highest-priority process, its worst-case response time will equal its own computation time (that is, $R = C$). Other processes will suffer **interference** from higher-priority processes; this is the time spent executing higher-priority processes when a low-priority process is runnable. So for a general process i:

$$R_i = C_i + I_i \tag{13.3}$$

where I_i is the maximum interference that process i can experience in any time interval $[t, t + R_i)$.[1] The maximum interference obviously occurs when all higher-priority processes are released at the same time as process i (that is, at a critical instant). Without loss of generality, it can be assumed that all processes are released at time 0. Consider one process (j) of higher priority than i. Within the interval $[0, R_i)$, it will be released a number of times (at least one). A simple expression for this number of releases is obtained using a ceiling function:

$$Number\_Of\_Releases = \left\lceil \frac{R_i}{T_j} \right\rceil$$

The ceiling function ($\lceil \ \rceil$) gives the smallest integer greater than the fractional number on which it acts. So the ceiling of 1/3 is 1, of 6/5 is 2, and of 6/3 is 2. The definitions of the ceilings of negative values need not be considered.

---

[1] Note that as a discrete time model is used in this analysis, all time intervals must be closed at the beginning (denoted by '[') and open at the end (denoted by a ')'). Thus a process can complete executing on the same tick as a higher-priority process is released.

So, if R_i is 15 and T_j is 6 then there are 3 releases of process j (at times 0, 6 and 12). Each release of process j will impose an interference of C_j. Hence

$$Maximum\_Interference = \left\lceil \frac{R_i}{T_j} \right\rceil C_j$$

If $C_j = 2$ then in the interval [0, 15) there are 6 units of interference. Each process of higher priority is interfering with process i, and hence:

$$I_i = \sum_{j \in hp(i)} \left\lceil \frac{R_i}{T_j} \right\rceil C_j$$

where $hp(i)$ is the set of higher-priority processes (than i). Substituting this value back into Equation (13.3) gives (Joseph and Pandya, 1986):

$$R_i = C_i + \sum_{j \in hp(i)} \left\lceil \frac{R_i}{T_j} \right\rceil C_j \tag{13.4}$$

Although the formulation of the interference equation is exact, the actual amounts of interference is unknown as R_i is unknown (it is the value being calculated). Equation (13.4) has R_i on both sides, but is difficult to solve due to the ceiling functions. It is actually an example of a fixed-point equation. In general, there will be many values of R_i that form solutions to Equation (13.4). The smallest such value of R_i represents the worst-case response time for the process. The simplest way of solving Equation (13.4) is to form a recurrence relationship (Audsley et al., 1993a):

$$w_i^{n+1} = C_i + \sum_{j \in hp(i)} \left\lceil \frac{w_i^n}{T_j} \right\rceil C_j \tag{13.5}$$

The set of values $\{w_i^0, w_i^1, w_i^2, ..., w_i^n, ...\}$ is, clearly, monotonically non-decreasing. When $w_i^n = w_i^{n+1}$, the solution to the equation has been found. If $w_i^0 < R_i$ then w_i^n is the smallest solution and hence is the value required. If the equation does not have a solution then the w values will continue to rise (this will occur for a low-priority process if the full set has a utilization greater than 100%). Once they get bigger than the process's period, T, it can be assumed that the process will not meet its deadline. The above analysis gives rise to the following algorithm for calculation response times:

```
for i in 1..N loop -- for each process in turn
    n := 0
    wⁿᵢ := Cᵢ
    loop
        calculate new wᵢⁿ⁺¹ from Equation (13.5)
        if wᵢⁿ⁺¹ = wᵢⁿ then
            Rᵢ := wᵢⁿ
            exit {value found}
```

```
      end if
      if w_i^{n+1} > T_i then
         exit {value not found}
      end if
      n := n + 1
   end loop
end loop
```

By implication, if a response time is found it will be less than T_i, and hence less than D_i, its deadline (remember with the simple process model $D_i = T_i$).

In the above discussion, w_i has been used merely as a mathematical entity for solving a fixed-point equation. It is, however, possible to get an intuition for w_i from the problem domain. Consider the point of release of process i. From that point, until the process completes, the processor will be executing processes with priority P_i or higher. The processor is said to be executing a P_i-**busy period**. Consider w_i to be a time window that is moving down the busy period. At time 0 (the notional release time of process i), all higher priority processes are assumed to have also been released, and hence

$$w_i^1 = C_i + \sum_{j \in hp(i)} C_j$$

This will be the end of the busy period unless some higher-priority process is released a second time. If it is, then the window will need to be pushed out further. This continues with the window expanding and, as a result, more computation time falling into the window. If this continues indefinitely then the busy period is unbounded (that is, there is no solution). However, if at any point, an expanding window does not suffer an extra 'hit' from a higher-priority process then the busy period has been completed, and the size of the busy period is the response time of the process.

To illustrate how the response time analysis is used, consider process set D given in Table 13.8.

The highest-priority process, a, will have a response time equal to its computation time (for example, $R_a = 3$). The next process will need to have its response time calculated. Let w_b^0 equal the computation time of process a, which is 3. Equation (13.5)

Process	Period, T	Computation time, C	Priority, P
a	7	3	3
b	12	3	2
c	20	5	1

Table 13.8   Process set D

Figure 13.5   Gantt chart for process set D.

is used to derive the next value of w:

$$w_b^1 = 3 + \left\lceil \frac{3}{7} \right\rceil 3$$

that is, $w_b^1 = 6$. This value now balances the Equation ($w_b^2 = w_b^1 = 6$) and the response time of process b has been found (that is, $R_b = 6$).

The final process will give rise to the following calculations:

$$w_c^0 = 5$$

$$w_c^1 = 5 + \left\lceil \frac{5}{7} \right\rceil 3 + \left\lceil \frac{5}{12} \right\rceil 3 \ = 11$$

$$w_c^2 = 5 + \left\lceil \frac{11}{7} \right\rceil 3 + \left\lceil \frac{11}{12} \right\rceil 3 \ = 14$$

$$w_c^3 = 5 + \left\lceil \frac{14}{7} \right\rceil 3 + \left\lceil \frac{14}{12} \right\rceil 3 \ = 17$$

$$w_c^4 = 5 + \left\lceil \frac{17}{7} \right\rceil 3 + \left\lceil \frac{17}{12} \right\rceil 3 \ = 20$$

$$w_c^5 = 5 + \left\lceil \frac{20}{7} \right\rceil 3 + \left\lceil \frac{20}{12} \right\rceil 3 \ = 20$$

Hence R_c has a worst-case response time of 20, which means that it will just meet its deadline. This behaviour is illustrated in the Gantt chart shown in Figure 13.5.

Consider again the process set C. This set failed the utilization-based test but was observed to meet all its deadlines up to time 80. Table 13.9 shows the response times calculated by the above method for this collection. Note that all processes are now predicted to complete before their deadlines.

The response time calculations have the advantage that they are sufficient and necessary – if the process set passes the test they will meet all their deadlines; if they

Process	Period, T	Computation time, C	Priority, P	Response time, R
a	80	40	1	80
b	40	10	2	15
c	20	5	3	5

Table 13.9   Response time for process set C.

Process	T(=D)	C
a	4	1
b	12	3
c	16	8

Table 13.10   A process set for EDF.

fail the test, then, at run-time, a process will miss its deadline (unless the computation time estimations, C, themselves turn out to be pessimistic). As these tests are superior to the utilization-based ones, this chapter will concentrate on extending the applicability of the response time method.

13.6   Response time analysis for EDF

One of the disadvantages of the EDF scheme is that the worst-case response time for each process does not occur when all processes are released at a critical instant. In that situation only processes with a shorter relative deadline will interfere. But later there may exist a position in which all (or at least more) processes have a shorter absolute deadline. For example, consider a three process system as depicted in Table 13.10. The behaviour of process b illustrates the problem. At time 0, a critical instant, b only gets interference from process a (once) and has a response time of 4. But at its next release (at time 12) process c is still active and has a shorted deadline (16 versus 24) and hence c takes precedence; the response time for this second release of b is 8, twice the value obtained at the critical instant. Later releases may give an even larger value, although it is bounded at 12 as the system is schedulable by EDF (utilization is 1). Hence to find the worst case is much more complex. It is necessary to consider all process releases to see which one suffers the maximum interference from other processes with shorter deadlines.

In the simple model with all periodic processes, the full process set will repeat its execution every *hyper-period*; that is, the least common multiple (LCM) of the process periods. For example, in a small system with only four processes but periods of 24, 50, 73 and 101 time units, the LCM is 4 423 800. To find the worst-case response time for

EDF requires each release within 4 423 800 to be considered – remember with FPS only the first release needs be analyzed (that is, the maximum time to consider is 101 time units).

Although more releases must be considered it is possible to derive a formula for computing each response time in a manner similar to that given above for FPS. We will not give that derivation here, but interested readers can find this (and other results relating to EDF scheduling) in the book on EDF included in the further reading section at the end of the chapter.

13.7   Worst-case execution time

In all the scheduling approaches described so far (that is, cyclic executives, FPS and EDF), it is assumed that the worst-case execution time of each process is known. This is the maximum any process invocation could require.

Worst-case execution time estimation (represented by the symbol C) can be obtained by either measurement or analysis. The problem with measurement is that it is difficult to be sure when the worst case has been observed. The drawback of analysis is that an effective model of the processor (including caches, pipelines, memory wait states and so on) must be available.

Most analysis techniques involve two distinct activities. The first takes the process and decomposes its code into a directed graph of basic blocks. These basic blocks represent straightline code. The second component of the analysis takes the machine code corresponding to a basic block and uses the processor model to estimate its worst-case execution time.

Once the times for all the basic blocks are known, the directed graph can be collapsed. For example, a simple choice construct between two basic blocks will be collapsed to a single value (that is, the largest of the two values for the alternative blocks). Loops are collapsed using knowledge about maximum bounds.

More sophisticated graph reduction techniques can be used if sufficient semantic information is available. To give just a simple example of this, consider the following code:

```
for I in 1.. 10 loop
  if Cond then
    -- basic block of cost 100
  else
    -- basic block of cost 10
  end if;
end loop;
```

With no further information, the total 'cost' of this construct would be $10 \times 100 +$ the cost of the loop construct itself, giving a total of, say, 1005 time units. It may, however, be possible to deduce (via static analysis of the code) that the condition Cond can only be true on at most three occasions. Hence a less pessimistic cost value would be 375 time units.

Other relationships within the code may reduce the number of feasible paths by eliminating those that cannot possibly occur; for instance, when the 'if' branch in one conditional statement precludes a later 'else' branch. Techniques that undertake this sort of semantic analysis usually require annotations to be added to the code. The graph reduction process can then make use of tools such as ILP (integer linear programming) to produce a tight estimate of worst-case execution time. They can also advise on the input data needed to drive the program down the path that gives rise to this estimation.

Clearly, if a process is to be analyzed for its worst-case execution time, the code itself needs to be restricted. For example, all loops and recursion must be bounded, otherwise it would be impossible to predict offline when the code terminates. Furthermore, the code generated by the compiler must also be analyzable.

The biggest challenge facing worst-case execution time analysis comes from the use of modern processors with on-chip caches, pipelines, branch predictors and so on. All of these features aim to reduce average execution time, but their impact on worst-case behaviour can be hard to predict. If one ignores these features the resulting estimates can be very pessimistic, but to include them is not always straightforward. One approach is to assume non-preemptive execution, and hence all the benefits from caching and so on can be taken into account. At a later phase of the analysis, the number of actual preemptions is calculated and a penalty applied for the resulting cache misses and pipeline refills.

To model in detail the temporal behaviour of a modern processor is non-trivial and may need proprietary information that can be hard to obtain. For real-time systems one is left with the choice of either using simpler (but less powerful) processor architectures or to put more effort into measurement. Given that all high-integrity real-time systems will be subject to considerable testing, an approach that combines testing and measurement for code units (basic blocks) but path analysis for complete components seems appropriate with today's technology.

13.8   Sporadic and aperiodic processes

To expand the simple model of Section 13.1 to include sporadic (and aperiodic) process requirements, the value T is interpreted as the minimum (or average) inter-arrival interval (Audsley et al., 1993a). A sporadic process with a T value of 20 ms is guaranteed not to arrive more than once in any 20 ms interval. In reality, it may arrive much less frequently than once every 20 ms, but the response time test will ensure that the maximum rate can be sustained (if the test is passed!).

The other requirement that the inclusion of sporadic processes demands concerns the definition of the deadline. The simple model assumes that $D = T$. For sporadic processes, this is unreasonable. Often a sporadic is used to encapsulate an error-handling routine or to respond to a warning signal. The fault model of the system may state that the error routine will be invoked very infrequently – but when it is, it is urgent and hence it has a short deadline. Our model must therefore distinguish between D and T, and allow $D < T$. Indeed, for many periodic processes, it will be useful to allow the application to define deadline values less than period.

An inspection of the response time algorithm for fixed priority scheduling, described in Section 13.5 reveals that:

- it works perfectly for values of D less than T as long as the stopping criterion becomes $w_i^{n+1} > D_i$,
- it works perfectly well with any priority ordering – $hp(i)$ always gives the set of higher-priority processes.

Although some priority orderings are better than others, the test will provide the worst-case response times for the given priority ordering.

In the Section 13.9, an optimal priority ordering for $D < T$ is defined (and proved). A later section will consider an extended algorithm and optimal priority ordering for the general case of $D < T, D = T$ or $D > T$.

13.8.1   Hard and soft processes

For sporadic processes, average and maximum arrival rates may be defined. Unfortunately, in many situations the worst-case figure is considerably higher than the average. Interrupts often arrive in bursts and an abnormal sensor reading may lead to significant additional computation. It follows that measuring schedulability with worst-case figures may lead to very low processor utilizations being observed in the actual running system. As a guideline for the minimum requirement, the following two rules should always be complied with:

- Rule 1 – all processes should be schedulable using average execution times and average arrival rates.
- Rule 2 – all hard real-time processes should be schedulable using worst-case execution times and worst-case arrival rates of all processes (including soft).

A consequent of Rule 1 is that there may be situations in which it is not possible to meet all current deadlines. This condition is known as a **transient overload**; Rule 2, however, ensures that no hard real-time process will miss its deadline. If Rule 2 gives rise to unacceptably low utilizations for 'normal execution', direct action should be taken to try and reduce the worst-case execution times (or arrival rates).

13.8.2   Aperiodic processes and fixed priority servers

One simple way of scheduling aperiodic processes, within a priority-based scheme, is to run such processes at a priority below the priorities assigned to hard processes. In effect, the aperiodic processes run as background activities, and therefore cannot steal, in a preemptive system, resources from the hard processes. Although a safe scheme, this does not provide adequate support to soft processes which will often miss their deadlines if they only run as background activities. To improve the situation for soft processes, a **server** can be employed. Servers protect the processing resources needed by hard processes, but otherwise allow soft processes to run as soon as possible.

Since they were first introduced in 1987, a number of server methods have been defined. Here only two will be considered: the Deferrable Server (DS) and the Sporadic Server (SS) (Lehoczky et al., 1987).

With the DS, an analysis is undertaken (using, for example, the response time approach) that enables a new process to be introduced at the highest priority.[2] This process, the server, thus has a period, T_s and a capacity C_s. These values are chosen so that all the hard processes in the system remain schedulable even if the server executes periodically with period T_s and execution time C_s. At run-time, whenever an aperiodic process arrives, and there is capacity available, it starts executing immediately and continues until either it finishes or the capacity is exhausted. In the latter case, the aperiodic process is suspended (or transferred to a background priority). With the DS model, the capacity is replenished every T_s time units.

The operation of the SS differs from DS in its replenishment policy. With SS, if a process arrives at time t and uses c capacity then the server has this c capacity replenished T_s time units after t. In general, SS can furnish higher capacity than DS but has increased implementational overheads. Section 13.14.2 describes how SS is supported by POSIX; DS and SS can be analyzed using response time analyses (Bernat and Burns, 1999).

As all servers limit the capacity that is available to aperiodic soft processes, they can also be used to ensure that sporadic processes do not execute more often than expected. If a sporadic process with interarrival interval of T_i and worst-case execution time of C_i is implemented not directly as a process, but via a server with $T_s = T_i$ and $C_s = C_i$, then its impact (interference) on lower-priority processes is bounded even if the sporadic process arrives too quickly (which would be an error condition).

All servers (DS, SS and others) can be described as *bandwidth preserving* in that they attempt to

- make CPU resources available immediately to aperiodic processes (if there is a capacity);
- retain the capacity for as long as possible if there are currently no aperiodic processes (by allowing the hard processes to execute).

Another bandwidth preserving scheme, which often performs better than the server techniques is **dual-priority scheduling** (Davis and Wellings, 1995). Here, the range of priorities is split into three bands: high, medium and low. All aperiodic processes run in the middle band. Hard processes, when they are released, run in the low band, but they are promoted to the top band in time to meet their deadlines. Hence in the first stage of execution they will give way to aperiodic activities (but will execute if there is no such activity). In the second phase they will move to a higher priority and then have precedence over the aperiodic work. In the high band, priorities are assigned

---

[2]Servers at other priorities are possible, but the description is more straightforward if the server is given a higher priority than all the hard processes.

according to the deadline monotonic approach (see below). Promotion to this band occurs at time $D - R$. To implement the dual-priority scheme requires a dynamic priority provision.

13.8.3   Aperiodic processes and EDF servers

Following the development of server technology for fixed priority systems, most of the common approaches have been reinterpreted within the context of dynamic EDF systems. For example there is a Dynamic Sporadic Server (Spuri and Buttazzo, 1994). Whereas the static system needs a priority to be assigned (which is done pre-run-time), the dynamic version needs to compute a deadline each time it needs to execute. In essence, the run-time algorithm assigns the server the shortest current deadline if (and only if) there is an outstanding aperiodic process to serve and there is capacity outstanding. Once the capacity is exhausted, the server is suspended until it is replenished.

A different scheme, that has a number of similarities with the dual-priority scheme of FPS, is the *earliest deadline last* (EDL) server defined by Chetto and Chetto (1989). Here hard processes switch between executing under EDF (if there are no aperiodic processes) to EDL (if there is aperiodic work to do). The EDL scheme ensures that every hard process will meet its deadline but postpones the release of the process as long as possible. Hence capacity is made available to aperiodic processes immediately (if there is spare capacity). A hard process will preempt the soft process when it is promoted and will compete its execution just at its deadline.

13.9   Process systems with $D < T$

In the above discussion on sporadic processes is was argued that, in general, it must be possible for a process to define a deadline that is less than its inter-arrival interval (or period). It was also noted earlier that for $D = T$ the rate monotonic priority ordering was optimal for a fixed priority scheme. Leung and Whitehead (1982) showed that for $D < T$, a similar formulation could be defined – the deadline monotonic priority ordering (DMPO). Here, the fixed priority of a process is inversely proportional to its deadline: $(D_i < D_j \Rightarrow P_i > P_j)$. Table 13.11 gives the appropriate priority assignments for a simple process set. It also includes the worst-case response time – as calculated by the algorithm in Section 13.5. Note that a rate monotonic priority ordering would not schedule these processes.

In the following subsection, the optimality of DMPO is proven. Given this result and the direct applicability of response time analysis to this process model, it is clear that fixed priority scheduling can adequately deal with this more general set of scheduling requirements. The same is not true for EDF scheduling. Once processes can have $D < T$ then the simple utilization test (total utilization less than one) cannot be applied. Moreover, the response time analysis, discussed in Section 13.6, is considerable more complex for EDF than it is for FPS.

Having raised this difficulty with EDF is must be remembered that EDF is the more effective scheduling scheme. Hence any process set that passes an FPS schedu-

Process	Period, T	Deadline, D	Computation time, C	Priority, P	Response time, R
a	20	5	3	4	3
b	15	7	3	3	6
c	10	10	4	2	10
d	20	20	3	1	20

Table 13.11   Example process set for DMPO.

lability test *will* also always meet its timing requirements if executed under EDF. The necessary and sufficient tests for FPS can thus be seen as sufficient tests for EDF.

13.9.1   Proof that DMPO is optimal

Deadline monotonic priority ordering (DMPO) is optimal if any process set, Q, that is schedulable by priority scheme, W, is also schedulable by DMPO. The proof of optimality of DMPO will involve transforming the priorities of Q (as assigned by W) until the ordering is DMPO. Each step of the transformation will preserve schedulability.

Let i and j be two processes (with adjacent priorities) in Q such that under W: $P_i > P_j$ and $D_i > D_j$. Define scheme W' to be identical to W except that processes i and j are swapped. Consider the schedulability of Q under W':

- All processes with priorities greater than P_i will be unaffected by this change to lower-priority processes.
- All processes with priorities lower than P_j will be unaffected. They will all experience the same interference from i and j.
- Process j, which was schedulable under W, now has a higher priority, suffers less interference, and hence must be schedulable under W'.

All that is left is the need to show that process i, which has had its priority lowered, is still schedulable.

Under W, $R_j \leq D_j$, $D_j < D_i$ and $D_i \leq T_i$ and hence process i only interferes once during the execution of j.

Once the processes have been switched, the new response time of i becomes equal to the old response time of j. This is true because under both priority orderings $C_j + C_i$ amount of computation time has been completed with the same level of interference from higher-priority processes. Process j was released only once during R_j, and hence interferes only once during the execution of i under W'. It follows that:

$$R'_i = R_j \leq D_j < D_i$$

It can be concluded that process i is schedulable after the switch.

Priority scheme W' can now be transformed (to W'') by choosing two more processes 'that are in the wrong order for DMPO' and switching them. Each such switch preserves schedulability. Eventually there will be no more processes to switch; the ordering will be exactly that required by DMPO and the process set will still be schedulable. Hence, DMPO is optimal.

Note that for the special case of $D = T$, the above proof can be used to show that, in this circumstance, rate monotonic ordering is also optimal.

13.10   Process interactions and blocking

One of the simplistic assumptions embodied in the system model, described in Section 13.1, is the need for processes to be independent. This is clearly unreasonable, as process interaction will be needed in almost all meaningful applications. In Chapters 8 and 9, it was noted that processes can interact safely by either some form of protected shared data (using, for example, semaphores, monitors or protected objects) or directly (using some form of rendezvous). All of these language features lead to the possibility of a process being suspended until some necessary future event has occurred (for example, waiting to gain a lock on a semaphore, or entry to a monitor, or until some other process is in a position to accept a rendezvous request). In general, synchronous communication leads to more pessimistic analysis as it is harder to define the real worst case when there are many dependencies between process executions. The following analysis is therefore more accurate when related to asynchronous communication where processes exchange data via protected shared resources. The majority of the material in the next two sections is concerned with fixed-priority scheduling. At the end of this discussion, the applicability of the results to EDF scheduling will be considered.

If a process is suspended waiting for a lower-priority process to complete some required computation then the priority model is, in some sense, being undermined. In an ideal world, such **priority inversion** (Lauer and Satterwaite, 1979) (that is, a high-priority process having to wait for a lower-priority process) should not exist. However, it cannot, in general, be totally eliminated. Nevertheless, its adverse effects can be minimized. If a process is waiting for a lower-priority process, it is said to be **blocked**. In order to test for schedulability, blocking must be bounded and measurable; it should also be small.

To illustrate an extreme example of priority inversion, consider the executions of four periodic processes: a, b, c and d. Assume they have been assigned priorities according to the deadline monotonic scheme, so that the priority of process d is the highest and that of process a the lowest. Further, assume that processes d and a (and processes d and c) share a critical section (resource), denoted by the symbol Q (and V), protected by mutual exclusion. Table 13.12 gives the details of the four processes and their execution sequences; in this table 'E' represents a single tick of execution time and 'Q' (or 'V') represent an execution tick with access to the Q (or V) critical section. Thus process c executes for four ticks; the middle two while it has access to critical section V.

Figure 13.6 illustrates the execution sequence for the start times given in the table.

Process	Priority	Execution sequence	Release time
a	1	EQQQQE	0
b	2	EE	2
c	3	EVVE	2
d	4	EEQVE	4

Table 13.12   Execution sequences.

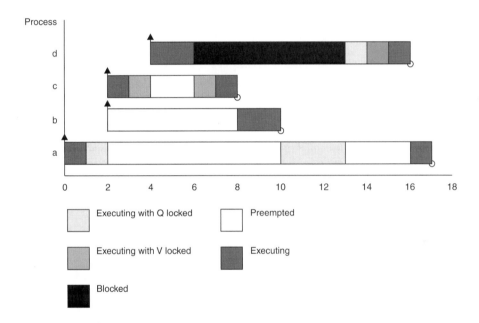

Figure 13.6   Example of priority inversion.

Process a is released first, executes and locks the critical section, Q. It is then preempted by the release of process c which executes for one tick, locks V and is then preempted by the release of process d. The higher-priority process then executes until it also wishes to lock the critical section, Q; it must then be suspended (as the section is already locked by a). At this point, c will regain the processor and continue. Once it has terminated, b will commence and run for its entitlement. Only when b has completed will a be able to execute again; it will then complete its use of the Q and allow d to continue and complete. With this behaviour, d finishes at time 16, and therefore has a response time of 12; c has a value of 6, b a value of 8, and a a value of 17.

An inspection of Figure 13.6 shows that process d suffers considerable priority inversion. Not only is it blocked by process a but also by processes b and c. Some

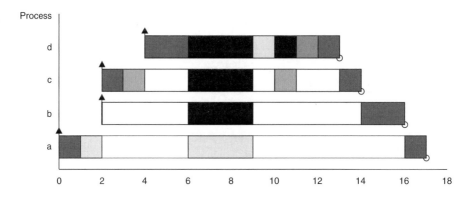

Figure 13.7   Example of priority inheritance.

blocking is inevitable; if the integrity of the critical section (and hence the shared data) is to be maintained then a must run in preference to d (while it has the lock). But the blocking of d by processes c and b is unproductive and will severely affect the schedulability of the system (as the blocking on process d is excessive).

This type of priority inversion is the result of a purely fixed-priority scheme. One method of limiting this effect is to use **priority inheritance** (Cornhill et al., 1987). With priority inheritance, a process's priority is no longer static; if a process p is suspended waiting for process q to undertake some computation then the priority of q becomes equal to the priority of p (if it were lower to start with). In the example just given, process a will be given the priority of process d and will, therefore, run in preference to process c and process b. This is illustrated in Figure 13.7. Note as a consequence of this algorithm, process b will now suffer blocking even though it does not use a shared object. Also note that process d now has a second block, but its response time has been reduced to 9.

With this simple inheritance rule, the priority of a process is the maximum of its own default priority and the priorities of all the other processes that are at that time dependent upon it.

In general, inheritance of priority would not be restricted to a single step. If process d is waiting for process c, but c cannot deal with d because it is waiting for process b then b as well as c would be given d's priority. The implication for the run-time dispatcher is that a process's priorities will often be changing and that it may be better to choose the appropriate process to run (or make runnable) at the time when the action is needed rather than try and manage a queue that is ordered by priority.

In the design of a real-time language, priority inheritance would seem to be of paramount importance. To have the most effective model, however, implies that the concurrency model should have a particular form. With standard semaphores and condition variables, there is no direct link between the act of becoming suspended and the identity of the process that will reverse this action. Inheritance is therefore not easily implemented. With synchronous message passing, indirect naming (for example, use of the channel in occam2) may also make it difficult to identify the process upon which one is waiting. To maximize the effectiveness of inheritance, direct symmetric naming would be the most appropriate.

Sha et al. (1990) show that with a priority inheritance protocol, there is a bound on the number of times a process can be blocked by lower priority processes. If a process has m critical sections that can lead to it being blocked then the maximum number of times it can be blocked is m. That is, in the worst case, each critical section will be locked by a lower-priority process (this is what happened in Figure 13.7). If there are only n ($n < m$) lower-priority processes then this maximum can be further reduced (to n).

If B_i is the maximum blocking time that process i can suffer then for this simple priority inheritance model, a formula for calculating B can easily be found. Let K be the number of critical sections (resources). Equation (13.6) thus provides an upper bound on B.

$$B_i = \sum_{k=1}^{K} usage(k,i)C(k) \tag{13.6}$$

where $usage$ is a 0/1 function: $usage(k,i) = 1$ if resource k is used by at least one process with a priority less than P_i, and at least one process with a priority greater or equal to P_i. Otherwise it gives the result 0. $C(k)$ is the worst-case execution time of the k critical section.

This algorithm is not optimal for this inheritance protocol, but serves to illustrate the factors that need to be taken into account when calculating B. In Section 13.11, better inheritance protocols will be described and an improved formulae for B will be given.

13.10.1   Response time calculations and blocking

Given that a value for B has been obtained, the response time algorithm can be modified to take the blocking factor into account:[3]

$$R = C + B + I$$

that is,

$$R_i = C_i + B_i + \sum_{j \in hp(i)} \left\lceil \frac{R_i}{T_j} \right\rceil C_j \tag{13.7}$$

---

[3]Blocking can also be incorporated into the utilization-based tests, but now each process must be considered individually.

which can again be solved by constructing a recurrence relationship:

$$w_i^{n+1} = C_i + B_i + \sum_{j \in hp(i)} \left\lceil \frac{w_i^n}{T_j} \right\rceil C_j \qquad (13.8)$$

Note that this formulation may now be pessimistic (that is, not necessarily sufficient and necessary). Whether a process actually suffers its maximum blocking will depend upon process phasings. For example, if all processes are periodic and all have the same period then no preemption will take place and hence no priority inversion will occur. However, in general, Equation (13.7) represents an effective scheduling test for real-time systems containing cooperating processes.

13.11   Priority ceiling protocols

While the standard inheritance protocol gives an upper bound on the number of blocks a high-priority process can encounter, this bound can still lead to an unacceptably pessimistic worst-case calculation. This is compounded by the possibility of chains of blocks developing (transitive blocking), that is, process c being blocked by process b which is blocked by process a and so on. As shared data is a system resource, from a resource management point of view not only should blocking be minimized, but failure conditions such as deadlock should be eliminated. All of these issues are addressed by the ceiling priority protocols (Sha et al., 1990); two of which will be considered in this chapter: the **original ceiling priority protocol** and the **immediate ceiling priority protocol**. The original protocol (OCPP) will be described first, followed by the somewhat more straightforward immediate variant (ICPP). When either of these protocols are used on a single-processor system:

- A high-priority process can be blocked at most once during its execution by lower-priority processes.
- Deadlocks are prevented.
- Transitive blocking is prevented.
- Mutual exclusive access to resources is ensured (by the protocol itself).

The ceiling protocols can best be described in terms of resources protected by critical sections. In essence, the protocol ensures that if a resource is locked, by process a say, and could lead to the blocking of a higher-priority process (b), then no other resource that could block b is allowed to be locked by any process other that a. A process can therefore be delayed by not only attempting to lock a previously locked resource but also when the lock could lead to multiple blocking on higher-priority processes.

The original protocol takes the following form:

(1) Each process has a static default priority assigned (perhaps by the deadline monotonic scheme).

(2) Each resource has a static ceiling value defined, this is the maximum priority of the processes that use it.

(3) A process has a dynamic priority that is the maximum of its own static priority and any it inherits due to it blocking higher-priority processes.

(4) A process can only lock a resource if its dynamic priority is higher than the ceiling of any currently locked resource (excluding any that it has already locked itself).

The locking of a first system resource is allowed. The effect of the protocol is to ensure that a second resource can only be locked if there does not exist a higher-priority process that uses both resources. Consequently, the maximum amount of time a process can be blocked is equal to the execution time of the longest critical section in any of the lower-priority processes that are accessed by higher-priority processes; that is, Equation (13.6) becomes:

$$B_i = \max_{k=1}^{K} usage(k, i)C(k) \qquad (13.9)$$

The benefit of the ceiling protocol is that a high-priority process can only be blocked once (per activation) by any lower-priority process. The cost of this result is that more processes will experience this block.

Not all the features of the algorithm can be illustrated by a single example, but the execution sequence shown in Figure 13.8 does give a good indication of how the algorithm works and provides a comparison with the earlier approaches (that is, this figure illustrates the same process sequence used in Figures 13.7 and 13.6).

In Figure 13.8, process a again locks the first critical section, as no other resources have been locked. It is again preempted by process c, but now the attempt by c to lock the second section (V) is not successful as its priority (3) is not higher than the current ceiling (which is 4, as Q is locked and is used by process d). At time 3, a is blocking c, and hence runs with its priority at the level 3, thereby blocking b. The higher-priority process, d, preempts a at time 4, but is subsequently blocked when it attempts to access Q. Hence a will continue (with priority 4) until it releases its lock on Q and has its priority drop back to 1. Now, d can continue until it completes (with a response time of 7).

The priority ceiling protocols ensure that a process is only blocked once during each invocation. Figure 13.8, however, appears to show process b (and process c) suffering two blocks. What is actually happening is that a single block is being broken in two by the preemption of process d. Equation (13.9) determines that all processes (apart from process a) will suffer a maximum single block of 4. Figure 13.8 shows that for this particular execution sequence process c and process d actually suffer a block of 3 and process d a block of only 2.

13.11.1 Immediate ceiling priority protocol

The immediate ceiling priority algorithm (ICPP) takes a more straightforward approach and raises the priority of a process as soon as it locks a resource (rather than only when

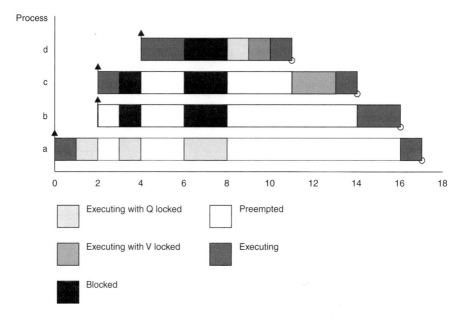

Figure 13.8   Example of priority inheritance – OCPP.

it is actually blocking a higher-priority process). The protocol is thus defined as follows:

- Each process has a static default priority assigned (perhaps by the deadline mono-tonic scheme).
- Each resource has a static ceiling value defined, this is the maximum priority of the processes that use it.
- A process has a dynamic priority that is the maximum of its own static priority and the ceiling values of any resources it has locked.

As a consequence of this final rule, a process will only suffer a block at the very be-ginning of its execution. Once the process starts actually executing, all the resources it needs must be free; if they were not, then some process would have an equal or higher priority and the process's execution would be postponed.

The same process set used in earlier illustrations can now be executed under ICPP (see Figure 13.9).

Process a having locked Q at time 1, runs for the next 4 ticks with priority 4. Hence neither process b, process c nor process d can begin. Once a unlocks Q (and has its priority reduced), the other processes execute in priority order. Note that all blocking is before actual execution and that d's response time is now only 6. This is somewhat misleading, however, as the worst-case blocking time for the two protocols is the same (see Equation (13.9)).

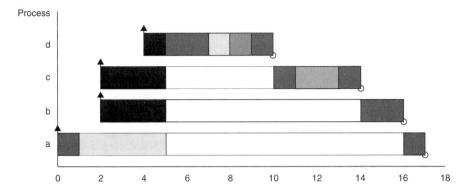

Figure 13.9   Example of priority inheritance – ICPP.

Although the worst-case behaviour of the two ceiling schemes is identical (from a scheduling view point), there are some points of difference:

- ICCP is easier to implement than the original (OCPP) as blocking relationships need not be monitored.
- ICPP leads to less context switches as blocking is prior to first execution.
- ICPP requires more priority movements as this happens with all resource usages; OCPP changes priority only if an actual block has occurred.

Finally, note that Protocol ICPP is called Priority Protect Protocol in POSIX and Priority Ceiling Emulation in Real-Time Java.

13.11.2   Ceiling protocols, mutual exclusion and deadlock

Although the above algorithms for the two ceiling protocols were defined in terms of locks on resources, it must be emphasized that the protocols themselves rather than some other synchronization primitive provided the mutual exclusion access to the resource (at least on a single processor system). Consider ICPP; if a process has access to some resource then it will be running with the ceiling value. No other process that uses that resource can have a higher priority, and hence the executing process will either execute unimpeded while using the resource, or, if it is preempted, the new process will not use this particular resource. Either way, mutual exclusion is ensured.

The other major property of the ceiling protocols (again for single-processor systems) is that they are deadlock-free. In Chapter 11, the issue of deadlock-free resource usage was considered in detail. The ceiling protocols are a form of deadlock prevention. If a process holds one resource while claiming another, then the ceiling of the second resource cannot be lower than the ceiling of the first. Indeed, if two resources are used in different orders (by different processes) then their ceilings must be identical. As one process is not preempted by another with merely the same priority, it follows that once a process has gained access to a resource then all other resources will be free when needed. There is no possibility of circular waits and deadlock is prevented.

13.11.3 Blocking and EDF

When considering shared resources and blocking, there is a direct analogy between EDF and FPS. Where FPS suffers priority inversion, EDF suffers deadline inversion. This is when a process requires a resource that is currently locked by another process with a longer deadline. Not surprisingly inheritance and ceiling protocols have been developed for EDF, but as with earlier comparisons, the EDF scheme is somewhat more complex.

Because priorities are static, it is easy to determine which processes can block the process currently being analyzed. With EDF, this relationship is dynamic; it depends on which processes (with longer deadlines) are active when the process is released. And this varies from one release to another through the hyper-period.

Probably the best scheme for EDF is the *Stack Resource Policy* (SRP) of Baker (1991). This works in a very similar way to the immediate ceiling priority protocol for FPS (indeed SRP influenced the development of ICPP). Each process, under SRP, is assigned a preemption level. Preemption levels reflect the relative deadlines of the processes, the shorter the deadline the higher the preemption level; so they actual designate the static priority of the process as assigned by the deadline monotonic scheme. At run-time, resources are given ceiling values based on the maximum preemption level of the processes that use the resource. When a process is released it can only preempt the currently executing process if its absolute deadline is shorter *and* its preemption level is higher than the highest ceiling of currently locked resources. The result of this protocol is identical to ICPP. Processes suffer only a single block, it is as they are released, deadlocks are prevented and a simple formulae is available for calculating the blocking time.

13.12 An extendible process model

It was noted earlier that the model outlined in Section 13.1 was too simplistic for practical use. In subsequent sections, three important restrictions were removed:

- Deadlines can be less than period ($D < T$).
- Sporadic and aperiodic processes, as well as periodic processes, can be supported.
- Process interactions are possible, with the resulting blocking being factored into the response time equations.

Within this section, five further generalizations will be given. Only fixed priority scheduling is considered, as EDF analysis is not as mature in these areas. The section will conclude with a general-purpose priority assignment algorithm.

13.12.1 Cooperative scheduling

The models described above have all required true preemptive dispatching. In this section, an alternative scheme is outlined (the use of deferred preemption). This has a number of advantages, but can still be analyzed by the scheduling technique embodied in Equation (13.7). In Equation (13.7), there is a blocking term B that accounts for the time a lower-priority process may be executing while a higher-priority process is runnable. In the application domain, this may be caused by the existence of data that is shared (under mutual exclusion) by processes of different priority. Blocking can, however, also be caused by the run-time system or kernel. Many systems will have the non-preemptable context switch as the longest blocking time (for example, the release of a higher-priority process being delayed by the time it takes to context switch to a lower-priority process – even though an immediate context switch to the higher-priority process will then ensue).

One of the advantages of using the immediate ceiling priority protocol (to calculate and bound B) is that blocking is not cumulative. A process cannot be blocked both by an application process and a kernel routine – only one could actually be happening when the higher-priority process is released.

Cooperative scheduling exploits this non-cumulative property by increasing the situation in which blocking can occur. Let B_{MAX} be the maximum blocking time in the system (using a conventional approach). The application code is then split into non-preemptive blocks, the execution times of which are bounded by B_{MAX}. At the end of each of these blocks, the application code offers a 'de-scheduling' request to the kernel. If a high-priority process is now runnable the kernel will instigate a context switch; if not, the currently running process will continue into the next non-preemptive block.

The normal execution of the application code is thus totally cooperative. A process will continue to execute until it offers to de-schedule. Hence, as long as any critical section is fully contained between de-scheduling calls, mutual exclusion is assured. This method does, therefore, require the careful placement of de-scheduling calls.

To give some level of protection over corrupted (or incorrect) software, a kernel could use an asynchronous signal, or abort, to remove the application process if any non-preemptive block lasts longer than B_{MAX}.

The use of deferred preemption has two important advantages. It increases the schedulability of the system, and it can lead to lower values of C. In the solution of Equation (13.4), as the value of w is being extended, new releases of higher-priority processes are possible that will further increase the value of w. With deferred preemption, no interference can occur during the last block of execution. Let F_i be the execution time of the final block, such that when the process has consumed $C_i - F_i$ time units, the last block has (just) started. Equation (13.4) is now solved for $C_i - F_i$ rather than C_i:

$$w_i^{n+1} = B_{MAX} + C_i - F_i + \sum_{j \in hp(i)} \left\lceil \frac{w_i^n}{T_j} \right\rceil C_j \qquad \textbf{(13.10)}$$

When this converges (that is, $w_i^{n+1} = w_i^n$), the response time is given by:

$$R_i = w_i^n + F_i \qquad \textbf{(13.11)}$$

In effect, the last block of the process has executed with a higher priority (the highest) than the rest of the processes.

The other advantage of deferred preemption comes from predicting more accurately the execution times of a process's non-preemptable basic blocks. Modern processors have caches, prefetch queues and pipelines that all significantly reduce the execution times of straightline code. Typically, simple estimations of worst-case execution time are forced to ignore these advantages and obtain very pessimistic results because preemption will invalidate caches and pipelines. Knowledge of non-preemption can be used to predict the speed up that will occur in practice. However, if the cost of offering a context switch is high, this will militate against these advantages. See Section 16.3.4 for a discussion on how to model the impact of cache effects on the schedulability analysis.

13.12.2   Release jitter

In the simple model, all processes are assumed to be periodic and to be released with perfect periodicity; that is, if process l has period T_l then it is released with exactly that frequency. Sporadic processes are incorporated into the model by assuming that their minimum inter-arrival interval is T. This is not, however, always a realistic assumption. Consider a sporadic process s being released by a periodic process l (on another processor). The period of the first process is T_l and the sporadic process will have the same rate, but it is incorrect to assume that the maximum load (interference) s exerts on low-priority processes can be represented in Equations (13.4) or (13.5) as a periodic process with period $T_s = T_l$.

To understand why this is insufficient, consider two consecutive executions of process l. Assume that the event that releases process s occurs at the very end of the periodic process's execution. On the first execution of process l, assume that the process does not complete until its latest possible time, that is, R_l. However, on the next invocation assume there is no interference on process l so it completes within C_l. As this value could be arbitrarily small, let it equal zero. The two executions of the sporadic process are not separated by T_l but by $T_l - R_l$. Figure 13.10 illustrates this behaviour for T_l equal to 20, R_l equal to 15 and minimum C_l equal to 1 (that is, two releases of the sporadic process within 6 time units). Note that this phenomenon is of interest only if process l is remote. If this was not the case then the variations in the release of process s would be accounted for by the standard equations, where a critical instant can be assumed between the releaser and the released.

To capture correctly the interference sporadic processes have upon other processes, the recurrence relationship must be modified. The maximum variation in a process's release is termed its *jitter* (and is represented by J). For example, in the above, process s would have a jitter value of 15. In terms of its maximum impact on lower-priority processes, this sporadic process will be released at time 0, 5, 25, 45 and so on. That is, at times $0, T - J, 2T - J, 3T - J$, and so on. Examination of the derivation of the schedulability equation implies that process i will suffer one interference from process s if R_i is between 0 and $T - J$, that is $R_i \in [0, T - J)$, two if $R_i \in [T - J, 2T - J)$,

Figure 13.10   Releases of sporadic processes.

three if $R_i \in [2T - J, 3T - J)$ and so on. A slight rearrangement of these conditions shows a single hit if $R_i + J \in [0, T)$, a double hit if $R_i + J \in [T, 2T)$ and so on. This can be represented in the same form as the previous response time equations as follows (Audsley et al., 1993a):

$$R_i = B_i + C_i + \sum_{j \in hp(i)} \left\lceil \frac{R_i + J_j}{T_j} \right\rceil C_j \qquad (13.12)$$

In general, periodic processes do not suffer release jitter. An implementation may, however, restrict the granularity of the system timer (which releases periodic processes). In this situation, a periodic process may also suffer release jitter. For example, a T value of 10 but a system granularity of 8 will imply a jitter value of 6 – at time 16 the periodic process will be released for its time '10' invocation. If response time (now denoted as $R_i^{periodic}$) is to be measured relative to the real release time then the jitter value must be added to that previously calculated:

$$R_i^{periodic} = R_i + J_i \qquad (13.13)$$

If this new value is greater than T_i then the following analysis must be used.

13.12.3   Arbitrary deadlines

To cater for situations where D_i (and hence potentially R_i) can be greater than T_i, the analysis must again be adapted. When deadline is less than (or equal) to period, it is necessary to consider only a single release of each process. The critical instant, when all higher-priority processes are released at the same time, represents the maximum interference and hence the response time following a release at the critical instant must be the worst case. However, when deadline is greater than period, a number of releases must be considered. The following assumes that the release of a process will be delayed until any previous releases of the same process have completed.

If a process executes into the next period then both releases must be analyzed to see which gives rise to the longest response time. Moreover, if the second release is not completed before a third occurs than this new release must also be considered, and so on.

For each potentially overlapping release, a separate window $w(q)$ is defined, where q is just an integer identifying a particular window (that is, $q = 0, 1, 2, ...$). Equation (13.5) can be extended to have the following form (ignoring jitter) (Tindell et al., 1994) :

$$w_i^{n+1}(q) = B_i + (q+1)C_i + \sum_{j \in hp(i)} \left\lceil \frac{w_i^n(q)}{T_j} \right\rceil C_j \tag{13.14}$$

For example, with q equal to 2, three releases of the process will occur in the window. For each value of q, a stable value of $w(q)$ can be found by iteration – as in Equation (13.5). The response time is then given as

$$R_i(q) = w_i^n(q) - qT_i \tag{13.15}$$

for example, with $q = 2$ the process started $2T_i$ into the window and hence the response time is the size of the window minus $2T_i$.

The number of releases that need to be considered is bounded by the lowest value of q for which the following relation is true:

$$R_i(q) \leq T_i \tag{13.16}$$

At this point, the process completes before the next release and hence subsequent windows do not overlap. The worst-case response time is then the maximum value found for each q:

$$R_i = \max_{q=0,1,2,...} R_i(q) \tag{13.17}$$

Note that for $D \leq T$, the relation in Equation (13.16) is true for $q = 0$ (if the process can be guaranteed), in which case Equations (13.14) and (13.15) simplify back to the original equation. If any $R > D$, then the process is not schedulable.

When this arbitrary deadline formulation is combined with the effect of release jitter, two alterations to the above analysis must be made. First, as before, the interference factor must be increased if any higher priority processes suffers release jitter:

$$w_i^{n+1}(q) = B_i + (q+1)C_i + \sum_{j \in hp(i)} \left\lceil \frac{w_i^n(q) + J_j}{T_j} \right\rceil C_j \tag{13.18}$$

The other change involves the process itself. If it can suffer release jitter then two consecutive windows could overlap if response time plus jitter is greater than period. To accommodate this, Equation (13.15) must be altered:

$$R_i(q) = w_i^n(q) - qT_i + J_i \tag{13.19}$$

13.12.4 Fault tolerance

Fault tolerance via either forward or backward error recovery always results in extra computation. This could be an exception handler or a recovery block. In a real-time fault tolerant system, deadlines should still be met even when a certain level of faults occur. This level of fault tolerance is know as the **fault model**. If C_i^f is the extra computation time that results from an error in process i, then the response time equation can easily be changed.

$$R_i = B_i + C_i + \sum_{j \in hp(i)} \left\lceil \frac{R_i}{T_j} \right\rceil C_j + \max_{k \in hep(i)} C_k^f \tag{13.20}$$

where $hep(i)$ is the set of processes with a priority equal or higher than i.

Here, the fault model defines a maximum of one fault and there is an assumption that a process will execute its recovery action at the same priority as its ordinary computation. Equation (13.20) is easily changed to increase the number of allowed faults (F):

$$R_i = B_i + C_i + \sum_{j \in hp(i)} \left\lceil \frac{R_i}{T_j} \right\rceil C_j + \max_{k \in hep(i)} FC_k^f \tag{13.21}$$

Indeed, a system can be analyzed for increasing values of F to see what number of faults (arriving in a burst) can be tolerated. Alternatively, the fault model may indicate a minimum arrival interval for faults, in this case the equation becomes:

$$R_i = B_i + C_i + \sum_{j \in hp(i)} \left\lceil \frac{R_i}{T_j} \right\rceil C_j + \max_{k \in hep(i)} \left(\left\lceil \frac{R_i}{T_f} \right\rceil C_k^f \right) \tag{13.22}$$

where T_f is the minimum inter-arrival time between faults.

In Equations (13.21) and (13.22), the assumption is made that in the worst case, the fault will always occur in the process that has the longest recovery time.

13.12.5 Introducing offsets

In the scheduling analysis presented so far in this chapter, it has been assumed that all processes share a common release time. This critical instant is when all processes are released simultaneously (this is usually taken to occur at time 0). For fixed priority

Process	T	D	C
a	8	5	4
b	20	10	4
c	20	12	4

Table 13.13   Example of a process set.

Process	T	D	C	O	R
a	8	5	4	0	4
b	20	10	4	0	8
c	20	12	4	10	8

Table 13.14   Response time analysis of the process set.

scheduling, this is a safe assumption; if all processes meet their timing requirements when released together then they will always be schedulable. There are, however, sets of periodic processes that can benefit from explicitly choosing their release times so that they do not share a critical instant. One process is said to have an **offset** with respect to the others. Consider for illustration the three processes defined in Table 13.13.

If a critical instant is assumed then process a has response time of 4, process b has a response time of 8, but the third process has a worst-case response time of 16, which is beyond its deadline. For process c the interference from process b is sufficient to force a further interference from a, and this is crucial. However, if process c is given an offset (O) of 10 (that is, retain the same period and relative deadline, but have its first release at time 10) then it will never execute at the same time as b. The result is a schedulable process set – see Table 13.14.

Unfortunately, process sets with arbitrary offsets are not amenable to analysis. It is a strongly NP-hard problem to choose offsets so that a process set is optimally schedulable. Indeed, it is far from trivial to even check if a set of processes with offsets share a critical instant.[4]

Notwithstanding this theoretical result, there are process sets that can be analyzed in a relatively straightforward (although not necessarily optimal) way. In most realistic systems, process periods are not arbitrary but are likely to be related to one another. As in the example just illustrated, two processes have a common period. In these situations it is ease to give one an offset (of $T/2$) and to analyze the resulting system using a transformation technique that removes the offset – and hence critical instant analysis applies. In the example, processes b and c (c having the offset of 10) are replaced by a

---

[4]One interesting result is that a process set with co-prime periods will always have a critical instant no matter what offsets are chosen (Audsley and Burns, 1998).

Process	T	D	C	O	R
a	8	5	4	0	4
n	10	10	4	0	8

Table 13.15   Response time analysis of the transformed process set.

single notional process with period 10, computation time 4, deadline 10 but no offset. This notional process has two important properties.

- If it is schedulable (when sharing a critical instant with all other processes), the two real process will meet their deadlines when one is given the half period offset.
- If all lower priority processes are schedulable when suffering interference from the notional process (and all other high-priority processes), they will remain schedulable when the notional process is replaced by the two real process (one with the offset).

These properties follow from the observation that the notional process always uses more (or equal) CPU time than the two real process. Table 13.15 shows the analysis that would apply to the transformed process set. The notional process is given the name 'n' in this table.

More generally the parameters of the notional process are calculated from the real processes a and b as follows:

$$T_n = T_a/2 \quad (or\ T_b/2\ as\ T_a = T_b)$$
$$C_n = Max(C_a, C_b)$$
$$D_n = Min(D_a, D_b)$$
$$P_n = Max(P_a, P_b)$$

where P denotes priority.

Clearly, what is possible for two processes is also applicable to three or more processes. A fuller description of these techniques is given in Bate and Burns (1997). In summary, although arbitrary offsets are effectively impossible to analyze, the judicious use of offsets and the transformation technique can return the analysis problem to one of a simple process set that shares a critical instant. All the analysis given in earlier sections of this chapter, therefore, applies.

13.12.6   Priority assignment

The formulation given for arbitrary deadlines has the property that no simple algorithms (such as rate or deadline monotonic) gives the optimal priority ordering. In this section, a theorem and algorithm for assigning priorities in arbitrary situations is given. The theorem considers the behaviour of the lowest priority process (Audsley et al., 1993b).

> **Theorem** *If process p is assigned the lowest priority and is feasible, then, if a feasible priority ordering exists for the complete process set, an ordering exists with process p assigned the lowest priority.*

The proof of this theorem comes from considering the schedulability equations – for example, Equation (13.14). If a process has the lowest priority, it suffers interference from all higher-priority processes. This interference is not dependent upon the actual ordering of these higher priorities. Hence if any process is schedulable at the bottom value it can be assigned that place, and all that is required is to assign the other $N - 1$ priorities. Fortunately, the theorem can be reapplied to the reduced process set. Hence through successive reapplication, a complete priority ordering is obtained (if one exists).

The following code in Ada implements the priority assignment algorithm; Set is an array of processes that is notionally ordered by priority; Set (N) being the highest priority, Set (1) being the lowest. The procedure Process_Test tests to see whether process K is feasible at that place in the array. The double loop works by first swapping processes into the lowest position until a feasible result is found, this process is then fixed at that position. The next priority position is then considered. If at any time the inner loop fails to find a feasible process, the whole procedure is abandoned. Note that a concise algorithm is possible if an extra swap is undertaken.

```ada
procedure Assign_Pri (Set : in out Process_Set; N : Natural;
                      Ok : out Boolean) is
begin
  for K in 1..N loop
    for Next in K..N loop
      Swap(Set, K, Next);
      Process_Test(Set, K, Ok);
      exit when Ok;
    end loop;
    exit when not Ok;   -- failed to find a schedulable process
  end loop;
end Assign_Pri;
```

If the test of feasibility is exact (necessary and sufficient) then the priority ordering is optimal. Thus for arbitrary deadlines (without blocking), an optimal ordering is found.

13.13   Dynamic systems and online analysis

Earlier in this chapter it was noted that there is a wide variety of scheduling schemes that have been developed for different application requirements. For hard real-time systems, offline analysis is desirable (indeed it is often mandatory). To undertake such analysis requires:

- arrival patterns of incoming work to be known and bounded (this leads to a fixed set of processes with known periods or worst-case arrival intervals);
- bounded computation times; and
- a scheduling scheme that leads to predictable execution of the application processes.

This chapter has shown how fixed-priority scheduling (and to a certain extent, EDF) can provide a predictable execution environment.

In contrast to hard systems, there are dynamic soft real-time applications in which arrival patterns and computation times are not known *a priori*. Although some level of offline analysis may still be applicable, this can no longer be complete and hence some form of online analysis is required.

The main task of an online scheduling scheme is to manage any overload that is likely to occur due to the dynamics of the system's environment. It was noted earlier that EDF is a dynamic scheme that is an optimal scheduling discipline. Unfortunately, EDF also has the property that during transient overloads it performs very badly. It is possible to get a cascade effect in which each process misses its deadline but uses sufficient resources to result in the next process also missing its deadline.

To counter this detrimental domino effect many online schemes have two mechanisms:

(1) an admissions control module that limits the number of processes that are allowed to compete for the processors, and
(2) an EDF dispatching routine for those processes that are admitted.

An ideal admissions algorithm prevents the processors getting overloaded so that the EDF routine works effectively.

If some processes are to be admitted, while others rejected, the relative importance of each process must be known. This is usually achieved by assigning *value*. Values can be classified as follows.

- Static – the process always has the same value whenever it is released.
- Dynamic – the process's value can only be computed at the time the process is released (because it is dependent on either environmental factors or the current state of the system).
- Adaptive – here the dynamic nature of the system is such that the value of the process will change during its execution.

To assign static values (or to construct the algorithm and define the input parameters for the dynamic or adaptive schemes) requires the domain specialists to articulate their understanding of the desirable behaviour of the system. As with other areas of computing, knowledge elicitation is not without its problems. But these issues will not be considered here (see Burns et al. (2000)).

One of the fundamental problems with online analysis is the trade-off that has to be made between the quality of the scheduling decision and the resources and time needed to make the decision. At one extreme, every time a new process arrives, the complete set of processes could be subject to an exact offline test such as those described in this chapter. If the process set is not schedulable, the lowest value process is dropped and the test repeated (until a schedulable set is obtained). This approach (which is known as *best-effort*) is optimal for static or dynamic value assignment - but only if the overheads of the tests are ignored. Once the overheads are factored in, the effectiveness of the approach is seriously compromised. In general, heuristics have to be used for online scheduling and it is unlikely that any single approach will work for all applications. This is still an active research area. It is clear, however, that what is required is not a single policy defined in a language or OS standard, but mechanisms from which applications can program their own schemes to meet their particular requirements.

The final topic to note in this section is hybrid systems that contain both hard and dynamic components. It is likely that these will become the norm in many application areas. Even in quite static systems, value-added computations, in the form of soft or firm processes that improve the quality of the hard processes, are an attractive way of structuring systems. In these circumstances, as was noted in Section 13.8.1, the hard processes must be protected from any overload induced by the behaviour of the non-hard processes. One way of achieving this is to use fixed priority scheduling for the hard processes and servers for the remaining work. The servers can embody whatever admissions policy is desirable and service the incoming dynamic work using EDF.

13.14   Programming priority-based systems

Few programming languages explicitly define priorities as part of their concurrency facilities. Those that do, often provide only a rudimentary model. For example, oc-cam2 has a variation of the PAR construct that indicates that static priorities should be assigned to the designated processes:

```
PRI PAR
   P1
   P2
   PAR
     P3
     P4
   P5
```

Here, relative priorities are used, with the textual order of the processes in the PRI PAR being significant. Hence P1 has the highest priority, P2 the second highest; P3 and P4 share the next priority level and P5 has the lowest priority. No minimum range of priorities need be supported by an implementation. There is no support for priority inheritance.

The one language that does attempt to give a more complete provision is Ada – this is, therefore, discussed in detail in the next subsection. Traditionally, priority-based scheduling has been more an issue for operating systems than languages. Hence, after a discussion of Ada, the facilities of POSIX are reviewed. Ada and POSIX assume that any schedulability analysis has been performed offline. More recently, Real-Time Java has attempted to provide the same facilities as Ada and POSIX but with the option of supporting online feasibility analysis. This is considered in Section 13.14.3.

It should, perhaps, be noted at this point that although most general-purpose operating systems provide the notion of process or thread priority, their facilities are often inadequate for hard real-time programming.

13.14.1   Ada

As indicated in the Preface, Ada is defined as a core language plus a number of annexes for specialized application domains. These annexes do not contain any new language features (in the way of new syntax) but define pragmas and library packages that must be supported if that particular annex is to be adhered to. This section considers some of the provisions of the Real-Time Systems Annex. In particular, those that allow priorities to be assigned to tasks (and protected objects).[5] In package System, there are the following declarations:

```
subtype Any_Priority is Integer range  implementation-defined;
subtype Priority is Any_Priority range
                    Any_Priority'First  ..  implementation-defined;
subtype Interrupt_Priority is Any_Priority range
                    Priority'Last+1  ..  Any_Priority'Last;

Default_Priority : constant Priority :=
                    (Priority'First + Priority'Last)/2;
```

An integer range is split between standard priorities and (the higher) interrupt priority range. An implementation must support a range for System.Priority of at least 30 values and at least one distinct System.Interrupt_Priority value.

A task has its initial priority set by including a pragma in its specification:

```
task Controller is
   pragma Priority(10);
end Controller;
```

If a task-type definition contains such a pragma, then all tasks of that type will have the same priority unless a discriminant is used:

```
task type Servers(Task_Priority : System.Priority) is
   entry Service1(...);
   entry Service2(...);
   pragma Priority(Task_Priority);
end Servers;
```

For entities acting as interrupt handlers, a special pragma is defined:

---

[5]Priorities can also be given to entry queues and the operation of the select statement. This section will, however, focus on task priorities and protected object ceiling priorities.

```
pragma Interrupt_Priority(Expression);
```

or simply

```
pragma Interrupt_Priority;
```

The definition, and use, of a different pragma for interrupt levels improves the readability of programs and helps to remove errors that can occur if task and interrupt priority levels are confused. However, the expression used in `Interrupt_Priority` evaluates down to `Any_Priority`, and hence it is possible to give a relatively low priority to an interrupt handler. If the expression is actually missing, the highest possible priority is assigned.

A priority assigned using one of these pragmas is called a **base priority**. A task may also have an **active priority** that is higher – this will be explained in due course.

The main program, which is executed by a notional environmental task, can have its priority set by placing the `Priority` pragma in the main subprogram. If this is not done, the default value, defined in `System`, is used. Any other task that fails to use the pragma has a default base priority equal to the base priority of the task that created it.

In order to make use of ICPP, an Ada program must include the following pragma:

```
pragma Locking_Policy(Ceiling_Locking);
```

An implementation may define other locking policies; only `Ceiling_Locking` is required by the Real-Time Systems Annex. The default policy, if the pragma is missing, is implementation defined. To specify the ceiling priority for each protected object, the `Priority` and `Interrupt_Priority` pragmas defined in the previous section are used. If the pragma is missing, a ceiling of `System.Priority'Last` is assumed.

The exception `Program_Error` is raised if a task calls a protected object with a priority greater than the defined ceiling. If such a call were allowed, then this could result in the mutually exclusive protection of the object being violated. If it is an interrupt handler that calls in with an inappropriate priority, then the program becomes erroneous. This must eventually be prevented through adequate testing and/or static analysis of the program.

With `Ceiling_Locking`, an effective implementation will use the thread of the calling task to execute not only the code of the protected call, but also the code of any other task that happens to have been released by the actions of the original call. For example, consider the following simple protected object:

```
protected Gate_Control is
   pragma Priority(28);
   entry Stop_And_Close;
   procedure Open;
private
   Gate: Boolean := False;
end Gate_Control;

protected body Gate_Control is
   entry Stop_And_Close when Gate is
```

```
   begin
      Gate := False;
   end Stop_And_Close;

   procedure Open is
   begin
      Gate := True;
   end Open;
end Gate_Control;
```

Assume a task T, priority 20, calls `Stop_And_Close` and is blocked. Later, task S (priority 27) calls `Open`. The thread that implements S will undertake the following actions:

(1) Execute the code of `Open` for S.

(2) Evaluate the barrier on the entry and note that T can now proceed.

(3) Execute the code of `Stop_And_Close` for T.

(4) Evaluate the barrier again.

(5) Continue with the execution of S after its call on the protected object.

As a result, there has been no context switch. The alternative is for S to make T runnable at point (2); T now has a higher priority (28) than S (27) and hence the system must switch to T to complete its execution within `Gate_Control`. As T leaves, a switch back to S is required. This is much more expensive.

As a task enters a protected object, its priority may rise above the base priority level defined by the `Priority` or `Interrupt_Priority` pragmas. The priority used to determine the order of dispatching is the **active priority** of a task. This active priority is the maximum of the task's base priority and any priority it has inherited.

The use of a protected object is one way in which a task can inherit a higher active priority. There are others, for example:

- During activation – a task will inherit the active priority of the parent task that created it; remember the parent task is blocked waiting for its child task to complete, and this could be a source of priority inversion without this inheritance rule.

- During a rendezvous – the task executing the accept statement will inherit the active priority of the task making the entry call (if it is greater than its own priority).

Note that the last case does not necessarily remove all possible cases of priority inversion. Consider a server task, S, with entry E and base priority L (low). A high-priority task makes a call on E. Once the rendezvous has started, S will execute with the higher priority. But before S reaches the accept statement for E, it will execute with priority L (even though the high-priority task is blocked). This, and other candidates for priority inheritance, can be supported by an implementation. The implementation must, however, provide a pragma that the user can employ to select the additional conditions explicitly.

The Real-Time Systems Annex attempts to provide flexible and extensible features. Clearly, this is not easy. Ada 83 suffered from being too prescriptive. However, the lack of a defined dispatching policy would be unfortunate, as it would not assist software development or portability. If base priorities have been defined, then it is assumed that preemptive priority-based scheduling is to be employed. On a multiprocessor system, it is implementation defined whether this is on a per-processor basis or across the entire processor cluster.

To give extensibility, the dispatching policy can be selected by using the following pragma:

```
pragma Task_Dispatching_Policy(Policy_Identifier);
```

The Real-Time Systems Annex defines one possible policy: FIFO_Within_-Priority. Where tasks share the same priority, then they are queued in FIFO order. Hence, as tasks become runnable, they are placed at the back of a notional run queue for that priority level. One exception to this case is when a task is preempted; here the task is placed at the front of the notional run queue for that priority level.

If a program specifies the Fifo_Within_Priority option, then it must also pick the Ceiling_Locking policy defined earlier. Together, they represent a consistent and usable model for building, implementing and analyzing real-time programs.

Other Ada facilities

Ada also provides other facilities which are useful for programming a wide variety of systems. For example, dynamic priorities, prioritized entry queues, task attributes, asynchronous task control facilities, and so on. The reader is referred to the Systems Programming and Real-Time Annexes of the Ada Reference Manual or Burns and Wellings (1998) for further details.

Currently, there is no support in Ada for sporadic servers. However, see Harbour et al. (1998) for a discussion on how they can be approximated.

13.14.2 POSIX

POSIX supports priority-based scheduling, and has options to support priority inheritance and ceiling protocols. Priorities may be set dynamically. Within the priority-based facilities, there are four policies:

- FIFO – a process/thread runs until it completes or it is blocked; if a process/thread is preempted by a higher-priority process/thread then it is placed at the head of the run queue for its priority.
- Round-Robin – a process/thread runs until it completes or it is blocked or its time quantum has expired; if a process/thread is preempted by a higher-priority process then it is placed at the head of the run queue for its priority; however, if its quantum expires it is placed at the back.

- Sporadic Server – a process/thread runs as a sporadic server (see below).
- OTHER – an implementation-defined policy (which must be documented).

For each scheduling policy, there is a minimum range of priorities that must be supported; for FIFO and round-robin, this must be at least 32. The scheduling policy can be set on a per process and a per thread basis.

Threads may be created with a 'system contention' option, in which case they compete with other system threads according to their policy and priority. Alternatively, threads can be created with a 'process contention' option; in this case they must compete with other threads (created with a process contention) in the parent process. It is unspecified how such threads are scheduled relative to threads in other processes or to threads with global contention. A specific implementation must decide whether to supports 'system contention' or 'process contention' or both.

As discusses in Section 13.8.2, a sporadic server assigns a limited amount of CPU capacity to handle events, has a replenishment period, a budget, and two priorities. The server runs at a high priority when it has some budget left and a low one when its budget is exhausted. When a server runs at the high priority, the amount of execution time it consumes is subtracted from its budget. The amount of budget consumed is replenished at the time the server was activated plus the replenishment period. When its budget reaches zero, the server's priority is set to the low value.

Program 13.1 illustrates a C interface to the POSIX scheduling facilities. The functions are divided into those which manipulate a process's scheduling policy and parameters, and those that manipulate a thread's scheduling policy and parameters. If a thread modifies the policy and parameters of its owning process, the effect on the thread will depend upon its contention scope (or level). If it is contending at a system level, the change will not affect the thread. If, however, it is contending at the process level, there will be an impact on the thread.

In order to prevent priority inversion, POSIX allows inheritance protocols to be associated with mutex variables. As well as catering for basic priority inheritance, the immediate ceiling priority protocol (called priority protect protocol by POSIX) is also supported.

Other POSIX facilities

POSIX provides other facilities that are useful for real-time systems. For example, it allows:

- message queues to be priority ordered;
- functions for dynamically getting and setting a thread's priority;
- threads to indicate whether their attributes should be inherited by any child thread they create.

Program 13.1 A typical C interface to some of the POSIX scheduling facilities.

```
#define SCHED_FIFO ...       /* preemptive priority scheduling */
#define SCHED_RR ...         /* preemptive priority with quantum */
#define SCHED_SPORADIC ... /* sporadic server */
#define SCHED_OTHER ...      /* implementation-defined scheduler */
#define PTHREAD_SCOPE_SYSTEM ... /* system-wide contention */
#define PTHREAD_SCOPE_PROCESS ...  /* local contention */
#define PTHREAD_PRIO_NONE ... /* no priority inheritance */
#define PTHREAD_PRIO_INHERIT ... /* basic priority inheritance */
#define PTHREAD_PRIO_PROTECT ... /* ICPP */

typedef ... pid_t;
struct sched_param {
   ...
   int sched_priority; /* used for SCHED_FIFO and SCHED_RR */
   int sched_ss_low_priority
   timespec sched_ss_repl_period
   timespec sched_ss_init_budget
   int  sched_ss_max_repl
   ... };

int sched_setparam(pid_t pid, const struct sched_param *param);
/* set the scheduling parameters of process pid */

int sched_getparam(pid_t pid, struct sched_param *param);
/* get the scheduling parameters of process pid */

int sched_setscheduler(pid_t pid, int policy,
                       const struct sched_param *param);
/* set the scheduling policy and parameters of process pid */

int sched_getscheduler(pid_t pid);
/* returns the scheduling policy of process pid */

int sched_yield(void);
/* causes the current thread/process to be placed at the back */
/* of the run queue */

int sched_get_priority_max(int policy);
/* returns the maximum priority for the policy specified */

int sched_get_priority_min(int policy);
/* returns the minimum priority for the policy specified */

int sched_rr_get_interval(pid_t pid, struct timespec *t);
/* if pid /= 0, the time quantum for the calling process/thread is *
 * set in the structure referenced by t                           *
 * if pid = 0, the calling process/threads time quantum is set     *
 * in the structure pointed to by t                               */

int pthread_attr_setscope(pthread_attr_t *attr,
                          int contentionscope);
```

```
/* set the contention scope attribute for a thread attribute object */

int pthread_attr_getscope(const pthread_attr_t *attr,
                          int *contentionscope);
/* get the contention scope attribute for a thread attribute object */

int pthread_attr_setschedpolicy(pthread_attr_t *attr,
                                int policy);
/* set the scheduling policy attribute for a thread attribute object */

int pthread_attr_getschedpolicy(const pthread_attr_t *attr,
                                int *policy);
/* get the scheduling policy attribute for a thread attribute object */

int pthread_attr_setschedparam(pthread_attr_t *attr,
                               const struct sched_param *param);
/* set the scheduling policy attribute for a thread attribute object */

int pthread_attr_getschedparam(const pthread_attr_t *attr,
                               struct sched_param *param);
/* get the scheduling policy attribute for a thread attribute object */

int pthread_mutexattr_setprotocol(pthread_mutexattr_t *attr,
                                  int protocol);
/* set the priority inheritance protocol */
int pthread_mutexattr_getprotocol(pthread_mutexattr_t *attr,
                                  int *protocol);
/* get the priority inheritance protocol */

int pthread_mutexattr_setprioceiling(pthread_mutexattr_t *attr,
                                     int prioceiling);
/* set the priority ceiling */
int pthread_mutexattr_getprioceiling(pthread_mutexattr_t *attr,
                                     int *prioceiling);
/* get the priority ceiling */

/* All the above integer functions except sched_get_priority_max  */
/* and sched_get_priority_min return 0 if successful */
```

13.14.3   Real-Time Java

Real-Time Java has the notion of a schedulable object. This is any object that supports the Schedulable interface given in Program 13.2. The classes RealtimeThread, NoHeapRealTimeThread and AsyncEventHandler all support this interface. Objects of these classes all have scheduling parameters (see Program 13.3). Real-Time Java implementations are required to support at least 28 real-time priority levels. As with Ada and POSIX, the larger the integer value, the higher the priority (and, therefore, the greater the execution eligibility). Non-real-time threads are given priority levels below

---

Program 13.2   The Real-Time Java `Schedulable` interface.

```
public interface Schedulable extends java.lang.Runnable
{

  public void addToFeasibility();
  public void removeFromFeasibility();

  public MemoryParameters getMemoryParameters();
  public void setMemoryParameters(MemoryParameters memory);

  public ReleaseParameters getReleaseParameters();
  public void setReleaseParameters(ReleaseParameters release);

  public SchedulingParameters getSchedulingParameters();
  public void setSchedulingParameters(SchedulingParameters scheduling);

  public Scheduler getScheduler();
  public void setScheduler(Scheduler scheduler);
}
```

Program 13.3   The Real-Time Java `SchedulingParameters` class and its subclasses.

```
public abstract class SchedulingParameters
{
  public SchedulingParameters();
}

public class PriorityParameters extends SchedulingParameters
{
  public PriorityParameters(int priority);

  public int getPriority();
  public void setPriority(int priority) throws
                        IllegalArgumentException;
  ...
}

public class ImportanceParameters extends PriorityParameters
{
  public ImportanceParameters(int priority, int importance);
  public int getImportance();
  public void setImportance(int importance);
  ...
}
```

Program 13.4 The Real-Time Java `Scheduler` class.

```
public abstract class Scheduler
{
  public Scheduler();

  protected abstract void addToFeasibility(Schedulable schedulable);
  protected abstract void removeFromFeasibility(Schedulable schedulable);

  public abstract boolean isFeasible();
  // checks the current set of schedulable objects

  public boolean changeIfFeasible(Schedulable schedulable,
                ReleaseParameters release, MemoryParameters memory);

  public static Scheduler getDefaultScheduler();
  public static void setDefaultScheduler(Scheduler scheduler);

  public abstract java.lang.String getPolicyName();
}
```

---

the minimum real-time priority. Note, scheduling parameters are bound to threads at thread creation time (see Program 12.11). If the parameter objects are changed, they have an immediate impact on the associated threads.

In common with Ada and Real-Time POSIX, Real-Time Java supports a preemptive priority-based dispatching policy. However, unlike Ada and Real-Time POSIX, Real-Time Java does not require a preempted thread to be placed at the head of the run queue associated with its priority level. Real-Time Java also supports a high-level scheduler whose goals are:

- to decide whether to admit new schedulable objects according to the resources available and a feasibility algorithm, and
- to set the priority of the schedulable objects according to the priority assignment algorithm associated with the feasibility algorithm.

Hence, while Ada and Real-Time POSIX focus on static offline schedulability analysis, Real-Time Java addresses more dynamic systems with the potential for online analysis.

The `Scheduler` abstract class is given in Program 13.4. The `isFeasible` method considers only the set of schedulable objects that have been added to its feasibility list (via the `addToFeasibility` and `removeFromFeasibility` methods). The method `changeIfFeasible` checks to see if its set of objects is still feasible if the given object has its release and memory parameters changed. If it is, the parameters are changed. Static methods allow the default scheduler to be queried or set.

One defined subclass of the `Scheduler` class is the `PriorityScheduler` class (defined in Program 13.5) which implements standard preemptive priority-based scheduling.

Program 13.5 The Real-Time Java `PriorityScheduler` class.

```
class PriorityScheduler extends Scheduler
{
  public PriorityScheduler()

  protected void addToFeasibility(Schedulable s);
  protected void removeFromFeasibility(Schedulable s);

  public boolean isFeasible();
  // checks the current set of schedulable objects

  public boolean changeIfFeasible(Schedulable schedulable,
               ReleaseParameters release, MemoryParameters memory);

  protected void addToFeasibility(Schedulable s);
  protected void removeFromFeasibility(Schedulable s);

  public abstract boolean isFeasible();
  // checks the current set of schedulable objects

  public void fireSchedulable(Schedulable schedulable);

  public int getMaxPriority();
  public int getMinPriority();
  public int getNormPriority();
  public java.lang.String getPolicyName();

  public static PriorityScheduler instance();


  ...
}
```

Again, it should be stressed that Real-Time Java does not require an implementation to provide an online feasibility algorithm. It is adequate to simply return false to the methods which test for feasibility.

Support for priority inheritance

Real-Time Java allows priority inheritance algorithms to be used when accessing synchronized classes. To achieve this, three classes are defined (see Program 13.6). Consider the following class:

```
public class SynchronizeClass
{
  public void Method1() { ... };
  public void Method2() { ... };
}
```

Program 13.6   Real-Time Java classes supporting priority inheritance.

```
public abstract class MonitorControl
{
  public MonitorControl();

  public static void setMonitorControl(MonitorControl policy);
  // set the default

  public static void setMonitorControl(java.lang.Object monitor,
                                       MonitorControl policy);
  // sets an individual objects policy
}

public class PriorityCeilingEmulation extends MonitorControl
{
  public PriorityCeilingEmulation(int ceiling);

  public int getDefaultCeiling();
  // get ceiling for this object
}

public class PriorityInheritance extends MonitorControl
{
  public PriorityInheritance();

  public static PriorityInheritance instance();
}
```

An instance of this class can have its control protocol set to immediate priority ceiling inheritance (called priority ceiling emulation by Real-Time Java) with a priority of 10 by the following code

```
SynchronizeClass SC = new SynchronizeClass();
PriorityCeilingEmulation PCI = new PriorityCeilingEmulation(10);
...
MonitorControl.setMonitorControl(SC, PCI);
```

13.14.4   Other Real-Time Java facilities

It is important to note that all queues in Real-Time Java are priority ordered.

One further facility is worth mentioning, Real-Time Java provides support for aperiodic threads in the form of processing groups. A group of aperiodic threads can be linked together and assigned characteristics which aid feasibility analysis. For example, the threads can be defined to consume no more than cost CPU time within a given period. The full definition of the class supporting process groups is given in the Appendix.

Summary

A scheduling scheme has two facets: it defines an algorithm for resource sharing; and a means of predicting the worst-case behaviour of an application when that form of resource sharing is used.

Most current periodic real-time systems are implemented using a cyclic executive. With this approach, the application code must be packed into a fixed number of 'minor cycles' such that the cyclic execution of the sequence of minor cycles (called a 'major cycle') will enable all system deadlines to be met. Although an effective implementation strategy for small systems, there are a number of drawbacks with this cyclic approach.

- The packing of the minor cycles becomes increasingly difficult as the system grows.

- Sporadic activities are difficult to accommodate.

- Processes with long periods (that is, longer than the major cycle) are supported inefficiently.

- Processes with large computation times must be split up so that they can be packed into a series of minor cycles.

- The structure of the cyclic executive makes it very difficult to alter to accommodate changing requirements.

Because of these difficulties, this chapter has focused on the use of a priority-based scheduling scheme. Following the description of a simple utilization-based test (which is only applicable to a restricted process model), the response time calculations were derived for a flexible model. This model can accommodate sporadic processes, process interactions, non-preemptive sections, release jitter, aperiodic servers, fault tolerant systems and an arbitrary relationship between process deadline (D) and its minimum arrival interval (T).

Interprocess synchronization, such as mutual exclusive access to shared data, can give rise to priority inversion unless some form of priority inheritance is used. Two particular protocols were described in detail in this chapter: 'original ceiling priority inheritance' and 'immediate ceiling priority inheritance'.

With priority-based scheduling, it is important that the priorities are assigned to reflect the temporal characteristic of the process load. Three algorithms have been described in this chapter:

- Rate monotonic – for $D = T$

- Deadline monotonic – for $D < T$

- Arbitrary – for $D > T$

The chapter concluded with illustrations of how fixed-priority scheduling can be accomplished in Ada, Real-Time Java and Real-Time POSIX.

Further reading

Audsley, N. C., Burns, A., Davis, R., Tindell, K. and Wellings, A. J. (1995) Fixed Priority Preemptive Scheduling: An Historical Perspective. *Real-Time Systems*, 8(3), 173–198.

Buttazzo, G. C. (1997) *Hard Real-Time Computing Systems: Predictable Scheduling Algorithms and Applications*. New York: Kluwer Academic.

Burns, A. and Wellings, A. J. (1995) *Concurrency in Ada*, 2nd edn. Cambridge: Cambridge University Press.

Gallmeister, B. O. (1995), *Programming for the Real World POSIX.4*. Sebastopol, CA: O'Reilly.

Halbwachs, N. (1993) *Synchronous Programming of Reactive Systems*. New York: Kluwer Academic.

Klein, M. H. et al. (1993) *A Practitioner's Handbook for Real-Time Analysis: Guide to Rate Monotonic Analysis for Real-Time Systems*. New York: Kluwer Academic.

Joseph, M. (ed.) (1996) *Real-time Systems: Specification, Verification and Analysis*. Englewood Cliffs, NJ: Prentice Hall.

Natarajan, S. (ed.) (1995) *Imprecise and Approximate Computation*. New York: Kluwer Academic.

Rajkumar, R. (1993) *Synchronization in Real-Time Systems: A Priority Inheritance Approach*. New York: Kluwer Academic.

Stankovic, J. A. et al. (1998) *Deadline Scheduling for Real-Time Systems: EDF and Related Algorithms*. New York: Kluwer Academic.

Exercises

13.1 Three logical processes P, Q and S have the following characteristics. P: period 3, required execution time 1; Q: period 6, required execution time 2; S: period 18, required execution time 5.

Show how these processes can be scheduled using the rate monotonic scheduling algorithm.

Show how a cyclic executive could be constructed to implement the three logical processes.

13.2 Consider three processes P, Q and S. P has a period of 100 milliseconds in which it requires 30 milliseconds of processing. The corresponding values for Q and S are (5,1) and (25,5) respectively. Assume that P is the most important process in the system, followed by S and then Q.

    (1) What is the behaviour of the scheduler if priority is based on importance?
    (2) What is the processor utilization of P, Q and S?
    (3) How should the processes be scheduled so that all deadlines are met?
    (4) Illustrate one of the schemes that allows these processes to be scheduled.

13.3 To the above process set is added a fourth process (R). Failure of this process will not lead to safety being undermined. R has a period of 50 milliseconds, but has a processing requirement that is data dependent and varies from 5 to 25 milliseconds. Discuss how this process should be integrated with P, Q and S.

13.4 Figure 13.11 illustrates the behaviour of four periodic processes w, x, y and z. These processes have priorities determined by the rate monotonic scheme, with the result that priority(w) > priority(x) > priority(y) > priority(z).

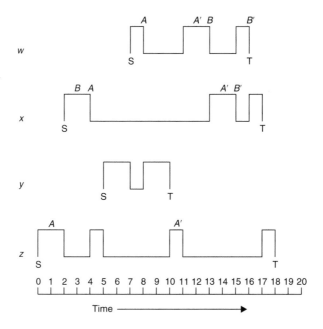

Figure 13.11   The behaviour of four periodic processes in Exercise 13.4.

Each process's period starts at time S and terminates at T. The four processes share 2 resources that are protected by binary semaphores A and B. On the diagram the tag A (and B) implies 'do a wait operation on the semaphore'; the tag A' (and B') implies 'do a signal operation on the semaphore'. Table 13.16 summaries the processes requirements:

The diagram shows the execution histories of the four processes using static priorities. For example, x starts at time 2, executes a successful wait operation on B at time 3 but unsuccessfully waits on A at time 4 (z has already locked A). At time 13 it executes again (that is, it now has lock on A), it releases A at time 14 and B at time 15. It is now preempted by Pw, but executes again at time 16. Finally it terminates at time 17.

Redraw the diagram given in Exercise 4 to illustrate the behaviour of these processes if priority inheritance is employed.

Process	Priority	Start time	Required processor time	Semaphores used
w	10	7	4	A,B
x	8	2	5	A,B
y	6	5	4	–
z	4	0	5	A

Table 13.16   Summary of the process's requirements for Exercise 13.4.

13.5 Redraw the diagram given in Exercise 4 to illustrate the behaviour of these processes if immediate priority ceiling inheritance is employed.

13.6 With the priority ceiling protocol, it is possible to calculate the maximum time any process can be blocked by the operation of a lower priority process. What is the rule for calculating this blocking? Illustrate the answer by calculating the maximum blocking time for each process in the following example. A program consists of five processes, a, b, c, d, e (these are listed in priority order with a having the highest priority), and six resources $R1$, ... $R6$ (protected by semaphores implementing the priority ceiling protocol). The resource accesses have worst case execution times given in Table 13.17.

R1	R2	R3	R4	R5	R6
50 ms	150 ms	75 ms	300 ms	250 ms	175 ms

Table 13.17   Summary of the processes' execution requirements for Exercise 13.6.

Resources are used by the processes according to Table 13.18.

Process	Uses
a	$R3$
b	$R1,R2$
c	$R3,R4,R5$
d	$R1,R5,R6$
e	$R2,R6$

Table 13.18   Summary of the processes' resource requirements for Exercise 13.6.

13.7 Is the process set shown in Table 13.19 schedulable using the simple utilization-based test given in Equation (13.1)? Is the process set schedulable using the response time analysis?

Process	Period	Execution time
a	50	10
b	40	10
c	30	9

Table 13.19   Summary of the processes' attributes for Exercise 13.7.

13.8 The process set shown in Table 13.20 is not schedulable using Equation (13.1) because a must be given the top priority due to its criticality. How can the process set be transformed so that it is schedulable. Note that the computations represented by a must still be given top priority.

Process	Period	Execution time	Criticality
a	60	10	HIGH
b	10	3	LOW
c	8	2	LOW

Table 13.20   Summary of the processes' attributes for Exercise 13.8.

13.9 The process set given in Table 13.21 is not schedulable using Equation (13.1), but does meet all deadlines when scheduled using fixed priorities. Explain why.

Process	Period	Execution time
a	75	35
b	40	10
c	20	5

Table 13.21   Summary of the processes' attributes for Exercise 13.9.

13.10 In Section 13.8, a sporadic process was defined as having a minimum inter-arrival time. Often sporadic processes come in bursts. Update Equation (13.4), to cope with a burst of sporadic activities such that N invocations can appear arbitrarily close together in a period of T.

13.11 Extend the answer given above to cope with sporadic activity which arrives in bursts, where there may be N invocations in a period of T and each invocation must be separated by at least M time units.

13.12 To what extent can the response time equations given in this chapter be applied to resources other than the CPU? For example, can the equations be used to schedule access to a disk?

13.13 In a safety-critical real-time system, a collection of processes can be used to monitor key environmental events. Typically, there will be a deadline defined between the event occurring and some output (which is in response to the event) being produced. Describe how periodic processes can be used to monitor such events.

13.14 Consider the list of events (shown in Table 13.22) together with the computation costs of responding to each event. If a separate process is used for each event (and these processes are implemented by preemptive priority-based scheduling) describe how Rate Monotonic Analysis can be applied to make sure all deadlines are met.

EVENT	Deadline	Computation time
A_Event	36	2
B_Event	24	1
C_Event	10	1
D_Event	48	4
E_Event	12	1

Table 13.22   Summary of events for Exercise 13.14.

13.15 How can the process set shown in Table 13.23 be optimally scheduled (using fixed priority scheduling)? Is this task set schedulable?

Process	T	C	B	D
a	8	4	2	8
b	10	2	2	5
c	30	5	2	30

Table 13.23   Summary of tasks for Exercise 13.15.

13.16 A real-time systems designer wishes to run a mixture of safety-critical, mission-critical and non-critical periodic and sporadic Ada tasks on the same processor. He or she is using preemptive priority-based scheduling and has used the response-time analysis equation to predict that all tasks meet their deadlines. Give reasons why the system might nevertheless fail to meet its deadlines at run-time. What enhancements could be provided to the Ada run-time support systems to help eliminate the problems?

13.17 Show how earliest deadline first scheduling can be implemented in Ada.

13.18 Outline (with code) how Ada supports sporadic tasks. How can the task protect itself from executing more often than its minimum inter-arrival time?

13.19 To what extent can sporadic servers be implemented in Ada?

13.20 Ada allows the base priority of a task to be set dynamically using the following package.

```
with Ada.Task_Identification;
with System;
package Ada.Dynamic_Priorities is

   procedure Set_Priority(Priority : System.Any_Priority;
              T : Ada.Task_Identification.Task_Id :=
              Ada.Task_Identification.Current_Task);
     -- raises Program_Error if T is the Null_Task_Id
     -- has no effect if the task has terminated

   function Get_Priority(T : Ada.Task_Identification.Task_Id :=
           Ada.Task_Identification.Current_Task)
           return System.Any_Priority;
     -- raises Tasking_Error if the task has terminated
     -- or Program_Error if T is the Null_Task_Id
private
   ... -- not required for this question
end Ada.Dynamic_Priorities;
```

Using this package, show how to implement a mode change protocol where a group of tasks must have their priorities changed as a single atomic operation.

13.21 Real-Time POSIX supports dynamic ceiling priorities, but Ada does not. Explain the pros and cons of supporting dynamic ceiling priorities.

13.22 To what extent can ProcessingGroupParameters be used by a Real-Time Java scheduler to support sporadic servers?

13.23 Show how earliest deadline first scheduling can be implemented in Real-Time Java with a feasibility test of total process utilization less that 100%.

Chapter 14
Distributed systems

Over the last thirty years, the cost of microprocessors and communications technology has continually decreased in real terms. This has made distributed computer systems a viable alternative to uniprocessor and centralized systems in many embedded application areas. The potential advantages of distribution include:

- improved performance through the exploitation of parallelism,
- increased availability and reliability through the exploitation of redundancy,
- dispersion of computing power to the locations in which it is used,
- the facility for incremental growth through the addition or enhancement of processors and communications links.

This chapter discusses some of the problems that are introduced when real-time systems are implemented on more than one processor.

14.1   Distributed system definition

For the purposes of this chapter, a **distributed computer system** is defined to be a system of multiple autonomous processing elements cooperating in a common purpose or to achieve a common goal. This definition is wide enough to satisfy most intuitive notions, without descending to details of physical dispersion, means of communication, and so on. The definition excludes pipeline and array processors, whose elements are not autonomous; it also excludes those computer networks (for example, the Internet)

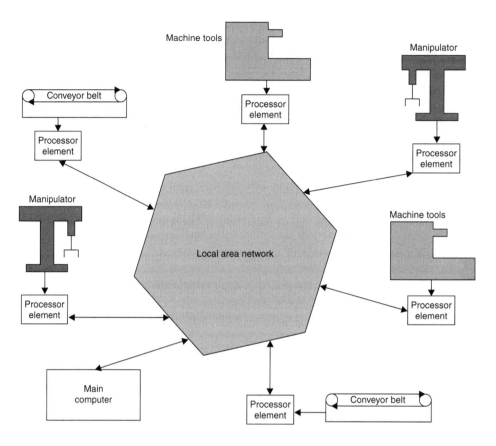

Figure 14.1   A manufacturing distributed embedded system.

where nodes work to no common purpose.[1] The majority of applications one might sensibly embed on multiprocessor architectures – for example command and control, banking (and other transaction-oriented commercial applications), and data acquisition – fall within the definition. A distributed manufacturing-based system is shown in Figure 14.1.

Even modern aircraft designs (both civil and military) have embedded distributed systems. For example, Integrated Modular Avionics (AEEC, 1991) allows more than one processing modules to be interconnected via an ARINC 629 bus, as illustrated in Figure 14.2.

It is useful to classify distributed systems as either **tightly coupled**, meaning that the processing elements, or nodes, have access to a common memory, and **loosely**

---

[1] However, as communication technology continues to improve, more and more internet-working will fit this definition of a distributed system.

Processing resource

Sensor/ actuator

Figure 14.2 A civil avionics distributed embedded system.

coupled, meaning that they do not. The significance of this classification is that synchronization and communication in a tightly coupled system can be effected through techniques based on the use of shared variables, whereas in a loosely coupled system some form of message passing is ultimately required. It is possible for a loosely coupled system to contain nodes which are themselves tightly coupled systems.

This chapter will use the term 'distributed system' to refer to loosely coupled architectures. Also, in general, full connectivity will be assumed between processors – issues associated with the routing of messages and so on will not be considered. For a full discussion on these topics, see Tanenbaum (1998). Furthermore, it will be assumed that each processor will have access to its own clock and that these clocks are loosely synchronized (that is, there is a bound by which they can differ).

A separate classification can be based on the variety of processors in the system. A **homogeneous** system is one in which all processors are of the same type; a **heterogeneous** system contains processors of different types. Heterogeneous systems pose problems of differing representations of program and data; these problems, while significant, are not considered here. This chapter assumes that all processors are homogeneous.

14.2   Overview of issues

So far in this book, the phrase concurrent programming has been used to discuss communication, synchronization and reliability without getting too involved with how processes are implemented. However, some of the issues which arise when distributed applications are considered raise fundamental questions that go beyond mere implementation details. The purpose of this chapter is to consider these issues and their implications for real-time applications. They are:

- **Language support** – The process of writing a distributed program is made much easier if the language and its programming environment support the partitioning, configuration, allocation and reconfiguration of the distributed application, along with location-independent access to remote resources.

- **Reliability** – The availability of multiple processors enables the application to become tolerant of processor failure – the application should be able to exploit this redundancy. Although the availability of multiple processors enables the application to become tolerant of processor failure, it also introduces the possibility of more faults occurring in the system which would not occur in a centralized single-processor system. These faults are associated with *partial* system failure and the application program must either be shielded from them, or be able to tolerate them.

- **Distributed control algorithms** – The presence of true parallelism in an application, physically distributed processors, and the possibility that processors and communication links may fail, means that many new algorithms are required for resource control. For example, it may be necessary to access files and data which are stored on other machines; furthermore, machine or network failure must not compromise the availability or consistency of those files or data. Also, as there is often no common time reference in a distributed system, each node having its own local notion of time, it is very difficult to obtain a consistent view of the overall system. This can cause problems when trying to provide mutual exclusion over distributed data.

- **Deadline scheduling** – In Chapter 13, the problems of scheduling processes to meet deadlines in a single processor system were discussed. When the processes are distributed, the optimal single processor algorithms are no longer optimal. New algorithms are needed.

These issues are now discussed in turn. However, in one chapter it is difficult to do justice to all the new activities in these areas.

14.3 Language support

The production of a distributed software system to execute on a distributed hardware system involves several steps which are not required when programs are produced for a single processor:

- **Partitioning** is the process of dividing the system into parts (units of distribution) suitable for placement onto the processing elements of the target system.

- **Configuration** takes place when the partitioned parts of the program are associated with particular processing elements in the target system.

- **Allocation** covers the actual process of turning the configured system into a collection of executable modules and downloading these to the processing elements of the target system.

- **Transparent execution** is the execution of the distributed software so that remote resources can be accessed in a manner which is independent of their location.

- **Reconfiguration** is the dynamic change to the location of a software component or resource.

Most languages which have been designed explicitly to address distributed programming will provide linguistic support for at least the partitioning stage of system development. For example, processes, objects, partitions, agents and guardians have all been proposed as units of distribution. All these constructs provide well-defined interfaces which allow them to encapsulate local resources and provide remote access. Some approaches will allow configuration information to be included in the program source, whereas others will provide a separate **configuration** language.

Allocation and reconfiguration, typically, require support from the programming support environment and operating system.

It is, perhaps, in the area of transparent execution where most efforts have been made to achieve a level of standardization across the various approaches. The goal is to make communication between distributed processes as easy and reliable as possible. Unfortunately, in reality, communication often takes places between heterogeneous processors across an unreliable network, and in practice complex communication protocols are required (see Section 14.5). What is needed is to provide mechanisms whereby:

- Processes do not have to deal with the underlying form of messages. For example, they do not need to translate data into bit strings suitable for transmission or to break up the message into packets.

- All messages received by user processes can be assumed to be intact and in good condition. For example, if messages are broken into packets, the run-time system will only deliver them when all packets have arrived at the receiving node and can be properly reassembled. Furthermore, if the bits in a message have been scrambled, the message either is not delivered or is reconstructed before delivery; clearly some redundant information is required for error checking and correction.

- Messages received by a process are the kind that the process expects. The process does not need to perform run-time checks.

- Processes are not restricted to communication only in terms of a predefined built-in set of types. Instead, processes can communicate in terms of values of interest to the application. Ideally, if the application is defined using abstract data types, then values of these types can be communicated in messages.

It is possible to identify three main *de facto* standards by which distributed programs can communicate with each other:

- by using an application programmers interface (API), such as *sockets*, to network transport protocols

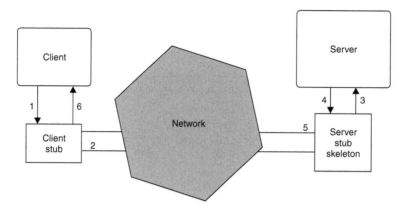

Figure 14.3   The relationship between client and server in an RPC.

- by using the remote procedure call (RPC) paradigm
- by using the distributed object paradigm.

The issue of network protocols will be discussed in Section 14.5 and a Java interface for sockets will be briefly considered in Section 14.4.3. The remainder of this subsection will consider RPC and distributed objects including the Common Object Request Broker Architecture (CORBA).

14.3.1   Remote procedure call

The overriding goal behind the remote procedure call paradigm is to make distributed communication as simply as possible. Typically, RPCs are used for communication between programs written in the same language, for example, Ada or Java. A procedure (server) is identified as being one that can be called remotely. From the server specification, it is possible to generate automatically two further procedures: a **client stub** and a **server stub**. The client stub is used in place of the server at the site on which the remote procedure call originates. The server stub is used on the same site as the server procedure. The purpose of these two procedures is to provide the link between the client and the server in a transparent way (and thereby meet all the requirements laid out in the previous section). Figure 14.3 illustrates the sequence of events in a RPC between a client and a server via the two stub procedures. The stubs are sometimes called **middleware** as they sit between the application and the operating system.

The role of the client stub is to:

- identify the address of the server (stub) procedure;

- convert the parameters of the remote call into a block of bytes suitable for transmission across the network – this activity is often call **parameter marshalling**;
- send the request to execute the procedure to the server (stub);
- wait for the reply from the server (stub) and unmarshal the parameters or any
exceptions propagated;
- return control to the client procedure along with the returned parameters, or raise
an exception in the client procedure.

The goal of the server stub is to:

- receive requests from client (stub) procedures;
- unmarshal the parameters;
- call the server;
- catch any exceptions that are raised by the server;
- marshal the return parameters (or exceptions) suitable for transmission across the
network;
- send the reply to the client (stub).

Where the client and server procedures are written in different languages or are
on different machine architectures, the parameter marshalling and unmarshalling mechanisms will convert the data into a machine- and language-independent format (see
Section 14.4.4).

14.3.2   The Distributed Object Model

The term **distributed objects** (or **remote objects**) has been used over the last few year
in a variety of contexts. In its most general sense, the distributed object model allows:

- the dynamic creation of an object (in any language) on a remote machine;
- the identification of an object to be determined and held on any machine;
- the transparent invocation of a remote method in an object as if it were a local
method and irrespective of the language in which the object is written;
- the transparent run-time dispatching of a method call across the network.

Not all systems which support distributed objects provide mechanisms to support all
this functionality. As will be shown in the following subsections:

Ada supports the static allocation of objects, allows the identification of remote Ada
objects, facilitates the transparent execution of remote methods, and supports distributed run-time dispatching of method calls;

Java allows the code of a Java object to be sent across the network and instances to be created remotely, the remote naming of a Java object, the transparent invocation of its methods, and distributed run-time dispatching;

CORBA allows objects to be created in different languages on different machines, facilitates the transparent execution of remote methods, and supports distributed run-time dispatching of method calls.

14.4 Distributed programming systems and environments

The number of distributed applications is vast, ranging from simple embedded control systems to large complex multi-language generic information processing platforms. It is beyond the scope of this book to discuss fully how these systems can be designed and implemented. However, four approaches will be considered:

(1) occam2 – for simple embedded control systems

(2) Ada – for more complex distributed real-time applications

(3) Java – for single-language Internet-type applications

(4) CORBA – for multi-language multi-platform applications

14.4.1 Occam2

Occam2 has been specifically designed so that programs can be executed in a distributed environment, that of a multi-transputer network. In general, occam2's processes do not share variables so the unit of partitioning is the process itself. Configuration is achieved by the PLACED PAR construct. A program constructed as a top-level PAR, such as:

```
PAR
   p1
   p2
   p3
   p4
   p5
```

can be distributed, for example as follows:

```
PLACED PAR
   PROCESSOR 1
      p1
   PROCESSOR 2
      PAR
         p2
         p3
   PROCESSOR 3
      PAR
         p4
         p5
```

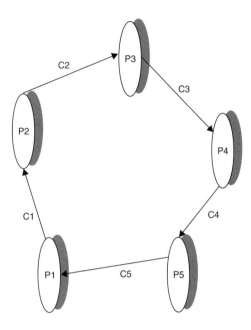

Figure 14.4   Five occam2 processes connected by five channels.

It is important to note that the transformation of the program from one that has a simple PAR to one that uses a PLACED PAR will not invalidate the program. However, occam2 does allow variables to be read by more than one process on the same processor. Therefore, a transformation may not be possible if the programmer has used this facility.

For the transputers, it is also necessary to associate each external channel with an appropriate transputer link. This is achieved by using the PLACE AT construct. For example, consider the above example with the following integer channels shown in Figure 14.4.

The program for execution on a single transputer is:

```
CHAN OF INT c1, c2, c3, c4, c5:
PAR
    p1
    p2
    p3
    p4
    p5
```

If the program is configured to three transputers, as illustrated in Figure 14.5, the occam2 program becomes:

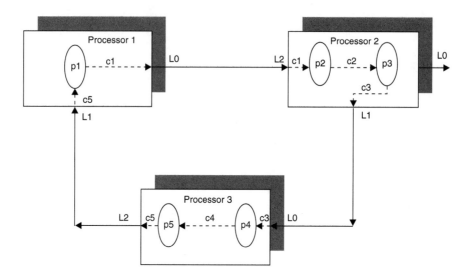

Figure 14.5 Five occam2 processes configured for three transputers.

```
CHAN OF INT c1, c3, c5:
PLACED PAR
  PROCESSOR 1
    PLACE c1 at 0:
    PLACE c5 at 1:
    p1
  PROCESSOR 2
    PLACE c1 at 2:
    PLACE c3 at 1:
    CHAN OF INT c2:
    PAR
      p2
      p3
  PROCESSOR 3
    PLACE c3 at 0:
    PLACE c5 at 2:
    CHAN OF INT c4:
    PAR
      p4
      p5
```

The ease with which occam2 programs can be configured for execution on a distributed system is one of the main attractions of occam2.

Allocation is not defined by the occam2 language nor are there any facilities for reconfiguration. Further, access to resources is not transparent.

Real-time perspective

The occam2 support for real-time is limited. However, within these limitations, the distributed system model is consistent.

14.4.2   Ada

Ada defines a distributed system as an

> interconnection of one or more processing nodes (a system resource that has both computational and storage capabilities), and zero or more storage nodes (a system resource that has only storage capabilities, with the storage addressable by more than one processing nodes).

The Ada model for programming distributed systems specifies a **partition** as the unit of distribution. Partitions comprised aggregations of library units (separately compiled library packages or subprograms) that collectively may execute in a distributed target execution environment. The configuration of library units into partitions is not defined by the language; it is assumed that an implementation will provide this, along with facilities for allocation and, if necessary, reconfiguration.

Each partition resides at a single execution site where all its library units occupy the same logical address space. More than one partition may, however, reside on the same execution site. Figure 14.6 illustrates one possible structure of a partition. The arrows represent the dependencies between library units. The principal interface between partitions consists of one or more package specifications (each labelled 'partition interface library unit' in Figure 14.6).

Partitions may be either **active** or **passive**. The library units comprising an active partition reside and execute upon the same processing element. In contrast, library units comprising a passive partition reside at a storage element that is directly accessible to the nodes of different active partitions that reference them. This model ensures that active partitions cannot directly access variables in other active partitions. Variables can only be shared directly between active partitions by encapsulating them in a passive partition. Communication between active partitions is defined in the language to be via remote subprogram calls (however, an implementation may provide other communication mechanisms).

Categorization pragmas

To aid the construction of distributed programs, Ada distinguishes between different categories of library units, and imposes restrictions on these categories to maintain type consistency across the distributed program. The categories (some of these are useful in their own right, irrespective of whether the program is to be distributed) are designated by the following pragmas:

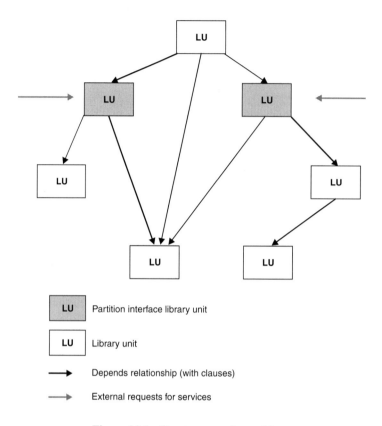

Figure 14.6   The structure of a partition.

Preelaborate

A preelaborable library unit is one that can be elaborated without execution of code at run-time.

Pure

Pure packages are preelaboratable packages with further restrictions which enable them to be freely replicated in different active or passive partitions without introducing any type inconsistencies. These restrictions concern the declaration of objects and types; in particular, variables and named access types are not allowed unless they are within a subprogram, task unit or protected unit.

Remote_Types

A `Remote_Types` package is a preelaboratable package that must not contain any variable declarations within the visible part.

Shared_Passive

`Shared_Passive` library units are used for managing global data shared between active partitions. They are, therefore, configured on storage nodes in the distributed system.

Remote_Call_Interface

A `Remote_Call_Interface` package defines the interface between active partitions. Its body exists only within a single partition. All other occurrences will have library stubs allocated.

The specification of a `Remote_Call_Interface` package must be preelaborable; in addition other restrictions apply, for example it must not contain the definition of a variable (to ensure no remote data access).

A package which is not categorized by any categorization pragma is called a *normal* library package. If it is included in more than one partition, then it is replicated and all types and objects are viewed as distinct. For example, the `Calendar` package is, in this regard, normal.

The above pragmas facilitate the distribution of an Ada program and ensure that illegal partitionings (which allow direct remote variable access between partitions) are easily identifiable.

Remote communication

The only predefined way in which active partitions can communicate directly is via remote subprogram calls. They can also communicate indirectly via data structures in passive partitions.

There are three different ways in which a calling partition can issue a remote subprogram call:

- by calling a subprogram which has been declared in a remote call interface package of another partition directly;
- by dereferencing a pointer to a remote subprogram;
- by using run-time dispatching to a method of a remote object.

It is important to note that, in the first type of communication, the calling and the called partitions are statically bound at compile time. However, in the latter two, the partitions are dynamically bound at run-time. Hence Ada can support transparent access to resources.

Program 14.1   The Ada `System.RPC` package.

```
with Ada.Streams;
package System.RPC is

   type Partition_ID is range 0 ..
implementation_defined;

   Communication_Error : exception;

   type Params_Stream_Type ...

   -- Synchronous call
   procedure Do_RPC(
          Partition  : in Partition_ID;
          Params     : access Params_Stream_Type;
          Result     : access Params_Stream_Type);

   -- Asynchronous call
   procedure Do_APC(
          Partition  : in Partition_ID;
          Params     : access Params_Stream_Type);

   -- The handler for incoming RPCs
   type RPC_Receiver is access procedure(
          Params     : access Params_Stream_Type;
          Result     : access Params_Stream_Type);

   procedure Establish_RPC_Receiver(Partition : Partition_ID;
          Receiver : in RPC_Receiver);

private
   ...
end System.RPC;
```

Many remote calls contain only 'in' or 'access' parameters (that is, data that is being passed in the same direction as the call) and a caller may wish to continue its execution as soon as possible. In these situations it is sometimes appropriate to designate the call as an *asynchronous* call. Whether a procedure is to be called synchronously or asynchronously is considered by Ada to be a property of the procedure and not of the call. This is indicated by using a pragma `Asynchronous` when the procedure is declared.

Ada has defined how distributed programs can be partitioned and what forms of remote communication must be supported. However, the language designers were keen not to overspecify the language and not to prescribe a distributed run-time support system for Ada programs. They wanted to allow implementors to provide their own network communication protocols and, where appropriate, allow other ISO standards to be used; for example the ISO Remote Procedure Call standard. To achieve these aims, the Ada language assumes the existence of a standard implementation-provided subsystem for handling all remote communication (the Partition Communication Subsystem, PCS). This allows compilers to generate calls to a standard interface without being concerned with the underlying implementation.

The package defined in Program 14.1 illustrates the interface to the remote procedure (subprogram) call (RPC) support system which is part of the PCS.

The type `Partition_Id` is used to identify partitions. For any library-level declaration, D, D' `Partition_Id` yields the identifier of the partition in which the declaration was elaborated. The exception `Communication_Error` is raised when an error is detected by `System.RPC` during a remote procedure call. An object of stream type `Params_Stream_Type` is used for marshalling (translating data into an appropriate stream-oriented form) and unmarshalling the parameters or results of a remote subprogram call, for the purposes of sending them between partitions. The object is also used to identify the particular subprogram in the called partition.

The procedure `Do_RPC` is invoked by the calling stub after the parameters are flattened into the message. After sending the message to the remote partition, it suspends the calling task until a reply arrives. The procedure `Do_APC` acts like `Do_RPC` except that it returns immediately after sending the message to the remote partition. It is called whenever the `Asynchronous` pragma is specified for the remotely called procedure. `Establish_RPC_Receiver` is called immediately after elaborating an active partition, but prior to invoking the main subprogram, if any. The `Receiver` parameter designates an implementation-provided procedure that receives a message and calls the appropriate remote call interface package and subprogram.

Real-time perspective

Although Ada defines a coherent real-time model for single and multiprocessor systems, it has very limited support for *distributed real-time* systems. There is no integration between the Distributed Systems Annex and the Real-Time Annex. Arguably, the technology of language support in this area is not sufficiently widely accepted to merit standardization.

14.4.3 Java

There are essentially two ways in which to construct distributed Java applications:

(1) execute Java programs on separate machines and use the Java networking facilities;

(2) use remote objects.

Java networking

In Section 14.5, two network communication protocols will be introduced: UDP and TCP. These are the prominent communication protocols in use today and the Java environment provide classes (in the `java.net` package) which allow easy access to them. The API to these protocols is via the `Socket` class (for the reliable TCP protocol) and the `DatagramSocket` class (for the UDP protocol). It is beyond the scope of this book to consider this approach in detail – see the Further Reading section at the end of this chapter for alternative sources of information.

Remote objects

Although Java provides a convenient way of accessing network protocols, these protocols are still complex and are a deterrent to writing distributed applications. Consequently, Java supports the distributed object communication model through the notion of **remote objects**.

The Java model is centred on the use of the `java.rmi` package which builds on top of the TCP protocol. In this package is the `Remote` interface:

```
public interface Remote { };
```

This is the starting point for writing distributed Java applications. Extensions of this interface are written to provide the link between the clients and servers. For example, consider a server which wishes to return details of the local weather forecast for its location. An appropriate interface might be:

```
public interface WeatherForecast extends java.rmi.Remote
  // shared between clients and server
{
  public Forecast getForecast() throws RemoteException;
}
```

The method `getForecast` must have a `RemoteException` class in its throws list so that the underlying implementation can indicate that the remote call has failed.

`Forecast` is an object which has details of today's forecast. As the object will be copied across the network, it must implement the `Serializable` interface[2]

```
public class Forecast implements java.io.Serializable
{
  public String Today() {
    String today = "Wet";

    return today ;
  }
}
```

---

[2]Like the `Remote` interface, the `Serializable` interface is empty. In both cases it acts as a tag to give information to the compiler. For the `Serializable` interface, it indicates that the object can be converted into a stream of bytes suitable for I/O.

Once the appropriate remote interface has been defined, a server class can be declared. Again, it is usual to indicate that objects of the class can potentially be called remotely by extending one of the predefined classes in the package `java.rmi.server`. Currently, there are two classes: `RemoteServer` (which is an abstract class derived from the `Remote` class) and `UnicastRemoteObject` which is a concrete extension of `RemoteServer`. The latter provides the class for servers which are non-replicated and have a point-to-point connection to each client using the TCP protocol. It is anticipated that future extension to Java might provide other classes such as a replicated server using a multicast communication protocol.

The following examples shows a server class which provides the weather forecast for the county of Yorkshire in the UK.

```
public class YorkshireWeatherForecast extends UnicastRemoteObject
                                       implements WeatherForecast
{

  public YorkshireWeatherForecast() throws RemoteException
  {
    super(); // call parent constructor
  }

  public Forecast getForecast() throws RemoteException
  {
    ...
  }
}
```

Once the server class has been written, it is necessary to generate the server and client stubs for each of the methods that can be called remotely. Note that Java uses the term **skeleton** for the server stub. The Java programming environment provides a tool called 'rmic' which will take a server class and automatically generate the appropriate client stub and server skeleton.

All that is now required is for the client to be able to acquire a client stub which accesses the server object. This is achieved via a registry. The registry is a separate Java program which executes on each host machine which has server objects. It listens on a standard TCP port and provides an object of the class `Naming` extracted in Program 14.2.

Each server object can use the `Naming` class to bind its remote object to a name. Clients then can access a remote registry to acquire a reference to the remote object. Of course, this is a reference to a client stub object for the server. The client stub is loaded into the client's machine. Once the reference has been obtained, the server's methods can be invoked.

Real-time perspective

The facilities described above are those of Standard Java which is not intended to operate within real-time constraints. Real-Time Java is currently silent on the issue of distributed

---

Program 14.2   An extract of the Java Naming class.

```
public final class Naming
{
  public static void bind(String name, Remote obj)
    throws AlreadyBoundException, java.net.MalformedURLException,
           UnknownHostException, RemoteException;
  // bind the name to the obj
  // name takes the form of a URL such as
  //             rmi://remoteHost:pot/objectName

  public static Remote lookup (String name)
    throws NotBoundException, java.net.MalformedURLException,
           UnknownHostException, RemoteException;
  // looks up the name in the registry and returns a remote object

  ...
}
```

---

real-time programming. However, this is a topic which will be addressed within the
next few years.

14.4.4 CORBA

The Common Object Request Broker Architecture (CORBA) provides the most general
distributed object model. Its goal is to facilitate interoperability between applications
written in different languages, for different platforms supported by middleware software
from different vendors. It was designed by the Object Management Group (OMG) – a
consortium of software vendors, software developers and end users – according to the
Object Management Architectural Model, which is depicted in Figure 14.7.

At the heart of the architecture is the **Object Request Broker** (ORB). This is a
software communication bus that provides the main infrastructure that facilitates interoperability between heterogeneous applications. The term CORBA often refers to the
ORB. The other components of the architecture are:

Object Services – a collection of basic services which support the ORB; for example,
support for object creation, naming and access control, and tracking relocated
objects.

Common Facilities – a set of functions which is common across a wide range of application domains; for example, user interfaces, document and database management.

Domain Interfaces – a group of interfaces which support particular application domains such as banking and finance or telecommunications.

Application Interfaces – the end users' specific application interfaces.

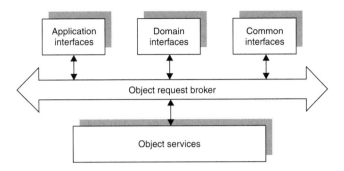

Figure 14.7   The Object Management Architecture Model.

To ensure interoperability between ORBs from different vendors, CORBA defines a General Inter-ORB Protocol which sits on top of TCP/IP (see section 14.5.2).

Central to writing CORBA applications is the **Interface Definition Language** (IDL) . A CORBA interface is similar in concept to the Java remote interface discussed in the previous section. The IDL (which is like the C++ language) is used to describe the facilities to be provided by an application object, the parameters to be passed with a given method and its return values, along with any object attributes. An example interface for the weather forecast application given in the previous section is shown below.

```
interface WeatherForecast {
  void GetForecast(out Forecast today);
}
```

Once the IDL for the application is defined, tools are used to 'compile' it. The IDL compiler generates several new files in one of a number of existing programming languages such as Java or Ada. The files include:

- client stubs that provide a communication channel between the client and the ORB; and
- a server skeleton which enables the ORB to call functions on the server.

The code for the server and clients can now be written. The server consists of two parts: the code for the application object itself and the code for the server process. The application object has to be associated with the server skeleton. The way this is achieved is dependent on the target language. For example in Java, it can be done by producing a class which is a subclass of the generated server skeleton. The methods for the application objects are then completed. The server process itself can be written as a main program which creates the application object and initializes the ORB and tells it that the object is ready to receive client requests. The structure of the client is similar.

In reality, CORBA provides many more facilities than those described above. As well as the static association between client and server, CORBA clients can dynamically discover a server's IDL interface without prior knowledge of the server details. Furthermore, the services that support the ORB allow for a wide range of functionality such as an event service, transaction and concurrency control, persistent objects and trading services. Applications access these services via the Portable Object Adapter (POA). This is a library which provides the run-time environment for a server object.

Real-time perspective

Although, in general, CORBA provides comprehensive support for distributed objects, from this book's perspective, one of the main limitation of CORBA has been its lack of support for real-time applications. The ORBs were not designed to operate within time constraints and the result is that many are inappropriate for soft real-time systems, let alone systems which have to operate within stringent timing constraints. Furthermore, the basic communication models provided by CORBA are: a synchronous RPC where the client must wait for the server to reply, and a deferred synchronous RPC where the client thread continues and subsequently polls for the reply. As was illustrated in Chapter 13, synchronous communication models are more difficult to analyze for their timing properties than asynchronous models and the results are more pessimistic.

For these reasons and the increasing use of CORBA in real-time applications, the OMG have set out over the last few years to address the performance problems associated with the main CORBA standard. They have tackled the problems from three perspectives:

(1) Minimum CORBA

(2) CORBA Messaging

(3) Real-Time CORBA

Minimum CORBA is a subset of the CORBA 2.2 specification which omits many services including all those associated with dynamic configurations between client and server objects. The subset is targeted at embedded systems with limited resources.

CORBA Messaging is an extension to the CORBA standard to support asynchronous message passing and quality of service parameters.

The Real-Time CORBA (RT CORBA) (Object Management Group, 1999) specification defines mechanisms that support predictability of distributed CORBA applications. It assumes that real-time behaviour is obtained by using fixed-priority based scheduling and is, therefore, compatible with most real-time operating systems – especially those supporting the Real-Time POSIX interfaces. The key aspect of RT CORBA is that it allows applications to configure and control both processor and communication resources. These facilities will now be briefly described.

Managing processor resources

The RT CORBA specification allows client and server applications to manage the following properties.

- The priority at which servers process client requests. RT CORBA specifies global CORBA priorities and mechanism to map these priorities onto the priority range of the particular real-time operating system hosting the RT ORB. Using these mapping, three global priority models are supported: (1) a server declared model in which the server specifies the priority of the requests it services, (2) a client propagated model in which the client specifies the priority and this is propagated to the server and (3) a priority transformation model in which the priority of a request is based on external factors such as current server load or the state of the global scheduling service.

- The degree of multithreading in a server. RT CORBA controls the degree of multithreading by the concept of thread pools. Using a Real-Time POA, server applications can specify: the default number of threads that are initially created, the maximum number of threads that can be created dynamically, and the default priority of all the threads. These threads are allocated from a thread pool which may or may not be shared between applications. Further flexibility is given by the concept of thread pools with lanes. Here, not only can the overall amount of concurrency be controlled, but also the amount of work performed at a particular priority.

- The impact of priority inheritance and priority ceiling protocols. RT CORBA defines POSIX-like mutexes to ensure consistency of synchronization protocols encapsulating shared resources.

Managing network resources

Although having transparent access to resources eases the writing of general-purpose distributed applications, it makes it impossible to do any realistic analysis of real-time performance. For this reason, RT CORBA allows explicit connections between client and server to be set up, for example, at system configuration time. It is also possible to control how client requests are sent over these connections. RT CORBA facilitates multiple connections between a client and a server in order to reduce priority inversion problems due to the use of non real-time transport protocols. Furthermore, private transport connections are also supported – so that a call from a client to a server can be made without any fear of the call having to compete with other calls which have been multiplexed on the same connection.

Even with the above support, it is still advantageous to be able to set any quality of service parameters of the specific communication protocols underlying the inter-ORB communication protocol. RT CORBA provides interfaces to select and configure these properties from both the client and the server side.

The scheduling service

From the above discussion it should be clear that RT CORBA provides many mechanisms to facilitate real-time distributed CORBA applications. However, setting up all the required parameters (so that a consistent scheduling policy is obtained) can be difficult. For this reason, RT CORBA allows an application to specify its scheduling requirements in terms of characteristics such as its period, its worst-case execution time, its criticality etc. This is done offline and each application scheduled entity (called an *activity*) is allocated a textual name. At run-time, interfaces are provided which allow the application to schedule a named activity via a *scheduling service*. This service sets all the necessary priority parameters to implement a specific scheduling policy such as deadline or rate monotonic scheduling.

14.5   Reliability

It seems almost paradoxical that distribution can provide the means by which systems can be made more reliable yet at the same time introduce more potential failures in the system. Although the availability of multiple processors enables the application to become tolerant of processor failure, it also introduces the possibility of faults occurring in the system which would not occur in a centralized single processor system. In particular, multiple processors introduce the concept of a partial system failure. In a single processor system, if the processor or memory fails then normally the whole system fails (sometimes the processor may be able to continue and recover from a partial memory failure, but in general the system will crash). However, in a distributed system, it is possible for a single processor to fail while others continue to operate. In addition, the propagation delay through the underlying communications network is variable and messages may take various routes. This, in conjunction with an unreliable transmission medium, may result in messages being lost, corrupted, or delivered in an order different to the order in which they were sent. The increased complexity of the software necessary to tolerate such failures can also threaten the reliability of the system.

14.5.1   Open systems interconnections

Much effort has been expended on communication protocols for networks and distributed systems. It is beyond the scope of this book to cover this in detail; rather the reader should refer to the Further Reading section at the end of this chapter. In general, communication protocols are layered to facilitate their design and implementation. However, many different networks exist, each with its own concept of a 'network architecture' and associated communication protocol. Consequently, without some international standards it is extremely difficult to contemplate interconnecting systems of different origins. Standards have been defined by the International Organization for Standardization (ISO) and involve the concept of *Open Systems Interconnections*, or *OSI*. The term 'open' is used to indicate that, by conforming to these standards, a system will be open to all other systems in the world that also obey the same standards.

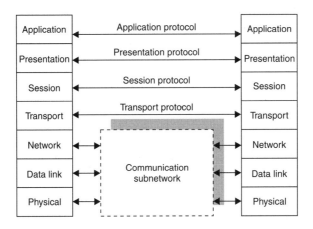

Figure 14.8   The OSI reference model.

These standards have become known as the *OSI Reference Model.* It should be stressed that this model is *not* concerned with specific applications of computer communication networks but with the *structuring* of the communication protocols required to provide a reliable, manufacturer independent communication service. The OSI Reference Model is a layered model. The layers are shown in Figure 14.8.

The basic idea of layering is that each layer adds to the services provided by the lower layers in order to present a service to higher layers. Viewed from above a particular layer, the ones below it may be considered as a black box which implements a service. The means by which one layer makes use of the service provided by the lower layers is through that layer's interface. The interface defines the rules and format for exchanging information across the boundary between adjacent layers. The modules which implement a layer are usually known as **entities**.

In networks and distributed systems, each layer may be distributed across more than one machine; in order to provide its service, entities in the same layer on different machines may need to exchange information. Such entities are known as **peer entities**. A **protocol** is the set of rules which governs communication between peer entities.

The OSI model itself does not define protocol standards; by breaking up the network's function into layers, it does suggest where protocol standards should be developed but these standards are outside the model itself. Such standards, however, have been developed.

The functions of each layer are now briefly described.

(1) **The Physical Layer**

The physical layer is concerned with transmitting raw data over a communication channel. Its job is to make sure that, in the absence of errors, when one side sends a 1 bit it is received as a 1 bit and not a 0 bit.

(2) **The Data Link Layer**

The data link layer converts a potentially unreliable transmission channel into a reliable one for use by the network layer. It is also responsible for resolving any contention for access to the transmission channel between nodes connected to the channel.

In order for the data link layer to provide a reliable communication channel, it must be able to correct errors. There are two basic and familiar techniques used: *forward error control* and *backward error control.* Forward error control requires enough redundant information in each message to correct any errors which may occur in its transmission. In general, the amount of redundancy required increases rapidly as the number of information bits increases. Backward error control requires only that the error be detected; once detected, a retransmission scheme can be employed to obtain the correct message (this is the job of the data link layer). Backward error control predominates in the world of networks and distributed systems.

Most backward error control techniques incorporate the notion of a calculated *checksum* which is sent with the message and describes the content of the message. On receipt, the checksum is recalculated and compared with the one sent. Any disagreement indicates that a transmission error has occurred. At this point, there are three basic classes of service that the Data Link Layer can offer: an unacknowledged connectionless service, an acknowledged connectionless service or a connection-oriented service. With the first, no further service is provided. The sender is unaware that the message has not been received intact. With the second, the sender is informed every time a message is received correctly; the absence of this acknowledgement message within a certain time period indicates that an error has occurred. The third service type establishes a connection between the send and the receiver and guarantees that all messages are received correctly and are received in order.

(3) **The Network Layer**

The network layer (or communication subnet layer) is concerned with how information from the transport layer is routed through the communication subnet to its destinations. Messages are broken down into packets which may be routed via different paths; the network layer must reassemble the packets and handle any congestion that may occur. There is no clear agreement as to whether the network layer should attempt to provide a perfect communication channel through the network. Two extremes in the services provided can be identified: *virtual circuits* (connection-oriented) and *datagrams* (connectionless). With virtual circuits, a perfect communication channel is provided. All messages packets arrive and do so in sequence. With a datagram service, the network layer attempts to deliver each packet in isolation from the others. Consequently, messages may arrive out of order, or may not arrive at all.

The physical, data link and network layers are network-dependent and their detailed operation may vary from one type of network to another.

(4) **The Transport Layer**

The transport layer (or host-to-host layer) provides reliable host-to-host communication for use by the session layer. It must hide all details of the communication subnet from the session layer in order that one subnet can be replaced by another. In effect, the transport layer shields the customer's portion of the network (layers 5–7) from the carrier's portion (layers 1–3).

(5) **The Session Layer**

The role of the session layer is to provide a communication path between two application-level processes using the facilities of the transport layer. The connection between users is usually called a session and may include a remote login or a file transfer. The operations involved in setting up a session (called binding) include authentication and accounting. Once the session has been initiated, the layer must control data exchange, and synchronize data operations between the two processes.

(6) **The Presentation Layer**

The presentation layer performs generally useful transformations on the data to overcome heterogeneous issues with respect to the presentation of data to the applications. For example, it allows an interactive program to converse with any one of a set of incompatible display terminals. It may undertake text compression or encryption.

(7) **The Application Layer**

The application layer provides the high-level functions of the network, such as access to databases, mail systems and so on. The choice of the application may dictate the level of services provided by the lower layers. Consequently, particular application areas may specify a set of protocols throughout all seven layers which are required to support the intended distributed processing function. For example, an initiative by General Motors has defined a set of protocols to achieve open interconnection within an automated manufacturing plant. These are called *manufacturing automation protocols* (MAP).

14.5.2 TCP/IP layers

The OSI model is now somewhat outdated and does not directly address the issue of Internet working. The TCP/IP Reference Model has only five layers and is shown in Figure 14.9.

The physical layer is equivalent to the ISO physical layer. The network interface layer performs the same functions as the ISO data link Layer. The Internet layer specifies the format of the packets to be sent across the internet and performs all the routing functions associated with the ISO network layer. It is here that the Internet Protocol (IP) is defined.

The transport layer is equivalent to the ISO transport layer; it provides two protocols: the User Data Protocol (UDP) and the Transmission Control Protocol (TCP). UDP provides an unreliable connectionless protocol which allows efficient access to the IP protocol in the layer below. The TCP protocol provides a reliable end-to-end byte stream protocol.

| Application |
| Transport |
| Internet |
| Network interface |
| Physical |

Figure 14.9   The TCP/IP Reference Model.

14.5.3 Lightweight protocols and local area networks

The OSI and TCP/IP model were developed primarily for wide area networks to enable open access; wide area networks were characterized by low bandwidth communication with high error rates. Most distributed embedded systems will use local area network technology and will be closed to the outside world. Local area networks are characterized by high bandwidth communication with low error rates. They may use a range of communication technologies, such as broadcast technology (for example, as does the Ethernet) or point-to-point switch-based technology (for example, ATM (Asynchronous Transfer Mode)). Consequently, although it is possible to implement language-level interprocess communication using the OSI or TCP/IP approach (for example, Java RMI), in practice the expense is often prohibitive. Thus many designers tailor the communication protocols to the requirements of the language (the application) and the communication medium. These are called *lightweight* protocols. A key issue in their design is the degree with which they tolerate communication failures.

At first glance, it appears that completely reliable communication is essential if efficient, reliable distributed applications are to be written. However, this may not always be the case. Consider the types of error that can be introduced by a distributed application. If two distributed processes are communicating and synchronizing their activities to provide a service, potential errors can occur from:

- transient errors resulting from interference on the physical communication medium
- design errors in the software responsible for masking out transient errors in the communication subsystems
- design errors in the protocols between the server processes and any other servers needed in the provision of the service
- design errors in the protocol between the two server processes themselves.

To protect against the latter error, it is necessary for the server processes to provide application-level checks (end-to-end checks). The **end-to-end** argument of system design (Saltzer et al., 1984) states that given the necessity of such checks for provision of a reliable service, it is not necessary to repeat these checks at lower levels in the protocol hierarchy, particularly when the communication medium (for example, local area networks such as an Ethernet or Token Ring) provides a low error rate (but not perfect) transmission facility. In these cases, it may be better to have a fast, less than 100% reliable, communication facility than a slower 100% reliable facility. Applications which require high reliability can trade off efficiency for reliability at the application level. However, applications that require fast (but not necessarily reliable) service *cannot* trade off reliability for efficiency if the other approach is taken.

There are standards for local area network communication protocols, particularly at the data link layer, which is divided into two sub-layers: Medium Access Control (MAC) and Logical Link Control (LLC). MAC is concerned with the interface to the physical communication media, and standards exists for CSMA/CD (Carrier Sense Multiple Access with Collision Detection) buses (for example, Ethernet), packet switching (for example, ATM), token buses and token rings. The LLC layer is concerned with providing a connectionless or connection-oriented protocol.

As described earlier, a common language-oriented lightweight protocol is the remote procedure call (ISO/IEC JTC1/SC21/WG8, 1992). This is normally implemented directly on top of a basic communication facility provided by the local area network (for example, the LLC layer). With languages like Java and Ada, remote procedure calls, in the absence of machine failures, are considered to be reliable. That is, for each remote procedure call, if the call returns then the procedure has been executed once and once only; this is often called **exactly once** RPC semantics. However, in the presence of machine failure, this is difficult to achieve because a procedure may be partially or totally executed several times depending on where the crash occurred and whether the program is restarted. Ada assumes that the call is executed *at most once* because there is no notion of restarting part of an Ada program following failure.

For a real-time local area network and its associated protocols, it is important to provide bounded and known delays in message transmissions. This topic will be returned to in Section 14.7.2.

14.5.4   Group communication protocols

The remote procedure call (or remote method call) is a common form of communication between clients and servers in a distributed systems. However, it does restrict communication to be between two processes. Often, when groups of processes are interacting (for example, performing an atomic action), it is necessary for communication to be sent to the whole group. A **multicast** communication paradigm provides such a facility. Some networks, for example Ethernet, provide a hardware multicast mechanism as part of their data link layer. If this is not the case, then further software protocols must be added.

All networks and processors are, to a greater or lesser extent, unreliable. It is therefore possible to design a family of group communication protocols, each of which provides a multicast communication facility with specific guarantees:

- **unreliable multicast** – no guarantees of delivery to the group is provided; the multicast protocol provides the equivalent of a datagram-level of service;

- **reliable multicast** – the protocol makes a best-effort attempt to deliver the message to the group, but offers no absolute guarantee of delivery;

- **atomic multicast** – the protocol guarantees that if one process in the group receives the message then all members of the group receive the message; hence the message is delivered to all of the group or none of them;

- **ordered atomic multicast** – as well as guaranteeing the atomicity of the multicast, the protocol also guarantees that all members of the group will receive messages from different senders in the same order.

The more guarantees the protocols give, the greater the cost of their implementation. Furthermore, the cost will also vary depending on the failure model used (see Section 5.2).

For atomic and ordered atomic multicasts, it is important to be able to bound the time taken by the implementation algorithms to terminate. Without this, it is impossible to predict their performance in a hard real-time system.

Consider a simple ordered atomic multicast which has the following failure model:

- processors fail silently

- all communication failures are fail omission

- no more than N consecutive network omission failures occur

- the network is fully connected and there is no network partitioning.

To achieve atomic message transmission, all that is required is to transmit each message $N + 1$ times; this is called message **diffusion**. To achieve the ordered property using diffusion requires that the time required to complete each message transmission be known. Assume that the worst-case transmission value for all messages is T_D and that clocks in the network are loosely synchronized with a maximum difference of C_Δ. Each message is time-stamped by its sender with the value of its local clock (C_{sender}). Each recipient can deliver the message to its process when its local clock is greater than $C_{sender} + T_D + C_\Delta$, as it is by this time that all recipients are guaranteed to have received the message and the message becomes **valid**. These messages can be ordered according to their validity times. If two messages have identical validity times an arbitrary order can be imposed (such as using the network address of the processor). Figure 14.10 illustrates the approach for $N = 1$.

Note that although the above simple algorithm guarantees that all processors receive and process the messages in the same order, it does not guarantee that the order is the actual order the messages were sent. This is because the value used to determine the order is based on the local clocks of the processors which can differ by C_Δ.

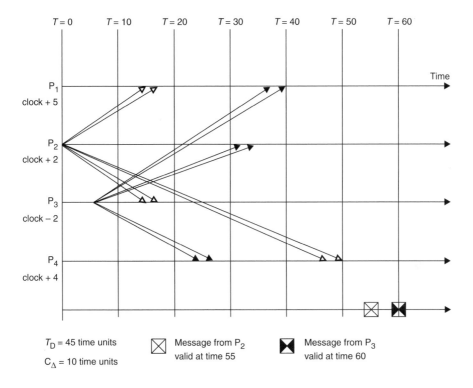

Figure 14.10 A simple ordered atomic multicast based on diffusion.

14.5.5 Processor failure

In Chapter 5, two general approaches for providing fault-tolerant hardware and software were identified; those with static (masking) and those with dynamic redundancy. Although hardware fault tolerance does have a major role to play in achieving reliability in the presence of processor and communication failure, an excessive amount of hardware is required to implement triple modular redundancy, and consequently it is expensive (but fast). This section, therefore, concentrates on the provision of fault tolerance through the use of software methods.

For the time being, it will be assumed that all processors in the system are **fail-silent**. This means that if a processor malfunctions in any way then it will suffer a permanent omission failure. If processors are not fail-silent then it is possible that they will send invalid messages to each other. This would introduce an extra level of complexity into the following discussion.

Tolerating processor failure through static redundancy

N-version programming was discussed in Chapter 5 in the context of achieving static tolerance to design faults. Clearly, if each of the versions in an *N*-version program resides on a different processor then this approach will also provide tolerance to processor failure. However, even if no design diversity is employed, it may still be desirable to replicate identical copies of some system components to obtain the required availability. This is often called **active replication**.

Suppose that an application is designed according to the distributed object model. It is possible to replicate objects on different processors and even vary the degree of replication according to the importance of the particular object.   For objects to be replicated transparently to the application programmer, they must have deterministic behaviour. This means that for a given sequence of requests to an object the behaviour of the object is predictable. If this was not the case, the states of each of the replicas in a replicated object set could end up being different. Consequently, any request made to that object set could produce a range of results. A set of objects must, therefore, be kept consistent. Its members must not diverge.

If objects are to be replicated, it is also necessary to replicate each remote method invocation. Furthermore, it is necessary to have exactly once RPC semantics. As is illustrated in Figure 14.11, each client object will potentially execute a one-to-many procedure call and each server procedure will receive a many-to-one request. The run-time system is responsible for coordinating these calls and ensuring the required semantics. This entails periodically probing server sites with outstanding calls to determine their status; a failure to respond will indicate a processor crash. In effect, the run-time system must support some form of membership protocol and an ordered atomic multicast group communication protocol.

An example of a language which explicitly allows replication (at the process level) is Fault-Tolerant Concurrent C (Cmelik et al., 1988). The language assumes that processors have a fail-stop failure model and provides a distributed consensus protocol to ensure that all replicas behave in a deterministic manner. Fault-Tolerant Concurrent C has a communication and synchronization model that is very similar to Ada, and therefore it has to ensure that if a particular branch of a select statement is taken in one replica then the same branch is taken in all replicas (even though the replicas are not executing in lock-step). There have also been attempts to make Ada fault-tolerant, for example, (Wellings and Burns, 1996; Wolf, 1998).

Although transparent replication of objects is an attractive approach to providing tolerance of processor failure, the cost of the underlying multicast and agreement protocols may be prohibitive for a hard real-time system. In particular, where objects are active and contain more than one task (with potentially nested tasks), it is necessary for the run-time agreement protocol (which ensures consistency between replicas) to be executed at every scheduling decision. Providing **warm** standbys with periodic state saving may offer a cheaper solution. With such an approach, an object would be replicated on more than one processor. However, unlike full replication, only one copy of the object is active at any one time. The state of this object is periodically saved (typically before and after communication with another object) on the processors with residing replicas. If the primary node fails a standby can be started from the last checkpoint.

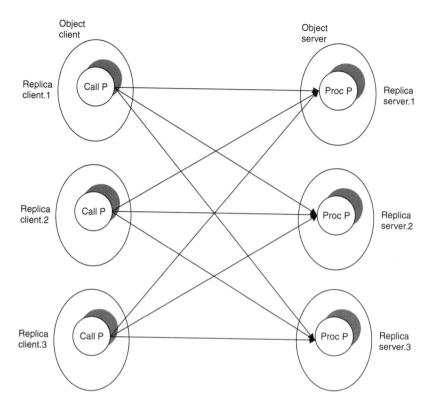

Figure 14.11   Replicated remote procedure calls.

There is clearly a trade-off between efficient use of the processing resources allocated to an object for availability and the time for it to recover from failures. Active replication is expensive in processing resources but requires little, if any, recovery time; in contrast warm replication (often called **passive** replication) is cheaper but has a slower recovery time. This has led to a compromise called **leader follower** replication (Barrett et al., 1990), where all replicas are active but one is deemed to be the primary version and takes all the decisions that are potentially non-deterministic. These decisions are then communicated to the followers. This form of replication is cheaper to support than active replication and does not have such a lengthy recovery time as passive replication.

Tolerating processor failure through dynamic redundancy

One of the problems of providing fault tolerance transparently to the application is that it is impossible for the programmer to specify degraded or safe execution. The alternative to static redundancy and replication is to allow processor(s) failure to be handled dynamically by the application programmer. Clearly, the techniques that have been discussed so far in this book which enable an application to tolerate software design faults (for example, atomic actions) will provide some measure of tolerance of hardware faults. In Chapter 5, the four phases of fault tolerance were described: error detection, damage confinement and assessment, error recovery and fault treatment with continued service. In the context of processor failure, the following actions must be performed:

(1) The failure of the processor(s) must be detected and communicated to the remaining processors in the system. Failure detection would normally be done by the underlying distributed run-time support system. However, there must be an appropriate way of communicating which processors have failed to the application software. Fault-Tolerant Concurrent C provides such a notification mechanism.

(2) The damage that has occurred because of the failure must be assessed; this requires knowledge of which processes were running on the failed processor(s), which processors and processes remain active (and their state). For this to be achieved, the application programmer must have control over which objects are placed on which machines. Furthermore, it must be clear what effect a processor failure has on the processes executing on the failed processor, and their data. Also, the effect of any interaction, either pending or future, with those processes and their data must be defined.

(3) Using the results of the damage assessment, the remaining software must agree on a response to the failure and carry out the necessary actions to effect that response. To achieve maximum tolerance, this part of the recovery procedure must be distributed. If only a single processor performs the recovery operations then failure of that processor will be catastrophic to the application. Recovery will require communication paths between processes being changed so that alternative services can be provided. Also, because the response selected will depend on the overall state of the application, it will be necessary for certain data to be made available on all machines and for this to be held in a consistent state. For example, the actions to be taken following a processor failure in an avionics system will depend on the altitude of the plane. If different processors have different values for this altitude then the chosen recovery procedures may work at cross purposes.

(4) As soon as is practicable, the failed processor and/or its associated software must be repaired and the system returned to its normal error-free state.

None of the real-time programming languages considered in this book provides adequate facilities to cope with dynamic reconfiguration after processor failure.

Ada and fault-tolerance

The Ada language makes no assumption about the failure model underlying the implementation of programs. All that is specified is that a pre-defined exception Communication_Error is raised if one partition attempts to communicate with another and an error is detected by the communication subsystem.

Ada also does not support any particular approach to fault tolerance but allows an implementation to provide appropriate mechanisms. The following discussion assumes that a distributed implementation of Ada is executed on top of fail-stop processors.

The ability to replicate partitions is also not explicitly provided by Ada (although an implementation is free to do so – for example see (Wolf, 1998)). However, the Partition Communication Subsystem (PCS) can be extended, so a replicated remote procedure call facility could be provided. Each replicated partition has an associated group identifier which can be used by the system. All remote procedure calls are potentially replicated calls. The body of the package would require access to an ordered multicast facility. Note, however, that this approach does not allow arbitrary partitions to be replicated with the full Ada run-time system being involved at every scheduling decision. Hence, further restriction would be required.

Asynchronous notification could be provided by providing a protected object in an extended PCS. The run-time system could then call a procedure when it detects processor failure. This can open an entry which can then cause an asynchronous transfer of control in one or more tasks. Alternatively, a single (or group of) task(s) can be waiting for a failure to occur. The following package illustrates the approach.

```
package System.RPC.Reliable is

   type Group_Id is range 0 .. implementation_defined;

   -- Synchronous replicated call
   procedure Do_Replicated_RPC(Group : in Group_Id;
            Params : access Params_Stream_Type;
            Results : out Param_Stream_Access);

   -- Asynchronous call
   procedure Do_Replicated_APC(Group : in Group_Id;
            Params : access Params_Stream_Type);

   type RRPC_Receiver is access procedure (Service : in Service_Id;
            Params : access Params_Stream_Type;
            Results : out Param_Stream_Access);

   procedure Establish_RRPC_Receiver(Partition : in Partition_Id;
            Receiver : in RRPC_Receiver);

   protected Failure_Notify is
      entry Failed_Partition(P : out Partition_Id);
   private
      procedure Signal_Failure(P : Partition_Id);
      ...
   end Failure_Notify;

private
      ...
end System.RPC.Reliable;
```

Once tasks have been notified, they must assess the damage that has been done to the system. This requires knowledge of the actual configuration. Reconfiguration is possible by using the dynamic binding facilities of the language (see Burns and Wellings (1998)).

Achieving reliable execution of occam2 programs

Although occam2 was designed for use in a distributed environment, it does not have any failure semantics. Processes which fail due to internal error (for example, array bound error) are equivalent to the STOP process. A process which is waiting for communication on a channel where the other process is on a failed processor will wait forever, unless it has employed a timeout. However, it is possible to imagine that suitable occam2 semantics for this event would be to consider both processes as STOPped and to provide a mechanism whereby some other process can be informed.

Achieving reliable execution of Real-Time Java programs

Java requires that each method that can be called remotely declares `RemoteExcep-tion` in its throws list. This allows the underlying implementation to give notification when a remote call fails. Furthermore, Java leaves open the possibility of defining remote services which support replication. Currently, Real-Time Java is silent on its use in a distributed system.

14.6   Distributed algorithms

So far, this chapter has concentrated on the expression of distributed programs in languages like Ada, Java and occam2, along with the general problems of tolerating processor and communication failure. It is beyond the scope of this book to consider the specific distributed algorithms which are required for controlling and coordinating access to resources in a distributed environment. However, it is useful to establish certain properties that can be relied on in a distributed environment. In particular, it is necessary to show how events can be ordered, how storage can be organized so that its contents survive a processor failure, and how agreement can be reached in the presence of faulty processors. These algorithms are often needed to implement atomic multicast protocols.

14.6.1   Ordering events in a distributed environment

In many applications, it is necessary to determine the order of events that have occurred in the system. This presents no difficulty for uniprocessor or tightly coupled systems, which have a common memory and a common clock. For distributed systems, however, there is no common clock and the delay which occurs in sending messages between processors means that these systems have two important properties:

- For any given sequence of events, it is impossible to prove that two different processes will observe, identically, the same sequence.

- As state changes can be viewed as events, it is impossible to prove that any two processes will have the same global view of a given subset of the system state. In Chapter 12, the notion of causal ordering of events was introduced to help solve this problem.

If processes in a distributed application are to coordinate and synchronize their activities in response to events as they occur, it is necessary to place a causal order on these events. For example, in order to detect deadlock between processes sharing resources, it is important to know that a process released resource A before requesting resource B. The algorithm presented here enables events in a distributed system to be ordered and is due to Lamport (1978).

Consider process P which executes the events $p0$, $p1$, $p2$, $p3$, $p4$ ... pn. As this is a sequential process the event $p0$ must have happened before event $p1$ which must have happened before event $p2$ and so on. This is written as $p0 \rightarrow p1 \rightarrow p2 \rightarrow ... \rightarrow pn$. Similarly for process $Q : q0 \rightarrow q1 \rightarrow q2 \rightarrow ... \rightarrow qn$. If these two processes are distributed and there is no communication between them, it is impossible to say whether $p0$ happened before or after $q0$, $q1$ and so on. Consider now the case where the event $p1$ is sending a message to Q, and $q3$ is the event which receives the message from P. Figure 14.12 illustrates this interaction.

As the act of receiving a message must occur *after* the message has been sent, then $p1 \rightarrow q3$, and as $q3 \rightarrow q4$, it follows that $p1 \rightarrow q4$ (that is, $p1$ could have a causal effect on $q4$). There is still no information as to whether $p0$ or $q0$ happened first. These events are termed **concurrent events** (as there is no causal ordering). As neither event can affect the other, it is of no real importance which one is considered to have occurred first. However, it is important that processes which make decisions based on this order all assume the same order.

To order all events totally in a distributed system, it is necessary to associate a *time-stamp* with each event. However, this is not a physical time-stamp but rather a logical time-stamp. Each processor in the system keeps a logical clock, which is incremented every time an event occurs on that processor. An event $p1$ in process P occurred before $p2$ in the same process if the value of the logical clock at $p1$ is less than the value of the logical clock at $p2$. Clearly, it is possible using this method for the logical clock associated with each process to get out of synchronization. For example, P's logical clock at $p1$ may be greater than Q's logical clock at $q3$; however, $p1$ must have occurred before $q3$ because a message cannot be received before it has been sent. To resolve this problem, it is necessary for every message sent between processes to carry the time-stamp of the event that sent the message. Furthermore, every time a process receives a message it must set its logical clock to a value which is the greater of its own value and:

- the time-stamp found in the message plus at least one – for asynchronous message passing; or

- the time-stamp – for synchronous message passing.

Figure 14.12   Two interacting processes.

This ensures that no message is received before it is sent.

Using the above algorithm, all events in the system have an associated time-stamp and can be partially ordered accordingly. If two events have the same time-stamp then it is sufficient to use an arbitrary condition, such as the numeric value of process identifiers, to give an artificial total order to the events.

14.6.2   Implementing global time

The approach to global ordering described above used logical clocks. An alternative scheme is to use a global time model based on physical time. This could be achieved by all nodes having access to a single time source, but it is more usual for nodes to have their own clocks. Hence it is necessary to coordinate these local clocks. There are many algorithms for doing this. All involve compensating for the inevitable clock drift that occurs even when clocks are notionally identical.

With quartz crystals, two clocks may drift apart by over one second in approximately six days. If timing events are significant at the millisecond level, drift becomes a problem after only eight minutes.

To bound clock drift, it is necessary to manipulate the time base at each node. Time must never move backwards and hence, although slow clocks can jump forward a defined number of ticks, fast clocks must be slowed down rather than be moved back-wards in time.

A clock coordination algorithm will provide a bound, Δ, on the maximum differ-ence between any two clocks (as would be perceived by an external reference clock). Event A can now be assumed to precede event B if (and only if):

$$t(A) \ + \ \Delta \ < \ t(B)$$

where $t(A)$ is the time of event A.

One way to achieve synchronization between nodes is for a central time server process, S, to supply the time according to its own clock upon request. The time server may be linked to an external time source or have a more accurate hardware clock. Alternatively, it may be an arbitrary node in the system that is deemed to be the source of system time. In a distributed system, communications are not instantaneous, and hence the time provided by S is subject to two sources of error – variability in the time taken for the message to be returned from S, and some non-determinism introduced by the responsiveness of the client once it receives the message. It is also important that S is not preempted between readings its clock and sending out the message.

To reduce the jitter introduced by the message round trip, S can periodically send out its 'time'. If, additionally, a high-priority message is used (and S itself has a high priority) then the other sources of variability can be minimized.

An alternative approach is for the client of S to send its own time reading with its message. Upon the receipt of a message, S looks at its clock and calculates a correction factor, δ:

$$\delta = t(client) + min - t(S)$$

where min is the minimum communication delay for the message from the client.

The correction factor is then transmitted back to the client. The transmission time of this second message is not time-critical. Upon receipt of this second message, the client will either advance its own clock by δ if its value is negative, or slow down its clock by this amount if δ is positive. The use of a single time source gives a simple scheme but is subject to the single point failure of S (or the node on which it is execut-ing). Other algorithms use a decentralized approach whereby all nodes broadcast their 'time' and a consensus vote is taken. Such a vote may omit outlying values. These clock synchronization algorithms must satisfy both an **agreement** and an **accuracy** property, where:

- the agreement condition is satisfied only if the skew between any two non-faulty clocks is bounded; and

- the accuracy condition is satisfied only if all non faulty clocks have a bounded drift with respect to real time.

14.6.3 Implementing stable storage

In many instances, it is necessary to have access to storage whose contents will survive a processor crash; this is called **stable storage**. As the main memory of any processor is volatile, it is necessary to use a disk (or any other form of non-volatile storage) as the stable storage device. Unfortunately, write operations to disks are not atomic in that the operation can crash part way through. When this happens, it is not possible for a recovery manager to determine whether the operation succeeded or not. To solve this problem, each block of data is stored twice on separate areas of the disk. These areas are chosen so that a head crash while reading one area will not destroy the other; if necessary, they can be on physically separate disk drives. It is assumed that the disk unit will indicate whether a single write operation completes successfully (using redundancy checks). The approach, in the absence of a processor failure, is to write the block of data to the first area of the disk (this operation may have to be repeated until it succeeds); only when this succeeds is the block written to the second area of the disk.

If a crash occurs while updating stable storage the following recovery routine can be executed.

```
read_block1;
read_block2;
if both_are_readable and block_1 = block2 then
    -- do nothing, the crash did not affect the stable storage
else
    if one_block_is_unreadable then
            -- copy good block to bad block
    else
        if both_are_readable_but_different then
                -- copy block1 to block2 (or visa versa)
        else
                -- a catastrophic failure has occurred and both
                -- blocks are unreadable
        end
    end;
end;
```

This algorithm will succeed even if there are subsequent crashes during its execution.

14.6.4 Reaching agreement in the presence of faulty processes

Early on in this chapter it was assumed that if a processor fails it fails silently. By this, it is meant that the processor effectively stops *all* execution and does not take part in communication with any other processors in the system. Indeed, even the algorithm for stable storage presented above assumes that a processor crash results in the processor immediately stopping its execution. Without this assumption, a malfunctioning processor might perform arbitrary state transitions and send spurious messages to other processors. Thus even a logically correct program could not be guaranteed to produce the desired result. This would make fault-tolerant systems seemingly impossible to achieve. Although every effort can be made to build processors that operate correctly in spite of component failure, *it is impossible* to guarantee this using a *finite* amount of hardware. Consequently, it is necessary to assume a bounded number of failures. This section considers the problem of how a group of processes executing on different processors can reach a consensus in the presence of a bounded number of faulty processes within the group. It is assumed that all communication is reliable (that is, sufficiently replicated to guarantee reliable service).

Byzantine generals problem

The problem of agreeing values between processes which may reside on faulty processors is often expressed as the **Byzantine Generals Problem** (Lamport et al., 1982). Several divisions of the Byzantine Army, each commanded by its own general, surround an enemy camp. The generals are able to communicate by messengers and must come to an agreement as to whether to attack the camp. To do this, each observes the enemy camp and communicates his or her observations to the others. Unfortunately, one or more of the generals may be traitors and liable to convey false information. The problem is for all loyal generals to obtain the same information. In general, $3m + 1$ generals can cope with m traitors if they have $m + 1$ rounds of message exchanges. For simplicity, the approach is illustrated with an algorithm for four generals that will cope with one traitor, and the following assumptions will be made:

(1) Every message that is sent is delivered correctly.

(2) The receiver of a message knows who sent it.

(3) The absence of a message can be detected.

The reader is referred to the literature for more general solutions (Pease et al., 1980; Lamport et al., 1982).

Consider general Gi and the information that he/she has observed Oi. Each general maintains a vector V of information he/she has received from the other generals. Initially Gi's vector contains only the value Oi; that is $Vi(j) = null(for\ i <> j)$ *and* $Vi(i) = Oi$. Each general sends a messenger to every other general indicating his or her observation; loyal generals will always send the correct observation; the traitor general may send a false observation and may send different false observations to different generals. On receiving the observations, each general updates his or her vector and then sends the value of the other three's observations to the other generals. Clearly, the traitor may send observations different from the ones he or she has received, or nothing at all. In the latter case, the generals can choose an arbitrary value.

After this exchange of messages, each loyal general can construct a vector from the majority value of the three values it has received for each general's observation. If no majority exists then they assume, in effect, that no observations have been made.

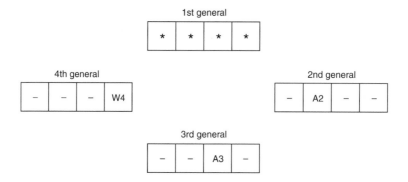

Figure 14.13   Byzantine generals – initial state.

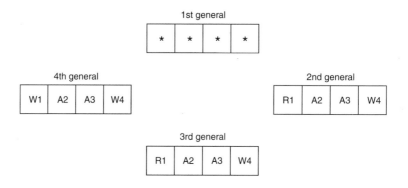

Figure 14.14   Byzantine generals – state after first message exchange.

For example, suppose that the observations of a general lead him or her to one of three conclusions: attack (A), retreat (R), or wait (W). Consider the case where $G1$ is a traitor, $G2$ concludes attack, $G3$: attack and $G4$: wait. Initially the state of each vector is given in Figure 14.13.

The index into the vector (1..4) gives the General number, the contents of the item at that index gives the observation from that general and who reported the observation. Initially then the fourth general stores 'Wait' in the fourth element of its vector indicating that the observation came from him- or herself. Of course, in the general case it might not be possible to authenticate who reported the observation. However, in this example it will be assumed that the traitor is not that devious.

After the first exchange of messages, the vectors are (assuming that the traitor realises the camp is vulnerable and sends the retreat and wait messages randomly to all

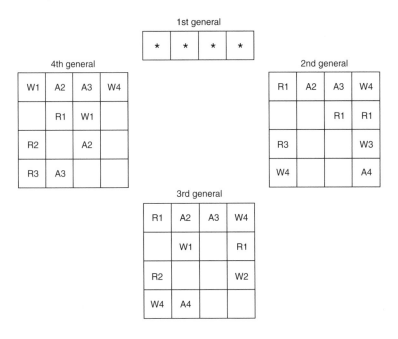

Figure 14.15   Byzantine generals – second message exchange

generals) shown in Figure 14.14. After the second exchange of messages, Figure 14.15 gives the information which is available to each general (again assuming the traitor sends retreat and wait messages randomly).

To illustrate how this table has been derived, consider the final row for the fourth general. This has been obtained, allegedly, from the third general (as the 3 indicates) and includes information about the decisions of the first and the second generals. Hence R3 in the first column indicates that the third general is of the view that the first general wishes to retreat.

Figure 14.16 gives a final (majority) vector. Loyal generals have a consistent view of each others' observations and, therefore, can make a uniform decision.

If it is possible to restrict the actions of the traitors further (that is, a stricter failure model), then the number of generals (processors) required to tolerate m traitors (failures) can be reduced. For example, if a traitor is unable to modify a loyal general's observation (say, he or she must pass a signed copy of the observation and the signature cannot be forged or modified), then only $2m + 1$ generals (processors) are required.

Using solutions to the Byzantine General problem, it is possible to construct a fail-silent processor by having internally replicated processors carry out a Byzantine agreement (Schneider, 1984). If the non-faulty processors detect a disagreement they stop execution.

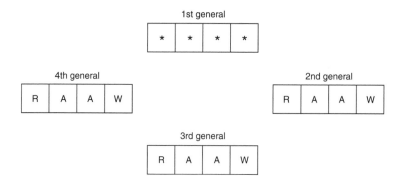

Figure 14.16   Byzantine generals – final state.

14.7   Deadline scheduling in a distributed environment

Having considered a number of distributed architectures, communication protocols and algorithms, it is now possible to return to the key issue of understanding the temporal behaviour of applications built upon a distributed environment. Here, parts of the system can be making progress at different rates and communication delays become significant. Not only must the time of the environment be linked to that of the computer system, but the different processors/nodes need to have some form of time linkage. The term **synchronous** is used (in this context) to designate a distributed system that has the following properties:

- There is an upper bound on message delays; this consists of the time it takes to send, transport and receive a message over some communications link.

- Every processor has a local clock, and there is a bounded drift rate between any two clocks.

- The processors themselves make progress at a minimum rate at least.

Note that this does not imply that faults cannot occur. Rather, the upper bound on message delay is taken to apply only when non-faulty processor are communicating over a non-faulty link. Indeed, the existence of the upper bound can be used to provide failure detection.

A system that does not have any of the above three properties is called **asynchronous**.

In this section only synchronous systems are considered. Two main topics will be investigated. First will be the issue of allocating processes to processors, and then the scheduling of communications will be discussed.

14.7.1 Allocation

The development of appropriate scheduling schemes for distributed (and multiprocessor) systems is problematic. Graham (1969) showed that multiprocessor systems can behave quite unpredictably in terms of the timing behaviour they exhibit. He used dynamic allocation (that is, processes are assigned to processors as they become runnable), and was able to illustrate the following anomalies:

- Decreasing the execution time of some process, P, could lead to it having an increased response time.

- Increasing the priority of process, P, could lead to it having an increased response time.

- Increasing the number of processors could lead to P having an increased response time.

All of these results are clearly counter-intuitive.

Mok and Dertouzos (1978) showed that the algorithms that are optimal for single processor systems are not optimal for increased numbers of processors. Consider, for example, three periodic processes P_1, P_2 and P_3 that must be executed on two processors. Let P_1 and P_2 have identical deadline requirements, namely a period and deadline of 50 time units and an execution requirement (per cycle) of 25 units; let P_3 have requirements of 100 and 80. If the rate monotonic algorithm (discussed in Chapter 13) is used, P_1 and P_2 will have highest priority and will run on the two processors (in parallel) for their required 25 units. This will leave P_3 with 80 units of execution to accomplish in the 75 units that are available. The fact that P_3 has two processors available is irrelevant (one will remain idle). As a result of applying the rate monotonic algorithm, P_3 will miss its deadline even though average processor utilization is only 65%. However, an allocation that maps P_1 and P_2 to one processor and P_3 to the other easily meets all deadlines.

Other examples can show that the earliest deadline first (EDF) formulation is similarly non-optimal. This difficulty with the optimal uniprocessor algorithms is not surprising as it is known that optimal scheduling for multiprocessor systems is NP-hard (Graham et al., 1979). It is, therefore, necessary to look for ways of simplifying the problem and to provide algorithms that give adequate sub-optimal results.

Allocation of periodic processes

The above discussion showed that judicious allocation of processes can significantly affect schedulability. Consider another example; this time let four processes be executing on the two processors, and let their cycle times be 10, 10, 14 and 14. If the two 10s are allocated to the same processor (and by implication the two 14s to the other) then 100% processor utilization can be achieved. The system is schedulable even if execution times for the four processes are 5, 5, 10 and 4 (say). However, if a 10 and a 14 were placed together on the same processor (as a result of dynamic allocation) then maximum utilization drops to 83%.

What this example appears to show is that it is better to allocate periodic processes statically rather than let them migrate and, as a consequence, unbalance the allocation and potentially downgrade the system's performance. Even on a tightly coupled system running a single run-time dispatcher, it is better to keep processes on the same processor rather than try to utilize an idle processor (and risk unbalancing the allocation).

If static deployment is used, then the deadline monotonic algorithm (or other optimal uniprocessor schemes) can test for schedulability on each processor. In performing the allocation, processes that are harmonically related should be deployed together (that is, to the same processor) as this will help increase utilization.

Allocation of sporadic and aperiodic processes

As it appears expedient to allocate periodic processes statically, a similar approach to sporadic processes would seem to be a useful model to employ. If all processes are statically mapped then the algorithms discussed in Chapter 13 can be used on each processor (that is, each processor, in effect, runs its own scheduler/dispatcher).

To calculate execution times (worst case or average) requires knowledge of potential blocking. Blocking within the local processor can be bounded by inheritance or ceiling protocols. However, in a multiprocessor system there is another form of blocking: this is when a processes is delayed by a process on another processor. This is called remote blocking and is not easily bounded. In a distributed system, remote blocking can be eliminated by adding processes to manage the distribution of data. For example, rather than be blocked waiting to read some data from a remote site, an extra process could be added to the remote site whose role is to forward the data to where it is needed. The data is thus available locally. This type of modification to a design can be done systematically; however, it does complicate the application (but does lead to a simpler scheduling model).

One of the drawbacks of a purely static allocation policy is that no benefits can be gained from spare capacity in one processor when another is experiencing a transient overload. For hard real-time systems, each processor would need to be able to deal with worst-case execution times for its periodic processes, and maximum arrival times and execution times for its sporadic load. To improve on this situation Stankovic et al. (1985) and Ramamritham and Stankovic (1984) have proposed more flexible task scheduling algorithms.

In their approach, all safety critical periodic and sporadic processes are statically allocated but non-critical aperiodic processes can migrate. The following protocol is used:

- Each aperiodic process arrives at some node in the network.

- The node at which the aperiodic process arrives checks to see if this new process can be scheduled together with the existing load. If it can, the process is said to be guaranteed by this node.

- If the node cannot guarantee the new processes, it looks for alternative nodes that may be able to guarantee it. It does this using knowledge of the state of the whole network and by bidding for spare capacity in other nodes.

- The process is thus moved to a new node where there is a high probability that it will be scheduled. However, because of race conditions, the new node may not be able to schedule it once it has arrived. Hence the guarantee test is undertaken locally; if the process fails the test then it must move again.

- In this way, an aperiodic process is either scheduled (guaranteed) or it fails to meet its deadline.

The usefulness of their approach is enhanced by the use of a linear heuristic algorithm for determining where a non-guaranteed process should move. This heuristic is not computationally expensive (unlike the optimal algorithm, which is NP-hard), but does give a high degree of success; that is, there is a high probability that the use of the heuristic will lead to an aperiodic process being scheduled (if it is schedulable at all).

The cost of executing the heuristic algorithm and moving the aperiodic processes is taken into account by the guarantee routine. Nevertheless, the scheme is workable only if aperiodic processes can be moved, and that this movement is efficient. Some aperiodic processes may be tightly coupled to hardware unique to one node and will have at least some component that must execute locally.

14.7.2 Scheduling access to communications links

Communication between processes on different machines in a distributed system requires messages to be transmitted and received on the underlying communication subsystem. In general, these messages will have to compete with each other to gain access to the network medium (for example, switch, bus or ring). In order for hard real-time processes to meet their deadlines, it will be necessary to schedule access to the communication subsystem in a manner which is consistent with the scheduling of processes on each processor. If this is not the case then priority inversion may occur when a high-priority process tries to access the communications link. Standard protocols such as those associated with Ethernet do not support hard deadline traffic, as they tend to queue messages in a FIFO order or use non-predictable back-off algorithms when there is a message collision.

Although the communication link is just another resource, there are at least four issues which distinguish the link scheduling problem from processor scheduling.

- Unlike a processor, which has a single point of access, a communications channel has many points of access – one for each attached physical node. A distributed protocol is therefore required.

- While preemptive algorithms are appropriate for scheduling processes on a single processor, preemption during message transmission will mean that the entire message will need retransmitting.

- In addition to the deadlines imposed by the application processes, deadlines may also be imposed by buffer availability – the contents of a buffer must be transmitted before new data can be placed in it.

Although many *ad hoc* approaches are used in distributed environments there are at least three schemes that do allow for predictable behaviour. These will now be briefly discussed.

TDMA

The natural extension to using a cyclic executive for uniprocessor scheduling, is to use a cyclic approach to communications. If all application processes are periodic, it is possible to produce a communications protocol that is slotted by time. Such protocols are call TDMA (Time Division Multiple Access). Each node has a clock that is synchronized to all other node clocks. During a communications cycle, each node is allocated time slots in which it can communicate. These are synchronized to the execution slots of each node's cyclic executive. No message collisions can occur, as each node knows when it can write and, moreover, each node knows when there is a message available that it needs to read.

The difficulty with the TDMA approach come from constructing the schedule. This difficulty increases exponentially with the number of nodes in the system. One architecture that has shown considerable success in using TDMA is the TTA (Time Triggered Architecture) (Kopetz, 1997). It uses a complex graph reduction heuristic to construct the schedules. The other drawback of TDMA is that it is difficult to plan when sporadic messages can be communicated.

Timed token-passing schemes

One approach for generalizing away from a purely time-slotted approach is to use a token-passing scheme. Here a special message (the **token**) is passed from node to node. Nodes can send out messages only when they hold the token. As there is only one token, no message collisions can occur. Each node can hold the token only for a maximum time, and hence there is a bounded **token rotation time**.

A number of protocols use this approach. An example being the fibre optic FDDI (Fiber Distributed Data Interface) protocol. Here messages are grouped into two classes called, confusingly, synchronous and asynchronous. Synchronous messages have hard time constraints and are used to define each node's token-holding time and hence the *target token rotation time*. Asynchronous messages are not deemed to have hard constraints; they can be communicated by a node if either it has no synchronous messages to send or the token has arrived early (because other nodes have had nothing to transmit). The worst-case behaviour of this protocol occurs when a message arrives at a node just as the token is being passed on. Moreover, up to that time no node has transmitted messages, and hence the token is being delivered very early. After the token has been passed on from the node with the new synchronous message, the rest of the nodes now have lots of messages to send. The first node sends its synchronous load and, as the token arrived very early, sends a full set of asynchronous messages; all subsequent nodes send their synchronous load. By the time the token arrives back at the node of interest, a time interval equal to twice the *target token rotation time* has passed. This is the bounded delivery time.

Priority-based protocols

Given the benefits that have been derived from using priority-based scheduling on processors, it is reasonable to assume that a priority-based approach to message scheduling would be useful. Such protocols tend to have two phases. In the first phase, each node indicates the priority of the message it wishes to transmit. This is obviously the maximum priority of the set of messages it may have outstanding. At the end of this first phase, one node has gained the right to transmit its message. The second phase is simply the communication of this message. In some protocols, the two phases can overlap (that is, while one message is being broadcast, parts of the message are modified so that the priority of the next message is determined).

While priority-based protocols have been defined for some time, they have tended to have the disadvantage that only a small range of priorities have been supported by communication protocols. They have been used to distinguish between broad classes of messages rather than for message scheduling. As indicated in Chapter 13, the best results of priority-based scheduling occur when each process (or message in this discussion) has a distinct priority. Fortunately, there are some protocols that do now provide for a large priority field. One example is CAN (Controller Area Network) (Tindell et al., 1995).

In CAN 2.0A, an 8 byte message is preceded by an 11 bit identifier that acts as a priority. At the start of a transmission sequence, each node writes (simultaneously) to the broadcast bus the first bit of its maximum priority message identifier. The CAN protocol acts like a large AND gate; if any node writes a 0 then all nodes read a 0. The 0 bit is said to be *dominant*. The protocol proceeds as follows (for each bit of the identifier):

- If a node transmits a zero it continues on to the next bit.
- If a node transmits a one and reads back a one then it continues on to the next bit.
- If a node transmits a one and reads back a zero, it backs off and takes no further part in this transmission round.

The lower the value of the identifier the higher the priority. As identifiers are unique, the protocol is forced to end up with just one node left in after the 11 rounds of bitwise arbitration. This node then transmits its message.

The value of CAN is that it is a genuine priority-based protocol and hence all the analysis presented in Chapter 13 can be applied. The disadvantage of the type of protocol used by CAN is that it restricts the speed of communication. In order for all nodes to write their identifiers' bits 'at the same time' and for them all to read the subsequent ANDed value (and act on this value before sending out, or not, the next bit) there must be a severe bound on the transmission speed. This bound is actually a function of the length of the wire used to transmit the bits, and hence CAN is not suitable for geographically dispersed environments. It was actually designed for the informatics within modern automobiles – where it is having considerable success.

ATM

ATM can be used across both wide area and local area networks. The goal is to support a wide range of communication requirements such as those needed for voice and video as well as data transmission. ATM supports point-to-point communication via one or more switches. Typically, each computer in the network is connected to a switch via two optical fibres: one taking traffic to the switch, the other relaying traffic from the switch.

All data to be transmitted is divided into fixed-sized packets call **cells**, where each cell has a 5-byte header and a 48-byte data field. Applications communicate via **virtual channels** (VC). The data to be transmitted on a particular VC can have certain timing behaviour associated with it, such as its bit rate, period or its deadline. An **adaptation layer** provides specific services to support the particular class of user data; the precise behaviour of this layer is variable to suit the data transmission needs of a particular system. It is within the adaption layer that end-to-end error correction and synchronization, and the segmentation and reassembly of user data into the ATM cells are performed.

A typical ATM network will contain multiple switches, each of which has an associated cell queuing policy - the basic FIFO policy was employed in most early commercial switches, but some now cater for priority-based queuing. Within an individual switch, a set of connections may be established between a number of switch input ports and output ports according to a connection table. Queuing of cells may occur at input and/or output ports.

A common approach taken in a real-time ATM solution is as follows:

- Pre-define all VC timing requirements;

- Pre-define the route and hence the network resources allocated to each VC;

- Control the total bandwidth required by each VC at each network resource through which it is routed;

- Calculate the resulting delays and hence assess the feasibility of a particular allocation of VCs to the network hardware.

The control of bandwidth usage by each VC is required in order to avoid congestion in the network. The motivation for this is to support predictable behaviour of each VC and consequently the network as a whole. When congestion is present, ATM cells are at risk of being discarded (under the normal rules of the ATM layer protocol) and worst-case delays are difficult to predict without excessive pessimism (allowing for detection of lost cells and possible retransmission).

14.7.3   Holistic scheduling

A reasonably large distributed real-time system may contain tens of processors and two or three distinct communication channels. Both the processor and the communication subsystems can be scheduled so that the worst-case timing behaviour is predictable. This is facilitated by a static approach to allocation. Having analyzed each component of the system it is then possible to link the predictions together to check compliance with system-wide timing requirements (Tindell and Clark, 1994; Palencia Gutierrez and Gonzalez Harbour, 1998; Palencia Gutierrez and Gonzalez Harbour, 1999). In addressing this *holistic scheduling* problem, two important factors need to be taken into consideration:

- Will variability in the behaviour of one component adversely affect the behaviour of another part of the system?
- Will the simple summation of each component's worst-case behaviour lead to pessimistic predictions?

The amount of variability will depend upon the approach to scheduling. If a purely time-triggered approach is used (that is, cyclic executives linked via TDMA channels), there is little room for deviation from the repeating behaviour. However, if priority-based scheduling is employed on the processors and channels then there could be considerable variation. For example, consider a sporadic process released by the execution of a periodic process on another node. On average the sporadic process will execute at the same rate as the periodic process (say, every 50 ms). But the periodic process (and the subsequent communication message to release the sporadic) will not take place at exactly the same time each period. It may be that the process executes relatively late on one invocation but earlier on the next. As a result the sporadic may be released for the second time only 30 ms after its previous release. To model the sporadic as a periodic process with a period of 50 ms would be incorrect and could lead to a false conclusion that all deadlines can be satisfied. Fortunately, this variability in release time can be accurately modelled using the release jitter analysis give in Section 13.12.2.

Whereas the response time analysis introduced for single processor scheduling is necessary and sufficient (that is, gives an accurate picture of the true behaviour of the processor), holistic scheduling can be pessimistic. This occurs when the worst-case behaviour on one subsystem implies that less than worst case will be experienced on some other component. Often only simulation studies will allow the level of pessimism to be determined (statistically). Further research is needed to accurately determine the effectiveness of holistic scheduling.

A final issue to note with holistic scheduling is that support can be given to the allocation problem. Static allocation seems to be the most appropriate to use. But deriving the best static allocation is still an NP-hard problem. Many heuristics have been considered for this problem. More recently, search techniques such as simulated annealing and genetic algorithms have been applied to the holistic scheduling problem. These have proved to be quite successful; and can be easily extended to systems that are replicated for fault tolerance (where it is necessary to come up with allocations that assign replicas to different components).

Summary

This chapter defined a distributed computer system to be a collection of autonomous processing elements, cooperating in a common purpose or to achieve a common goal. Some of the issues which arise when considering distributed applications raise fundamental questions that go beyond simple aspects of implementation. They are: language support, reliability, distributed control algorithms and deadline scheduling.

Language support

The production of a distributed software system to execute on a distributed hardware system involves: **partitioning** – the process of dividing the system into parts (units of distribution) suitable for placement onto the processing elements of the target system; **configuration** – associating the partitioned components with particular processing elements in the target system; **allocation** – the actual process of turning the configured system into a collection of executable modules and downloading these to the processing elements; **transparent execution** – executing the distributed software so that remote resources are accessed in a manner which is independent of their location (usually via remote procedure call); and **reconfiguration** – changing the location of a software component or resource.

Occam2, although designed for use in a distributed environment, is fairly low-level; the process is the unit of partitioning; configuration is explicit in the language but neither allocation nor reconfiguration are supported. Furthermore, remote access to resources is not transparent.

Ada allows collection of library units to be grouped into 'partitions' which communicate via remote procedure calls and remote objects. Neither configuration, nor allocation nor reconfiguration are supported directly by the language.

Java allows objects to be distributed which can communication via remote procedure calls or via sockets. None of configuration, allocation or reconfiguration is supported directly by the language.

CORBA facilitates distributed objects and interoperability between applications written in different languages for different platforms supported by middleware software from different vendors.

Reliability

Although the availability of multiple processors enables the application to become tolerant of processor failure, it also introduces the possibility of new types of faults occurring which would not be present in a centralized single-processor system. In particular, multiple processors introduce the concept of a partial system failure. Furthermore, the communication media may lose, corrupt, or change the order of messages.

Communication between processes across machine boundaries requires layers of protocols so that transient error conditions can be tolerated. Standards have been defined to support these layers of protocols. The OSI Reference Model is a layered model consisting of the Application, Presentation, Session Transport, Network, Data Link and Physical layers. It was developed primarily for wide area networks to enable open access; wide area networks were characterized by low-bandwidth communication with high error rates. TCP/IP is another protocol reference model aimed primarily at wide area networks. Most distributed embedded systems will, however, use local area network technology and will be closed to the outside world. Local area networks are characterized by high-bandwidth communication with low error rates. Consequently, although it is possible to implement language-level interprocess communication using the OSI approach, in practice the expense is often prohibitive. Thus, many designers tailor the communication protocols to the requirements of the language (the application) and the communication medium. These are called lightweight protocols.

When groups of processes are interacting, it is necessary for communication to be sent to the whole group. A **multicast** communication paradigm provides such a facility. It is possible to design a family of group communication protocols, each of which provides a multicast communication facility with specific guarantees: **unreliable multicast** – no guarantees of delivery to the group is provided; **reliable multicast** – the protocol makes a best-effort attempt to deliver the message to the group; **atomic multicast** – the protocol guarantees that if one process in the group receives the message then all members of the group receive the message; **ordered atomic multicast** – as well as guaranteeing the atomicity of the multicast, the protocol also guarantees that all members of the group will receive messages from different senders in the same order.

Processor failure can be tolerated through static or dynamic redundancy. Static redundancy involves replicating application components on different processors. The degree of replication can be varied according to the importance of a particular component. One of the problems of providing fault tolerance transparently to the application is that it is impossible for the programmer to specify degraded or safe execution. The alternative to static redundancy is to allow processor failure to be handled dynamically by the application programmer. This requires: the failure of the processor to be detected and communicated to the remaining processors in the system; the damage that has occurred must then be assessed; using these results the remaining software must agree on a response and carry out the necessary actions to effect that response; and as soon as is practicable the failed processor and/or its associated software must be repaired and the system returned to its normal error free state. Few of the real-time programming languages provide adequate facilities to cope with dynamic reconfiguration after processor failure.

Distributed control algorithms

The presence of true parallelism in an application together with physically distributed processors and the possibility that processors and communication links may fail, require many new algorithms for resource control. The following algorithms were considered: event ordering, stable storage implementation, and Byzantine agreement protocols. Many distributed algorithms assume that processors are "fail-stop"; this means either they work correctly or they halt immediately a fault occurs.

Deadline scheduling

Unfortunately, the general problem of dynamically allocating processes to processors (so that system-wide deadlines are met) is computationally expensive. It is therefore necessary to implement a less flexible allocation scheme. One rigid approach is to deploy all processes statically or to allow only the non-critical ones to migrate.

Once processors have been allocated, it is necessary to schedule the communications medium. TDMA, timed token passing and priority-based scheduling are appropriate real-time communication protocols. Finally, end-to-end timing requirements must be verified by considering the holistic scheduling of the entire system.

Further reading

Brown, C. (1994) *Distributed Programming with Unix*. Englewood Cliffs, NJ: Prentice Hall.

Comer, D. E. (1999) *Computer Networks and Internets*. New York: Prentice Hall.

Coulouris, G. F., Dollimore, J. and Kindberg, T. (2000) *Distributed Systems, Concepts and Design*, 3rd Edition. Harlow: Addison-Wesley.

Farley, J. (1998) *Java Distributed Computing*. Sebastopol, CA: O'Reilly.

Harold, E. (1997) *Java Network Programming*. Sebastopol, CA: O'Reilly.

Halsall, F. (1995) *Data Communications, Computer Networks and OSI* 2nd Edition. Reading, MA: Addison-Wesley.

Hoque, R. (1998) *CORBA 3*. Foster City, CA: IDG Books Worldwide.

Horstmann, C. S. and Cornell, G. (2000) *Core Java 2, Volume II – Advanced Features*. Sun Microsystems.

Kopetz, H. (1997) *Real-Time Systems: Design Principles for Distributed Embedded Applications*: New York: Kluwer International.

Lynch, N. (1996) *Distributed Algorithms*. San Mateo, CA: Morgan Kaufmann.

Mullender, S. (ed.) (1993) *Distributed Systems*, 2nd Edition. Reading, MA: Addison-Wesley.

Tanenbaum, A. S. (1994) *Distributed Operating Systems*. Englewood Cliffs, NJ: Prentice Hall.

Tanenbaum, A. S. (1998), *Computer Networks*. Englewood Cliffs, NJ: Prentice Hall.

Exercises

14.1 Discuss some of the *disadvantages* of distributed systems.

14.2 Ada supports a Real-Time Systems Annex and a Distributed Systems Annex. Discuss the extent to which these two annexes constitute a Distributed Real-Time Systems Annex.

14.3 From a data abstraction viewpoint, discuss why variables should not be visible in the interface to a remote object.

14.4 Consider the implications of having timed and conditional entry calls in a distributed Ada environment.

14.5 The following occam2 process has five input channels and three output channels. All integers received down the input channels are output to all output channels:

```
INT I,J,temp:
WHILE TRUE
  ALT I = 1 FOR 5
    in[I] ? temp
      PAR J = 1 FOR 3
        out[J] ! temp
```

Because this process has an eight channel interface it cannot be implemented on a single transputer unless its client processes are on the same transputer. Transform the code so that it can be implemented on three transputers. (Assume a transputer has only four links.)

14.6 Compare and contrast the Ada, Java and CORBA remote object models.

14.7 To what extent can CORBA's Message Passing Services be implemented in Java?

14.8 Sketch the layers of communication that are involved when the French delegate at the United Nations Security Council wishes to talk to the Russian delegate. Assume that there are interpreters who translate into a common language (say English) and then pass on the message to telephone operators. Does this layered communication follow the ISO OSI model?

14.9 Why do the semantics of remote procedure calls differ from the semantics of ordinary procedure calls?

14.10 If the OSI network layer is used to implement an RPC facility, should a datagram or a virtual circuit service be used?

14.11 Compare and contrast the stable storage and replicated data approaches for achieving reliable system data which will survive a processor failure.

14.12 Redo the Byzantine Generals problem given in Section 14.6.4 with G1 as the traitor, G2 concluding retreat, G3 concluding wait and G4 concluding attack.

14.13 Given the choice between an Ethernet and a token ring as the real-time communication subsystem, which should be used if deterministic access under heavy loads is the primary concern?

14.14 Update the algorithm given in Section 10.8.2 for forward error recovery in a distributed system

Chapter 15
Low-level programming

One of the main characteristics of an embedded system is the requirement that it interacts with special-purpose input and output (I/O) devices. Unfortunately, there are many different types of device interfaces and control mechanisms. This is mainly because: different computers provide different methods of interfacing with devices; different devices have separate requirements for their control; and similar devices from different manufacturers have different interfaces and control requirements.

   To provide a rationale for the high-level language facilities needed to program low-level devices, one must understand the basic hardware I/O functions. Therefore this chapter considers these mechanisms first, then deals with language features in general, and finally gives details of particular languages.

   Embedded systems often have limited memory capacity. Consequently, the programmer must ensure that the compiler allocates only the memory needed for the job in hand. Furthermore, dynamic memory allocation must be carefully controlled to ensure that time-critical code is not preempted by the inopportune execution of system functions such as a garbage collector.

15.1   Hardware input/output mechanisms

As far as input and output devices are concerned, there are two general classes of computer architecture: one with a logically separate bus for memory and I/O and the other with memory and I/O devices on the same logical bus. These are represented diagrammatically in Figures 15.1 and 15.2.

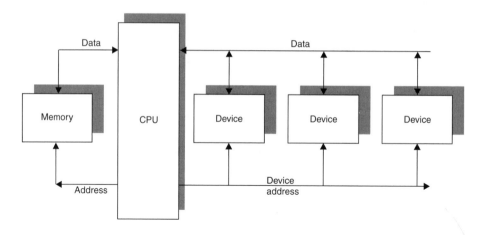

Figure 15.1   Architecture with separate buses.

The interface to a device is normally through a set of registers. With logically separate buses for memory and I/O devices, the computer must have two sets of assembly instructions: one for accessing memory and one for accessing device registers. The latter normally take the form of:

```
IN    AC, PORT
OUT   AC, PORT
```

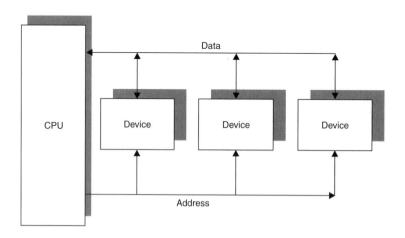

Figure 15.2   Memory-mapped architecture

Where IN reads the contents of the device register identified by PORT into the accumulator AC, and OUT writes the contents of the accumulator to the device register. (The term PORT is used here to indicate an address on the I/O device bus.) There may also be other instructions for reading a device's status. The Intel 486 and the Pentium are examples of an architecture which allows devices to be accessed via special instructions.

With devices on the same logical bus, certain addresses will access a memory location and others will access a device. This approach is called **memory-mapped I/O**. The Motorola M68000 and PowerPC range of computers have memory mapped I/O.

It is necessary to interface with a device in order to control the device's operations (for example, initializing the device and preparing the device for the transfer of data) and to control the data transfer (for example, initiating or performing the data transfer). It is possible to describe two general mechanisms for performing and controlling input/output; these are status-driven control mechanisms and interrupt-driven control mechanisms.

15.1.1 Status driven

With this type of control mechanism, a program performs explicit tests in order to determine the status of a given device. Once the status of the device has been determined, the program is able to carry out the appropriate actions. Typically there are three kinds of hardware instruction supporting this type of mechanism. These are:

- test operations that enable the program to determine the status of the given device;
- control operations that direct the device to perform non-transfer device dependent actions such as positioning disk read heads;
- I/O operations that perform the actual transfer of data between the device and the CPU.

Although devices with status-driven I/O were common a few years ago, as they were inexpensive, nowadays, because of the continuing decrease in hardware cost, most devices are interrupt-driven. However, interrupts can of course be turned off and polling of device status used instead. Interrupts also add to the non-deterministic behaviour of real-time systems and are sometimes prohibited on safety grounds – for example if it is not possible to bound the number of interrupts.

15.1.2 Interrupt-driven

Even with the interrupt-driven mechanism, there are many possible variations depending on how the transfers need to be initiated and controlled. Three of these variations are: interrupt-driven program-controlled, interrupt-driven program-initiated, and interrupt-driven channel-program controlled.

Interrupt-driven program-controlled

Here, a device requests an interrupt as a result of encountering certain events, for example the arrival of data. When the request is acknowledged, the processor suspends the executing process and invokes a designated interrupt-handling process which performs appropriate actions in response to the interrupt. When the interrupt-handling process has performed its function, the state of the processor is restored to its state prior to the interrupt, and control of the processor is returned to the suspended process.

Interrupt-driven program-initiated

This type of input/output mechanism is often referred to as **Direct Memory Access** (or DMA). A DMA device is positioned between the input/output device and main memory. The DMA device takes the place of the processor in the transfer of data between the I/O device and memory. Although the I/O is initiated by the program, the DMA device controls the actual transfers of data (one block at a time). For each piece of data to be transferred, a request is made by the DMA device for a memory cycle and the transfer is made when the request is granted. When the transfer of the entire block is completed, a *transfer complete* interrupt is generated by the device. This is handled by the interrupt-driven program-controlled mechanism.

The term **cycle stealing** is often used to refer to the impact that DMA devices have on the access to memory. It can lead to non-deterministic behaviour and makes it very difficult to calculate the worst-case execution time of a program (see Section 13.7).

Interrupt-driven channel-program controlled

Channel-program controlled input/output extends the concept of program-initiated input-output by eliminating as much as possible the involvement of the central processor in the handling of input/output devices. The mechanism consists of three major components: the hardware channel and connected devices, the channel program (often called a 'script') and the input/output instructions.

The hardware channel's operations include those of the DMA devices given above. In addition, the channel directs device control operations as instructed by the channel program. The execution of channel programs is initiated from within the application. Once a channel has been instructed to execute a channel program, the selected channel and device proceed independent of the central processor until the specified channel program has been completed or some exceptional condition has occurred. Channel programs normally consist of one or more channel control words which are decoded and executed one at a time by the channel.

In many respects, a hardware channel can be viewed as an autonomous processor sharing memory with the central processor. Its impact on memory access times of the central processor can be unpredictable (as with DMA devices).

15.1.3   Elements required for interrupt-driven devices

As can be seen from the foregoing section, the role of interrupts in controlling input/output is an important one. They allow input/output to be performed asynchronously and so avoid the 'busy waiting' or constant status checking that is necessary if a purely status-controlled mechanism is used.

In order to support interrupt-driven input and output, the following mechanisms are required.

Context-switching mechanisms

When an interrupt occurs, the current processor state must be preserved and the appropriate service routine activated. Once the interrupt has been serviced, the original process is resumed and execution continues. Alternatively, a new process may be selected by the scheduler as a consequence of the interrupt. This whole process is known as **context switching** and its actions can be summarized as follows:

- preserving the state of the processor immediately prior to the occurrence of the interrupt;
- placing the processor in the required state for processing the interrupt;
- restoring the suspended process state after the interrupt processing has been completed.

The state of the process executing on a processor consists of:

- the memory address of the current (or next) instruction in the execution sequence;
- the program status information (this may contain information concerning the mode of processing, current priority, memory protection, allowed interrupts, and so on);
- the contents of the programmable registers.

The type of context switching provided can be characterized by the extent of the process state preservation, and restoration, that is performed by the hardware. Three levels of context switching can be distinguished:

- basic – just the program counter is saved and a new one loaded;
- partial – the program counter and the program status registers are saved and new ones loaded;
- complete – the full context of the process is saved and a new context loaded.

Depending on the degree of processor state preservation required, it may be necessary to supplement the actions of the hardware by explicit software support. For example, a partial context switch may be adequate for an interrupt-handling model which views the handler as a procedure or subroutine. However, if the handler is viewed as being a separate process with its own stack and data areas, there will need to be a low-level handler which does a full context switch between the interrupted process and the handling process. If, on the other hand, the hardware undertakes a full context switch, no such low-level handler is required. Most processors provide only a partial context switch. However, the ARM processor does supply a fast interrupt where some of the general-purpose registers are also saved.

It should be noted, some modern processors allow instructions to be fetched, decoded and executed in parallel. Some also allow instructions to be executed out of order from that specified in the program. This chapter will assume that interrupts are **precise** (Walker and Cragon, 1995) in that, when an interrupt handler executes:

- all instructions issued before the interrupted instruction have finished executing and modified the program state correctly;
- instructions issued after the interrupted instruction have not been executed and no program state has been modified;
- if the interrupted instruction itself caused the interrupt (for example, an instruction which causes memory violation) then either the instruction has been completely executed or not executed at all.

If an interrupt is not precise, it is assumed that the recovery is transparent to the interrupt handling software. See Walker and Cragon (1995) for a taxonomy of interrupt handling.

Interrupting device identification

Devices differ in the way they must be controlled; consequently, they will require different interrupt-handling routines. In order to invoke the appropriate handler, some means of identifying the interrupting device must exist. Four interrupting device identification mechanisms can be distinguished: vectored, status, polling and high-level language primitive.

A **vectored** mechanism for identifying the interrupting device consists of a set of dedicated (and usually contiguous) memory locations called an **interrupt vector** and a hardware mapping of device addresses onto the interrupt vector. An interrupt vector may be used by one particular device or may be shared by several devices. The programmer must associate a particular interrupt vector location explicitly with an interrupt-service routine. This may be done either by setting the vector location to the address of the service routine, or by setting it to an instruction that causes a branch to occur to the required routine. In this way, the service routine is directly tied to an interrupt vector location, which in turn is indirectly tied to a device or set of devices. Therefore, when a particular service routine is invoked and executed, the interrupting device has been implicitly identified.

A **status** mechanism for identifying an interrupting device is used for machine configurations on which several devices are connected to a device controller and they do not have unique interrupt vectors. It is also used in the case where a generalized service routine will initially handle all interrupts. With this mechanism, each interrupt has an associated status word which specifies the device causing the interrupt and the reason for the interrupt (among other things). The status information may be provided automatically by the hardware in a dedicated memory location for a given interrupt or class of interrupts, or it may need to be retrieved by means of some appropriate instruction.

The **polling** device identification mechanism is the simplest of all. When an interrupt occurs, a general interrupt-service routine is invoked to handle the interrupt. The status of each device is interrogated in order to determine which device has requested the interrupt. When the interrupting device has been identified, the interrupt is serviced in the appropriate manner.

With some modern computer architectures, interrupt handling is directly associated with a **high-level language primitive**. With these systems, an interrupt is often viewed as a synchronization message down an associated channel. In this case, the device is identified by the channel which becomes active.

Interrupt identification

Once the device has been identified, the appropriate interrupt-handling routine must determine why it generated the interrupt. In general, this can be supplied either by status information provided by the device or by having different interrupts from the same device occurring through different vectored locations or channels.

Interrupt control

Once a device is switched on and has been initialized, although it may be able to produce interrupts, they will be ignored unless the device has had its interrupts enabled. This control (enabling/disabling) of interrupts may be performed by means of the following interrupt control mechanisms.

Status interrupt control mechanisms provide flags, either in an interrupt state table or via device and program status words, to enable and disable the interrupts. The flags are accessible (and may be modified) by normal bit-oriented instructions or special bit-testing instructions.

Mask interrupt control mechanisms associate each device interrupt with a particular bit position in a word. If the bit is set to one the interrupt will be blocked; if it is set to zero then it will be allowed. The interrupt mask word may be addressable by normal bit-oriented (or word-oriented) instructions or may be accessible only through special interrupt-masking instructions.

Level interrupt control mechanisms have devices associated with certain levels. The current level of the processor determines which devices may or may not interrupt. Only those devices with a higher logical level may interrupt. When the highest logical level is active, only those interrupts which cannot be disabled (for example, power fail) are allowed. This does not explicitly disable interrupts, so interrupts at a lower logical level than the current processor level will still be generated, and will not need to be re-enabled when the processor level falls appropriately.

Priority control

Some devices have higher urgency than others, and therefore a priority facility is often associated with interrupts. This mechanism may be static or dynamic and is usually related to the device interrupt control facility and the priority levels of the processor.

15.1.4   A simple example I/O system

In order to illustrate the various components of an I/O system, a simple machine is described. It is loosely based on the Motorola 68000 series of computers.

Each device supported on the machine has as many different types of register as are necessary for its operation. These registers are memory-mapped. The most common types used are **control and status** registers which contain all the information on a device's status, and allow the device's interrupts to be enabled and disabled. **Data buffer** registers act as buffer registers for temporarily storing data to be transferred into or out of the machine via the device.

A typical control and status register for the computer has the following structure:

```
bits
  15 - 12  : Errors              -- set when device errors occur
  11       : Busy                -- set when the device is busy
  10 -  8  : Unit select         -- where more than one device is
                                 -- being controlled
   7       : Done/ready          -- I/O completed or device ready
   6       : Interrupt enable    -- when set enables interrupts
   5 -  3  : reserved            -- reserved for future use
   2 -  1  : Device function     -- set to indicate required function
   0       : Device enable       -- set to enable the device
```

The typical structure of a data buffer register used for a character-orientated device is:

```
bits
  15 - 8    : Unused
   7 - 0    : Data
```

Bit 0 is the least significant bit of the register.

A device may have more than one of each of these registers, the exact number being dependent on the nature of the device. For example, one particular Motorola parallel interface and timer device has 14 registers.

Interrupts allow devices to notify the processor when they require service; they are vectored. When an interrupt occurs, the processor stores the current program counter (PC) and the current processor status word (PSW) on the system stack. The PSW will contain, among other things, the processor priority. Its actual layout is given below:

```
bits
  15 - 11   : Mode information
  10 -  8   : Unused
   7 -  5   : Priority
   4 -  0   : Condition codes
```

The condition codes contain information on the result of the last processor operation.

The new PC and PSW are loaded from two preassigned consecutive memory locations (the interrupt vector). The first word contains the address of the interrupt service routine and the second contains the PSW, including the priority at which the interrupt is to be handled. A low-priority interrupt handler can be interrupted by a higher-priority interrupt.

This example I/O system will be returned to later.

15.2   Language requirements

As noted above, one of the main characteristics of an embedded system is the need to interact with input and output devices, all of which have their particular characteristics. The programming of such devices has traditionally been the stronghold of the assembly language programmer, but languages like C, Modula-1, Java, occam2 and Ada have now attempted to provide progressively higher-level mechanisms for these low-level functions. This makes device-driving and interrupt-handling routines easier to read, write and maintain. A major difficulty, however, lies in deciding what features are required in a high-level language in order to program usable device handlers conveniently. Although the subject is still not mature, **encapsulation facilities** and an **abstract model** of device handling can be identified as being particular requirements.

15.2.1   Modularity and encapsulation facilities

Low-level device interfacing is necessarily machine-dependent, and therefore in general it is not portable.[1]

In any software system, it is important to separate the non-portable sections of code from the portable ones. Wherever possible, it is advisable to encapsulate all the machine-dependent code into units which are clearly identifiable. With Modula-1, the code associated with devices must be encapsulated into a special type of module called a **device module**. In Ada, the package and protected type facilities are used. In Java, classes and packages are the appropriate encapsulation mechanisms. In occam2, the only facility is the proc; in C it is a file.

15.2.2   Abstract models of device handling

A device can be considered to be a processor performing a fixed task. A computer system can, therefore, be considered to be several parallel processes. There are several models by which the device 'process' can communicate and synchronize with the processes executing inside the main processor. All models must provide:

---

[1]Note that in recent years there has been some attempt to produce a Uniform Driver Interface (UDI). UDI defines an architecture and a set of operating-system neutral (and hardware neutral) interfaces for use between the device driver and the surrounding system. This allows device drivers and operating systems to be developed independently, and multiple operating systems and hardware platforms to use the same driver.

(1) **Facilities for representing, addressing and manipulating device registers**
    A device register may be represented as a program variable, an object, or even a communication channel.

(2) **A suitable representation of interrupts**
    The following representations are possible:

   (a) **Procedure**
       The interrupt is viewed as a procedure call (in a sense, it is a remote procedure call coming from the device process). Any communication and synchronization required must be programmed in the interrupt handler procedure. The procedure is non-nested: only global state or state local to the handler can be accessed.

   (b) **Sporadic process**
       The interrupt is viewed as a request to execute a process. The handler is a sporadic process and it can access both local persistent data and global data (if shared-variable communication is available in the concurrency model).

   (c) **Asynchronous notification**
       The interrupt is viewed as an asynchronous notification directed at a process. The handler can access both the local state of the process and the global state. Both the resumption model and the termination are possible.

   (d) **Shared-variable condition synchronization**
       The interrupt is viewed as a condition synchronization within a shared-variable synchronization mechanism; for example, a signal operation on a semaphore or a send operation on a condition variable in a monitor. The handler can access both the local state of the process/monitor and the global state.

   (e) **Message-based synchronization**
       The interrupt is viewed as a content-less message sent down a communication channel. The receiving process can access the local state of the process.

All of the above approaches, except the procedural approach, require a full context switch as the handler executes in the scope of a process. Optimizations are possible if the handlers are restricted. For example, if the handler in the asynchronous notification model has resumption semantics and it does not access any data local to the process, then the interrupt can be handled with only a partial context switch.

Not all these models can be found in real-time languages and operating systems. The most popular one is the procedural model as this requires little support. Usually, real-time systems implemented in C and C++ adopt this model with device registers represented as program variables. For sequential systems, the asynchronous event model is identical in effect to the procedural model, as there is only one process to interrupt and therefore there is no need to identify the process or the event. The Ada model is a hybrid between a procedure model and a shared-variable condition synchronization model. The interrupt is mapped to a protected procedure and registers are accessed via program variables. Real-Time Java views an interrupt as an asynchronous event where the handler is a schedulable object. Modula-1 and Real-Time Euclid map interrupts to condition variables and semaphores respectively (again registers are represented as program variables) and are, therefore, pure shared-variable models. Occam2 views an interrupt as a message down a channel, device registers are also represented as channels.

This section now consider five languages in detail: Modula-1, Ada, Real-Time Java, occam2 and C.

15.3   Modula-1

Modula-1 was one of the first high-level programming languages which had facilities for programming device drivers.

In Modula-1, the unit of modularity and encapsulation is the module. A special type of module, called an **interface module**, which has the properties of a monitor, is used to control access to shared resources. Processes interact via signals (condition variables) using the operators WAIT, SEND and AWAITED (see Chapter 8). A third type of module, called a **device module** is a special type of interface module used to encapsulate the interaction with a device. It is only from within a device module that the facilities for handling interrupts can be used.

15.3.1   Addressing and manipulating device registers

Associating a variable with a register is fairly straightforward. In Modula-1, this is expressed by an octal address following the name in a declaration. For example, a data buffer register for the simple I/O architecture described in Section 15.1.4 would be defined as:

```
var rdbr[177562B] char;
```

where 177562B denotes an octal address which is the location of the register in memory.

The mapping of a character into a character buffer register is also a straightforward activity, since the type has no internal structure. A control and status register is more interesting. In Modula-1, only scalar data types can be mapped onto a device register; consequently registers which have internal structures are considered to be of the predefined type *bits* whose definition is:

```
TYPE BITS = ARRAY 0:no_of_bits_in_word OF BOOLEAN;
```

Variables of this type are packed into a single word. A control and status register at octal address 177560B can, therefore, be defined by the following Modula-1 code:

```
VAR rcsr[177560B] : BITS;
```

To access the various fields in the register, an index into the array is supplied by the programmer. For example, the following code will enable the device:

```
rcsr[0] := TRUE;
```

and the following turns off interrupts:

```
rcsr[6] := FALSE;
```

In general, these facilities are not powerful enough to handle all types of register conveniently. The general structure of the control and status register was given earlier:

```
bits
 15 - 12  : Errors
 11       : Busy
 10 -  8  : Unit select
  7       : Done/ready
  6       : Interrupt enable
  5 -  3  : reserved
  2 -  1  : Device function
  0       : Device enable
```

To set the selected unit (bits 8–10) using boolean values is very clumsy. For example, the following statements set the device unit to the value 5.

```
rcsr[10] := TRUE;
rcsr[9]  := FALSE;
rcsr[8]  := TRUE;
```

It is worth noting that on many machines more than one device register can be mapped to the same physical address. Consequently, several variables may be mapped to the same location in memory. Furthermore, these registers are often read or write only. Care, therefore, must be taken when manipulating device registers. In the above example, if the control and status register was a pair of registers mapped to the same location, the code presented will probably not have the desired effect. This is because to set a particular bit may require code to be generated which reads the current value into the machine accumulator. As the control register is write-only, this would produce the value of the status register. It is advisable, therefore, to have other variables in a program which represent device registers. These can be manipulated in the normal way. When the required register format has been constructed, it may then be assigned to the actual device register. Such variables are often called **shadow device registers**.

15.3.2 Interrupt handling

The facilities for handling interrupts in Modula-1 are based around the concept of an ideal hardware device. This device has the following properties (Wirth, 1977a):

- For each device operation, it is known how many interrupts are produced.
- After an interrupt has occurred, the device status indicates whether or not another associated interrupt will occur.

- No interrupt arrives unexpectedly.
- Each device has a unique interrupt location.

The facilities provided by Modula-1 may be summarized by the following points.

- Each device has an associated device module.
- Each device module has a hardware priority specified in its header following the module name.
- *All code within the module executes at the specified hardware priority.*
- Each interrupt to be handled within a device module requires a process called a **device process**.
- When the device process is executing, it has sole access to the module (that is, it holds the monitor lock using the ceiling priority specified in the device module header).
- A device process is not allowed to call any non-local procedures and cannot send signals to other device processes. This is to ensure that device processes will not be inadvertently blocked.
- When a device process sends a signal, the semantics of the send operation are different from those for ordinary Modula-1 processes; in this case the receiving process is not resumed, but the signalling process continues. Again this is to ensure that the process is not blocked.
- WAIT statements within device processes may only be of rank 1 (highest level).
- An interrupt is considered to be a form of signal. The device process, however, instead of issuing a WAIT request issues a DOIO request.
- The address of the vector through which the device interrupts is specified in the header of the process.
- *Only device processes can contain DOIO statements.*
- DOIO and WAIT calls lower the processor priority and, therefore, release the monitor lock.
- Only one instance of a device process may be activated.

For example, consider a device module which handles a real-time clock for the simple machine architecture outlined in Section 15.1.4. On receipt of an interrupt, the handler sends a signal to a process which is waiting for the clock to tick.

```
DEVICE MODULE rtc[6]; (* hardware priority 6 *)

    DEFINE tick;
    VAR tick : SIGNAL;

    PROCESS clock[100B];
        VAR csr[177546B] : BITS;
    BEGIN
        csr[0] := TRUE;  (* enable device *)
```

```
            csr[6] := TRUE;   (* enable interrupts *)
            LOOP
                DOIO;
                WHILE AWAITED(tick) DO
                    SEND(tick);
                END
            END
        END;
BEGIN
    clock; (* create one instance of the clock process *)
END rtc;
```

The heading of the device module specifies an interrupt priority of 6, at which all code within the module will be executed. The value 100B on the process header indicates that the device will interrupt through the vector at address (octal) 100. After enabling interrupts, the device process enters a simple loop of waiting for an interrupt (the DOIO) and then sending sufficient signals (that is, one per waiting process). Note that the device process does not give up its mutually exclusive access to the module when it sends a signal, but continues until it executes a WAIT or a DOIO statement.

The following illustrates how Modula-1 deals with the general characteristics of an interrupt driven device which were outlined in Sections 15.1.2 and 15.1.3.

- **Device control** – I/O registers are represented by variables.

- **Context switching** – The interrupt causes an immediate context switch to the interrupt-handling process, which waits using the DOIO.

- **Interrupt device identification** – The address of the interrupt vector is given with the device process's header.

- **Interrupt identification** – In the above example, only one interrupt was possible. In other cases, however, the device status register should be checked to identify the cause of the interrupt.

- **Interrupt control** – The interrupt control is status driven and provided by a flag in the device register.

- **Priority control** – The priority of the device is given in the device module header. *All* code in the module runs at this priority (that is, the device module has a hardware ceiling priority and executes with the Immediate Priority Ceiling Protocol (see Section 13.11)).

15.3.3   An example terminal driver

To illustrate further the Modula-1 approach to device driving, a simple terminal device module is presented. The terminal has two components: a display and a keyboard. Each component has an associated control and status register, a buffer register and an interrupt.

Two procedures are provided to allow other processes in the program to read and write characters. These procedures access a bounded buffer to allow characters to be typed ahead for input and buffered for output. These buffers must be included in the device module because device processes *cannot* call non-local procedures. Although separate modules for the display and keyboard could have been used, they have been combined to illustrate that a device module can handle more than one interrupt.

```
DEVICE MODULE terminal[4];

  DEFINE readch, writech;

  CONST n=64;                    (* buffer size *)

  VAR KBS[177560B]: BITS; (* keyboard status *)
      KBB[177562B]: CHAR; (* keyboard buffer *)
      DPS[177564B]: BITS; (* display status  *)
      DPB[177566B]: CHAR; (* display buffer  *)
      in1, in2, out1, out2 : INTEGER;
      n1, n2 : INTEGER;
      nonfull1, nonfull2,
      nonempty1, nonempty2 : SIGNAL;
      buf1, buf2 : ARRAY 1:n OF CHAR;


  PROCEDURE readch(VAR ch : CHAR);
  BEGIN
    IF n1 = 0 THEN WAIT(nonempty1) END;
    ch := buf1[out1];
    out1 := (out1 MOD n)+1;
    DEC(n1);
    SEND(nonfull1)
  END readch;

  PROCEDURE writech(ch : CHAR);
  BEGIN
    IF n2 = n THEN WAIT(nonfull2) END;
    buf2[in2] := ch;
    in2 := (in2 MOD n)+1;
    INC(n2);
    SEND(nonempty2)
  END writech;


  PROCESS keyboarddriver[60B];
  BEGIN
    KBS[0] := TRUE;  (* enable device *)
    LOOP
      IF n1 = n THEN WAIT(nonfull1) END;
      KBS[6] := TRUE;
      DOIO;
      KBS[6] := FALSE;
      buf1[in1] := KBB;
      in1 := (in1 MOD n)+1;
```

```
      INC(n1);
      SEND(nonempty1)
    END
  END keyboarddriver;

  PROCESS displaydriver[64B];
  BEGIN
    DPS[0] := TRUE;   (* enable device *)
    LOOP
      IF n2 = 0 THEN WAIT(nonempty2) END;
      DPB := buf2[out2];
      out2 := (out2 MOD n)+1;
      DPS[6] := TRUE;
      DOIO;
      DPS[6] := FALSE;
      DEC(n2);
      SEND(nonfull2)
    END
  END displaydriver;

BEGIN
  in1 :=1; in2 := 1;
  out1 := 1; out2 :=1;
  n1 :=0; n2 := 0;
  keyboarddriver;
  displaydriver
END terminal;
```

Timing facilities

Modula-1 provides no direct facilities for manipulating time; these have to be provided by the application. This requires a device module which handles the clock interrupt and then issues a regular signal, say, every second. This module is now presented; it is a modified version of the one previously defined. The hardware clock is assumed to tick every fiftieth of a second.

```
DEVICE MODULE hardwareclock[6];
    DEFINE tick;
    VAR tick : SIGNAL;

    PROCESS handler[100B];
        VAR count : INTEGER;
            statusreg[177546B] : BITS;
    BEGIN
        count := 0;
        statusreg[0] := TRUE;
        statusreg[6] := TRUE;
        LOOP
            DOIO;
            count := (count+1) MOD 50;
            IF count = 0 THEN
                WHILE AWAITED(tick) DO
```

```
                    SEND(tick)
                END
            END
        END
    END handler;
BEGIN
    handler
END hardwareclock;
```

An interface module which maintains the time of day can now be easily provided.

```
INTERFACE MODULE SystemClock;
    (* defines procedures for getting and setting the time of day *)
    DEFINE GetTime, SetTime;

    (* import the abstract data type time, and the tick signal *)
    USE time, initialise, add, tick;

    VAR TimeOfDay, onesec : time;

    PROCEDURE SetTime(t: time);
    BEGIN
        TimeOfDay := t
    END SetTime;

    PROCEDURE GetTime(VAR t: time);
    BEGIN
        t := TimeOfDay
    END GetTime;

    PROCESS clock;
    BEGIN
        LOOP
            WAIT(tick);
            addtime(TimeOfDay, onesec)
        END
    END clock;
BEGIN
    inittime(TimeOfDay, 0, 0, 0);
    inittime(onesec, 0, 0, 1);
    clock;
END SystemClock;
```

Note that the clock process is logically redundant. The device process could increment systemtime directly, thereby saving a context switch. However, it is not allowed in Modula-1 for a device process to call a non-local procedure.

Delaying a process

In real-time systems, it is often necessary to delay a process for a period (see Chapter 12). Although Modula-1 has no direct facilities for achieving this, they can be programmed. This is left as an exercise for the reader (see Exercise 15.6).

15.3.4   Problems with the Modula-1 approach to device driving

Modula-1 was designed to attack the stronghold of assembly language programming – that of interfacing to devices. In general, it has been considered a success; however, there are a few criticisms that have been levelled at its facilities.

- Modula-1 does not allow a device process to call a non-local procedure because device processes must be kept as small as possible and must run at the hardware priority of the device. To call procedures defined in other modules, whose implementation is hidden from the process, might lead to unacceptable delays. Furthermore, it would require these procedures to execute at the device's priority. Unfortunately, as a result of this restriction, programmers either have to incorporate extra functionality into a device module which is *not* directly associated with driving the device (as in the terminal driver example, where a bounded buffer was included in the device module), or they have to introduce extra processes to wait for a signal sent by a device process. In the former case, this can lead to very large device modules and in the latter, unnecessary inefficiency.

- Modula-1 only allows a single instance of a device process because the process header contains the information necessary to associate the process with the interrupt. This makes the sharing of code between similar devices more difficult; the problem is compounded by not being able to call non-local procedures.

- Modula-1 was designed for memory-mapped machines and consequently it is difficult to use its facilities for programming devices which are controlled by special instructions. However, it is easy to imagine a simple extension to solve this problem. Young (1982) suggests the possibility of using the following notation:

```
VAR x AT PORT 46B : INTEGER;
```

The compiler is then able to recognize when a port is being addressed and can generate the correct instructions.

- It has already been pointed out that many device registers are read- or write-only. It is not possible to define variables that are read- or write-only in Modula-1. Furthermore, there is an implicit assumption that a compiler will not optimize access to device registers and cache them in local registers.

15.4   Ada

In Ada, there are three ways in which tasks can synchronize and communicate with each other:

- through the rendezvous;
- using protected units; and
- via shared variables.

In general, Ada assumes that the device and the program have access to shared memory device registers which can be specified using its representation specification techniques. In Ada 83, interrupts were represented by hardware-generated task entry calls. In the current version of Ada, this facility is considered obsolete and will probably be removed from the language at the next revision. Consequently, it will not be discussed in this book.

The preferred method of device driving is to encapsulate the device operations in a protected unit. An interrupt may be handled by a protected procedure call.

15.4.1   Addressing and manipulating device registers

Ada presents the programmer with a comprehensive set of facilities for specifying the implementation of data types. These are collectively known as **representation clauses**, and they indicate how the types of the language are to be mapped onto the underlying hardware. A type can only have a single representation. The representation is specified separately from the logical structure of the type. Of course, the specification of the representation of a type is optional and can be left to the compiler.

Representation clauses are a compromise between abstract and concrete structures. Four distinct specifications are available:

(1) **Attribute definition clause** – allows various attributes of an object, task or subprogram to be set; for example, the size (in bits) of objects, the storage alignment, the maximum storage space for a task, the address of an object.

(2) **Enumeration representation clause** – the literals of an enumeration type may be given specific internal values.

(3) **Record representation clause** – record components can be assigned offsets and lengths within single storage units.

(4) **At clause** – this was the main Ada 83 mechanism for positioning an object at a specific address; this facility is now obsolete (attributes can be used) and will not, therefore, be discussed further.

If an implementation cannot obey a specification request then the compiler must either reject the program or raise an exception at run-time.

In order to illustrate the use of these mechanisms, consider the following type declarations which represent a typical control and status register of the simple machine defined earlier.

```
type Error_T is (None, Read_Error, Write_Error,
                 Power_Fail, Other);
type Function_T is (Read, Write, Seek);
type Unit_T is new Integer range 0 .. 7;

type Csr_T is record
    Errors   : Error_T;
    Busy     : Boolean;
```

```
   Unit       : Unit_T;
   Done       : Boolean;
   Ienable    : Boolean;
   Dfun       : Function_T;
   Denable    : Boolean;
end record;
```

An enumeration representation clause specifies the internal codes for the literals of the enumeration type. For example, the internal codes for the function required by the device above may be:

```
01   --    READ
10   --    WRITE
11   --    SEEK
```

In Ada, this is specified by:

```
type Function_T is (Read, Write, Seek);
for Function_T use (Read => 1, Write => 2, Seek => 3);
```

Similarly, for Error_t:

```
type Error_T is (None, Read_Error, Write_Error, Power_Fail, Other);
for Error_T use (None => 0, Read_Error => 1, Write_Error => 2,
                 Power_Fail => 3, Other => 4);
-- note, this is in fact the default assignment
```

A record representation clause specifies the storage representation of records; that is, the order, position and size of its components. The bits in the record are numbered from 0; the range in the component clause specifies the number of bits to be allocated. For example, the control status register is given by:

```
Word : constant := 2; -- number of storage units in a word
Bits_In_Word : constant := 16; -- bits in word
for Csr_T use
  record
    Denable   at 0*Word range 0..0; -- at word 0 bit 0
    Dfun      at 0*Word range 1..2;
    Ienable   at 0*Word range 6..6;
    Done      at 0*Word range 7..7;
    Unit      at 0*Word range 8 .. 10;
    Busy      at 0*Word range 11 .. 11;
    Errors    at 0*Word range 12 .. 15;
end record;
```

```
for Csr_T'Size use Bits_In_Word; -- the size of object of Csr type
for Csr_T'Alignment use Word; -- object should be word aligned
for Csr_T'Bit_order use Low_Order_First;
-- first bit is least significant bit of byte
```

A size attribute specifies the amount of storage that is to be associated with a type. In this example, the register is a single 16-bit word. The alignment attribute specifies that the compiler should always place objects on an integral number of storage units boundary, in this case a word boundary. The bit-ordering attribute specifies whether the machine numbers the most significant bit as 0 (big endian) or the least significant bit (little endian). Note that bits 3, 4 and 5 (which were reserved for future use) have not been specified.

Finally, an actual register needs to be declared and placed at the required location in memory. In Ada, Address is an implementation-defined type defined in package System. A child package (System.Storage_Elements.To_Address) provides a function for converting an integer value into the address type.

```
Tcsr : Csr_T;
for Tcsr'Address use System.Storage_Elements.To_Address(8#177566#);
```

Having now constructed the abstract data representation of the register, and placed an appropriately defined variable at the correct address, the hardware register can be manipulated by assignments to this variable:

```
Tcsr := (Denable => True, Dfun => Read,
         Ienable => True, Done => False,
         Unit => 4, Errors => None);
```

The use of this record aggregate assumes that the entire register will be assigned values at the same time. To ensure that Dfun is not set before the other fields of the record it may be necessary to use a temporary (shadow) control register:

```
Temp_Cr : Csr_T;
```

This temporary register is then assigned control values and copied into the real register variable:

```
Tcsr := Temp_Cr;
```

The code for this assignment will in most cases ensure that the entire control register is updated in a single action. If any doubt still remains, then the pragma Atomic can be used (which instructs the compiler to generate the update as a simple operation or produce an error message).

After the completion of the I/O operation, the device itself may alter the values on the register; this is recognized in the program as changes in the values of the record components:

```
if Tcsr.Error = Read_Error then
  raise Disk_Error;
end if;
```

The object Tcsr is therefore a collection of shared variables, which are shared between the device control task and the device itself. Mutual exclusion between these two concurrent (and parallel) processes is necessary to give reliability and performance. This is achieved in Ada by using a protected object.

15.4.2   Interrupt handling

Ada defines the following model of an interrupt:

- An interrupt represents a class of events that are detected by the hardware or the system software.
- The **occurrence** of an interrupt consists of its **generation** and its **delivery**.
- The generation of an interrupt is the event in the underlying hardware or system which makes the interrupt available to the program.
- Delivery is the action which invokes a part of the program (called the interrupt handler) in response to the interrupt occurrence. In between the generation of the interrupt and its delivery, the interrupt is said to be **pending**. The handler is invoked once for each delivery of the interrupt. The **latency** of an interrupt is the time spent while in the pending state.
- While an interrupt is being handled, further interrupts from the same source are **blocked**; all future occurrences of the interrupt are prevented from being delivered. It is usually device-dependent as to whether a blocked interrupt remains pending or is lost.
- Certain interrupts are **reserved**. The programmer is not allowed to provide a handler for a reserved interrupt. Usually, a reserved interrupt is handled directly by the run-time support system of Ada (for example, a clock interrupt used to implement the delay statement).
- Each non-reserved interrupt has a default handler that is assigned by the run-time support system.

Handling interrupts using protected procedures

The main representation of an interrupt handler in Ada is a parameterless protected procedure. Each interrupt has a unique discrete identifier which is supported by the system. How this unique identifier is represented is implementation-defined; it might, for example, be the address of the hardware interrupt vector associated with the interrupt. Where Ada is implemented on top of an operating system that supports signals, each signal may be mapped to a particular interrupt identifier. Thus allowing signal handlers to be programmed in the language.

Identifying interrupt-handling protected procedures is done using one of two pragmas:

```
pragma Attach_Handler(Handler_Name, Expression);
   -- This can appear in the specification or body of a
   -- library-level protected object and allows the
```

```
-- static association of a named handler with the
-- interrupt identified by the expression; the handler
-- becomes attached when the protected object is created.
-- Raises Program_Error:
--    (a) when the protected object is created and
--        the interrupt is reserved,
--    (b) if the interrupt already has a
--        user-defined handler, or
--    (c) if any ceiling priority defined is
--        not in the range Ada.Interrupt_Priority.

pragma Interrupt_Handler(Handler_Name);
    -- This can appear in the specification of a library-level
    -- protected object and allows the dynamic association of
    -- the named parameterless procedure as an interrupt
    -- handler for one or more interrupts. Objects created
    -- from such a protected type must be library level.
```

Program 15.1 defines the Systems Programming Annex's support for interrupt identification and the dynamic attachment of handlers. In all cases where `Program_Error` is raised, the currently attached handler is not changed.

It should be noted that the `Reference` function provides the mechanisms by which interrupt task entries are supported. As mentioned earlier, this model of interrupt handling is considered obsolete and should, therefore, not be used.

It is possible that an implementation will also allow the association of names with interrupts via Program 15.2. This will be used in the following examples.

15.4.3   A simple driver example

A common class of equipment to be attached to an embedded computer system is the analogue to digital converter (ADC). The converter samples some environmental factors, such as temperature or pressure; it translates the measurements it receives, which are usually in millivolts, and provides scaled integer values on a hardware register. Consider a single converter that has a 16-bit result register at hardware address 8#150000# and a control register at 8#150002#. The computer is a 16-bit machine and the control register is structured as follows:

```
Bit       Name            Meaning
0         A/D Start       Set to 1 to start a conversion.
6         Interrupt       Set to 1 to enable interrupts
          Enable/Disable
7         Done            Set to 1 when conversion is complete.
8-13      Channel         The converter has 64 analogue inputs,
                          the particular one required is
                          indicated by the value of the channel.
15        Error           Set to 1 by the converter if device
                          malfunctions.
```

Program 15.1 Package Ada.Interrupts.

```
package Ada.Interrupts is
  type Interrupt_Id is implementation_defined; -- must be discrete
  type Parameterless_Handler is access protected procedure;

  function Is_Reserved(Interrupt : Interrupt_Id) return Boolean;
    -- Returns True if the interrupt is reserved,
    -- returns False otherwise.
  function Is_Attached(Interrupt : Interrupt_Id) return Boolean;
    -- Returns True if the interrupt is attached to a
    -- handler, returns False otherwise.
    -- Raises Program_Error if the interrupt is reserved.
  function Current_Handler(Interrupt : Interrupt_Id)
                          return Parameterless_Handler;
    -- Returns an access variable to the current handler for
    -- the interrupt. If no user handler has been attached, a
    -- value is returned which represents the default handler.
    -- Raises Program_Error if the interrupt is reserved.
  procedure Attach_Handler(New_Handler : Parameterless_Handler;
                          Interrupt : Interrupt_Id);
    -- Assigns New_Handler as the current handler.
    -- If New_Handler is null, the default handler is restored.
    -- Raises Program_Error:
    --      (a) if the protected object associated with the
    --          New_Handler has not been identified with a
    --          pragma Interrupt_Handler,
    --      (b) if the interrupt is reserved,
    --      (c) if the current handler was attached statically
    --          using pragma Attach_Handler.
  procedure Exchange_Handler(
            Old_Handler : out Parameterless_Handler;
            New_Handler : Parameterless_Handler;
            Interrupt : Interrupt_Id);
    -- Assigns New_Handler as the current handler for the
    -- Interrupt and returns the previous handler in
    -- Old_Handler.
    -- If New_Handler is null, the default handler is restored.
    -- Raises Program_Error:
    --      (a) if the protected object associated with the
    --          New_Handler has not been identified with a
    --          pragma Interrupt_Handler,
    --      (b) if the interrupt is reserved,
    --      (c) if the current handler was attached statically
    --          using pragma Attach_Handler.
  procedure Detach_Handler(Interrupt : Interrupt_Id);
    -- Restores the default handler for the specified interrupt.
    -- Raises Program_Error:
    --      (a) if the interrupt is reserved,
    --      (b) if the current handler was attached statically
    --          using pragma Attach_Handler.
  function Reference(Interrupt : Interrupt_Id)
          return System.Address;
```

```
   -- Returns an Address which can be used to attach
   -- a task entry to an interrupt via an address
   -- clause on an entry.
   -- Raises Program_Error if the interrupt cannot be
   -- attached in this way.
private
   ... -- not specified by the language
end Ada.Interrupts;
```

Program 15.2 Package Ada.Interrupts.Names.

```
package Ada.Interrupts.Names is
   implementation defined : constant Interrupt_Id := implementation defined;
   ...
   implementation defined : constant Interrupt_Id := implementation defined;
private
   ... -- not specified by the language
end Ada.Interrupts.Names;
```

The driver for this ADC will be structured as a protected type within a package, so that the interrupt it generates can be processed as a protected procedure call, and so that more than one ADC can be catered for:

```
package Adc_Device_Driver is
   Max_Measure : constant := (2**16)-1;
   type Channel is range 0..63;
   subtype Measurement is Integer range 0..Max_Measure;
   procedure Read(Ch: Channel; M : out Measurement);
      -- potentially blocking
   Conversion_Error : exception;

private
   for Channel'Size use 6;
   -- indicates that six bits only must be used
end Adc_Device_Driver;
```

For any request, the driver will make three attempts before raising the exception. The package body follows:

```
with Ada.Interrupts.Names; use Ada.Interrupts;
with System; use System;
with System.Storage_Elements; use System.Storage_Elements;
package body Adc_Device_Driver is
   Bits_In_Word : constant := 16;
   Word : constant := 2; -- bytes in word
   type Flag is (Down, Set);
```

```ada
type Control_Register is
record
  Ad_Start : Flag;
  Ienable  : Flag;
  Done     : Flag;
  Ch       : Channel;
  Error    : Flag;
end record;

for Control_Register use
  -- specifies the layout of the control register
  record
    Ad_Start at 0*Word range 0..0;
    Ienable  at 0*Word range 6..6;
    Done     at 0*Word range 7..7;
    Ch       at 0*Word range 8..13;
    Error    at 0*Word range 15..15;
end record;

for Control_Register'Size use Bits_In_Word;
  -- the register is 16-bits long
for Control_Register'Alignment use Word;
  -- on a word boundary
for Control_Register'Bit_order use Low_Order_First;

type Data_Register is range 0 .. Max_Measure;
for Data_Register'Size use Bits_In_Word;
  -- the register is 16-bits long

Contr_Reg_Addr : constant Address := To_Address(8#150002#);
Data_Reg_Addr : constant Address  := To_Address(8#150000#);
Adc_Priority : constant Interrupt_Priority := 63;
Control_Reg : aliased Control_Register;
    -- aliased indicates that pointers are used to access it
for Control_Reg'Address use Contr_Reg_Addr;
    -- specifies the address of the control register
Data_Reg : aliased Data_Register;
for Data_Reg'Address use Data_Reg_Addr;
    -- specifies the address of the data register

protected type Interrupt_Interface(Int_Id : Interrupt_Id;
                Cr : access Control_Register;
                Dr : access Data_Register) is
  entry Read(Chan : Channel; M : out Measurement);
private
  entry Done(Chan : Channel; M : out Measurement);
  procedure Handler;
  pragma Attach_Handler(Handler, Int_Id);
  pragma Interrupt_Priority(Adc_Priority);
    -- see Section 13.11 for discussion on priorities
  Interrupt_Occurred : Boolean := False;
  Next_Request : Boolean := True;
end Interrupt_Interface;
```

```
Adc_Interface : Interrupt_Interface(Names.Adc,
                Control_Reg'Access,
                Data_Reg'Access);
   -- this assumes that 'Adc' is registered as an
   -- Interrupt_Id in Ada.Interrupts.Names
   -- 'Access gives the address of the object



protected body Interrupt_Interface is

   entry Read(Chan : Channel; M : out Measurement)
        when Next_Request is
     Shadow_Register : Control_Register;
   begin
     Shadow_Register := (Ad_Start => Set, Ienable => Set,
         Done => Down, Ch   => Chan, Error => Down);
     Cr.all := Shadow_Register;
     Interrupt_Occurred := False;
     Next_Request := False;
     requeue Done;
   end Read;

   procedure Handler is
   begin
     Interrupt_Occurred := True;
   end Handler;

   entry Done(Chan : Channel; M : out Measurement)
                            when Interrupt_Occurred is
   begin
     Next_Request := True;
     if Cr.Done = Set and Cr. Error = Down then
         M := Measurement(Dr.all);
     else
       raise Conversion_Error;
     end if;
   end Done;
  end Interrupt_Interface;



  procedure Read(Ch : Channel; M : out Measurement) is
  begin
    for I in 1..3 loop
      begin
        Adc_Interface.Read(Ch,M);
        return;
      exception
        when Conversion_Error => null;
      end;
    end loop;
    raise Conversion_Error;
  end Read;
end Adc_Device_Driver;
```

The client tasks simply call the Read procedure indicating the channel number from which to read, and an output variable for the actual value read. Inside the procedure, an inner loop attempts three conversions by calling the Read entry in the protected object associated with the converter. Inside this entry, the control register, Cr, is set up with appropriate values. Once the control register has been assigned, the client task is requeued on a private entry to await the interrupt. The Next_Request flag is used to ensure only one call to Read is outstanding.

Once the interrupt has arrived (as a parameterless protected procedure call), the barrier on the Done entry is set to true; this results in the Done entry being executed (as part of the interrupt handler), which ensures that Cr.Done has been set and that the error flag has not been raised. If this is the case, the out parameter M is constructed, using a type conversion, from the value on the buffer register. (Note that this value cannot be out of range for the subtype Measurement.) If the conversion has not been successful, the exception Conversion_Error is raised; this is trapped by the Read procedure, which makes three attempts in total at a conversion before allowing the error to propagate.

The above example illustrates that it is often necessary when writing device drivers to convert objects from one type to another. In these circumstances the strong typing features of Ada can be an irritant. It is, however, possible to circumvent this difficulty by using a generic function that is provided as a predefined library unit:

```
generic
  type Source (<>) is limited private;
  type Target (<>) is limited private;
function Ada.Unchecked_Conversion(S : Source) return Target;
pragma Convention(Intrinsic, Ada.Unchecked_Conversion);
pragma Pure(Ada.Unchecked_Conversion);
```

The effect of unchecked conversion is to copy the bit pattern of the source over to the target. The programmer must make sure that the conversion is sensible and that all possible patterns are acceptable to the target.

15.4.4 Accessing I/O devices through special instructions

If special instructions are required, assembler code may have to be integrated with Ada code. The machine code insertion mechanism enables programmers to write Ada code which contains visible non-Ada objects. This is achieved in a controlled way by only allowing machine code instructions to operate within the context of a subprogram body. Moreover, if a subprogram contains code statements then it can contain only code statements and 'use' clauses (comments and pragmas being allowed as usual).

As would be expected, the details and characteristics of using code inserts are largely implementation dependent; implementation-specific pragmas and attributes may be used to impose particular restrictions and calling conventions on the use of objects defining code instructions. A code statement has the following structure:

```
code_statement ::= qualified_expression
```

The qualified expression should be of a type declared within a predefined library package called System.Machine_Code. It is this package that provides record declarations (in standard Ada) to represent the instructions of the target machine. The following example illustrates the approach:

```
D : Data; -- to be input

procedure In_Op; pragma Inline(In_Op);

procedure In_Op is
  use System.Machine_Code;
begin
  My_Machine_Format'(Code => In_Instruction,  Reg => 1, Port => 1);
  My_Machine_Format'(CODE => SAVE, REG =>, S'Address);
end;
```

The pragma Inline instructs the compiler to include inline code, rather than a procedure call, whenever the subprogram is used.

Even though this code insertion method is defined in Ada, the language makes it quite clear (ARM 13.8.4) that an implementation need not provide a Machine_Code package unless the Systems Programming Annex is supported. If it does not, the use of machine code inserts is prohibited.

15.5   Real-Time Java

Although Java was initially designed for embedded system and is awash with facilities for graphics programming and file handling, the language says nothing about how to program device drivers or handle interrupts. Real-Time Java attempts to correct this situation, but currently provides only limited support.

15.5.1   Addressing and manipulating device registers

Real-Time Java supports the ability to access device registers through the notion of raw memory. An implementation is allowed to support a range of memory types such as DMA memory or shared memory. One such memory could be the memory where I/O registers are allocated: IO_Page. The RawMemoryAccess class (defined in Program 15.3) can then be used to read and write to that memory. The approach does not allow user-defined objects to be mapped to raw memory, as this could potentially allow violations of the typing mechanism. Consequently, it is necessary to access individual registers as primitive data types (byte, int, short, long) and use low-level bit-wise operations.

Program 15.3 An excerpt of the `RawMemoryClass` class.

```
public class RawMemoryAccess
{
  protected RawMemoryAccess(long base, long size);
  protected RawMemoryAccess(RawMemoryAccess memory, long base,
                                                  long size);

  public static RawMemoryAccess create(java.lang.Object type, long size)
         throws SecurityException, OffsetOutOfBoundsException,
                SizeOutOfBoundsException,
                UnsupportedPhysicalMemoryException;

  public static RawMemoryAccess create(java.lang.Object type,
                                       long base, long size)
         throws SecurityException, OffsetOutOfBoundsException,
                SizeOutOfBoundsException,
                UnsupportedPhysicalMemoryException;

  public byte getByte(long offset)
         throws SizeOutOfBoundsException, OffsetOutOfBoundsException;

  public void getBytes(long offset, byte[] bytes, int low,
                       int number) throws
             SizeOutOfBoundsException, OffsetOutOfBoundsException;

  // similarly for integers, long integers and short integers

  public void setByte(long offset, byte value) throws
             SizeOutOfBoundsException, OffsetOutOfBoundsException;

  public void setBytes(long offset, byte[] bytes, int low,
                       int number) throws
             SizeOutOfBoundsException, OffsetOutOfBoundsException;

  // similarly for integers, long integers and short integers
  . . .
}
```

Consider again the control and status register for the simple ADC given in Section 15.4.3.

Bit	Name	Meaning
0	A/D Start	Set to 1 to start a conversion.
6	Interrupt Enable/Disable	Set to 1 to enable interrupts
7	Done	Set to 1 when conversion is complete.
8-13	Channel	The converter has 64 analogue inputs, the particular one required is indicated by the value of the channel.
15	Error	Set to 1 by the converter if device malfunctions.

First it is necessary to create a class for the register. The constructor for this class creates an instance of the `RawMemoryAccess` class indicating the memory type as being the `IO_Page`. The `setControlWord` method can then be used to access the register itself.

```
public class ControlAndStatusRegister
{
  RawMemoryAccess rawMemory;

  public ControlAndStatusRegister(long base, long size)
  {
    rawMemory = RawMemoryAccess.create(IO_Page, base, size);
  }

  public void setControlWord(short value)
  {
    rawMemory.setShort(0, value);
  }
}
```

Now, using a shadow device register and bitwise logical operators, the correct bit pattern can be constructed. For example, to start a conversion on channel 6:

```
byte shadow, channel;
final byte start = 01;
final byte enable = 040;
final long csrAddress = 015002;
final long csrSize = 2;
ControlAndStatusRegister csr = new
        ControlAndStatusRegister(csrAddress, csrSize);

channel = 6;
shadow = (channel << 8) | start | enable);
csr.setControlWord(shadow);
```

15.5.2   Interrupt handling

Real-Time Java views an interrupt as an asynchronous event (see Section 10.7). An interrupt occurring is thus equivalent to the `fire` method being called. The association between the interrupt and the event is achieved by calling the `bindTo` method in the `AsyncEvent` class. The parameter is of string type, and this is used in an implementation-dependent manner – one approach might be to pass the address of the interrupt vector. When the interrupt occurs, the appropriate handler's fire method is called. Now, it is possible to associate the handler with a schedulable object and give it an appropriate priority and release parameters.

```
AsyncEvent Interrupt = new AsyncEvent();
AsyncEventHandler InterruptHandler = new BoundAsyncEventHandler(
            priParams, releaseParams, null, null, null);
```

Program 15.4 An excerpt of the `POSIXSignalHandler` class.

```
public final class POSIXSignalHandler
{
  public static final int SIGABRT;
  public static final int SIGALRM;
  public static final int SIGBUS
  . . .

  public static synchronized void addHandler(int signal,
                  AsyncEventHandler handler);

  public static synchronized void removeHandler(int signal,
                  AsyncEventHandler handler);

  public static synchronized void setHandler(int signal,
                  AsyncEventHandler handler);


}
```

```
Interrupt.addHandler(InterruptHandler);
Interrupt.bindTo("177760");
```

For the case where the Real-Time Java program is executing on top of a POSIX-compliant operating system, the class `POSIXSignalHandler` (see Program 15.4) can be used to associate asynchronous event handlers with the occurrence of a POSIX signal. Interestingly, POSIX's real-time signals are not supported.

15.6 Occam2

Earlier sections of this chapter have showed how a basically shared-variable model of communication and synchronization can be mapped onto machines with memory mapped I/O. However, the models did not handle machines with special instructions elegantly and resorted to special procedures, embedded assembly code or variables of a special type which were recognized by the compiler. In this section, the occam2 language is examined as an example of a message-based concurrent programming language which uses messages to control devices.

Although occam2 was designed for the transputer, in the following discussion it is considered as a machine-independent language. The model is presented first, and then consideration is given to its implementation on memory-mapped and special-instruction machines. As with shared variable device driving, the three issues of device encapsulation, register manipulation and interrupt handling must be considered.

Modularity and encapsulation facility

The only encapsulation facility provided by occam2 is the procedure, and it is this that must, therefore, be used to encapsulate device drivers.

Addressing and manipulating device registers

Device registers are mapped onto PORTs, which are conceptually similar to occam2 channels. For instance, if a 16-bit register is at address X then a PORT P is defined by:

```
PORT OF INT16 P:
PLACE P AT X:
```

Note that this address can be interpreted as either a memory address or a device address depending on the implementation. Interaction with the device register is obtained by reading or writing to this port:

```
P ! A   -- write value of A to the port

P ? B   -- read value of port into B
```

A port cannot be defined as read or write only.

The distinction between ports and channels in occam2, which is a significant one, is that there is no synchronization associated with the port interaction. Neither reads nor writes can lead to the executing process being suspended; a value is always written to the address specified and, similarly, a value is always read. A port is thus a channel in which the partner is always ready to communicate.

Occam2 provides facilities for manipulating device registers using shift operations and bitwise logical expressions. There is, however, no equivalent to Modula-1's bit type or Ada representation specifications.

Interrupt handling

An interrupt is handled in occam2 as a rendezvous with the hardware process. Associated with the interrupt, there must be an implementation-dependent address which, in the simple input/output system described in this chapter, is the address of the interrupt vector; a channel is then mapped onto this address (ADDR):

```
CHAN OF ANY Interrupt:
PLACE Interrupt AT ADDR:
```

Note that this is a channel and not a port. This is because there is synchronization associated with an interrupt where there is none associated with access to a device register. The data protocol for this channel will also be implementation-dependent.

The interrupt handler can wait for an input from the designated channel thus:

```
INT ANY:  -- define ANY to be of the protocol type
SEQ
  -- using ports enable interrupt
  Interrupt ? ANY
  -- actions necessary when interrupt has occurred.
```

The run-time support system must, therefore, synchronize with the designated channel when an external interrupt occurs. To obtain responsiveness, the process handling the interrupt will usually be given a high priority. Therefore not only will it be made executable by the interrupt event, but it will, within a short period of time, actually be executing (assuming that no other high-priority process is running).

To cater for interrupts which are lost if not handled within a specified period, it is necessary to view the hardware as issuing a timeout on the communication. The hardware must therefore conceptually issue:

```
ALT
  Interrupt ? ANY
    SKIP
  CLOCK ? AFTER Time PLUS Timeout
    SKIP
```

and the handler must execute:

```
Interrupt ! ANY
```

This is because only an input request can have a timeout associated with it.

Implementation on memory-mapped and special-instruction machines

To map the occam2 model of device driving to memory-mapped machines simply requires that input and output requests on ports be mapped to read and write operations on the device registers. To map the model to special-instruction machines requires the following:

- an occam2 PORT to be associated with an I/O port using the PLACE statement;
- the data which is sent to an occam2 PORT to be placed in an appropriate accumulator for use with the output machine instruction;
- the data which is received from an occam2 PORT to become available, via an appropriate accumulator, after the execution of the input instruction.

15.6.1 An example device driver

To illustrate the use of the low-level input/output facilities that occam2 provides, a process will be developed that controls an analogue to digital converter (ADC) for a memory-mapped machine. The converter is the same as the one described in Section

15.4.3 and implemented in Ada and Java. In order to read a particular analogue input, a channel address (not to be confused with an occam2 channel) is given in bits 8 to 13 and then bit 0 is set to start the converter. When a value has been loaded into the results register, the device will interrupt the processor. The error flag will then be checked before the results register is read. During this interaction it may be desirable to disable the interrupt.

The device driver will loop round receiving requests and providing results; it is programmed as a PROC with a two-channel interface. When an address (for one of the eight analogue input channels) is passed down input, a 16-bit result will be returned via channel output.

```
CHAN OF INT16 request:
CHAN OF INT16 return:
PROC ADC(CHAN OF INT16 input, output)
  -- body of PROC, see below
PRI PAR
  ADC(request, return)
  PAR
    -- rest of program
```

A PRI PAR is desirable as the ADC must handle an interrupt each time it is used, and therefore should run at the highest priority.

Within the body of the PROC, the interrupt channel and the two PORTs must first be declared:

```
PORT OF INT16 Control.Register:
PLACE Control.Register AT #AA12#:
PORT OF INT16 Buffer.Register:
PLACE Buffer.Register AT #AA14#:
CHAN OF ANY Interrupt:
PLACE Interrupt AT #40#:
INT16 Control.R:   -- variable representing control register
```

Where #AA12# and #AA14# are the defined hexadecimal addresses for the two registers and #40# is the interrupt vector address.

To instruct the hardware to undertake an operation requires bits 0 and 6 to be set on the control register; at the same time all other bits apart from those between 8 and 13 (inclusive) must be set to zero. This is achieved by using the following constants;

```
VAL INT16 zero IS 0:
VAL INT16 Go IS 65:
```

Having received an address from channel 'input', its value must be assigned to bits 8 through 10 in the control register. This is accomplished by using a shift operation. The actions that must be taken in order to start a conversion are, therefore:

```
INT16 Address:
SEQ
  input ? Address
```

```
IF
  (Address < 0) OR (Address > 63)
    output ! MOSTNEG INT16  -- error condition
  TRUE
    SEQ
      Control.R := zero
      Control.R := Address << 8
      Control.R := Control.R BITOR Go
      Control.Register ! Control.R
```

Once an interrupt has arrived, the control register is read and the error flag and 'Done' checked. To do this, the control register must be masked against appropriate constants:

```
VAL INT16 Done IS 128:
VAL INT16 Error IS MOSTNEG INT16:
```

MOSTNEG has the representation 1 000 000 000 000 000.
  The checks are thus:

```
SEQ
  Control.Register ? Control.R
  IF
    ((Done BITAND Control.R) = 0) OR
    ((Error BITAND Control.R) <> zero)
      -- error
    TRUE
      -- appropriate value is in buffer register
```

Although the device driver will be run at a high priority, the client process in general will not, and hence the driver would be delayed if it attempted to call the client directly and the client was not ready. With input devices that generate data asynchronously, this delay could lead to the driver missing an interrupt. To overcome this, the input data must be buffered. A suitable circular buffer is given below. Note that because the client wishes to read from the buffer and because the ALT in the buffer cannot have output guards, another single buffer item is needed. To ensure that the device driver is not delayed by the scheduling algorithm, the two buffer processes (as well as the driver) must execute at high priority.

```
PROC buffer(CHAN OF INT put, get)
  CHAN OF INT Request, Reply:
  PAR
    VAL INT Buf.Size IS 32:
    INT top, base, contents:
    [Buf.Size]buffer:
    SEQ
      contents := 0
      top := 0
      base := 0
      INT ANY:
      WHILE TRUE
        ALT
```

```
              contents < Buf.Size & put ? buffer [top]
                SEQ
                  contents := contents + 1
                  top := (top + 1) REM Buf.Size
              contents > 0 & Request ? ANY
                SEQ
                  Reply ! buffer[base]
                  contents := contents - 1
                  base := (base + 1) REM Buf.Size
    INT Temp:    -- single buffer process
    VAL INT ANY IS 0:    -- dummy value
    WHILE TRUE
      SEQ
        Request ! ANY
        Reply ? Temp
        get ! Temp
:
```

The full code for the PROC can now be given. The device driver is again structured so that three attempts are made to get a correct reading.

```
PROC ADC(CHAN OF INT16 input, output)
  PORT OF INT16 Control.Register:
  PLACE Control.Register AT #AA12#:
  PORT OF INT16 Buffer.Register:
  PLACE Buffer.Register AT #AA14#:

  CHAN OF ANY Interrupt:
  PLACE Interrupt AT #40#:
  TIMER CLOCK:

  INT16 Control.R:    -- variable representing control buffer
  INT16 Buffer.R:    -- variable representing results buffer
  INT Time:

  VAL INT16 zero IS 0:
  VAL INT16 Go IS 65:
  VAL INT16 Done IS 128:
  VAL INT16 Error IS MOSTNEG INT16:
  VAL INT Timeout IS 600000:    -- or some other appropriate value
  INT ANY:
  INT16 Address:
  BOOL Found, Error:
  CHAN OF INT16 Buff.In:

  PAR
    buffer(Buff.In, output)
    INT16  Try:
    WHILE TRUE
      SEQ
        input ? Address
        IF
          (Address < 0) OR (Address > 63)
            Buff.In ! MOSTNEG INT16
                      -- error condition
```

```
TRUE
  SEQ
    Try := 0
    Error := FALSE
    Found := FALSE
    WHILE (Try < 3) AND ((NOT Found) AND (NOT Error))
      -- Three attempts are made to get a reading from
      -- the ADC. This reading may be either correct or
      -- is flagged as being an error.
      SEQ
        Control.R := zero
        Control.R := Address << 8
        Control.R := Control.R BITOR Go
        Control.Register ! Control.R
        CLOCK ? Time
        ALT
          Interrupt ? ANY
            SEQ
              Control.Register ? Control.R
              IF
                ((Done BITAND Control.R) = 0) OR
                    ((Error BITAND Control.R) <> zero)
                  SEQ
                    Error := TRUE
                    Buff.In ! MOSTNEG INT16 -- error condition
                TRUE
                  SEQ
                    Found := TRUE
                    Buffer.Register ? Buffer.R
                    Buff.In ! Buffer.R
          CLOCK ? AFTER Time PLUS Timeout
            -- The device is not responding
            Try := Try + 1
    IF
      (NOT Found) AND (NOT Error)
        Buff.In ! MOSTNEG INT16
      TRUE
        SKIP
:
```

15.6.2 Difficulties with device driving in occam2

The above example illustrates some of the difficulties in writing device drivers and
interrupt handlers in occam2. In particular, there is no direct relationship between the
hardware priority of the device and the priority assigned to the driver process. To ensure
that high-priority devices are given preference, it is necessary to order all the device
drivers appropriately at the outer level of the program in a PRI PAR construct.

The other main difficulty stems from the lack of data structures for representing
device registers. This results in the programmer having to use low-level bit manipulation
techniques, which can be error-prone.

15.7   C and older real-time languages

The first generation of real-time programming languages (RTL/2, Coral 66 and so on)
provide no real support for concurrent programming or for the programming of devices.
Interrupts are typically viewed as procedure calls, and very often the only facility available for accessing device registers is to allow assembly language code to be embedded
in the program. For example, RTL/2(Barnes, 1976) has a code statement as follows:

```
code code_size, stack_size
    mov  R3,@variable
    ...
    ...
@rtl
```

One disadvantage of this approach is that in order to access RTL/2 variables,
knowledge of the structure of the code generated from the compiler is needed.

Another common feature with early real-time languages is that they tend to be
weakly typed. Therefore variables can be treated as fixed-length bit strings. This allows
the individual bits and fields of registers to be manipulated using low-level operators,
such as logical shift and rotate instructions. However, the disadvantages of having weak
typing by far outweigh the benefits of this flexibility.

The language C, although more recent than RTL/2 and Coral 66, has continued
with this tradition. Device registers are addressed by pointer variables which can be
assigned to the memory location of the register. They are manipulated either by low-
level bitwise logical operators or by the use of bitfields in structure definitions. The
latter appears to be similar to record representation clauses in Ada, but in fact is both
machine- and compiler-dependent. To illustrate the use of the bit manipulation facilities
of C, two examples are presented, the first using low-level bitwise logical operators and
the second using bitfields.

Consider again the control and status register for the simple ADC given in Section
15.4.3.

Using bitwise logical operators, it is first necessary to define a set of masks corresponding to each bit position.

```
#define START   01 /* numbers beginning with 0 are in hexadecimal */
#define ENABLE  040
#define ERROR   0100000
```

The 'Channel' field can either be defined on a per bit basis, or the value can be
shifted to its correct position. The latter approach is used below, where the channel
number 6 is required:

```
unsigned short int *register, shadow, channel;

register = 0xAA12;
channel = 6;
shadow = 0;

shadow |= (channel << 8) | START | ENABLE
*register = shadow
```

With bitfields, this becomes:

```
struct {
  unsigned int start      : 1; field 1-bit long
  unsigned int            : 5; unnamed field 5-bits long
  unsigned int interrupt  : 1; field 1-bit long
  unsigned int Done       : 1; field 1-bit long
  unsigned int Channel    : 6; field 6-bits long
  unsigned int error      : 1; field 1-bit long
} control_register;

control_register *register, shadow;
register = 0xAA12;
shadow.start = 1;
shadow.Interrupt = 1;
shadow.channel = 6;
shadow.error = 0;

*register = shadow;
```

There are two points to note about this example:

- C gives no guarantee of the ordering of fields; hence the compiler may decide to pack the fields in the word in a different order to that implied by the programmer.
- C does not attempt to address whether the machine numbers bits from left to right or right to left.

Given these two points, it is clear that bitfields should not be used to access device registers unless the programmer has knowledge of how they are implemented by the particular compiler for the specific machine being used. Even in this case, the code will not be portable.

For portability, the C programmer is therefore forced to use low-level bitwise logical operators. The following example shows how these can quickly become unreadable (although arguably they produce more efficient code). The following procedure sets n bits starting at position p in the register pointed at by reg to x.

```
unsigned int setbits(unsigned int *reg, unsigned int n,
        unsigned int p, unsigned int x)
{
  unsigned int data, mask;

  data = (x & (~(~0 << n))) << (p); /* data to be masked in */
  mask = ~(~0 << n); /* mask */
  *reg &= ~(mask << (p)); /* clear current bits */
  *reg |= data; /* OR in the data */
}
```

The C code is somewhat terse in this example: ~ means a bitwise complement, << is a shift left (with a 0 fill), & is a bitwise 'and', and | is a bitwise 'or'.

With the simple I/O architecture outlined in Section 15.1.4, interrupt handlers are assigned by placing the address of a parameterless procedure in the appropriate interrupt vector location. Once the procedure is executed, any communication and synchronization with the rest of the program must be programmed directly.

Although POSIX provides alternative mechanisms which, in theory, could be used to provide an alternative model of interrupt handling (for example, associating an interrupt with a condition variable), there is currently no standard mechanism for attaching user-defined handlers to interrupts.

15.8   Scheduling device drivers

As many real-time systems have I/O components, it is important that the scheduling analysis incorporates any features which are particular to this low-level programming. It has already been noted that DMA and channel-program controlled techniques are often too unpredictable (in their temporal behaviour) to be analyzed. Attention in this section is therefore focused upon the interrupt-driven program-controlled and status driven approaches.

Where an interrupt releases a sporadic process for execution, there is a cost that must be allocated to the interrupt handler itself. The priority of the handler is likely to be greater than that of the sporadic process, which means that processes with priority greater than the sporadic process (but less than the interrupt handler) will suffer an interference. Indeed, this is an example of priority inversion, as the handler's only job is to release the sporadic process – its priority should ideally be the same as the sporadic process. Unfortunately, most hardware platforms require the interrupt priorities to be higher than the ordinary software priorities. To model the interrupt handler, an extra 'process' is included in the schedulability test. It has a 'period' equal to the sporadic process, a priority equal to the interrupt priority level and an execution time equal to its own worst-case behaviour.

With status-driven devices, the control code can be analyzed in the usual way. Such devices, however, do introduce a particular difficulty. Often the protocol for using an input device is as follows: ask for a reading, wait for the reading to be taken by the hardware, and then access a register to bring the reading into the program. The problem is how to manage the delay while the reading is being taken. Depending on the likely duration of the delay, three approaches are possible:

- busy wait on the 'done' flag
- reschedule the process to some future time
- for periodic processes, split the action between periods.

With small delays, a busy wait is acceptable. From a scheduling point of view, the 'delay' is all computation time and hence as long as the 'delay' is bounded, there is no change to the analysis approach. To protect against a failure in the device (that is, it never sets the done bit), a timeout algorithm can be used (see Section 12.4).

If the delay is sizable, it is more effective to suspend the process, execute other work and then return to the I/O process at some future time when the value should be available. So if the reading time was 30 ms, the code would be:

```
begin
  --set up reading
  delay Milliseconds(30);
  -- take reading and use
end;
```

From a scheduling perspective, this structure has three significant implications. Firstly, the response times are not as easy to calculate. Each half of the process must be analyzed separately. The total response time is obtained by adding together both sub-response times, and the 30 ms delay. Although there is a delay in the process, this is ignored when considering the impact that this process has on lower-priority processes. Secondly, the extra computation time involved in delaying and being rescheduled again must be added to the worst-case execution time of the process (see Section 16.3 for a discussion on how to include system overheads). Thirdly, there is an impact on blocking. Recall that the simple equation for calculating the response time of a process is (see Section 13.7)

$$R_i = C_i + B_i + I_i$$

B_i is the blocking time (that is, the maximum time the process can be delayed by the actions of a lower-priority process). Various protocols for resource sharing were considered in Section 13.10. The effective ones all had the property that B_i consisted of just one block. However, when a process delays (and lets lower priority processes execute), it can be blocked again when it is released from the delay queue. Hence the response time equation becomes:

$$R_i = C_i + (N + 1)B_i + I_i$$

where N is the number of internal delays.

With periodic processes, there is another way of managing this explicit delay. This method is called **period displacement** and involves initiating the reading in one period but taking the reading in the next. For example:

```
-- set up first reading
loop
  delay until Next_Release;
  -- check done flag set
  -- take reading and use
  -- set up for next reading
  Next_Release := Next_Release + Period;
end loop;
```

This is a straightforward approach with no impact on scheduling. Of course, the reading is one period old, which may not be acceptable to the application. To ensure that there is sufficient gap between the end of one execution and the start of the next, the deadline of the process can be adjusted. So, if S is the settling time for the device the required constraint is $D \leq T - S$. Note that the maximum staleness of the reading is bounded by $T + D$ (or $T + R$ once the worst-case response time is calculated).

15.9 Memory management

Embedded real-time systems often have only a limited amount of memory available; this is either because of the cost or because of other constraints associated with the surrounding system (for example, size, power or weight constraints). It may, therefore, be necessary to control how this memory is allocated so that it can be used effectively. Furthermore, where there is more than one type of memory (with different access characteristics) within the system, it may be necessary to instruct the compiler to place certain data types at certain locations. By doing this, the program is able to increase performance and predictability as well as interact with the outside world.

   This chapter has already considered how data items can be allocated to particular memory locations, and how certain fields within storage units can be used to represent specific data types. This section considers the more general issues of storage management. Attention is focused on management of the two basic components that compilers use to manage data at run-time: the heap and the stack.

15.9.1 Heap management

The run-time implementations of most programming languages provide a large amount of memory (called the **heap**) so that the programmer can make run-time requests for chunks to be allocated (for example, to contain an array whose bounds were not known at compile time). An allocator (usually the **new** operator) is used for this purpose. It returns a pointer to memory within the heap of adequate size for the program's data structure. The run-time support system is responsible for managing the heap. Key problems are deciding how much space is required and when allocated space can be released. The first of these problems, in general, requires application knowledge. The second can be handled in several ways, including:

- require the programmer to return the memory explicitly – this is error-prone but is easy to implement; it is the approach taken by the C programming language where the functions `malloc` and `free` are used – the function `sizeof` allows the size of data types in bytes to be obtained (from the compiler);

- require the run-time support system to monitor the memory and determine when it can logically no longer be accessed – the scope rules of Ada allows an implementation to adopt this approach; when an access type goes out of scope, all the memory associated with that access type can be freed;

- require the run-time support system to monitor the memory and release chunks which are no longer being used (**garbage collection**) – this is, perhaps, the most general approach, as it allows memory to be freed even though its associated access type is still in scope.

From a real-time perspective, the above approaches have an increasing impact on the ability to analyze the timing properties of the program. In particular, garbage collection may be performed either when the heap is empty or by an asynchronous activity (incremental garbage collection). In either case, running the garbage collector may have a significant impact on the response time of a time-critical task. Although there has been much work on real-time garbage collection and progress continues to be made (for example, see Lim et al. (1999), Siebert (1999) and Kim et al. (1999)), there is still a reluctance to rely on these techniques in time-critical systems.

The following subsections will explore in more depth the facilities provided by Ada and Real-Time Java.

Heap management in Ada

In Ada, the heap is represented by one or more **storage pools**. Storage pools are associated with a particular Ada partition (for a non-distributable Ada system this is simply the whole program). Each object which is of an access type has an associated storage pool. The allocator ('new') takes its memory from the target pool. The `Ada.Unchecked_Deallocation` facility returns data to the pool. An implementation may support a single global pool which will be reclaimed when the partition terminates, or it may support pools defined at different accessibility levels which will be reclaimed when the associated scope is exited. By default, the implementation chooses a standard storage pool per access type. Note that all objects accessed directly (not via a pointer) are placed on the stack, not the heap.

To give more user control over storage management, Ada defines a package called `System.Storage_Elements` which is given in Program 15.5.

Programmers can implement their own storage pools by extending the `Root_Storage_Pool` type and providing concrete implementations for the subprogram bodies. To associate an access type with a storage pool, the pool is first declared and then the `Storage_Pool` attribute is used:

```
My_Pool : Some_Storage_Pool_Type;

type A is access Some_Object;
for A'Storage_Pool use My_Pool;
```

Now all calls to 'new' using A will automatically call `Allocate`; calls to `Ada.Unchecked_Deallocation` will call `Deallocate`; both referring to `My_Pool`. Furthermore, the implementation will call `Deallocate` when the access type goes out of scope.

Finally, it should be noted that Ada does not require an implementation to support garbage collection. However, it does support a pragma `Controlled` which indicates that garbage collection on a particular type should *not* be performed.

Program 15.5   The Ada `System.Storage_Pools` package.

```
with Ada.Finalization;
with System.Storage_Elements;

package System.Storage_Pools is

  pragma Preelaborate(System.Storage_Pools);

  type Root_Storage_Pool is abstract new
      Ada.Finalization.Limited_Controlled with private;

  procedure Allocate(Pool : in out Root_Storage_Pool;
            Storage_Address : out Address;
            Size_In_Storage_Elements : in System.
                Storage_Elements.Storage_Count;
            Alignment : in System.Storage_Elements.Storage_Count)
            is abstract;

  procedure Deallocate(Pool : in out Root_Storage_Pool;
            Storage_Address : in Address;
            Size_In_Storage_Elements : in System.
                Storage_Elements.Storage_Count;
            Alignment : in System.Storage_Elements.Storage_Count)
            is abstract;

  function Storage_Size(Pool : Root_Storage_Pool) return
            System.Storage_Elements.Storage_Count is abstract;
private
  ...
end System.Storage_Pools;
```

Heap management in Real-Time Java

In contrast to Ada, all objects in Java are allocated on the heap and the language requires garbage collection for an effective implementation. Real-Time Java recognizes that it is necessary to allow memory management which is not affected by the vagaries of garbage collection. To this end, it introduces the notion of **memory areas**, some of which exist outside the traditional Java heap and never suffer garbage collection. Program 15.6 defines the abstract class for all memory areas. When a particular memory area is entered, all object allocation is performed within that area.

Using this abstract class, Real-Time Java defines various kinds of memory including the following.

Program 15.6 The Java `MemoryArea` abstract class.

```
public abstract class MemoryArea
{
  protected MemoryArea(long sizeInBytes);

  public void enter(java.lang.Runnable logic);
  // associate this memory area to the current thread
  // for the duration of the logic.run method

  public static MemoryArea getMemoryArea(java.lang.Object object);
  // get the memory area associated with the object

  public long memoryConsumed();
  // number of bytes consumed in this memory area
  public long memoryRemaining();
  // number of bytes remaining

  public synchronized java.lang.Object newArray(java.lang.class type,
          int number) throws IllegalAccessException,
          InstantiationException, OutOfMemoryError;
  // allocate an array

  public synchronized java.lang.Object newInstance(java.lang.class type)
          throws IllegalAccessException, InstantiationException,
          OutOfMemoryError;
  // allocate an object

  public long size(); // the size of the memory area
}
```

- *Immortal memory*

  Immortal memory is shared among all threads in an application. Objects created in immortal memory are never subject to garbage collection and are freed only when the program terminates.

  ```
  public final class ImmortalMemory extends MemoryArea
  {
    public static ImmortalMemory instance();
  }
  ```

  There is also a class called `ImmortalPhysicalMemory` which has the same characteristics as immortal memory but allows objects to be allocated from within a range of physical addresses.

- *Scoped memory*

  Scoped memory is a memory area where objects which have a well-defined life-time can be allocated. A scoped memory may be entered explicitly (by the use of the `enter` method) or implicitly by attaching it to a `RealtimeThread` at thread creation time. Associated with each scoped memory is a reference count. This is incremented for every call to `enter` and at every associated thread creation. It is decremented when the `enter` method returns and at every associated thread exit. When the reference count reaches 0, all objects resident in the scoped memory have their finalization method executed and the memory is reclaimed. Scoped memory can be nested by nested calls to the `enter` method.

The `ScopedMemory` class (defined in Program 15.7) is an abstract class which has several subclasses including

- `VTMemory` – allocations may take variable amounts of time;
- `LTMemory` – allocations occur in linear time (related to the size of the object);
- `ScopedPhysicalMemory` – allowing objects to be allocated at physical memory locations.

The definition of these subclasses is given in Appendix A.

To avoid the possibility of dangling pointers, a set of access restrictions are placed on the use of the various memory areas.

- Heap objects – can reference other heap objects and objects in immortal memory only (i.e. it cannot access scoped memory);

- Immortal objects – can reference heap objects and immortal memory objects only;

- Scoped objects – can reference heaped objects, immortal objects and objects in the same scope or an outer scope only.

Memory parameters can be given when real-time threads and asynchronous event handlers are created. They can be used by the scheduler as part of an admission control policy and/or for the purpose of ensuring adequate garbage collection. Program 15.8 defines the class.

Consider, for example, a real-time thread which wishes to have all its memory allocated, by default, from immortal memory. However, during certain parts of its computation it wishes to create some temporary objects with a well-defined lifetime. First, the code for the thread is defined. The method `computation` represents the part of the code where temporary storage is required. It creates some linear time scoped memory indicating the minimum and maximum size it requires. It then defines a local `Runnable` to contain the actual computation. The code `myMem.enter` limits the scope of the memory.

```
import javax.realtime.*;
public class ThreadCode implements Runnable
{
  private void computation()
  {
    final int min = 1*1024;
    final int max = 1*1024;
    final LTMemory myMem = new LTMemory(min, max);
```

Program 15.7   The Real-Time Java `ScopedMemory` class.

```
public abstract class ScopedMemory extends MemoryArea
{
  public ScopedMemory(long size);

  public void enter(java.lang.Runnable logic);

  public int getMaximumSize();

  public MemoryArea getOuterScope();

  public java.lang.Object getPortal();

  public void setPortal(java.lang.Object object);
}
```

Program 15.8   The Real-Time Java `MemoryParameters` class.

```
public class MemoryParameters
{
  public static final long NO_MAX;

  public MemoryParameters(long maxMemoryArea, long maxImmortal)
         throws IllegalArgumentException;

  public MemoryParameters(long maxMemoryArea, long maxImmortal,
                          long allocationRate)
         throws IllegalArgumentException;

  public long getAllocationRate();
  public long getMaxImmortal();
  public long getMaxMemoryArea();

  public void setAllocationRate(long rate);
  public boolean setMaxImmortal(long maximum);
  public boolean setMaxMemoryArea(long maximum);
}
```

```
    myMem.enter(new Runnable()
    {
      public void run()
      {
        // code here which requires access
        // to temporary memory
      }
```

```
      } );
   }

   public void run()
   {
      . . .
      computation();
      . . .
   }
}
```

The thread can now be created. Note that in this example no parameters other than the memory area and the `Runnable` are given.

```
ThreadCode code = new ThreadCode();

RealtimeThread myThread = new RealtimeThread(
        null, null, null, ImmortalMemory.instance(),
        null, code);
```

15.9.2 Stack management

As well as managing the heap, embedded programmers also have to be concerned with stack size. While specifying the stack size of a task/thread requires trivial support (for example, in Ada it is via the `Storage_Size` attribute applied to a task; in POSIX it is via pthread attributes), calculating the stack size is more difficult. As tasks enter blocks and execute procedures their stacks grow. To accurately estimate the maximum extent of this growth requires knowledge of the execution behaviour of each task. This knowledge is similar to that required to undertake worst-case execution time (WCET) analysis (see Section 13.7). Hence both WCET and worst-case stack usage bounds can be obtained from a single tool performing control flow analysis of the task's code.

Summary

One of the main characteristics of an embedded system is the requirement that it interacts with special-purpose input and output devices. To program device drivers in high-level languages requires:

- the ability to pass data and control information to and from the device;
- the ability to handle interrupts.

Normally control and data information is passed to devices through device registers. These registers are either accessed by special addresses in a memory-mapped I/O architecture, or via special machine instructions. Interrupt handling requires context switching, device and interrupt identification, interrupt control, and device prioritization.

The programming of devices has traditionally been the stronghold of the assembly language programmer, but languages like C, Modula-1, occam2 and Ada have progressively attempted to provide high-level mechanisms for these low-level functions. This makes device driver and interrupt-handling routines easier to read, write and maintain. The main requirement on a high-level language is that it provides an abstract model of device handling. Encapsulation facilities are also required so that the non-portable code of the program can be separated from the portable part.

The model of device handling is built on top of the language's model of concurrency. A device can be considered to be a processor performing a fixed process. A computer system can therefore be modelled as several parallel processes which need to communicate and synchronize. There are several ways in which interrupts can be modelled. They must all have:

(1) Facilities for addressing and manipulating device registers.

(2) A suitable representation of interrupts.

In a pure shared-variable model of device driving, the driver and the device communicate using the shared device registers, and the interrupt provides condition synchronization. Modula-1 presents the programmer with such a model. Driver processes are encapsulated in device modules which have the functionality of monitors. Device registers are accessed as scalar objects or arrays of bits, and an interrupt is viewed as a signal on a condition variable.

In Ada, device registers can be defined as scalars and user-defined record types, with a comprehensive set of facilities for mapping types onto the underlying hardware. Interrupts are viewed as hardware-generated procedure calls to a protected object.

Only occam2 presents a message-based view of device driving to the programmer. Device registers are accessed as special channels, called ports, and interrupts are treated as content-free messages passing down channels.

Real-Time Java supports the access to memory-mapped I/O registers through the `RawMemoryClass`; however, it lacks expressive power for manipulating device registers. Interrupts are viewed as asynchronous events.

Low-level programming also involves the more general issue of managing the memory resources of the processor. This chapter has considered both stack and heap management. Ada does not require a garbage collector – memory can be explicitly deallocated and the scope rules of the language allow automatic deallocation when an access type goes out of scope. The language also allows user-defined storage pools to be defined which enable programmers to define their own memory management policies.

Real-Time Java recognizes that the memory allocation policy of Java is not sustainable for real-time systems. Consequently, it allows memory to be allocated outside of the heap, and supports the notion of scoped memory which allows automatic reclamation of memory without garbage collection.

Further reading

Barr, M. (1999) *Programming Embedded Systems in C and C++*. Sebastopol, CA: O'Reilly.

Bollella, G., Brosgol, B., Dibble, P., Furr, S., Gosling, J., Hardin, D. and Turnbull, M. (2000) *The Real-Time Specification for Java*. Reading, MA: Addison-Wesley.

Project UDI (2000) *Uniform Driver Interface (UDI)* `http://www.project-udi.org/`, accessed June 2000.

Exercises

15.1 Consider a computer which is embedded in a patient-monitoring system (assume the simple I/O system given in this chapter). The system is arranged so that an interrupt is generated at the highest hardware priority, through vector location 100 (octal) every time the patient's heart beats. In addition, a mild electric shock can be administered via a device control register, the address of which is 177760 (octal). The register is set up so that every time an integer value x is assigned to it the patient receives x volts over a small period of time.

If no heartbeat is recorded within a 5 second period the patient's life is in danger. Two actions should be taken when the patient's heart fails: the first is that a 'supervisor' task should be notified so that it may sound the hospital alarm, the second is that a single electric shock of 5 volts should be administered. If the patient fails to respond, the voltage should be increased by 1 volt for every further 5 seconds.

Write an Ada program which monitors the patient's heart and initiates the actions described above. You may assume that the supervisor task is given by the following specification:

```
task Supervisor is
    entry Sound_Alarm;
end Supervisor;
```

15.2 The Spanish government is considering introducing charges for the use of motorways. One possible mechanism is that detector stations can be set up at regular intervals along all motorways; as a vehicle passes the detector station its details are logged and a road charge is recorded. At the end of each month the vehicle owner can be sent a bill for his or her motorway usage.

Each vehicle will require an interface device which interrupts an on-board computer when a detector station requests its details. The computer has a word size of 16 bits and has memory-mapped I/O, with all I/O registers 16 bits in length. Interrupts are vectored, and the address of the interrupt vector associated with the detector station is 8#60#. After an interrupt has been received, a read-only input register located at 8#177760# contains the basic cost of using the current stretch of motorway (in pesetas). The hardware priority of the interrupt is 4.

The computer software must respond to the interrupt within a period of 5 seconds, and pass its ownership details to the detector station via the interface device. It does this by writing to a bank of five control and status registers located at 8#177762#. The structure of these registers is shown in Table 15.1.

Register	Bits	Meaning
1	0–7	Vehicle registration character 1
1	8–15	Vehicle registration character 2
2	0–7	Vehicle registration character 3
2	8–15	Vehicle registration character 4
3	0–7	Vehicle registration character 5
3	8–15	Vehicle registration character 6
4	0–7	Vehicle registration character 5
4	8–15	Vehicle registration character 8
5	0	set to 1 to transmit data
5	1–4	travel details
		1 = business
		2 = pleasure
		3 = overseas tourist
		4 = police
		5 = military
		6 = emergency services
5	5–15	security code (0–2047)

Table 15.1   Register structure for road charging.

The bank of CSR registers is write-only.

Write an Ada task to interface with the detector station. The task should respond to interrupts from the interface device and be responsible for sending the correct vehicle details. It should also read the data register containing the cost of the road usage, and pass the current total cost of the journey to a task which will output it on a visual display unit on the vehicles dashboard. You may assume the following is available:

```
package Journey_Details is
  Registration_Number : constant String(1..8) :=
                        "........";

  type Travel_Details is
        (Business, Pleasure, Overseas_Tourist,
         Police, Military, Emergency_Service);
  for Travel_Details use
        (Business   => 1, Pleasure => 2,
         Overseas_Tourist => 3, Police => 4,
         Military => 5 , Emergency_Service => 6);
```

Figure 15.3 A slotted ring.

```
    subtype Security_Code is Integer range 0 .. 2047;

    function Current_Journey return Travel_Details;

    function Code return Security_Code;
end Journey_Details;

package Display_Interface is

    task Display_Driver is
        entry Put_Cost(C : Integer);
        -- prints the cost on the dashboard display
    end Display_Driver;

end Display_Interface;
```

Assume that the compiler represents the type `Character` as an 8-bit value and the type `Integer` as a 16-bit value.

15.3 A slotted ring-based local area network is one which contains slots in which data can be placed for transmission; these slots continually circulate the ring. Consider a particular ring which has a *single* slot, called a packet, which is 40 bits wide. The structure of the packet is shown in Figure 15.3

Bit 39 indicates the start of a packet; it is always set to 1. Bit 36 indicates whether the packet is full or empty (that is, if the slot is being used), bits 27–34 are used to indicate the destination address of the data, bits 19–26 are used to contain the source address of the data, bits 3–18 are used to contain the data to be transmitted, bit 0 is a parity bit which may be ignored for the purpose of this question. The response bits (bits 1–2) and monitor bit (bit 35) are described below.

A transmitting process on finding an empty packet will set the packet full bit, clear the response bits to zero, set the destination and source addresses, and place the data to be transmitted. The packet circulates the ring; each station on the ring checks the packet to see if it is the destination address for that packet. If it is, it copies the data out of the packet and sets the response bits (to binary 11) to indicate that the data has been received. The original sender checks the response bits and removes the data by setting the full bit to 0 thereby indicating that the packet is empty. The empty packet is then transmitted. If the sender wishes to send another message it must wait until it again receives an empty packet; this stops one sender from monopolizing the ring.

Although the ring has a low error rate it is possible for the data in the packet to become corrupted. In particular, it is possible that the sender address could be corrupted. To avoid the possibility of the same full packet continually circulating the ring, a monitor station is introduced. The monitor station reads every packet and sets the monitor bit to one. A transmitting station will set the monitor bit to 0 when it transmits a packet. If the monitor station therefore reads a packet which is full and has the monitor bit set, then this packet has been all the way around the ring and hence the address has been corrupted. If this error condition occurs the full/empty bit should be set to zero to indicate that the packet may be reused. A station's interface to the ring is controlled by four 16-bit memory-mapped registers. The first register is a control and status register which resides at octal location 177760. The structure of the register is given in Table 15.2.

Bits	Meaning
0	parity bit
1, 2	response
3	monitor bit
4	full/empty bit
6	interrupt enable
10	transmit packet

Table 15.2   Control register structure for slotted ring.

The second and third registers are source and destination address registers which reside at octal locations 177762 and 177764 respectively. Their structure is shown in Table 15.3.

Bits	Meaning
0–7	address
8–15	not used

Table 15.3   Address registers structure for slotted ring.

The final register is the data register, and it resides at octal location 177766. All four device registers can be read and written.

An interrupt will signal the arrival of a packet. The interrupt is vectored at octal location 60; the priority of the interrupt is 6. On interrupt the control and status register will indicate the value of the full bit, the monitor bits, the response bits and the parity bit. The bits can be altered by writing to the control and status register. If bit 10 is set by the interrupt-handling process the packet is transmitted. The contents of the data, the source and destination addresses can similarly be read and modified.

Write an Ada package to transmit and receive integers via the single slotted ring. The specification of your package is given below:

```
package Slotted_Ring_Driver is

    type Station_Id is private;
    Station1 : constant Station_Id;
    Station2 : constant Station_Id;
    Station3 : constant Station_Id;
    Station4 : constant Station_Id;

    -- etc

    procedure Transmit (To_Station : Station_Id;
                        Data : Integer);

    procedure Receive (From_Station : out Station_Id;
                       Data : out Integer);
private

    type Station_Id is new Short_Integer;    -- 16 bits
    Station1 : constant Station_Id := 1;
    Station2 : constant Station_Id := 2;
    -- etc
end Slotted_Ring_Driver;
```

You may assume that if the response bits in the packet are set to 0 when the packet returns to the sender, the data has not been received. However, no retry is necessary – the data should just be discarded.

You may also ignore parity checks, and can assume that a 'short integer' occupies 16 bits of memory.

15.4 Rewrite your answer to Exercise 15.2 in occam2, Modula-1 and Real-Time Java.

15.5 Consider a simple robot arm, connected to a computer with a simple I/O system, which can only be moved along the horizontal axis. The device is controlled by two registers: a data register at octal location 177234 and a control register at octal location 177326. When the device is enabled (by setting bit 6 in the control register) and a coordinate is placed in the data register, the robot arm moves to that coordinate, and an interrupt is generated (through location octal 56 and at a hardware priority of 4) when the arm is in the new position.

Define a Modula-1 device module so that a Modula-1 process may move the arm to a particular position by calling the routine MOVETOPOSITION, defined by the device module, with a parameter indicating the required position. The procedure should return when the arm is located at the new position. You may assume that only one process at a time will call MOVETOPOSITION.

15.6 Design a Modula-1 device module which enables a calling process to be delayed for a number of clock ticks. Calling processes should interact with the device module by a procedure called DELAY which takes an integer parameter indicating the duration of the delay in ticks. The procedure returns when the delay time has expired. You may assume the priority of the clock device is 6; its interrupt vector location is at octal location 100 and its control and status register is at address octal 177546 and is 16 bits long. Bit 6 of this register when set enables interrupts.

15.7 Rewrite the keyboard device driver, given in Section 15.3.3, in occam2.

15.8 Compare and contrast the restrictions that Ada and Modula-1 place on the programming of device drivers.

15.9 The British government is concerned about the speed of cars using motorways. In the future, beacons will be set up at regular intervals along all motorways; they will continuously transmit the current speed limit. New cars will contain computers which will monitor the current speed limit and inform the driver when he or she exceeds the limit.

One car currently being designed (the Yorkmobile) already has the necessary hardware interfaces. They are as follows.

- Each car has a 'speed control' 16-bit computer which has memory-mapped I/O, with all I/O registers 16 bits in length.
- A register located at octal location 177760 interfaces to a device which monitors the road side beacons. The register always contains the value of the last speed limit received from the roadside beacons.
- A pair of registers interface to an intelligent speedometer device which checks the speed of the car against a set limit. If the speed limit is broken, the device generates an interrupt through octal location 60. The priority of the interrupt is 5. This interrupt is repeated every 5 seconds until the car is no longer speeding.
- The register pair consists of a 'control and status' register (CSR), and a data buffer register (DBR). The structure of CSR register is show in Table 15.4.

Bits	Meaning
0	enable device
1	when set the value found in the DBR is used as the car's current speed limit
5–2	not used
6	interrupt enable
11–7	not used
15–12	error bits (0 = no error, > 0 illegal limit)

Table 15.4   Control register structure speed computer.

The CSR register may be both read from and written to, and resides at address octal 177762. The DBR register simply contains an integer value representing the car's speed limit to be set. If this value falls outside the range 0 - 70 then an illegal limit has been specified, and the device continues with the current limit. The address of the DBR register is octal 177764.

- A flashing light (on the car dashboard) can be turned on by setting the register, located at octal address 177750, to 1. The light will flash for 5 seconds only. A zero value turns the light off.

Design an occam2 device driver which will implement the following speed control algorithm.

Every 60 seconds the current speed limit should be read from the roadside beacon by the speed control computer. This value is passed unchecked to the speedometer device which interrupts if the car exceeds the set speed limit or if the speed limit is illegal. If the car exceeds the limit then the dashboard light should be flashed until the car returns to the current limit.

15.10 Redo Exercise 15.9 using Modula-1, Ada and Real-Time Java.

15.11 Compare and contrast the Modula-1 shared memory model of device driving with the occam-2 message passing model.

Chapter 16
The execution environment

By their very nature, real-time systems have to exhibit a timely response to events occurring in their surrounding environment. This has led to the view that real-time systems must be as fast as possible, and that any overheads introduced by language or operating system features that support high-level abstractions (such as monitors, exceptions, atomic actions and so on) cannot be tolerated. The term 'efficiency' is often used to express the quality of the code produced by a compiler or the level of abstraction provided by mechanisms supported by an operating system or run-time support system. This term, however, is not well-defined. Furthermore, efficiency is in many ways a poor metric for assessing an application and its implementation. In real-time systems, what is actually important is the meeting of deadlines or the attainment of adequate response times in a particular execution environment. This chapter considers some of the issues associated with meeting this goal. Firstly, the impact of the execution environment on the design and implementation of real-time systems is considered. Then, ways in which the software execution environment can be tailored to the needs of the application are discussed. Scheduling models of kernels are then reviewed so as to facilitate the complete schedulability analysis of an application. This is followed by illustrations of how some of the abstractions presented in this book can be supported by hardware in the execution environment.

16.1   The role of the execution environment

In Chapter 13, schedulability analysis was considered to be essential for predicting the real-time properties of software. It is difficult to undertake this analysis unless the details

635

of the proposed execution environment are known. The term 'execution environment' is used to mean those components that are used together with the application's code to make the complete system: the processors, networks, operating systems and so on. The nature of the proposed execution environment will dictate whether a particular design will meet its real-time requirements. Clearly, the more 'efficient' use of the execution environment, the more likely the requirements will be met. But this is not always the case, and a poorly structured design may fail to meet its requirements irrespective of how efficiently it is implemented. For example, a design suffering from significant priority inversion will fail to meet attainable deadlines irrespective of how efficiently it is implemented – as was so poignantly illustrated in the Mars Pathfinder mission (Jones, 1997; Reeves, 1997).

The design process can be viewed as a progression of increasingly specific **commitments** and **obligations**. The commitments define properties of the system design which designers operating at a more detailed level are not at liberty to change. Those aspects of a design to which no commitment is made at some particular level in the design hierarchy are effectively the subject of obligations that lower levels of design must address.

The process of refining a design – transforming obligations into commitments – is often subject to **constraints** imposed primarily by the execution environment. The choice of the execution environment and how it is used may also be constrained. For example, there may be a requirement which dictates that a space-hardened processor be used, or there may be a certification requirement which dictates that the capacity of the processor (or network) shall not exceed 50%.

Many design methods distinguish between a logical and physical design. The logical design focuses on meeting the functional requirements of the application and assumes a sufficiently fast execution environment. The physical architecture is the result of combining the functional and the proposed execution environment to produce a complete software and hardware architecture design.

The physical architecture forms the basis for asserting that all the application's requirements will be met once the detailed design and implementation have taken place. It addresses timing (and even dependability) analysis that will ensure (guarantee) that the system once built will (within some stated failure hypotheses) satisfy the real-time requirements. To undertake this analysis, it will be necessary to make some initial estimations of resource usage of the proposed system (hardware and software). For example, initial estimates of the timing properties of the application can be made and schedulability analysis undertaken to give confidence that deadlines will be met once the final system has been implemented.

The focus of physical architecture design is to take the functional architecture and to map it on to the facilities provided by the execution environment. Any mismatch between the assumptions made by the functional architecture and the facilities provided by the execution environment must be addressed during this activity. For example, the functional architecture might assume that all functions are immediately visible from all other functions. When functions are mapped to processors in the physical architecture, there may be no direct communication path provided by the infrastructure, and consequently it may be necessary to add extra application-level router functions. Furthermore, the infrastructure may only support low-level message passing, whereas the functions may communicate using procedure calls; consequently it will be necessary to provide an application-level RPC facility. There is clearly a trade-off between the sophistication of the execution environment and the need to add extra application facilities to the functional architecture during the production of the physical architecture. However, it is also important not to provide sophisticated mechanisms in the execution environment if they are not needed by the application, or worse, the application needs more primitive facilities which it must then try to construct from high-level ones. This is often called **abstraction inversion**.

Once the initial architectural design activities are complete, the detailed design can begin in earnest and all components for the application produced. When this has been achieved, each component must be analyzed using tools to measure characteristics of the application such as its worst-case execution time (or its complexity, for example, if dependability is being considered) to confirm that estimated worst-case execution times are accurate, (or that certain modules were complex and therefore prone to software errors, resulting in design diversity being needed). If these estimations were not accurate (which will usually be the case for a new application), then either the detailed design must be revisited (if there are small deviations), or the designer must return to the architectural design activities (if serious problems exist). If the estimation indicates that all is well, then testing of the application proceeds. This should involve measuring the actual timing of code, the number of bugs found and so on. The process is illustrated in Figure 16.1 (this is actually the life cycle supported by the HRT-HOOD design methods considered in Chapter 2 and used in the case study presented in Chapter 17).

What is important, therefore, is not so much efficiency of compiled code or operating systems overheads, but rather that timing analysis be undertaken as early on in the life cycle as possible. Having said this, a grossly inefficient compiler would clearly be an inappropriate tool to employ; such inefficiencies being an indication of a poorly engineered product.

16.2   Tailoring the execution environment

Modern operating systems, and the run-time support systems associated with languages like Ada, are awash with functionality because they try to be as general purpose as possible. Clearly, if a particular application does not use certain features of an operating system, it would be advantageous to customize its run-time existence. This ability is essential for three main reasons:

(1) it avoids unnecessary resource usage, be it processor time or memory;

(2) it reduces the amount of software whose correctness has to be argued during any certification process;

(3) many development standards require 'dead code' to be removed.

This section considers the facilities provided by Ada and POSIX that aid this process. Real-Time Java does not, in general, support optional components as it is contrary to

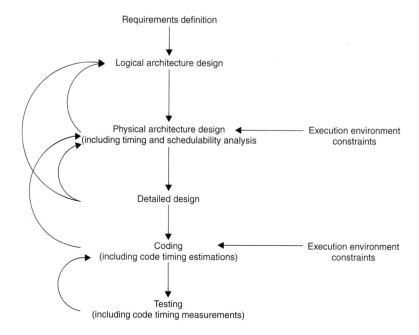

Figure 16.1   A hard real-time life cycle.

the *Write Once Run Anywhere* principle. However, it does accept that some components cannot be implemented if the underlying support system does not provide that functionality. The most obvious case being the class that interfaces to POSIX signals.

16.2.1 Restricted tasking in Ada

The Real-Time Annex of Ada allows the programmer to specify a set of restrictions that a run-time system should recognize and 'reward' by giving more effective support. The following are examples of restrictions which are identified by pragmas, and are checked and enforced before run-time:

- `No_Task_Hierarchy` – This significantly simplifies the support required for task termination.
- `No_Abort_Statement` – This affects all aspects of the run-time support system, as there is no need to worry about a task being aborted while in a rendezvous, in a protected operation, propagating an exception, waiting for child termination and so on.
- `No_Terminate_Alternatives` – Again simplifies the support required for task termination.

- `No_Task_Allocators` – Allows the run-time system to be configured for a static number of tasks and removes a need for dynamic memory allocation.

- `No_Dynamic_Priorities` – Simplifies many aspects of the support for task priorities as priority will not change dynamically (other than via the use of ceiling priorities).

- `No_Asynchronous_Control` – This affects all aspects of the run-time support system as there is no need to worry about a task receiving an asynchronous event while in a rendezvous, in a protected operation, propagating an exception, waiting for child termination and so on.

- `Max_Select_Alternatives` – Allows the use of static data structures and removes a need for dynamic memory allocation.

- `Max_Task_Entries` – Again allows the use of static data structures and removes a need for dynamic memory allocation. A value of zero indicates that no rendezvous are possible.

- `Max_Protected_Entries` – Again allows the use of static data structures and removes a need for dynamic memory allocation. A value of zero indicates that no condition synchronization is allowed for protected objects.

- `Max_Tasks` – Specifies the maximum number of tasks and therefore allows the run-time to provide a fixed amount of static support structures.

Note that Ada also has a Safety and Security Annex which sets all the above restrictions to zero (that is *no tasking*!). It also introduces a further restriction that disallows protected types and objects. Current practice, in the safety critical application area, forbids the use of tasks or interrupts. This is unfortunate, as it is possible to define a subset of the tasking facilities that is both predictable and amenable to analysis. It is also possible to specify run-time systems so that they can be implemented to a high level of integrity.

One of the challenges facing Ada practitioners over the coming decade is to demonstrate that concurrent programming is an effective and safe technique for even the most stringent of requirements. Towards this goal, the 8th International Real-Time Ada Workshop (Burns, 1999) defined a tasking profile (known as the *Ravenscar Profile*) for use in high-integrity or performance-sensitive applications. In the Ravenscar Profile, use of the following features is forbidden:

- Task types and object declarations other than at the library level. Thus, there is no hierarchy of task types.

- Unchecked deallocation of protected and task objects (and hence finalization). Dynamic allocation of such objects may be allowed, but only if the sequential part of the high-integrity language profile allows dynamic allocation of other objects.

- Requeue.

- ATC (asynchronous transfer of control via the *select then abort* statement).

- Abort statements.

- Task entries.

- Dynamic priorities.
- Package `Calendar`.
- Relative delays.
- Protected types other than at the library level.
- Protected types with more than one entry.
- Protected entries with barriers other than a single boolean variable declared within the same protected type.
- Attempts to queue more than one task on a single protected entry.
- Locking policies other than *Ceiling locking*.
- Scheduling policies other than *FIFO within priorities*.
- All forms of the select statement.
- User-defined task attributes.

In addition to these restrictions, an implementation can make the assumption that none of the program's tasks will terminate. Note that most, but not all, of these constraints can be defined using the `Restrictions` pragma. Even with these limitations, an application conforming to the Ravenscar Profile still has:

- Task objects, restricted as above.
- Protected objects, restricted as above.
- Suspension objects.
- Atomic and volatile pragmas.
- 'Delay until' statements.
- *Ceiling locking* policy and *FIFO within priority* dispatching.
- The Count attribute (but not within entry barriers).
- Task identifiers.
- Task discriminants.
- The `Real_Time` package.
- Protected procedures as interrupt handlers.

Protected types with only subprogram interfaces are provided for simple mutual exclusion. The special form of protected entry (that is, only one per protected object and a maximum of one possible caller of that entry) is available as an event signalling mechanism to allow aperiodic or sporadic tasks to be supported.

In addition to the features described above, the Real-Time Systems Annex defines a number of implementation requirements, documentation requirements and metrics. The metrics allow the costs (in processor cycles) of the run-time system to be obtained. They also indicate which primitives can lead to blocking, and which must not.

The timing features (that is, real-time clock and delay primitives) are defined precisely. It is thus, for example, possible to know the maximum time between a task's delay value expiring and it being placed on the run queue. All this information is needed for the analysis of an application within the context of its execution environment.

16.2.2 POSIX

POSIX consists of a variety of standards. There is the base standard, the real-time extensions, the threads extensions and so on. If implemented in a single system, it would contain a huge amount of software. To help produce more compact versions of operating systems which conform to the POSIX specifications, a set of application environment **profiles** have been developed, the idea being that implementors can support one or more profiles. For real-time systems, four profiles have been defined:

- PSE50 – Minimal real-time system profile – intended for small single/multiprocessor embedded systems controlling one or more external devices; no operator interaction is required and there is no file system. Only a single multithreaded process is supported.

- PSE51 – Real-time controller system profile – an extended PSE50 for potentially multiple processors with a file system interface and asynchronous I/O.

- PSE52 – Dedicated real-time system profile – an extension of PSE50 for single or multiple processor systems with memory management units; includes multiple multithreaded processes, but no file system.

- PSE53 – Multi-purpose real-time system profile – capable of running a mix of real-time and non real-time processes executing on single/multiprocessor systems with memory management units, mass storage devices, networks and so on.

Table 16.1 illustrates the type of functionality provided by PSE50, PSE51 and PSE52.

In general, a POSIX system is also free not to support any of the optional units of functionality it chooses, and so much finer control over the supported functionality is possible. All of the real-time and the thread extensions are optional. However, conforming to one of the profiles means that all the required units of functionality must be supported.

16.3 Scheduling models

The execution environment has a significant impact on the timing properties of an application. Where there is a software kernel, the overheads incurred by the kernel must be taken into account during the schedulability analysis of the application. The following characteristics are typical of many real-time software kernels:

- The cost of a context switch between processes is not negligible and may not be a single value. The cost of a context switch to a higher-priority periodic process (following, for example, a clock interrupt) may be higher than a context switch

Functionality	PSE50	PSE51	PSE52
pthreads	√	√	√
fork	×	×	√
semaphores	√	√	√
mutexes	√	√	√
message passing	√	√	√
signals	√	√	√
timers	√	√	√
synchronous I/O	√	√	√
asynchronous I/O	×	√	√
priority scheduling	√	√	√
shared memory objects	√	√	√
file system	×	√	×

Table 16.1   POSIX real-time profile functionality.

from a process to a lower-priority process (at the end of the high-priority process's execution). For systems with a large number of periodic processes, an additional cost will be incurred for manipulating the delay queue (for periodic tasks when they execute, say, an Ada 'delay until' statement).

- All context switch operations are non preemptive.

- The cost of handling an interrupt (other than the clock) and releasing an application sporadic process is not insignificant. Furthermore, for DMA and channel-program controlled devices, the impact of shared-memory access can have a non-trivial impact on worst-case performance; such devices are best avoided in hard real-time systems.

- A clock interrupt (say every 10 ms) could result in periodic processes being moved from a delay queue to the dispatch queue. The costs for this operation varies depending on the number of processes to be moved.

In addition to the above, the scheduling analysis must take into account the features of the underlying hardware, such as the impact of the cache and pipeline.

16.3.1   Modelling non-trivial context switch times

Most scheduling models ignore context switch times. This approach is, however, too simplistic if the total cost of the context switches is not trivial when compared with the application's own code. Figure 16.2 illustrates a number of significant events in the execution of a typical periodic process.

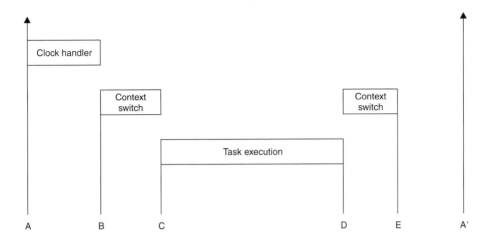

Figure 16.2   Overheads when executing processes.

A − the clock interrupt that designates the notional time at which the process should start (assuming no release jitter or non-preemptive delay, if the interrupts were disabled due to the operation of the context switch then the clock handler would have its execution delayed; this is taken into account in the scheduling equations by the blocking factor B).

B − the earliest time that the clock handler can complete, this signifies the start of the context switch to the process (assume it is the highest priority runnable process)

C − the actual start of the execution of the process

D − the completion of the process (the process may be preempted a number of times between C and D)

E − the completion of the context switch away from the process

A′ − the next release of the process

The typical requirement for this process is that it completes before its next release (that is, D < A′), or before some deadline prior to its next release. Either way, D is the significant time, not E. Another form of requirement puts a bound on the time between the start of execution and termination (that is, D–C). This occurs when the first action is an input and the last an output (and there is a deadline requirement between the two). While these factors affect the meaning of the process's own deadline (and hence its response time) they do not affect the interference this process has on lower-priority processes; here the full cost of both context switches counts. Recall that the basic scheduling equation (13.7) has the form:

$$R_i = C_i + B_i + \sum_{j \in hp(i)} \left\lceil \frac{R_i}{T_j} \right\rceil C_j$$

This now becomes (for periodic processes only):

$$R_i = CS^1 + C_i + B_i + \sum_{j \in hp(i)} \left\lceil \frac{R_i}{T_j} \right\rceil (CS^1 + CS^2 + C_j) \qquad \textbf{(16.1)}$$

where CS^1 is the cost of the initial context switch (to the process) and CS^2 is the cost of the context switch away from each process at the end of its execution. The cost of putting the process into the delay queue (if it is periodic) is incorporated into C_i. Note that in practice this value may depend on the size of the queue; a maximum value would need to be incorporated into C_i.

This measure of the response time is from point B in Figure 16.2. To measure from point C, the first CS^1 term is removed. To measure from point A (the notional true release time of the process) requires the clock behaviour to be measured (see Section 16.3.3).

16.3.2 Modelling sporadic processes

For sporadic processes released by other sporadic processes, or by periodic processes, Equation (16.1) is a valid model of behaviour. However, the computation time for the process, C_i, must include the overheads of blocking on the agent that controls its release.

When sporadics are released by an interrupt, priority inversion can occur. Even if the sporadic has a low priority (due to it having a long deadline) the interrupt itself will be executed at a high hardware priority level. Let Γs be the set of sporadic processes released by interrupts. Each interrupt source will be assumed to have the same arrival characteristics as the sporadic that it releases. The additional interference these interrupt handlers have on each application process is given by:

$$\sum_{k \in \Gamma s} \left\lceil \frac{R_i}{T_k} \right\rceil IH$$

where IH is the cost of handling the interrupt (and returning to the running process, having released the sporadic process).

This representation assumes that all interrupt handlers give rise to the same cost; if this is not the case then IH must be defined for each k. Equation (16.1) now becomes:

$$R_i = CS^1 + C_i + B_i + \sum_{j \in hp(i)} \left\lceil \frac{R_i}{T_j} \right\rceil (CS^1 + CS^2 + C_j)$$

Queue state	Clock handling time, μs
No processes on queue	16
Processes on queue but none removed	24
One process removed	88
Two processes removed	128
Twenty five processes removed	1048

Table 16.2   Clock handling overheads.

$$+ \sum_{k \in \Gamma s} \left\lceil \frac{R_i}{T_k} \right\rceil IH \qquad\qquad (16.2)$$

16.3.3 Modelling the real-time clock handler

To support periodic processes, the execution environment must have access to a real-time clock that will generate interrupts at appropriate times. An ideal system will use an interval timer, and will interrupt only when a periodic process needs to be released. The more common approach, however, is one in which the clock interrupts at a regular rate (say once every 10 ms) and the handler must decide if none, one, or a number of periodic processes must be released. The ideal approach can be modelled in an identical way to that introduced for sporadic processes (see Section 16.3.2). With the regular clock method, it is necessary to develop a more detailed model as the execution times of the clock handler can vary considerably. Table 16.2 gives possible times for this handler (for a clock period of 10 ms). Note that if the worst case was ˙assumed to occur on all occasions over 100% of the processor would have to be assigned to the clock handler. Moreover, all this computation occurs at a high (highest) hardware priority level, and hence considerable priority inversion is occurring. For example, with the figures given in the table, at the LCM (least common multiple) of 25 periodic processes 1048 μs of interference would be suffered by the highest priority application process that was released. If the process was released on its own then only 88 μs would be suffered. The time interval is represented by B–A in Figure 16.2.

In general, the cost of moving N periodic processes from the delay queue to the dispatch queue can be represented by the following formulae:

$$C_{clk} = CT^c + CT^s + (N - 1)CT^m$$

Where CT^c is the constant cost (assuming there is always at least one process on the delay queue), CT^s is the cost of making a single move, and CT^m is the cost of each subsequent move. This model is appropriate due to the observation that the cost of moving just one process is often high when compared with the additional cost of moving extra processes. With the kernel considered here, these costs were:

CT^c	24 μs
CT^s	64 μs
CT^m	40 μs

To reduce the pessimism of assuming that a computational cost of C_{clk} is consumed on each execution of the clock handler, this load can be spread over a number of clock ticks. This is valid if the shortest period of any application process, T_{min} is greater than the clock period, T_{clk}. Let M be defined by:

$$ M = \left\lceil \frac{T_{min}}{T_{clk}} \right\rceil $$

If M is greater than 1 then the load from the clock handler can be spread over M executions. In this situation, the clock handler is modelled as a process with period T_{min} and computation time C'_{clk}:

$$ C'_{clk} = M(CT^c + CT^s) + (N - M)CT^m $$

This assumes $M <= N$.

Equation (16.2) now becomes

$$ R_i = CS^1 + C_i + B_i + \sum_{j \in hp(i)} \left\lceil \frac{R_i}{T_j} \right\rceil (CS^1 + CS^2 + C_j) $$

$$ + \sum_{k \in \Gamma s} \left\lceil \frac{R_i}{T_k} \right\rceil IH $$

$$ + \left\lceil \frac{R_i}{T_{min}} \right\rceil C'_{clk} \tag{16.3} $$

To give further improvements (to the model) requires a more exact representation of the clock handlers actual execution. For example, using just CT^c and CT^s the following equation can easily be derived:

$$ R_i = CS^1 + C_i + B_i + \sum_{j \in hp(i)} \left\lceil \frac{R_i}{T_j} \right\rceil (CS^1 + CS^2 + C_j) $$

$$ + \sum_{k \in \Gamma s} \left\lceil \frac{R_i}{T_k} \right\rceil IH + \left\lceil \frac{R_i}{T_{clk}} \right\rceil CT_c $$

$$ + \sum_{g \in \Gamma p} \left\lceil \frac{R_i}{T_g} \right\rceil CT_s $$

$$ \tag{16.4} $$

where Γp is the set of periodic processes.

It is left as an exercise for the reader to incorporate the three-parameter model of clock handling (see Exercise 16.2).

16.3.4   The impact of the cache on worst-case execution time analysis

The problems of undertaking WCET analysis for processes executing on modern processors has already been mentioned in Section 13.12.1. In particular, it is necessary to model the behaviour of the processor's cache and pipeline. In Equation (16.4), C_i and C_j are the values that are affected. If these values are calculated following a detailed analysis of the processor's architecture, preemptions caused by interrupts need to be taken into account in the scheduling equations. Otherwise, the values used will be optimistic. Fortunately, for hard real-time systems, it is necessary to place bounds on how often interrupts can occur. Each interrupt handler is treated as a sporadic process of a high priority and is considered in the same way as a periodic process of higher priority. Equation (16.4) already specifies the number of preemptions that can occur while process i is executing. It is simply the number of times each higher-priority process can be released during process's i response time. Each preemption will potentially flush the cache and the pipeline. This leads to the following approaches to integrating the preemption penalties. Assume C_i is the worst-case value calculated using models which account for the benefits gained by caches and pipelining in *the absence* of interrupt. Calculate γ, the maximum possible penalty that can be accrued from an interrupt, this being the time taken to refill the cache and the pipeline. Equation (16.4) can now be modified to calculate the effect of interrupts on process i (Busquets and Wellings, 1996):

$$
\begin{aligned}
R_i \;=\; & CS^1 + C_i + B_i + \sum_{j \in hp(i)} \left\lceil \frac{R_i}{T_j} \right\rceil (CS^1 + CS^2 + C_j) \\
& + \sum_{k \in \Gamma s} \left\lceil \frac{R_i}{T_k} \right\rceil (IH + \gamma) + \left\lceil \frac{R_i}{T_{clk}} \right\rceil (CT_c + \gamma) \\
& + \sum_{g \in \Gamma p} \left\lceil \frac{R_i}{T_g} \right\rceil CT_s
\end{aligned}
$$

$$(16.5)$$

Of course, this is quite pessimistic because not all preemptions will require the whole cache to be refilled. Furthermore, some memory blocks which are replaced would have been replaced anyway. A less pessimistic approach tries to identify the number of cache blocks.

16.4   Hardware support

When concurrent processes are introduced into the solution to any real-time problem, overheads with scheduling, interprocess communication, and so on, occur. Section 16.3.3 has attempted to model these overheads in the schedulability analysis. Several attempts have also been made to reduce these overheads by providing direct hardware support. This section briefly considers two hardware kernels. The first is the transputer which was designed to execute occam2 programs efficiently, and the second is the Ada Tasking Coprocessor (ATAC).

In more recent years, there have been moves to support the Java Virtual Machine directly in hardware (for example, Sun Microsystems' picoJava processor (Sun Microsystems, 2000) or the aJ-100 from aJile Systems Inc (aJile Systems, 2000)). This support goes beyond the support for just concurrent execution and attempts to improve the performance over interpreting Java byte code.

16.4.1   The transputer and occam2

The transputer was designed as an occam2 machine which, on a single chip, has a 32-bit processor, a 64-bit floating-point coprocessor, internal memory and a number of communication links for direct connection to other transputers. An address bus joins external memory to the internal provision by means of a continuous address space. Typically a transputer will have 16 kbyte of internal memory; this acts as, in effect, a large collection of non-sharable registers for the executing processes.

The links are connected to the main processor via link interfaces. These interfaces can independently manage the communications of the link (including direct access to memory). As a result, a transputer can simultaneously communicate on all links (in both directions), execute an internal process and undertake a floating-point operation.

The transputer has a reduced instruction set but with an operations stack of only three registers. Each instruction has been designed to be of use in the code generation phase of the occam2 compiler; direct programming in assembler, although allowed, has not been taken into account in the design of the instruction set. Being a reduced instruction machine, not all instructions are immediately available; those that are directly accessible are precisely those that are commonly generated from real occam2 programs.

Unfortunately the transputer can only support a limited priority model. But by this restriction, a run-time support system that is essentially cast in silicon can be provided. The result of this architecture (plus the axiom that context switches only take place when the operations stack is empty) is very small context switch times.

Although the operational characteristics of a single transputer are impressive it is only when they are grouped together that their full potential is realized. Transputers use point-to-point communication, which has the disadvantage that a message may have to be forwarded to its destination via intermediates if no direct link is available. Nevertheless link transfer rates are very high and transmission failure rates very low, giving a real-time engine of considerable power and reliability.

16.4.2 ATAC and Ada

There have been several attempts to produce Ada machines, for example (Ericsson, 1986; Runner and Warshawsky, 1988). The one considered here is an Ada tasking coprocessor (ATAC) designed by Roos (1991).

The ATAC is a hardware device designed to support the Ada 83 tasking and clock models. It also anticipated some of the Ada 95 features such as support for priority inheritance and 'delay until'. It goal is to remove the burden of supporting Ada tasking from the application CPU, thereby allowing tasks to proceed efficiently without the overheads normally incurred by the Ada run-time support system.

Communication between CPU and the ATAC is based on standard memory-mapped read and write instructions. A set of primitive operations provide the interface; they include:

- `CreateTask` – create a new task;
- `ActTasks` – activate one or more created tasks;
- `Activated` – signal activation to creating task;
- `EnterTBlock` – enter a new task block;
- `ExitTBlock` – wait for dependent tasks to exit a task block;
- `EntryCall` – make an entry call;
- `TimedECall` – make a timed entry call;
- `SelectArg` – open a select alternative;
- `SelectRes` – choose an alternative in a select;
- `RndvCompl` – set caller runnable after the rendezvous is complete;
- `Activate` – make a suspended task runnable;
- `Suspend` – suspend the current task;
- `Switch` – perform a reschedule;
- `Delay` – delay a task.

The ATAC also fields all interrupt and interrupts the CPU only if a higher-priority task becomes runnable. An internal timer is used to support the Ada delay facilities and package calendar.

The overall goal of ATAC is to increase the performance of Ada tasking by two orders of magnitude over a pure software run-time system.

Summary

The execution environment is a key component of any implemented real-time system. It supports the application, but also introduces overheads and constrains the facilities that the application can use. A full-blown operating system (OS) could be used to provide the execution environment, but this is usually rejected due to:

- size of the OS (that is, memory occupancy);
- efficiency of key functions (such as context switching);
- complexity and hence reliability of the complete OS.

In this chapter it has been shown how an execution environment can be tailored to an application's specific needs, how its overheads can be modelled, and how hardware support can be provided. Other parts of the book have also introduced issues of significance to the execution environment. For example:

- its role in providing damage confinement (that is, firewalls);
- its role in error detection;
- its role in supporting communications in a distributed system.

The second issue has a number of facets. Various aspects of the application's execution can be monitored (array bounds violation, memory violation, time overruns). Also 'built-in test' facilities can be run in background mode to exercise parts of the hardware in order to isolate faulty components and generate maintenance data for fault removal.

As many features of an execution environment are important to a wide range of applications, there is a need to reuse trusted components and to move towards the provision of standard environments. The use of standardized languages and operating system interfaces will help to bring this about.

Further reading

Allen, R. K., Burns, A. and Wellings, A. J. (1995) Sporadic Tasks in Hard Real-Time Systems. *Ada Letters*, XV(5), 46–51.

Burns, A., Tindell, K. and Wellings, A. J. (1995) Effective Analysis for Engineering Real-Time Fixed Priority Schedulers. *IEEE Transactions on Software Engineering*, 21(5), 475–480.

Venners, B. (1999) *Inside the Java 1.2 Virtual Machine*. New York: Osborne McGraw-Hill.

Exercises

16.1 Should the real-time system's programmer be aware of the implementation cost of all the implementation language's features?

16.2 Develop a model of clock handling which incorporates the three parameters CT^c, CT^s and CT^m (see Section 16.3.3).

16.3 Rather than using a clock interrupt to schedule periodic processes, what would be the ramifications of only having access to a real-time clock?

16.4 A periodic process of period 40 ms is controlled by a clock interrupt that has a granularity of 30 ms. How can the worst-case response time of this process be calculated?

Chapter 17

A case study in Ada

In this chapter, a case study is presented which includes many of the facilities described in this book. Ideally, the study should be given in Ada, Real-Time Java, C (and POSIX) and occam2. Unfortunately, space is limited so the study is restricted to Ada only.

17.1 Mine drainage

The example that has been chosen is based on one which commonly appears in the literature. It concerns the software necessary to manage a simplified pump control system for a mining environment (Kramer et al., 1983; Sloman and Kramer, 1987; Shrivastava et al., 1987; Burns and Lister, 1991; Joseph, 1996; de la Puente et al., 1996); it possesses many of the characteristics which typify embedded real-time systems. It is assumed that the system will be implemented on a single processor with a simple memory-mapped I/O architecture.

The system is used to pump mine water, which collects in a sump at the bottom of the shaft, to the surface. The main safety requirement is that the pump should not be operated when the level of methane gas in the mine reaches a high value due to the risk of explosion. A simple schematic diagram of the system is given in Figure 17.1.

The relationship between the control system and the external devices is shown in Figure 17.2. Note that only the high and low water sensors communicate via interrupts (indicated by dashed arrows); all the other devices are either polled or directly controlled.

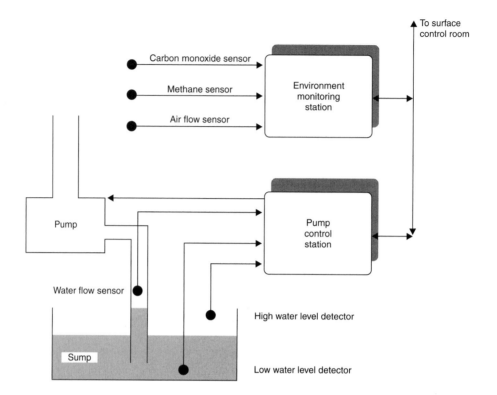

Figure 17.1   A mine drainage control system.

17.1.1 Functional requirements

The functional specification of the system may be divided into four components: the pump operation, the environment monitoring, the operator interaction, and system monitoring.

Pump operation

The required behaviour of the pump controller is that it monitors the water levels in the sump. When the water reaches a high level (or when requested by the operator), the pump is turned on and the sump is drained until the water reaches the low level. At this point (or when requested by the operator), the pump is turned off. A flow of water in the pipes can be detected if required.

The pump should only be allowed to operate if the methane level in the mine is below a critical level.

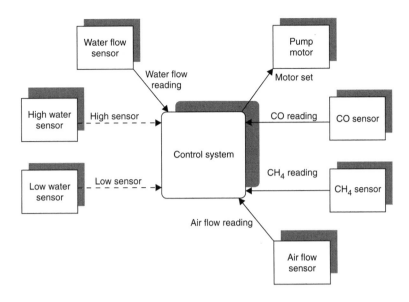

Figure 17.2   Graph showing external devices.

Environment monitoring

The environment must be monitored to detect the level of methane in the air; there is a level beyond which it is not safe to cut coal or operate the pump. The monitoring also measures the level of carbon monoxide in the mine and detects whether there is an adequate flow of air. Alarms must be signalled if gas levels or air-flow become critical.

Operator interaction

The system is controlled from the surface via an operator's console. The operator is informed of all critical events.

System monitoring

All the system events are to be stored in an archival database, and may be retrieved and displayed upon request.

17.1.2   Non-functional requirements

The non-functional requirements can be divided into three components: timing, dependability, and security. This case study is mainly concerned with the timing requirements and consequently dependability and security will not be addressed (see Burns and Lister (1991) for a full consideration of dependability and security aspects).

There are several requirements which relate to the timeliness of system actions. The following list is adapted from Burns and Lister (1991):

(i) Monitoring periods

The maximum periods for reading the environment sensors may be dictated by legislation. For the purpose of this example, it is assumed that these periods are the same for all sensors, namely 100 ms. In the case of methane, there may be a more stringent requirement based on the proximity of the pump and the need to ensure that it never operates when the methane level is critically high. This is discussed in (ii) below. In Section 15.8, it was described how a device driver can be analyzed. In the case study, the 'period displacement' approach will be used for the CH_4 and CO sensors. These environmental sensors each require 40 ms in order for a reading to become available. Hence they require a deadline of 60 ms.

The water flow object executes periodically and has two roles. While the pump is operational it checks that there is a water flow; but while the pump is off (or disabled) it also checks that the water has stopped flowing. This latter check is used as confirmation that the pump has indeed been stopped. Due to a time lag in the flow of water, this object is given a period of 1 second, and it uses the results of two consecutive readings to determine the actual state of the pump. To make sure that two consecutive readings are actually one second apart (approximately), the object is given a tight deadline of 40 ms (that is, two readings will be at least 960 ms, but no more than 1040 ms, apart).

It is assumed that the water level detectors are event-driven and that the system should respond within 200 ms. The physics of the application indicates that there must be at least 6 seconds between interrupts from the two water level indicators.

(ii) Shut-down deadline

To avoid explosions, there is a deadline within which the pump must be switched off once the methane level exceeds a critical threshold. This deadline is related to the methane-sampling period, to the rate at which methane can accumulate, and to the margin of safety between the level of methane regarded as critical and the level at which it explodes. With a direct reading of the sensor, the relationship can be expressed by the inequality:

```
R(T + D) < M
```

where

      R is the rate at which methane can accumulate
      T is the sampling period
      D is the shut-down deadline
      M is the safety margin.

	Periodic/sporadic	'Period'	Deadline
CH$_4$ sensor	P	80	30
CO sensor	P	100	60
Air flow	P	100	100
Water flow	P	1000	40
Water level detectors	S	6000	200

Table 17.1   Attributes of periodic and sporadic entities.

If 'period displacement' is used then a further period of time is needed:

```
R(2T + D) < M
```

Note that the period T and the deadline D can be traded off against each other, and both can be traded off against the safety margin M. The longer the period or the deadline, the more conservative must be the safety margin; the shorter the period or deadline, the closer to its safety limits the mine can operate. The designer may therefore vary any of D, T or M in satisfying the deadline and periodicity requirements.

In this example, it is assumed that the presence of methane pockets may cause levels to rise rapidly, and therefore a deadline requirement (from methane going high to the pump been disabled) of 200 ms is assumed. This can be met by setting the rate for the methane sensor at 80 ms, with a deadline of 30 ms. Note that this level will ensure that correct readings are taken from the sensor (that is, the displacement between two readings is at least 50 ms).

(iii) Operator information deadline

The operator must be informed within 1 second of detection of critically high methane or carbon monoxide readings, within 2 seconds of a critically low air-flow reading, and within 3 seconds of a failure in the operation of the pump. These requirements are easily met when compared with the other timing requirements.

In summary, Table 17.1 defines the periods, or minimum inter-arrival times ('period') and deadlines (in milliseconds) for the sensors.

17.2   The HRT-HOOD design method

In Chapter 2 the HRT-HOOD development process was introduced. It focuses on the design of logical and physical architectures and uses an object-based notation. A simplified version of this method is used in this chapter.

HRT-HOOD facilitates the logical architectural design of a system by providing different object types. They are:

- **Passive** – reentrant objects which have no control over when invocations of their operations are executed, and do not spontaneously invoke operations in other objects.

- **Active** – objects which may control when invocations of their operations are executed, and may spontaneously invoke operations in other objects. Active objects are the most general class of objects and have no restrictions placed on them.

- **Protected** – objects which may control when invocations of their operations are executed, but do not spontaneously invoke operations in other objects; in general protected objects may **not** have arbitrary synchronization constraints and must be analyzable for the blocking times they impose on their callers.

- **Cyclic** – objects which represent periodic activities, they may spontaneously invoke operations in other objects and only have very restrictive interfaces.

- **Sporadic** – objects which represent sporadic activities; sporadic objects may spontaneously invoke operations in other objects; each sporadic has a **single** operation which is called to invoke the sporadic.

A hard real-time program designed using HRT-HOOD will contain at the terminal level (that is, after full design decomposition) only cyclic, sporadic, protected and passive objects. Active objects, because they cannot be fully analyzed, are only allowed for background activity. Active object types may be used during decomposition of the main system but must be transformed into one of the above types before reaching the terminal level.

Figure 17.3 illustrates the diagrammatic representation of an HRT-HOOD design. It shows the hierarchical decomposition of a 'Parent' object into two child objects ('Child1', 'Child2'). The 'Parent' object is an active object (indicated by the letter 'A' in the top left-hand corner of the object) and has two operations 'Operation1' and 'Operation2'. The child objects each implement the functionality of one of the operations. To implement the functionality of 'Operation1', 'Child1' uses the facilities provided by 'Child2' (a passive object) and an 'Uncle'. An uncle object is an object which is defined at a higher level of decomposition. The diagram also shows data flow and exception flow.

17.3   The logical architecture design

The logical architecture addresses those requirements which are independent of the physical constraints (for example, processor speeds) imposed by the execution environment. The functional requirements identified in Section 17.1.1 fall into this category. Consideration of the other system requirements is deferred until the design of the physical architecture, described later.

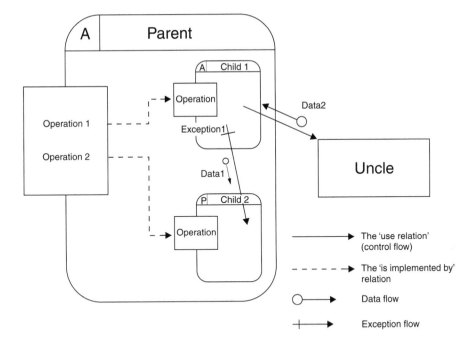

Figure 17.3   HRT-HOOD diagrammatic notation.

17.3.1   First level decomposition

The first step in developing the logical architecture is the identification of appropriate classes of object from which the system can be built. The functional requirements of the system suggest four distinct subsystems:

(1) pump controller subsystem – responsible for operating the pump;

(2) environment monitor subsystem – responsible for monitoring the environment;

(3) operator console subsystem – responsible for the interface to operators;

(4) data logger subsystem – responsible for logging operational and environmental data.

Figure 17.4 illustrates this decomposition. The pump controller has four operations: The operations 'not safe' and 'is safe' are called by the environment monitor to indicate to the pump controller whether it is safe to operate the pump (due to the level of methane in the environment). The 'request status' and 'set pump' operations are called by the operator console. As an additional reliability feature, the pump controller will always check that the methane level is low before starting the pump (by calling 'check safe' in the environment monitor). If the pump controller finds that the pump cannot be

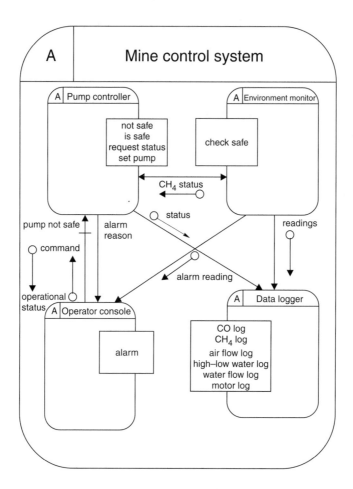

Figure 17.4   First-level hierarchical decomposition of the control system.

started (or that the water does not appear to be flowing when the pump is notionally on) then it raises an operator alarm.

The environment monitor has the single operation 'check safe' which is called by the pump controller.

The operator console has the alarm operation, which as well as being called by the pump controller, is also called by the environmental monitor if any of its readings are too high. As well as receiving the alarm calls, the operator console can request the status of the pump and attempt to override the high and low water sensors by directly operating the pump. However, in the latter case the methane check is still made, with an exception being used to inform the operator that the pump cannot be turned on.

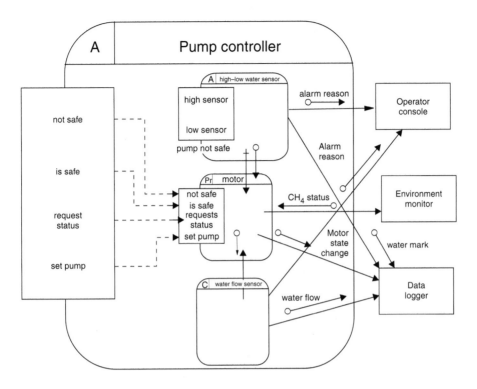

Figure 17.5   Hierarchical decomposition of the pump object.

The data logger has six operations which are merely data logging actions that are called by the pump controller and the environment monitor.

17.3.2 Pump controller

The decomposition appropriate to the pump controller is shown in Figure 17.5. The pump controller is decomposed into three objects. The first object controls the pump motor. As this object simply responds to commands, requires mutual exclusion for its operations, and does not spontaneously call other objects, it is a *protected* object. All of the pump controller's operations are implemented by the motor object. As the system is real-time, none of the operations can be arbitrarily blocked (although they require mutual exclusion). The motor object will make calls to all its uncle objects.

The other two objects control the water sensors. The flow sensor object is a *cyclic* object which continually monitors the flow of water from the mine. The high–low water sensor is an *active* object which handles the interrupts from the high–low water sensors. It decomposes into a *protected* and a *sporadic* object, as shown in Figure 17.6.

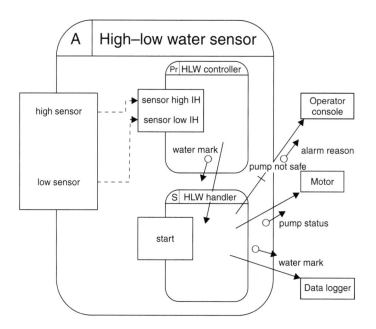

Figure 17.6   Decomposition of the high–low water sensor.

17.3.3   The environment monitor

The environment monitor decomposes into four terminal objects, as shown in Figure 17.7. Three of the objects are *cyclic* objects which monitor the CH_4 level, CO level and the air flow in the mine environment. Only the CH_4 level is requested by other objects in the system; consequently a *protected* object is used to control access to the current value.

17.3.4   The data logger and the operator console

This case study is not concerned with the details of the data logger or the operator console. However, it is a requirement that they only delay the real-time threads for a bounded time. It is assumed, therefore, that their interfaces contain protected objects.

17.4   The physical architecture design

HRT-HOOD supports the design of a physical architecture by:

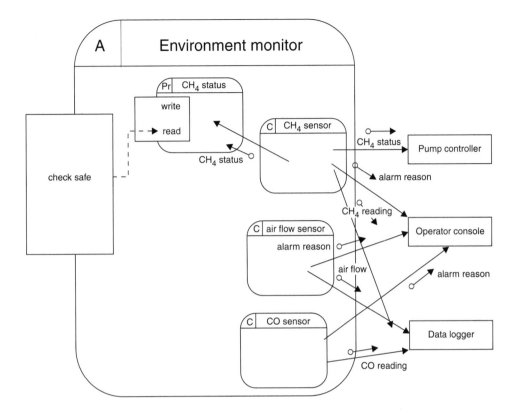

Figure 17.7   Hierarchical decomposition of the environment monitor.

- allowing timing attributes to be associated with objects,

- providing a framework from within which a schedulability approach can be defined and the analysis of the terminal objects undertaken, and

- providing the abstractions with which the designer can express the handling of timing errors.

The non-functional timing requirements identified in Section 17.1.2 are transformed into annotations on methods and threads. To illustrate the analysis described in Chapter 13, fixed priority scheduling will be used and the response-time form of analysis will be undertaken. Table 17.2 summarizes the timing attributes of the objects introduced in the logical architecture.

	Type	'Period'	Deadline	Priority
CH$_4$ sensor	Periodic	80	30	10
CO sensor	Periodic	100	60	8
Air-flow sensor	Periodic	100	100	7
Water-flow sensor	Periodic	1000	40	9
HLW handler	Sporadic	6000	200	6
Motor	Protected			10
HLW controller	Protected			11
CH$_4$ status	Protected			10
Operator console	Protected			10
Data logger	Protected			10

Table 17.2   Attributes of design objects.

	Type	WCET
CH$_4$ sensor	Periodic	12
CO sensor	Periodic	10
Air flow sensor	Periodic	10
Water flow sensor	Periodic	10
HLW handler	Sporadic	20
Interrupt	Sporadic	2

Table 17.3   Worst-case execution times.

17.4.1 Scheduling analysis

Once the code has been developed, it must be analyzed to obtain its worst-case execution times. As indicated in Section 15.8, these values can be obtained via either direct measurement or by modelling the hardware. None of the code derived is particularly extensive, so it is reasonable to assume that a low speed processor is adequate. Table 17.3 contains some representative values for the worst-case execution times (in milliseconds) for each object in the design. Note the times for each thread include time spent executing within other objects, the time spent executing exception handlers and the associated context switch times. To model the effect of the interrupt handler a 'pseudo' sporadic object is introduced (the maximum handler execution time is 2ms).

The execution environment imposes its own set of important parameters – these are given in Table 17.4. Note that the clock interrupt is of sufficient granularity to ensure no release jitter for the periodic threads.

The maximum blocking time, for all threads, occurs when the operator console makes a call upon the motor object. It can be assumed that the thread that makes the call is of low priority. The worst-case execution time for this protected operation is assumed to be 3 ms.

	Symbol	Time
Clock period	T_{CLK}	20
Clock overhead	CT^c	2
Cost of single task move	CT^s	1

Table 17.4   Overheads.

	Type	T	B	C	D	R
CH$_4$ sensor	Periodic	80	3	12	30	25
CO sensor	Periodic	100	3	10	60	47
Air flow sensor	Periodic	100	3	10	100	57
Water flow sensor	Periodic	1000	3	10	40	35
HLW handler	Sporadic	6000	3	20	200	79

Table 17.5   Analysis results.

The above information can now be synthesized to provide a comprehensive analysis of the response times of all threads in the system. This analysis is given in Table 17.5. The conclusion of the analysis is that all deadlines are met.

17.5   Translation to Ada

HRT-HOOD supports a systematic translation to Ada. For each terminal object, two packages are generated: the first simply contains a collection of data types and variables defining the object's real-time attributes; the second contains the code for the object itself.

Each of the objects shown in Figure 17.4 can potentially be implemented on a separate processor. However, for the purpose of this example, a single-processor implementation is considered.

The decomposition appropriate to the pump controller was shown in Figure 17.5 and the high–low water sensor object is given in Figure 17.6. It is now possible to give the code for these objects.

17.5.1   The pump controller object

The motor

The real-time attributes for the motor object are given first. For simplicity, only the ceiling priority attribute is shown.

```
package Motor_Rtatt is
  Ceiling_Priority: constant := 10;
end Motor_Rtatt;
```

The interface for the motor object is:

```
package Motor is -- PROTECTED
  type Pump_Status is (On, Off);
  type Pump_Condition is (Enabled, Disabled);

  type Motor_State_Changes is (Motor_Started,
      Motor_Stopped, Motor_Safe, Motor_Unsafe);

  type Operational_Status is
    record
      Ps : Pump_Status;
      Pc : Pump_Condition;
    end record;

  Pump_Not_Safe : exception;

  procedure Not_Safe;
  procedure Is_Safe;

  function Request_Status return Operational_Status;
  procedure Set_Pump(To : Pump_Status);
end Motor;
```

The state of the motor is defined by two variables. One which indicates whether the pump should be on or off, and the other whether the pump is enabled or disabled. The pump is disabled when it is unsafe to operate. The type Motor_State_Changes is used to indicate state changes to the data logger.

A state transition diagram for the motor is shown in Figure 17.8. Only in the 'On-Enabled' state will the pump actually be operating.

The body of the package, therefore, implements the state changes. As these must be done atomically, a protected object is used. In this chapter, all protected objects generated to implement synchronization constraints are called Agent. The code assumes that devices register types are declared in a package called Device_Register_Types.

```
package Device_Register_Types is
  Word : constant := 2;        -- two bytes in a word
  One_Word : constant := 16; -- 16 bits in a word
  -- register field types
  type Device_Error is (Clear, Set);
  type Device_Operation is (Clear, Set);
  type Interrupt_Status is (I_Disabled, I_Enabled);
  type Device_Status is (D_Disabled, D_Enabled);

  -- register type itself
  type Csr is
```

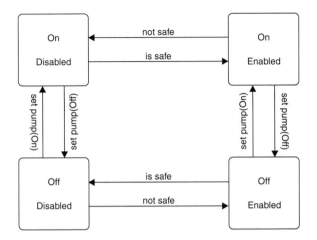

Figure 17.8   State transition diagram for the motor.

```
record
    Error_Bit   : Device_Error;
    Operation   : Device_Operation;
    Done        : Boolean;
    Interrupt   : Interrupt_Status;
    Device      : Device_Status;
end record;
-- bit representation of the register field
for Device_Error use (Clear => 0, Set => 1);
for Device_Operation use (Clear => 0, Set => 1);
for Interrupt_Status use (I_Disabled => 0,
                          I_Enabled => 1);
for Device_Status use (D_Disabled => 0,
                       D_Enabled => 1);
for Csr use
  record at mod Word;
    Error_Bit   at 0 range 15 ..15;
    Operation   at 0 range 10 ..10;
    Done        at 0 range 7 .. 7;
    Interrupt   at 0 range 6 .. 6;
    Device      at 0 range 0 .. 0;
  end record;
for Csr'Size use One_Word;
for Csr'Alignment use Word;
for Csr'Bit_order use Low_Order_First;
end Device_Register_Types;
```

The body of the Motor package simply contains the implementation of the Agent protected type. The external operations simply call the protected subprograms.

```ada
with Data_Logger;
with Ch4_Status; use  Ch4_Status;
with Device_Register_Types; use Device_Register_Types;
with System; use System;
with Motor_Rtatt; use Motor_Rtatt;
with System.Storage_Elements; use System.Storage_Elements;
package body Motor is
   Control_Reg_Addr : constant Address := To_Address(16#Aa14#);
   Pcsr : Device_Register_Types.Csr :=
        (Error_Bit => Clear, Operation => Set,
         Done => False, Interrupt => I_Enabled,
         Device => D_Enabled);
   for Pcsr'Address use Control_Reg_Addr;

   protected Agent is
     pragma Priority(Motor_Rtatt.
                        Ceiling_Priority);
     procedure Not_Safe;
     procedure Is_Safe;
     function Request_Status return Operational_Status;
     procedure Set_Pump(To : Pump_Status);
   private
     Motor_Status : Pump_Status := Off;
     Motor_Condition : Pump_Condition := Disabled;
   end Agent;

   procedure Not_Safe is
   begin
      Agent.Not_Safe;
   end Not_Safe;

   procedure Is_Safe is
   begin
      Agent.Is_Safe;
   end Is_Safe;

   function Request_Status return Pump_Status is
   begin
      return Agent.Request_Status;
   end Request_Status;

   procedure Set_Pump(To : Pump_Status) is
   begin
      Agent.Set_Pump(To);
   end Set_Pump;

   protected body Agent is
     procedure Not_Safe is
     begin
       if Motor_Status = On then
          Pcsr.Operation := Clear; -- turn off motor
          Data_Logger.Motor_Log(Motor_Stopped);
       end if;
       Motor_Condition := Disabled;
       Data_Logger.Motor_Log(Motor_Unsafe);
```

```
      end Not_Safe;

      procedure Is_Safe is
      begin
        if Motor_Status = On then
          Pcsr.Operation := Set; -- start motor
          Data_Logger.Motor_Log(Motor_Started);
        end if;
        Motor_Condition := Enabled;
        Data_Logger.Motor_Log(Motor_Safe);
      end Is_Safe;

      function Request_Status return Operational_Status is
      begin
        return (Ps => Motor_Status, Pc => Motor_Condition);
      end Request_Status;

      procedure Set_Pump(To : Pump_Status) is
      begin
        if To = On then
          if Motor_Status = Off then
            if Motor_Condition = Disabled then
              raise Pump_Not_Safe;
            end if;
            if Ch4_Status.Read  = Motor_Safe then
              Motor_Status := On;
              Pcsr.Operation := Set; -- turn on motor
              Data_Logger.Motor_Log(Motor_Started);
            else
              raise Pump_Not_Safe;
            end if;
          end if;
        else
          if Motor_Status = On then
            Motor_Status:= Off;
            if Motor_Condition = Enabled then
              Pcsr.Operation := Clear; -- turn off motor
              Data_Logger.Motor_Log(Motor_Stopped);
            end if;
          end if;
        end if;
      end Set_Pump;
    end Agent;
end Motor;
```

Water flow sensor handling object

The water-flow sensor is a cyclic object, and therefore has the following real-time attributes.

```
with System; use System;
with Ada.Real_Time; use Ada.Real_Time;
```

```
package Water_Flow_Sensor_Rtatt is
  Period : Time_Span := Milliseconds(1000);
  Thread_Priority : constant Priority := 9;
end Water_Flow_Sensor_Rtatt;
```

There is no provided interface to the object, although a type declaration is required for the data logger. The pragma is needed to ensure the body of the package is elaborated.

```
package Water_Flow_Sensor is -- CYCLIC
  pragma Elaborate_Body;
  type Water_Flow is (Yes, No);
                      -- calls Operator_Console.Alarm
                      -- calls Data_Logger.Water_Flow_Log
                      -- calls Motor.Request_Status
end Water_Flow_Sensor;
```

The body contains two subprograms: one for initializing the sensor (Initialize), and the other for the code to be executed each period (Periodic_Code). Every invocation, the task simply checks that if the pump is on, water is flowing and if the pump is off, no water flows. Alarms are sounded if these two invariants are violated. The task Thread implements the correct periodic timing attributes.

```
with Ada.Real_Time; use Ada.Real_Time;
with Device_Register_Types; use Device_Register_Types;
with System; use System;
with Water_Flow_Sensor_Rtatt; use Water_Flow_Sensor_Rtatt;
with Motor; use Motor;
with Operator_Console; use Operator_Console;
with Data_Logger; use Data_Logger;
with System.Storage_Elements; use System.Storage_Elements;
package body Water_Flow_Sensor is
  Flow : Water_Flow := No;
  Current_Pump_Status, Last_Pump_Status : Pump_Status := Off;

  Control_Reg_Addr : constant Address := To_Address(16#Aa14#);
  Wfcsr : Device_Register_Types.Csr;
  for Wfcsr'Address use Control_Reg_Addr;

  procedure Initialize is
  begin
    -- enable device
    Wfcsr.Device := D_Enabled;
  end Initialize;

  procedure Periodic_Code is
  begin
    Current_Pump_Status := Motor.Request_Status;
    if (Wfcsr.Operation = Set) then
      Flow := Yes;
    else
      Flow := No;
    end if;
```

```
  if Current_Pump_Status = On and
     Last_Pump_Status = On and Flow = No  then
    Operator_Console.Alarm(Pump_Fault);
  elsif Current_Pump_Status = Off and
     Last_Pump_Status = Off and Flow = Yes  then
    Operator_Console.Alarm(Pump_Fault);
  end if;
  Last_Pump_Status := Current_Pump_Status;
  Data_Logger.Water_Flow_Log(Flow);
end Periodic_Code;


task Thread is
  pragma Priority(Water_Flow_Sensor_Rtatt.Thread_Priority);
end Thread;


task body Thread is
  T: Time;
  Period : Time_Span := Water_Flow_Sensor_Rtatt.Period;
begin
  T:= Clock;
  Initialize;
  loop
    Periodic_Code;
    T := T + Period;
    delay until(T);
  end loop;
end Thread;
end Water_Flow_Sensor;
```

The HLW controller object

The HLW controller object is responsible for handling interrupts from the high and low water detectors. Its purpose is to map the two interrupts to a call to a single sporadic object called 'HLW handler'. It is necessary because HRT-HOOD does not allow a sporadic object to be invoked by more than one start operation. The interrupt handlers are procedures in an Ada protected object.

```
with System; use System;
with Ada.Real_Time; use Ada.Real_Time;
package Hlw_Controller_Rtatt is
  Ceiling_Priority :  constant Priority :=  11;
end Hlw_Controller_Rtatt;

with Hlw_Controller_Rtatt; use Hlw_Controller_Rtatt;
package Hlw_Controller is -- PROTECTED
  procedure Sensor_High_Ih;
  procedure Sensor_Low_Ih;
end Hlw_Controller;

with Hlw_Handler; use Hlw_Handler;
with System; use System;
with Ada.Interrupts; use Ada.Interrupts;
```

```ada
with Ada.Interrupts.Names; use Ada.Interrupts.Names;
-- Ada.Interrupts.Names defines Waterh_Interrupt and Waterl_Interrupt
package body Hlw_Controller is
  protected Agent is
    pragma Priority(Hlw_Controller_Rtatt.
                      Ceiling_Priority);
    procedure Sensor_High_Ih;
    pragma Attach_Handler(Sensor_High_Ih, Waterh_Interrupt);
          -- assigns interrupt handler
    procedure Sensor_Low_Ih;
    pragma Attach_Handler(Sensor_Low_Ih, Waterl_Interrupt);
          -- assigns interrupt handler
  end Agent;

  procedure Sensor_High_Ih is
  begin
    Agent.Sensor_High_Ih;
  end Sensor_High_Ih;

  procedure Sensor_Low_Ih is
  begin
    Agent.Sensor_Low_Ih;
  end Sensor_Low_Ih;

  protected body Agent is
    procedure Sensor_High_Ih is
    begin
      Hlw_Handler.Start(High);
    end Sensor_High_Ih;

    procedure Sensor_Low_Ih is
    begin
      Hlw_Handler.Start(Low);
    end Sensor_Low_Ih;
  end Agent;
end Hlw_Controller;
```

HLW handler

The HLW handler object handles the application's response to the interrupt; that is, requesting the pump be turned on and off. It contains a task which is waiting for the interrupt via a protected object entry (Wait_Start). The interrupt is signalled by the HLW controller object by a call to the Start operation. (A more sophisticated mapping would enable overruns on the interrupting device to be detected and handled.)

```ada
with System; use System;
package Hlw_Handler_Rtatt is
  Ceiling_Priority :  constant Priority := 11;
  Thread_Priority :  constant Priority := 6;
end Hlw_Handler_Rtatt;
```

```ada
with Hlw_Handler_Rtatt; use Hlw_Handler_Rtatt;
package Hlw_Handler is -- SPORADIC
  type Water_Mark is (High, Low);
  procedure Start(Int : Water_Mark);
end Hlw_Handler;


with Device_Register_Types; use Device_Register_Types;
with System; use System;
with Motor; use Motor;
with Data_Logger;
with System.Storage_Elements; use System.Storage_Elements;
package body Hlw_Handler is
  Hw_Control_Reg_Addr : constant Address := To_Address(16#Aa10#);
  Lw_Control_Reg_Addr : constant Address :=  To_Address(16#Aa12#);
  Hwcsr : Device_Register_Types.Csr;
  for Hwcsraddress use Hw_Control_Reg_Addr;
  Lwcsr : Device_Register_Types.Csr;
  for Lwcsr'Address use Lw_Control_Reg_Addr;

  procedure Sporadic_Code(Int : Water_Mark) is
  begin
    if Int = High then
      Motor.Set_Pump(On);
      Data_Logger.High_Low_Water_Log(High);
      Lwcsr.Interrupt := I_Enabled;
      Hwcsr.Interrupt := I_Disabled;
    else
      Motor.Set_Pump(Off);
      Data_Logger.High_Low_Water_Log(Low);
      Hwcsr.Interrupt := I_Enabled;
      Lwcsr.Interrupt := I_Disabled;
    end if;
  end Sporadic_Code;

  procedure Initialize is
  begin
    Hwcsr.Device :=D_Enabled;
    Hwcsr.Interrupt := I_Enabled;
    Lwcsr.Device :=D_Enabled;
    Lwcsr.Interrupt := I_Enabled;
  end Initialize;

  task Thread is
    pragma Priority(Hlw_Handler_Rtatt.Thread_Priority);
  end Thread;

  protected Agent is
    pragma Priority(Hlw_Handler_Rtatt.
                    Ceiling_Priority);
    -- for the Start operation
    procedure Start(Int : Water_Mark);
    entry Wait_Start(Int : out Water_Mark);
  private
    Start_Open : Boolean := False;
    W : Water_Mark;
  end Agent;
```

```
procedure Start(Int : Water_Mark) is
begin
  Agent.Start(Int);
end Start;

protected body Agent is
  procedure Start(Int : Water_Mark) is
  begin
    W := Int;
    Start_Open := True;
  end Start;

  entry Wait_Start(Int : out Water_Mark)
        when Start_Open is
  begin
    Int := W;
    Start_Open := False;
  end Wait_Start;
end Agent;

task body Thread is
  Int : Water_Mark;
begin
  Initialize;
  loop
    Agent.Wait_Start(Int);
    Sporadic_Code(Int);
  end loop;
end Thread;
end Hlw_Handler;
```

17.5.2   Environment monitoring

The decomposition of the environment monitor subsystem is shown in Figure 17.7. Note that the check_safe subprogram allows the pump controller to observe the current state of the methane level without blocking, via the CH_4 status protected object. All other components are periodic activities.

CH4 status object

The CH4 status object simply contains data which indicates whether it is safe to operate the pump.

```
with System; use System;
with Ada.Real_Time; use Ada.Real_Time;
package Ch4_Status_Rtatt is
  -- for PROTECTED objects
  Ceiling_Priority :  constant Priority :=  10;
end Ch4_Status_Rtatt;
```

```
package Ch4_Status is -- PROTECTED
  type Methane_Status is (Motor_Safe, Motor_Unsafe);

  function Read return Methane_Status;
  procedure Write (Current_Status : Methane_Status);
end Ch4_Status;



with Ch4_Status_Rtatt; use Ch4_Status_Rtatt;
package body Ch4_Status is
 protected Agent is
    pragma Priority(Ch4_Status_Rtatt.
                      Ceiling_Priority);
    procedure Write (Current_Status : Methane_Status);
    function Read return Methane_Status;
 private
    Environment_Status : Methane_Status := Motor_Unsafe;
 end Agent;

  function Read return Methane_Status is
  begin
    return Agent.Read;
  end Read;

  procedure Write (Current_Status : Methane_Status) is
  begin
    Agent.Write(Current_Status);
  end Write;

  protected body Agent is
    procedure Write (Current_Status : Methane_Status) is
    begin
      Environment_Status := Current_Status;
    end Write;

    function Read return Methane_Status is
    begin
      return Environment_Status;
    end Read;
  end Agent;
end Ch4_Status;
```

CH$_4$ sensor handling object

The function of the CH$_4$ sensor is to measure the level of methane in the environment.
The requirements are that it should not rise above a threshold. Inevitably, around this
threshold the sensor will continually signal safe and unsafe. To avoid this jitter, lower
and upper bounds on the threshold are used. Note that, as the ADC takes some time to
produce its result, the conversion is requested at the end of one period to be used at the
start of the next.

```ada
with System; use System;
with Ada.Real_Time; use Ada.Real_Time;
package Ch4_Sensor_Rtatt is

  Period : Time_Span := Milliseconds(80);
  Thread_Priority : constant Priority := 10;

end Ch4_Sensor_Rtatt;



package Ch4_Sensor is -- CYCLIC
  pragma Elaborate_Body;
  type Ch4_Reading is new Integer range 0 .. 1023;
  Ch4_High : constant Ch4_Reading := 400;
                      -- calls Motor.Is_Safe
                      -- calls Motor.Not_Safe
                      -- calls Operator_Console.Alarm
                      -- calls Data_Logger.Ch4_Log
end Ch4_Sensor;



with Ada.Real_Time; use Ada.Real_Time;
with System; use System;
with Ch4_Sensor_Rtatt; use Ch4_Sensor_Rtatt;
with Device_Register_Types; use Device_Register_Types;
with Operator_Console; use Operator_Console;
with Motor; use Motor;
with Data_Logger; use Data_Logger;
with Ch4_Status; use Ch4_Status;
with System.Storage_Elements; use System.Storage_Elements;
package body Ch4_Sensor is
  Ch4_Present : Ch4_Reading;

  Control_Reg_Addr : constant Address := To_Address(16#Aa18#);
  Data_Reg_Addr : constant Address := To_Address(16#Aa1a#);
  Ch4csr : Device_Register_Types.Csr;
  for Ch4csr'Address use Control_Reg_Addr;
  -- define the data register
  Ch4dbr : Ch4_Reading;
  for Ch4dbraddress use Data_Reg_Addr;
  Jitter_Range : constant Ch4_Reading := 40;

  procedure Initialize is
  begin
    -- enable device
    Ch4csr.Device := D_Enabled;
    Ch4csr.Operation := Set;
  end Initialize;

  procedure Periodic_Code is
  begin
    if not Ch4csr.Done then
      Operator_Console.Alarm(Ch4_Device_Error);
    else
```

```
      -- read device register for sensor value
      Ch4_Present := Ch4dbr;
      if Ch4_Present > Ch4_High then
        if Ch4_Status.Read = Motor_Safe then
          Motor.Not_Safe;
          Ch4_Status.Write(Motor_Unsafe);
          Operator_Console.Alarm(High_Methane);
        end if;
      elsif (Ch4_Present < (Ch4_High - Jitter_Range)) and
            (Ch4_Status.Read = Motor_Unsafe) then
        Motor.Is_Safe;
        Ch4_Status.Write(Motor_Safe);
      end if;
      Data_Logger.Ch4_Log(Ch4_Present);
    end if;
    Ch4csr.Operation := Set; -- start conversion for next iteration
  end Periodic_Code;

  task Thread is
    pragma Priority(Ch4_Sensor_Rtatt.
                    Thread_Priority);
  end Thread;

  task body Thread is
    T: Time;
    Period : Time_Span := Ch4_Sensor_Rtatt.Period;
  begin
    T:= Clock + Period;
    Initialize;
    loop
      delay until(T);
      Periodic_Code;
      T := T + Period;
    end loop;
  end Thread;
end Ch4_Sensor;
```

17.5.3 Air flow sensor handling object

The air flow sensor is another periodic object which simply monitors the flow of air in the mine.

```
with System; use System;
with Ada.Real_Time; use Ada.Real_Time;
package Air_Flow_Sensor_Rtatt is
  Period : Time_Span :=  Milliseconds(100);
  Thread_Priority : constant Priority := 7;
end Air_Flow_Sensor_Rtatt;


package Air_Flow_Sensor is -- CYCLIC
  pragma Elaborate_Body;
```

```ada
   type Air_Flow_Status is (Air_Flow, No_Air_Flow);
                           -- calls Data_Logger.Air_Flow_Log
                           -- calls Operator_Console.Alarm
end Air_Flow_Sensor;




with Device_Register_Types; use Device_Register_Types;
with System; use System;
with Ada.Real_Time; use Ada.Real_Time;
with Air_Flow_Sensor_Rtatt; use Air_Flow_Sensor_Rtatt;
with Operator_Console; use Operator_Console;
with Data_Logger; use Data_Logger;
with System.Storage_Elements; use System.Storage_Elements;
package body Air_Flow_Sensor is
  Air_Flow_Reading : Boolean;

  Control_Reg_Addr : constant Address := To_Address(16#Aa120#);
  Afcsr : Device_Register_Types.Csr;
  for Afcsr'Address use Control_Reg_Addr;

  task Thread is
    pragma Priority(Air_Flow_Sensor_Rtatt.
                      Initial_Thread_Priority);
  end Thread;

  procedure Initialize is
  begin
    -- enable device
    Afcsr.Device := D_Enabled;
  end Initialize;

  procedure Periodic_Code is
  begin
    -- read device register for flow indication
    -- (operation bit set to 1);
    Air_Flow_Reading := Afcsr.Operation = Set;
    if not Air_Flow_Reading then
      Operator_Console.Alarm(No_Air_Flow);
      Data_Logger.Air_Flow_Log(No_Air_Flow);
    else
      Data_Logger.Air_Flow_Log(Air_Flow);
    end if;
  end Periodic_Code;

  task body Thread is
    T: Time;
    Period : Time_Span := Air_Flow_Sensor_Rtatt.Period;
  begin
    T:= Clock;
    Initialize;
    loop
      delay until(T);
      Periodic_Code;
      T := T + Period;
```

```
      end loop;
   end Thread;
end Air_Flow_Sensor;
```

17.5.4 CO sensor handling object

The CO sensor is, again, straightforward in its implementation.

```ada
with System; use System;
with Ada.Real_Time; use Ada.Real_Time;
package Co_Sensor_Rtatt is

   Period : Time_Span :=  Milliseconds(1000);
   Thread_Priority : constant Priority := 8;
end Co_Sensor_Rtatt;
```

```ada
package Co_Sensor is  -- CYCLIC
   pragma Elaborate_Body;
   type Co_Reading is new Integer range 0 .. 1023;
   Co_High : constant Co_Reading := 600;
                        -- calls Data_Logger.Co_log
                        -- calls Operator_Console.Alarm
end Co_Sensor;
```

```ada
with Ada.Real_Time; use Ada.Real_Time;
with System; use System;
with Device_Register_Types; use Device_Register_Types;
with Co_Sensor_Rtatt; use Co_Sensor_Rtatt;
with Operator_Console; use Operator_Console;
with Data_Logger; use Data_Logger;
with System.Storage_Elements; use System.Storage_Elements;
package body Co_Sensor is
   Co_Present : Co_Reading;

   Control_Reg_Addr : constant Address := To_Address(16#Aa1c#);
   Data_Reg_Addr : constant Address := To_Address(16#Aa1e#);
   Cocsr : Device_Register_Types.Csr;
   for Cocsr'Addres use Control_Reg_Addr;
   -- define the data register
   Codbr : Co_Reading;
   for Codbr'Address use Data_Reg_Addr;

   procedure Initialize is
   begin
      -- enable device
      Cocsr.Device := D_Enabled;
      Cocsr.Operation := Set; -- start conversion
   end Initialize;
```

```ada
procedure Periodic_Code is
begin
  if not Cocsr.Done then
    Operator_Console.Alarm(Co_Device_Error);
  else
    -- read device register for sensor value
    Co_Present := Codbr;
    if Co_Present > Co_High then
      Operator_Console.Alarm(High_Co);
    end if;
    Data_Logger.Co_Log(Co_Present);
  end if;
  Cocsr.Operation := Set; -- start conversion
end Periodic_Code;

task Thread is
  pragma Priority(Co_Sensor_Rtatt.Thread_Priority);
end Thread;

task body Thread is
  T : Time;
  Period : Time_Span := Co_Sensor_Rtatt.Period;
begin
  T := Clock + Period;
  Initialize;
  loop
    delay until(T);
    Periodic_Code;
    T := T + Period;
  end loop;
end Thread;
end Co_Sensor;
```

17.5.5 Data logger

Only the interface to the Data logger object is shown.

```ada
with Co_Sensor; use Co_Sensor;
with Ch4_Sensor; use Ch4_Sensor;
with Air_Flow_Sensor; use Air_Flow_Sensor;
with Hlw_Handler; use Hlw_Handler;
with Water_Flow_Sensor; use Water_Flow_Sensor;
with Motor; use Motor;
package Data_Logger is -- ACTIVE
  procedure Co_Log(Reading : Co_Reading);
  procedure Ch4_Log(Reading : Ch4_Reading);
  procedure Air_Flow_Log(Reading : Air_Flow_Status);
  procedure High_Low_Water_Log(Mark : Water_Mark);
  procedure Water_Flow_Log(Reading : Water_Flow);
  procedure Motor_Log(State : Motor_State_Changes);
end Data_Logger;
```

17.5.6   Operator console

Only the interface to the 'Operator console' object is shown.

```
package Operator_Console is -- ACTIVE
  type Alarm_Reason is (High_Methane, High_Co, No_Air_Flow,
                Ch4_Device_Error, Co_Device_Error,
                Pump_Fault, Unknown_Error);
  procedure Alarm(Reason: Alarm_Reason;
                Name : String := "Unknown";
                Details : String:= "");

  -- calls Request_Status in Pump_Controller
  -- calls Set_Pump in Pump_Controller
end Operator_Console;
```

17.6   Fault tolerance and distribution

Chapter 5 identified four sources of faults which can result in an embedded system software failure.

(1) Inadequate specification.

(2) Faults introduced from design errors in software components.

(3) Faults introduced by failure of one or more processor components of the embedded systems.

(4) Faults introduced by transient or permanent interference in the supporting communication subsystem.

It is these last three on which this book has concentrated. They are now discussed in turn in relation to the case study. Ada's approach to software fault tolerance is to use exception handling as a framework from which error recovery can be built.

17.6.1   Design errors

As this case study is necessarily simplified, the scope for fault tolerance of software design errors is small. In the example, the HRT-HOOD design methodology, in conjunction with the Ada data abstraction facilities, has been used in an attempt to prevent faults from entering the system during the design and implementation phases. In a real application, this would then be followed by a comprehensive testing phase to remove any faults that had, nevertheless, been introduced. Simulations may also be used.

Any residual design faults in the program will cause unanticipated errors to occur. Although backward error recovery or *N*-version programming is ideal for recovering from these types of errors, there is little scope in the example for design diversity. If the example were to assume that all unanticipated errors will result in exceptions being raised, each task or operation could be protected by a 'when other' exception handler. For example, the water-flow thread could be modified to inform the operator if an unexpected error occurs.

```
task Thread;

task body Thread is
  T: Time;
  Period : Time_Span := Water_Flow_Sensor_Rtatt.Period;
  use Ada.Exceptions;
begin
  T:= Clock;
  Initialize;
  loop
    Periodic_Code;
    T := T + Period;
    delay until(T);
  end loop;
exception
  when E: others =>
    Operator_Console.Alarm(Unknown_Error, Exception_Name(E),
                           Exception_Information(E) );
    Motor.Not_Safe; -- Pump_Controller.Not_Safe
    Ch4_Status.Write(Motor_Unsafe);
    -- try and turn motor off before terminating
end Thread;
end Water_Flow_Sensor;
```

Although mine flooding is serious, the application's requirements dictate that fire is more dangerous; therefore error handling always attempts to ensure that the pump is turned off (fail safe).

It should be noticed that all interactions which manipulate the pump and the status of methane should be in the form of atomic actions. The code given above allows another task to determine that the motor is in an unsafe position, even though the methane status might indicate that the pump is safe to operate (see Exercise 17.2).

17.6.2 Processor and communication failure

In general, if the mine control system was implemented on a single processor computer and any part of the processor failed then the whole system would be in jeopardy. Consequently, either some form of hardware redundancy must be applied or distribution is required. Control systems of the kind found in mines are naturally distributed. The top level decomposition illustrated in Figure 17.4 shows four components that could clearly execute on distinct processes (see Exercise 17.4).

It was noted in Chapter 14 that Ada does not define failure semantics for partially failed programs. However, an exception Communication_Error will be raised by the underlying implementation when it is unable to make contact with a remote partition.

It has been assumed that all transient communication failures will be masked out by the underlying distributed system's implementation. If a more permanent failure occurs then an appropriate exception should be raised by the implementation, which the application can then handle. For example, if the remote call to `Is_Safe` generates an exception, the pump should be disabled.

17.6.3   Other hardware failures

The above assumes that only the processor and the communications subsystem can fail. Clearly, it is equally likely that the sensors may fail either through deterioration or through damage. In the example presented in this chapter, no attempt has been made to increase the reliability of the sensors, as this book has only touched upon hardware redundancy techniques. One approach would be to replicate each sensor and have each replica controlled by a different task. The tasks would then have to communicate in order to compare results. These results would inevitably be slightly different, and therefore some form of matching algorithm would be required.

Summary

This case study has been included to illustrate some of the issues discussed in this book. Unfortunately a single, relatively small, application cannot exercise all the important concepts that have been covered. In particular, issues of size and complexity are clearly not addressable within this context.

Nevertheless, it is hoped that the case study has helped to consolidate the reader's understanding of a number of topics, for example.

- top-down design and decomposition
- concurrency and Ada's model of interprocess communication
- forward error recovery techniques and fault tolerant design
- periodic and sporadic processes
- priority assignment and scheduling analysis
- distributed programming.

Further reading

The case study given in this Chapter is discussed by several other authors in the following references:

Burns, A. and Lister, A. M. (1991) A Framework for Building Dependable Systems. *Computer Journal*, 34(2), 173–181.

Joseph, M. (ed.) (1996). *Real-Time Systems: Specification, Verification and Analysis*. Englewood Cliffs, NJ: Prentice Hall.

Shrivastava, S. K., Mancini, L. and Randell, B. (1987) *On The Duality of Fault Tolerant Structures*. Berlin: Springer-Verlag, pp. 19–37.

Sloman, M. and Kramer, J. (1987) *Distributed Systems and Computer Networks*. Englewood Cliffs, NJ: Prentice Hall.

Exercises

17.1 If water is seeping into the mine at approximately the same rate as the pump is taking water out, the high water interrupt could be generated many times. Will this effect the behaviour of the software?

17.2 Identify which of the task interactions, given in the mine control system design, should be atomic actions. How could the solution be modified to support these actions?

17.3 All of the periodic tasks given in this chapter have a similar structure. Can they be represented as instantiations of a single generic task (encapsulated in a package) or a parameterized task?

17.4 Modify the solution given in this chapter so that it can be executed on a distributed system. Assume that each of the top-level objects, given in Figure 17.4, are active partitions.

17.5 To what extent can the solution to Exercise 17.4 be analyzed for its timing properties?

17.6 Can the data logger determine the actual order of events that have occurred? If not, how could the code be modified to give a valid global ordering? What are the implications for a distributed implementation?

17.7 In the analysis of the mine control system, what would be the consequences of running the clock at 100 ms? (or 10 ms?)

17.8 Undertake a sensitivity analysis on the mine control tasks set. Taking each task in turn consider by how much its computation time must increase before the task set becomes unschedulable. Express this value as a percentage of the original C value.

17.9 If the deadlines for the CO sensor and air flow sensor were both 50 then the system would not be schedulable. How could the fact that both sensors have the same period be exploited to obtain a schedulable system?

Chapter 18
Conclusions

The distinguishing characteristic of real-time systems is that correctness is not just a function of the logical results of program execution but of the time at which these results are produced. This one characteristic makes the study of real-time systems quite separate from other areas of computing. The importance of many real-time systems also places unique responsibilities on the practitioner. As more and more computers are being embedded in engineering applications, the greater is the risk of human, ecological or economic catastrophe. These risks arise from the problem of not being able to prove (or at least convincingly demonstrate) that all temporal and functional constraints will be met in all situations.

Real-time systems can be classified in a number of ways. First is the degree to which the application can tolerate tardiness in the system's responses. Those which have some flexibility are termed *soft* real-time systems; those with temporal rigidity are called *hard*. A deadline of three hours may be hard but easily attainable; one of three microseconds (hard or soft) presents the developer with considerable difficulty. Where deadlines, or response times, are very short the system is often called *real* real-time.

A non-real-time system can wait almost indefinitely for processors and other system resources. As long as such a system possesses *liveness* then it will execute appropriately. This is not the case with a real-time system. Because time is bounded and processors are not infinitely fast, a real-time program must be seen to be executing on a system with limited resources. It becomes necessary, therefore, to schedule the use of these resources between competing requests from different parts of the same program; a far from trivial endeavour.

Other characteristics of a typical modern real-time system are:

- they are often geographically distributed;
- they may contain a very large and complex software component;
- they must interact with concurrent real-world entities;
- they may contain processing elements which are subject to cost, size or weight constraints.

It follows from the very nature of most real-time applications that there is a stringent requirement for high reliability. This can also be formulated as a need for dependability and safety. Often, there is an almost symbiotic relationship between the computer system and its immediate environment. One cannot function without the other, as in a fly-by-wire aircraft. To give high levels of reliability requires fault-tolerant hardware and software. There is a need for tolerance of loss of functionality and missed deadlines (even for hard real-time systems).

The combination of temporal requirements, limited resources, concurrent environmental entities and high reliability requirements (together with distributed processing) presents the system engineer with unique problems. Real-time systems engineering is now recognized as a distinct discipline. It has its own body of knowledge and theoretical foundation. From an understanding of the science of large real-time systems, the following will emerge:

- specification techniques that can capture temporal and fault tolerance requirements

- design methods that have at their heart temporal requirements, and that can deal with methods of providing fault tolerance and distribution

- programming languages and operating systems that can be used to implement these designs.

This book has been concerned with the characteristics and requirements of real-time systems, fault tolerance techniques, models of concurrency, time-related language features, resource control, distribution and low-level programming techniques. Throughout, attention has been given to the facilities provided by current real-time languages, in particular Ada, Java (and its Real-Time extensions), C (augmented with the POSIX Real-Time and Threads extensions) and occam2. Table 18.1 summarizes the facilities provided by these languages.

Ada is still the most appropriate language for high-integrity system and those systems which have hard real-time constraints. Real-Time Java now rivals Ada in terms of its expressive power. However, it remains to be seen if implementations can be made efficient enough for effective deployment. Indeed, it may well be the case that Real-Time Java, the language, is appropriate, but Real-Time Java, the virtual machine, is not. Consequently, either programs will need to be compiled rather than interpreted, or a hardware-assisted virtual machine will be needed. Perhaps where Real-Time Java does have the edge over Ada is with its support for more dynamic soft real-time systems. It is in this application domain that the language will find its initial use, particularly, in those applications where portability is essential.

The C language, augmented with a real-time operating system (with or without POSIX compliancy) will continue to be used for those small embedded systems which are resource constrained. Occam2, in comparison, will continue to fade from use. Academically it has some interesting properties, but its lack of support for large-scale programming will condemn it to be little more than an esoteric language.

One trend that has occurred over the last five years, and will continue for the foreseeable future, is the use of more than one language for a single application. This is a result of the requirement to use legacy code, and the recognition that it is not appropriate to use the same language for all classes of applications. For example, a real-time

	Ada	Real-Time Java	C/POSIX	occam2
Support for programming in the large	Packages Generics	Packages Interfaces	Files	None
Support for concurrent programming	Tasks Rendezvous Protected types	Threads Synchronized methods and statements	Processes Threads Mutexes	Processes Rendezvous
Support for execution in a distributed environment	RPC Partitions Distributed objects	Remote methods Distributed objects	To be defined	Distributed processes
Facilities for fault-tolerant programming	Exceptions ATC	Exceptions ATC Events	Signals	None
Real-time facilities	Clocks and delay	Clocks and timers	Clocks and timers	Clocks and delay
Scheduling facilities	Coherent priority model Dynamic priorities	Coherent priority model Dynamic priorities	Coherent priority model Dynamic priorities	Limited priority model Static priorities
Model of device handling	Shared memory	Limited shared memory	None defined	Message passing
Execution environment	Restricted tasking ATAC	No subsets	Profiles	Transputer

Table 18.1.   Summary of the facilities provided by Ada, Real-Time Java, C/POSIX and occam2.

application with a significant user interface component might be written in a mixture of Ada and Java. An 'intelligent' real-time systems might require a rule-based component for which the most appropriate language might be Prolog.

To give an actual example of a real-time system, a case study has been described. Of necessity this was a relatively small system. Many of the challenges facing real-time computing are, however, manifest only in large complex applications. In order to give an impression of the kind of system that will be deployed in the near future, consider the International Space Station. The primary function of its computer systems is mission and life support. Other activities include flight control (particularly of the orbital transfer vehicle), external monitoring, the control and coordination of experiments, and the management of the mission database. A particularly important aspect of the on-board software is the interface it presents to the flight personnel.

The on-board execution environment for the space station has the following pertinent characteristics:

- It is large and complex (that is, there are a large variety of activities to be computerized).
- It must have non-stop execution.
- It will have a long operational life (perhaps over 30 years).
- It will experience evolutionary software changes (without stopping).
- It must have highly dependable execution.
- It will have components with hard and soft real-time deadlines.
- The distributed system will contain heterogeneous processors.

To meet the challenges of this kind of application, the science of real-time systems must itself develop. There are still many research themes to explore. Even the current state of understanding, which has been the focus of attention in this book, is rarely put into practice. In a search for the 'next generation' of real-time systems, Stankovic identified several research issues (Stankovic, 1988). Although much progress has been made since 1988, the following research topics are still crucial to the development of the discipline.

- Specification and verification techniques that can handle the needs of real-time systems with a large number of interacting components.
- Design methodologies that consider timing properties from the very beginning of the design process.
- Programming languages with explicit constructs to express time-related behaviour (in particular, relating to distributed computation).
- Scheduling algorithms that can handle complex process structures and resource constraints, timing requirements of varying granularity, and probabilistic guarantees.
- Real-time queuing models.
- Run-time support, or operating system functions, designed to deal with fault tolerant resource usage.
- Tool support for predicting the worst-case and average execution times for software on complex modern processors.
- The integration of worst-case and average case performance metrics.
- Communication architectures and protocols for efficiently dealing with messages that require timely delivery across the Internet.
- Architecture support for fault tolerance and dynamic reconfiguration.
- Integrated support for Artificial Intelligence (for example, machine learning) components.

- Programming language and operating system support for atomic actions, recovery blocks, conversations or group communication protocols.
- Programming languages with explicit support for change management (i.e. the ability to do software upgrades to non-stop systems).
- Real-time virtual machines to support 'write once run anywhere' real-time applications with stringent timing constraints.
- Real-time reflective (self-modifying) architectures allowing applications to adapt their behaviour in response to changing environments.

It is to be hoped that some readers of this book will be able to contribute to these research themes.

Appendix A
Real-Time Java specification

This appendix contains the specifications for the Real-Time Java classes discussed in this book. These specifications are conformant with that presented in Bollella et al. (2000). However, it should be noted that Real-Time Java is an evolving specification and, at the time of writing, has not been tested by an implementation. The reader should therefore refer to the Web site maintained by the The Real-Time for Java Expert Group (http://www.rtj.org/) for the current status of the project.

The specification is given as class headers in alphabetical order. Note that, although not part of the Real-Time Java Specification, the Thread and ThreadGroup class specification are also given in this appendix.

A.1 AbsoluteTime

```
package javax.realtime;
public class AbsoluteTime extends HighResolutionTime
{
  // constructors
  public AbsoluteTime();
  public AbsoluteTime(AbsoluteTime time);
  public AbsoluteTime(java.util.Date date);
  public AbsoluteTime(long millis, int nanos);

  // methods
  public AbsoluteTime absolute(Clock clock, AbsoluteTime destination);
  public AbsoluteTime add(long millis, int nanos);
  public AbsoluteTime add(long millis, int nanos,
                          AbsoluteTime destination);
  public final AbsoluteTime add(RelativeTime time);
  public AbsoluteTime add(RelativeTime time,
                          AbsoluteTime destination);
  public java.util.Date getDate();
```

```
  public void set(java.util.Date date);
  public final RelativeTime subtract(AbsoluteTime time);
  public RelativeTime subtract(AbsoluteTime time,
                                RelativeTime destination);
  public final AbsoluteTime subtract(RelativeTime time);
  public AbsoluteTime subtract(RelativeTime time,
                                AbsoluteTime destination);
  public java.lang.String toString();
}
```

A.2 AperiodicParameters

```
package javax.realtime;
public class AperiodicParameters extends ReleaseParameters
{
  // constructors
  public AperiodicParameters(RelativeTime cost, RelativeTime deadline,
       AsyncEventHandler overrunHandler,
       AsyncEventHandler missHandler);
}
```

A.3 AsyncEvent

```
package javax.realtime;
public class AsyncEvent
{
  // constructors
  public AsyncEvent();

  // methods
  public synchronized void addHandler(AsyncEventHandler handler);
  public void bindTo(java.lang.String happening);
  public ReleaseParameters createReleaseParameters();
  public synchronized void fire();
  public boolean handledBy(AsyncEventHandler target);
  public synchronized void removeHandler(AsyncEventHandler handler);
  public void setHandler(AsyncEventHandler handler);
}
```

A.4 AsyncEventHandler

```
package javax.realtime;
public abstract class AsyncEventHandler implements Schedulable
```

```
{
  //constructors
  public AsyncEventHandler();
  public AsyncEventHandler(boolean nonheap);
  public AsyncEventHandler(SchedulingParameters scheduling,
          ReleaseParameters release, MemoryParameters memory,
          MemoryArea area, ProcessingGroupParameters group);
  public AsyncEventHandler(SchedulingParameters scheduling,
          ReleaseParameters release, MemoryParameters memory,
          MemoryArea area, ProcessingGroupParameters group,
          boolean nonheap);

  //methods
  public void addToFeasibility();
  protected final synchronized int getAndClearPendingFireCount();
  protected synchronized int getAndDecrementPendingFireCount();
  protected synchronized int getAndIncrementPendingFireCount();
  public MemoryArea getMemoryArea();
  public MemoryParameters getMemoryParameters();
  public ProcessingGroupParameters getProcessingGroupParameters();
  public ReleaseParameters getReleaseParameters();
  public Scheduler getScheduler();
  public SchedulingParameters getSchedulingParameters();
  public abstract void handleAsyncEvent();
  public void removeFromFeasibility();
  public final void run();
  public void setMemoryParameters(MemoryParameters memory);
  public void setProcessingGroupParameters(
              ProcessingGroupParameters parameters);
  public void setReleaseParameters(ReleaseParameters parameters);
  public void setScheduler(Scheduler scheduler);
  public void setSchedulingParameters(
              SchedulingParameters parameters);
}
```

A.5   AsynchronouslyInterruptedException

```
package javax.realtime;
public class AsynchronouslyInterruptedException
       extends java.lang.InterruptedException
{
  // constructors
  public  AsynchronouslyInterruptedException();

  // methods
  public synchronized boolean disable();
  public boolean doInterruptible (Interruptible logic);
  public synchronized boolean enable();
  public synchronized boolean fire();
  public static AsynchronouslyInterruptedException getGeneric();
```

```
  public boolean happened (boolean propagate);
  public boolean isEnabled();
  public void propagate();
}
```

A.6 BoundAsyncEventHandler

```
package javax.realtime;
public abstract class BoundAsyncEventHandler
                extends AsyncEventHandler
{
  // constructors
  public BoundAsyncEventHandler();
  public BoundAsyncEventHandler(SchedulingParameters scheduling,
        ReleaseParameters release, MemoryParameters memory,
        MemoryArea area, ProcessingGroupParameters group,
        boolean nonheap);
}
```

A.7 Clock

```
package javax.realtime;
public abstract class Clock
{
  // constrcutors
  public Clock();

  // methods
  public static Clock getRealtimeClock();
  public abstract RelativeTime getResolution();
  public AbsoluteTime getTime();
  public abstract void getTime(AbsoluteTime time);
  public abstract void setResolution(RelativeTime resolution);
}
```

A.8 HighResolutionTime

```
package javax.realtime;
public abstract class HighResolutionTime
      implements java.lang.Comparable
{
  // methods
  public abstract AbsoluteTime absolute(Clock clock,
                                    AbsoluteTime destination);
  public int compareTo(HighResolutionTime time);
```

```
public int compareTo(java.lang.Object object);
public boolean equals(HighResolutionTime time);
public boolean equals(java.lang.Object object);
public final long getMilliseconds();
public final int getNanoseconds();
public int hashCode();
public void set(HighResolutionTime time);
public void set(long millis);
public void set(long millis, int nanos);
}
```

A.9   ImmortalMemory

```
package javax.realtime;
public final class ImmortalMemory extends MemoryArea
{
  // methods
  public static ImmortalMemory instance();
}
```

A.10   ImportanceParameters

```
package javax.realtime;
public class ImportanceParameters extends PriorityParameters
{
  // constructors
  public ImportanceParameters(int priority, int importance);

  // methods
  public int getImportance();
  public void setImportance(int importance);
  public java.lang.String toString();
}
```

A.11   Interruptible

```
package javax.realtime;
public interface Interruptible
{
  public void interruptAction(
            AsynchronouslyInterruptedException exception);
  public void run(AsynchronouslyInterruptedException exception)
        throws AsynchronouslyInterruptedException;
}
```

A.12 LTMemory

```
public class LTMemory extends ScopedMemory
{
  //constructors
  public LTMemory(long initialSizeInBytes, long maxSizeInBytes);
}
```

A.13 MemoryArea

```
public abstract class MemoryArea
{
  // constructors
  protected MemoryArea(long sizeInBytes);

  // methods
  public void enter(java.lang.Runnable logic);
  public static MemoryArea getMemoryArea(java.lang.Object object);
  public long memoryConsumed();
  public long memoryRemaining();
  public synchronized java.lang.Object newArray(
        java.lang.class type, int number)
        throws IllegalAccessException, InstantiationException,
        OutOfMemoryError;
  public synchronized java.lang.Object newInstance(
        java.lang.class type)
        throws IllegalAccessException, InstantiationException,
        OutOfMemoryError;
  public long size();
}
```

A.14 MemoryParameters

```
public class MemoryParameters
{
  // fields
  public static final long NO_MAX;

  // constructors
  public MemoryParameters(long maxMemoryArea, long maxImmortal)
        throws IllegalArgumentException;

  public MemoryParameters(long maxMemoryArea, long maxImmortal,
                          long allocationRate)
        throws IllegalArgumentException;
```

```java
  // methods
  public long getAllocationRate();
  public long getMaxImmortal();
  public long getMaxMemoryArea();
  public void setAllocationRate(long rate);
  public boolean setMaxImmortal(long maximum);
  public boolean setMaxMemoryArea(long maximum);
}
```

A.15 MonitorControl

```java
package javax.realtime;
public abstract class MonitorControl
{
  // constructors
  public MonitorControl();

  // methods
  public static void setMonitorControl(MonitorControl policy);
  public static void setMonitorControl(java.lang.Object monitor,
                                       MonitorControl policy);
}
```

A.16 NoHeapRealtimeThread

```java
package javax.realtime;
public class NoHeapRealtimeThread extends RealtimeThread
{
  //constructors
  public NoHeapRealtimeThread(SchedulingParameters scheduling,
         MemoryArea area) throws IllegalArgumentException;

  public NoHeapRealtimeThread(SchedulingParameters scheduling,
         ReleaseParameters release, MemoryArea area)
         throws IllegalArgumentException;

  public NoHeapRealtimeThread(SchedulingParameters scheduling,
         ReleaseParameters release, MemoryParameters memory,
         MemoryArea area, ProcessingGroupParameters group,
         java.lang.Runnable logic)
               throws IllegalArgumentException;
}
```

A.17   OneShotTimer

```
package javax.realtime;
public class OneShotTimer extends Timer
{
  // constructors
  public OneShotTimer(HighResolutionTime time,
                      AsyncEventHandler handler);
  public OneShotTimer(HighResolutionTime start, Clock clock,
                      AsyncEventHandler handler);
}
```

A.18   PeriodicParameters

```
package javax.realtime;
public class PeriodicParameters extends ReleaseParameters
{
  // constructors
  public PeriodicParameters(HighResolutionTime start,
        RelativeTime period, RelativeTime cost,
        RelativeTime deadline, AsyncEventHandler overrunHandler,
        AsyncEventHandler missHandler);

  // methods
  public RelativeTime getPeriod();
  public HighResolutionTime getStart();
  public void setPeriod(RelativeTime period);
  public void setStart(HighResolutionTime start);
}
```

A.19   PeriodicTimer

```
package javax.realtime;
public class PeriodicTimer extends Timer
{
  // constructors
  public PeriodicTimer(HighResolutionTime start,
                       RelativeTime interval,
                       AsyncEventHandler handler);
  public PeriodicTimer(HighResolutionTime start,
                       RelativeTime interval,
                       Clock clock, AsyncEventHandler handler);

  // methods
  public ReleaseParameters createReleaseParameters();
  public void fire();
  public AbsoluteTime getFireTime();
```

```
  public RelativeTime getInterval();
  public void setInterval(RelativeTime interval);
}
```

A.20   POSIXSignalHandler

```
package javax.realtime;
public final class POSIXSignalHandler
{
  //fields
  public static final int SIGABRT;
  public static final int SIGALRM;
  public static final int SIGBUS;
  public static final int SIGCANCEL;
  public static final int SIGCHLD;
  public static final int SIGCLD;
  public static final int SIGCONT;
  public static final int SIGEMPT;
  public static final int SIGFPE;
  public static final int SIGFREEZE;
  public static final int SIGHUP;
  public static final int SIGILL;
  public static final int SIGINT;
  public static final int SIGIO;
  public static final int SIGIOT;
  public static final int SIGKILL;
  public static final int SIGLOST;
  public static final int SIGLWP;
  public static final int SIGPIPE;
  public static final int SIGPOLL;
  public static final int SIGPROF;
  public static final int SIGPWF;
  public static final int SIGQUIT;
  public static final int SIGSEGV;
  public static final int SIGSTOP;
  public static final int SIGSYS;
  public static final int SIGTERM;
  public static final int SIGTHAW;
  public static final int SIGTRAP;
  public static final int SIGTSTP;
  public static final int SIGTTIN;
  public static final int SIGTTOU;
  public static final int SIGURG;
  public static final int SIGUSR1;
  public static final int SIGUSR2;
  public static final int SIGVTALRM;
  public static final int SIGWINCH;
  public static final int SIGXCPU;
  public static final int SIGXFSZ;
```

```
  // methods
  public static synchronized void addHandler(int signal,
        AsyncEventHandler handler);
  public static synchronized void removeHandler(int signal
        AsyncEventHandler handler);
  public static synchronized void setHandler(int signal,
        AsyncEventHandler handler);
}
```

A.21   PriorityCeilingEmulation

```
package javax.realtime;
public class PriorityCeilingEmulation extends MonitorControl
{
  // constructors
  public PriorityCeilingEmulation(int ceiling);

  // methods
  public int getDefaultCeiling();
}
```

A.22   PriorityInheritance

```
package javax.realtime;
public class PriorityInheritance extends MonitorControl
{
  // constructors
  public PriorityInheritance();

  // methods
  public static PriorityInheritance instance();
}
```

A.23   PriorityParameters

```
package javax.realtime;
public class PriorityParameters extends SchedulingParameters
{
  // constructors
  public PriorityParameters(int priority);

  // methods
  public int getPriority();
  public void setPriority(int priority) throws IllegalArgumentException;
```

```
  public java.lang.String toString();
}
```

A.24   PriorityScheduler

```
package javax.realtime;
public class PriorityScheduler extends Scheduler
{
  // constructors
  public PriorityScheduler() ;

  // methods
  protected void addToFeasibility(Schedulable schedulable);
  boolean changeIfFeasible(Schedulable schedulable,
          ReleaseParameters release, MemoryParameters memory);
  public void fireSchedulable(Schedulable schedulable);
  public int getMaxPriority();
  public static int getMaxPriority(java.lang.Thread thread);
  public int getMinPriority();
  public static int getMinPriority(java.lang.Thread thread);
  public int getNormPriority();
  public static int getNormPriority(java.lang.Thread thread);
  public java.lang.String getPolicyName();
  public static PriorityScheduler instance();
  public boolean isFeasible();
  protected void removeFromFeasibility(Schedulable schedulable);
}
```

A.25   ProcessingGroupParameters

```
package javax.realtime;
public class ProcessingGroupParameters
{
  // constructors
  public ProcessingGroupParameters(HighResolutionTime start,
          RelativeTime period, RelativeTime cost,
          RelativeTime deadline, AsyncEventHandler overrunHandler,
          AsyncEventHandler missHandler);

  // methods
  public RelativeTime getCost();
  public AsyncEventHandler getCostOverrunHandler();
  public RelativeTime getDeadline();
  public AsyncEventHandler getDeadlineMissHandler();
  public RelativeTime getPeriod();
  public HighResolutionTime getStart();
  public void setCost(RelativeTime cost);
  public void setCostOverrunHandler(AsyncEventHandler handler);
```

```java
  public void setDeadline(RelativeTime deadline);
  public void setDeadlineMissHandler(AsyncEventHandler handler);
  public void setPeriod(RelativeTime period);
  public void setStart(HighResolutionTime start);
}
```

A.26   RationalTime

```java
package javax.realtime;
public class RationalTime extends RelativeTime
{
  // constructors
  public RationalTime(int frequency);
  public RationalTime(int frequency, long millis, int nanos)
        throws IllegalArgumentException;
  public RationalTime(int frequency, RelativeTime interval)
        throws IllegalArgumentException;

  // methods
  public AbsoluteTime absolute(Clock clock, AbsoluteTime destination);
  public void addInterarrivalTo(AbsoluteTime destination);
  public int getFrequency();
  public RelativeTime getInterarrivalTime(RelativeTime destination);
  public void set(long millis, int nanos)
        throws IllegalArgumentException;
  public void setFrequency(int frequency)
        throws ArithmeticException;
}
```

A.27   RawMemoryAccess

```java
package javax.realtime;
public class RawMemoryAccess
{
  // constructors
  protected RawMemoryAccess(long base, long size);
  protected RawMemoryAccess(RawMemoryAccess memory, long base,
                            long size);

  // methods
  public static RawMemoryAccess create(java.lang.Object type,
        long size) throws SecurityException, OffsetOutOfBoundsException,
        SizeOutOfBoundsException, UnsupportedPhysicalMemoryException;

  public static RawMemoryAccess create(java.lang.Object type,
                                       long base, long size)
        throws SecurityException, OffsetOutOfBoundsException,
        SizeOutOfBoundsException, UnsupportedPhysicalMemoryException;
```

```
public byte getByte(long offset) throws SizeOutOfBoundsException,
        OffsetOutOfBoundsException;
public void getBytes(long offset, byte[] bytes, int low,
                     int number) throws
            SizeOutOfBoundsException, OffsetOutOfBoundsException;
public int getInt(long offset) throws SizeOutOfBoundsException,
        OffsetOutOfBoundsException;
public void getInts(long offset, int[] ints, int low,
                     int number) throws
            SizeOutOfBoundsException, OffsetOutOfBoundsException;
public long getLong(long offset) throws SizeOutOfBoundsException,
        OffsetOutOfBoundsException;
public void getLongs(long offset, long[] longs, int low,
                     int number) throws
            SizeOutOfBoundsException, OffsetOutOfBoundsException;
public long getMapped Address();
public short getshort(long offset) throws SizeOutOfBoundsException,
        OffsetOutOfBoundsException;
public void getshorts(long offset, short[] shorts, int low,
                     int number) throws
            SizeOutOfBoundsException, OffsetOutOfBoundsException;
public long map();
public long map(long base);
public long map(long base, long size);
public void setByte(long offset, byte value) throws
            SizeOutOfBoundsException, OffsetOutOfBoundsException;
public void setBytes(long offset, byte[] bytes, int low,
                     int number) throws
            SizeOutOfBoundsException, OffsetOutOfBoundsException;
public void setInt(long offset, int value) throws
            SizeOutOfBoundsException, OffsetOutOfBoundsException;
public void setInts(long offset, int[] ints, int low,
                     int number) throws
            SizeOutOfBoundsException, OffsetOutOfBoundsException;
public void setLong(long offset, long value) throws
            SizeOutOfBoundsException, OffsetOutOfBoundsException;
public void setLongs(long offset, long[] longs, int low,
                     int number) throws
            SizeOutOfBoundsException, OffsetOutOfBoundsException;
public void setShort(long offset, short value) throws
            SizeOutOfBoundsException, OffsetOutOfBoundsException;
public void setShorts(long offset, short[] shorts, int low,
                     int number) throws
            SizeOutOfBoundsException, OffsetOutOfBoundsException;
public void unmap();
}
```

A.28   Realtime Security

```
package javax.realtime;
public class RealtimeSecurity
```

```
{
  // constructors
  public RealtimeSecurity();

  // methods
  public void checkAccessPhysical() throws
        SecurityException;
  public void checkAccessPhysicalRange(long base, long size) throws
        SecurityException;
  public void checkSetFactory() throws
        SecurityException;
  public void checkSetScheduler() throws
        SecurityException;
}
```

A.29   Realtime System

```
package javax.realtime;
public class RealtimeSystem
{
  // fields
  public static final byte BIG_ENDIAN;
  public static final byte BYTE_ORDER;
  public static final byte LITTLE_ENDIAN;

  // methods
  public static GarbageCollector currentGC();
  public int getConcurrentLocksUsed();
  public int getMaximumConcurrentLocks();
  public static RealtimeSecurity getSecurityManager();
  public void setMaximumConcurrentLocks(int number);
  public void setMaximumConcurrentLocks(int number, boolean hard);
  public static voidgetSecurityManager(RealtimeSecurity manager) throws
        SecurityException;
}
```

A.30   RealtimeThread

```
package javax.realtime;
public class RealtimeThread extends java.lang.Thread
        implements Schedulable
{
  // constructors
  public RealtimeThread();
  public RealtimeThread(SchedulingParameters scheduling);
  public RealtimeThread(SchedulingParameters scheduling,
                        ReleaseParameters release);
  public RealtimeThread(SchedulingParameters scheduling,
```

```
            ReleaseParameters release, MemoryParameters memory,
            MemoryArea area, ProcessingGroupParameters group,
            java.lang.Runnable logic);

   // methods
   public void addToFeasibility();
   public static RealtimeThread currentRealtimeThread();
   public synchronized void deschedulePeriodic();
   public MemoryArea getMemoryArea();
   public MemoryParameters getMemoryParameters();
   public ProcessingGroupParameters getProcessingGroupParameters();
   public ReleaseParameters getReleaseParameters();
   public Scheduler getScheduler();
   public SchedulingParameters getSchedulingParameters();
   public synchronized void interrupt();
   public void removeFromFeasibility();
   public synchronized void schedulePeriodic();
   public void setMemoryParameters(MemoryParameters parameters);
   public void setProcessingGroupParameters(
                ProcessingGroupParameters parameters);
   public void setReleaseParameters(ReleaseParameters parameters);
   public void setScheduler(Scheduler scheduler)
         throws IllegalThreadStateException;
   public void setSchedulingParameters(
                SchedulingParameters scheduling);
   public static void sleep(Clock clock, HighResolutionTime time)
         throws InterruptedException;
   public static void sleep(HighResolutionTime time)
         throws InterruptedException;
   public boolean waitForNextPeriod()
         throws IllegalThreadStateException ;
}
```

A.31   RelativeTime

```
package javax.realtime;
public class RelativeTime extends HighResolutionTime
{
   // constructors
   public RelativeTime();
   public RelativeTime(long millis, int nanos);
   public RelativeTime(RelativeTime time);

   // methods
   public AbsoluteTime absolute(Clock clock,
                                AbsoluteTime destination);
   public RelativeTime add(long millis, int nanos);
   public RelativeTime add(long millis, int nanos,
                           RelativeTime destination);
   public final RelativeTime add(RelativeTime time);
   public RelativeTime add(RelativeTime time, RelativeTime destination);
```

```
  public void addInterarrivalTo(AbsoluteTime destination);
  public RelativeTime getInterarrivalTime(RelativeTime destination);
  public final RelativeTime subtract(RelativeTime time);
  public RelativeTime subtract(RelativeTime time,
                                 RelativeTime destination);
  public java.lang.String toString();
}
```

A.32   ReleaseParameters

```
package javax.realtime;
public abstract class ReleaseParameters
{
  // constructors
  protected ReleaseParameters(RelativeTime cost, RelativeTime deadline,
            AsyncEventHandler overrunHandler,
            AsyncEventHandler missHandler);

  // methods
  public RelativeTime getCost();
  public AsyncEventHandler getCostOverrunHandler();
  public RelativeTime getDeadline();
  public AsyncEventHandler getDeadlineMissHandler();
  public void setCost(RelativeTime cost);
  public void setCostOverrunHandler(AsyncEventHandler handler);
  public void setDeadline(RelativeTime deadline);
  public void setDeadlineMissHandler(AsyncEventHandler handler);
}
```

A.33   Schedulable

```
package javax.realtime;
public interface Schedulable extends java.lang.Runnable
{
  // methods
  public void addToFeasibility();
  public MemoryParameters getMemoryParameters();
  public ReleaseParameters getReleaseParameters();
  public Scheduler getScheduler();
  public SchedulingParameters getSchedulingParameters();
  public void removeFromFeasibility();
  public void setMemoryParameters(MemoryParameters memory);
  public void setReleaseParameters(ReleaseParameters release);
  public void setScheduler(Scheduler scheduler);
  public void setSchedulingParameters(SchedulingParameters scheduling);
}
```

A.34   Scheduler

```
package javax.realtime;
public abstract class Scheduler
{
  // constructors
  public Scheduler();

  // methods
  protected abstract void addToFeasibility(Schedulable schedulable);
  public boolean changeIfFeasible(Schedulable schedulable,
                  ReleaseParameters release, MemoryParameters memory);
  public static Scheduler getDefaultScheduler();
  public abstract java.lang.String getPolicyName();
  public abstract boolean isFeasible();
  protected abstract void removeFromFeasibility(Schedulable schedulable);
  public static void setDefaultScheduler(Scheduler scheduler);
}
```

A.35   SchedulingParameters

```
package javax.realtime;
public abstract class SchedulingParameters
{
  // constructors
  public SchedulingParameters();
}
```

A.36   ScopedMemory

```
package javax.realtime;
public abstract class ScopedMemory extends MemoryArea
{
  // constructors
  public ScopedMemory(long size);

  // methods
  public void enter(java.lang.Runnable logic);
  public int getMaximumSize();
  public MemoryArea getOuterScope();
  public java.lang.Object getPortal();
  public void setPortal(java.lang.Object object);
}
```

A.37   ScopedPhysicalMemory

```
package javax.realtime;
public class ScopedPhysicalMemory extends ScopedMemory;
{
  // constructors
  protected ScopedPhysicalMemory(long base, long size);
  protected ScopedPhysicalMemory(ScopedPhysicalMemory memory,
                                 long base, long size);

  //methods
  public static ScopedPhysicalMemory create(java.lang.Object type,
               long base, long size) throws SecurityException,
               OffsetOutOfBoundsException, SizeOutOfBoundsException,
               UnsupportedPhysicalMemoryException;
  public static void setFactory(PhysicalMemoryFactory factory);
}
```

A.38   SporadicParameters

```
package javax.realtime;
public class SporadicParameters extends AperiodicParameters
{
  //constructors
  public SporadicParameters(RelativeTime minInterarrival,
         RelativeTime cost, RelativeTime deadline,
         AsyncEventHandler overrunHandler,
         AsyncEventHandler missHandler);

  // methods
  public RelativeTime getMinimumInterarrival();
  public void setMinimumInterarrival(RelativeTime minimum);

}
```

A.39   Thread

```
// Not in package javax.realtime;
public class Thread extends Object implements Runnable
{
  // fields
  static int MAX_PRIORITY;
  static int MIN_PRIORITY;
  static int NORM_PRIORITY;

  // constructors
  public Thread();
```

```
public Thread(Runnable target);
public Thread(Runnable target, String name);
public Thread(String name);
public Thread(ThreadGroup group, String name);
      throws SecurityException, IllegalThreadStateException
public Thread(ThreadGroup group, Runnable target);
      throws SecurityException, IllegalThreadStateException
public Thread(ThreadGroup group, Runnable target, String name);
        throws SecurityException, IllegalThreadStateException

// methods
static int activeCount();
void checkAccess() throws SecurityException;
int countStackFrames()
    throws IllegalThreadStateException;
public static Thread currentThread();
public void destroy() throws SecurityException;
static void dumpStack();
static int enumerate(Thread[] tarray)
      throws SecurityException;
ClassLoader getContextClassLoader() throws SecurityException;
String getName();
int getPriority();
ThreadGroup getThreadGroup();.
void interrupt() throws SecurityException;
static boolean interrupted();
public final native boolean isAlive();
public final boolean isDaemon();
boolean isInterrupted();
public final void join() throws InterruptedException;
public final void join(long millis)
      throws InterruptedException;
public final void join(long millis, int nanos)
      throws InterruptedException;
public void resume()
      throws SecurityException;  // DEPRECATED
public void run();
public void setContextClassLoader(ClassLoader cl)
      throws SecurityException;
public final void setDaemon()
      throws SecurityException, IllegalThreadStateException;
public void setName(String name)
      throws SecurityException;
public void setPriority(int newPriority)
      throws class IllegalArgumentException, InterruptedException;
public static void sleep(long millis)
      throws InterruptedException;
public static void sleep(long millis, int nanos)
      throws class IllegalArgumentException, InterruptedException;
public native synchronized void start()
      throws IllegalThreadStateException;
public final void stop()
      throws SecurityException;  // DEPRECATED
public final synchronized void stop(Throwable o);
      throws SecurityException, NullPointerException;  // DEPRECATED
```

```
  public void suspend()
        throws SecurityException;  // DEPRECATED
  public String toString();
  public static void yield();
}
```

A.40   ThreadGroup

```
// Not in package javax.realtime;
public class ThreadGroup {
  // constructors
  public ThreadGroup(String name)
        throws SecurityException;
  public ThreadGroup(ThreadGroup parent, String name)
        throws SecurityException, NullPointerException;

  // methods
  public int activeCount();
  public int activeGroupCount();
  public boolean allowThreadSuspension(boolean b);  // DEPRECATED
  public final void checkAccess()
        throws SecurityException;
  public final void destroy()
        throws IllegalThreadStateException, SecurityException;
  public int enumerate(Thread[] list)
        throws SecurityException;
  public int enumerate(Thread[] list, boolean recurse)
        throws SecurityException;
  public int enumerate(ThreadGroup[] list)
        throws SecurityException;
  public int enumerate(ThreadGroup[] list, boolean recurse)
  public int getMaxPriority()
  public String getName()
  public final ThreadGroup getParent()
        throws SecurityException;
  public void interrupt()
        throws SecurityException;
  public final boolean isDaemon();
  public synchronized boolean isDestroyed();
  public void list()
  public final boolean parentOf(ThreadGroup g);
  public void resume()
        throws SecurityException;  // DEPRECATED
  public final void setDaemon(boolean daemon);
            throws SecurityException;
  public void setMaxPriority(int pri)
        throws SecurityException;
  public final void stop()
            throws SecurityException;  // DEPRECATED
  public void suspend()
        throws SecurityException;  // DEPRECATED
```

```
  public String toString();
  public void uncaughtException(Thread t, Throwable e)
}
```

A.41 Timed

```
package javax.realtime;
public class Timed extends AsynchronouslyInterruptedException
                    implements java.io.Serializable
{
  // constructors
  public Timed(HighResolutionTime time) throws
              IllegalArgumentException;
  // methods
  public boolean doInterruptible(Interruptible logic);
  public void resetTime(HighResolutionTime time);
}
```

A.42 Timer

```
package javax.realtime;
public abstract class Timer extends AsyncEvent
{
  // constructors
  protected Timer(HighResolutionTime time, Clock clock,
                  AsyncEventHandler handler);
  // methods
  public ReleaseParameters createReleaseParameters();
  public void disable();
  public void enable();
  public Clock getClock();
  public AbsoluteTime getFireTime();
  public void reschedule(HighResolutionTime time);
  public void start();
}
```

A.43 VTMemory

```
package javax.realtime;
public class VTMemory extends ScopedMemory
{
  // constructors
  VTMemory(int initial, int maximum);
}
```

References

AEEC (1991). Design guidance for integrated mondular avionics, *ARINC 651 (Draft 9)*, AEEC.

aJile Systems (2000). aJ-100 datasheet, *http://www.ajile.com/ aJ-100_datasheet.htm*, aJile Systems.

Allworth, S. and Zobel, R. (1987). *Introduction to Real-Time Software Design*, MacMillan.

Ammann, P. and Knight, J. (1988). Data diversity: An approach to software fault tolerance, *IEEE Transactions on Computers* **C-37**(4): 418–425.

Anderson, T. and Lee, P. (1990). *Fault Tolerance Principles and Practice:*, 2nd edn, Prentice Hall International.

Andrews, G. and Olsson, R. (1993). *The SR Programming Language - Concurrency in Practice*, Benjamin/Cummings.

ARINC AEE Committee (1999). Avionics application software standard interface.

Audsley, N. and Burns, A. (1998). On fixed priority scheduling, offsets and co-prime task periods, *Information Processing Letters, Elsevier* **67**: 65–69,.

Audsley, N. et al. (1993a). Applying new scheduling theory to static priority preemptive scheduling, *Software Engineering Journal* **8**(5): 284–292.

Audsley, N., Tindell, K. and Burns, A. (1993b). The end of the line for static cyclic scheduling?, *Proceedings of the 5th Euromicro Workshop on Real-Time Systems*, IEEE Computer Society Press, Oulu, Finland, pp. 36–41.

Avizienis, A. and Ball, D. (1987). On the achievement of a highly dependable and fault-tolerant air traffic control system, *Computer* **20**(2): 84–90.

Avizienis, A., Lyu, M. and Schutz, W. (1988). Multi-version software developmnt: A UCLA/Honeywell joint project for fault-tolerant flight control systems, *CSD-880034*, Department of Computer Science, University of California, Los Angeles.

Bach, M. (1986). *The Design of the UNIX Operating System*, Prentice Hall.

Baker, T. P. (1991). Stack-based scheduling of realtime processes, *Real Time Systems*.

Barnes, J. (1976). *RTL/2 Design and Philosophy*, Heyden International Topics in Science.

Barrett, P., Hilborne, A., Verissimo, P., Rodrigues, L., Bond, P., Seaton, D. and Speirs, N. (1990). The Delta-4 extra performance architecture(XPA), *Digest of Papers, The Twentieth Annual International Symposium on Fault-Tolerant Computing*, Newcastle, pp. 481–488.

Barringer, H. and Kuiper, R. (1983). Towards the hierarchical, temporal logic, specification of concurrent systems, *Proceedings of the STL/SERC workshop on the analysis of concurrent systems*, Spinger-Verlag.

Bate, I. and Burns, A. (1997). Timing analysis of fixed priority real-time systems with offsets, *9th Euromicro Workshop on Real-Time Systems*, pp. 153–160.

Ben-Ari, M. (1982). *Principles of Concurrent Programming*, Prentice Hall.

Bennett, P. (1994). Software development for the Channel Tunnel: A summary, *High Integrity Systems* **1**(2): 213–220.

Bernat, G. and Burns, A. (1999). New results on fixed priority aperiodic servers, *Proceedings of the 20th IEEE Real-Time Systems Symposium*, pp. 68–78.

Berry, G. (1989). Real time programming: Special purpose or general purpose languages, *in* G. Ritter (ed.), *Proceedings of Information Processing '89*, Elsevier Science Publishers.

Bloom, T. (1979). Evaluating synchronisation mechanisms, *Proceedings of the Seventh ACM Symposium on Operating System Principles*, Pacific Grove, pp. 24–32.

Bois, P. D. (1995). Semantic definition of the Albert II language, *Technical Report RP-95-007*, Computer Science Dept., University of Namur, Namur, Belgium.

Bollella, G., Brosgol, B., Dibble, P., Furr, S., Gosling, J., Hardin, D. and Turnbull, M. (2000). *The Real-Time Specification for Java*, Addison-Wesley.

Booch, G. (1986). *Software Engineering with Ada*, 2nd edn, The Benjamin/Cummings Publishing Company, Inc.

Booch, G., Rumbaugh, J. and Jacobson, I. (1999). *The Unified Modeling Language User Guide*, Addoson-Wesley.

Boussinot, F. and de Simone, R. (1991). The Esterel langauge, *Proceedings of IEEE*, pp. 1293–1304.

Brauer, W. (1980). Net theory and applications, *Lecture Notes in Computer Science*, Springer-Verlag.

Brilliant, S., Knight, J. and Leveson, N. (1987). The consistent comparison problem in N-version software, *ACM Software Engineering Notes* **12**(1): 29–34.

Brilliant, S., Knight, J. and Leveson, N. (1990). Analysis of faults in an N-version software experiment, *IEEE Transactions on Software Engineering* **16**(2): 238–47.

Brinch-Hansen, P. (1973). *Operating System Principles*, Prentice Hall, New Jersey.

Brinch-Hansen, P. (1981). Edison: A multiprocessor language, *Software-Practice and Experience* **11**(4): 325–361.

Bull, G. and Lewis, A. (1983). Real-Time BASIC, *Software - Practice and Experience* **13**(11): 1075–1092.

Burns, A. (1983). Enhanced input/output on Pascal, *SIGPLAN Notices*.

Burns, A. (1988). *Programming in occam 2*, Addison Wesley.

Burns, A. (1999). The Ravenscar Profile, *ACM Ada Letters* **XIX**(4): 49–52.

Burns, A. and Lister, A. M. (1991). A framework for building dependable systems, *Computer Journal* **34**(2): 173–181.

Burns, A. and Wellings, A. J. (1994). HRT-HOOD: A design method for hard real-time Ada, *Real-Time Systems* **6**(1): 73–114.

Burns, A. and Wellings, A. J. (1995). *Hard Real-Time HOOD: A Structured Design Method for Hard Real-Time Ada Systems*, Elsevier.

Burns, A. and Wellings, A. J. (1998). *Concurrency in Ada*, second edn, Cambridge University Press.

Burns, A., Lister, A. and Wellings, A. J. (1987). A review of Ada tasking, *Lecture Notes in Computer Science, Volume 262*, Springer-Verlag.

Burns, A., Prasad, D., Bondavalli, A., Giandomenico, F. D., Ramamritham, K., Stankovic, J. and Stringini, L. (2000). The meaning and role of value in scheduling flexible real-time systems, *Journal of Systems Architecture* **46**: 305–325.

Busquets, J. and Wellings, A. J. (1996). Adding instruction cache effect to schedulability analysis of preemptive real-time systems, *Proceedings of RTAS96*.

Cairns, P. (1999). Enumeration types in Java, *Software-Practice and Experience* **29**(3): 291–297.

Calvez, J. (1993). *Embedded Real-Time Systems: A Specification and Design Methodology*, Wiley.

Campbell, R. and Randell, B. (1986). Error recovery in asynchronous systems, *IEEE Transactions on Software Engineering* **1**(8): 811–826.

CCITT (1980). CCITT high level language (CHILL) recommendation Z.200.

Chen, L. and Avizienis, A. (1978). N-version programming: A fault-tolerance approach to reliability of software operation, *Digest of Papers, The Eighth Annual International Conference on Fault-Tolerant Computing*, Toulouse, France, pp. 3–9.

Cherry, G. (1986). *Pamela Designers Handbook*, Thought Tools Incorporated.

Chetto, H. and Chetto, M. (1989). Some results of the earliest deadline scheduling algorithm, *IEEE Transactions on Software Engineering* **15**(10): 1261–1269.

Cmelik, R., Gehani, N. and Roome, W. (1988). Fault Tolerant Concurrent C: A tool for writing fault tolerant distributed programs, *The Eighteenth Annual International Symposium on Fault-Tolerant Computing Digest of Papers*.

Coleman, D. et al. (1994). *Object-Oriented Development: The Fusion Method*, Prentice Hall.

Conway, M. E. (1963). Design of a separable transition-diagram compiler, *Communications of the ACM* **6**(7): 396–408.

Cooling, J. (1991). *Software Design for Real-Time Systems*, Chapman and Hall.

Cornhill, D., Sha, L., Lehoczky, J., Rajkumar, R. and Tokuda, H. (1987). Limitations of Ada for real-time scheduling, *Proceedings of the International Workshop on Real Time Ada Issues, ACM Ada Letters*, pp. 33–39.

Davis, R. and Wellings, A. J. (1995). Dual priority scheduling, *IEEE Proceedings of Real-Time Systems Symposium.*

de la Puente, J., Alonso, A. and Alvarez, A. (1996). Mapping HRT-HOOD designs to Ada 95 hierarchical libraries, *Ada-Europe'96 Conference, Springer-Verlag.*

Dijkstra, E. (1965). Solution of a problem in concurrent program control, *Communications of the ACM* **8**(9): 569–.

Dijkstra, E. (1968a). Cooperating sequential processes, *in* F. Genuys (ed.), *Programming Languages*, Academic Press, London.

Dijkstra, E. (1968b). The structure of THE multiprogramming system, *Communications of the ACM* **11**(5): 341–.

Dijkstra, E. (1975). Guarded commands, nondeterminacy, and formal derivation of programs, *CACM* **18**(8): 453–457.

Dix, A., M.D.Harrison and C.Runciman (1987). Interactive models and the principled design of interactive systems, *Proc ESEC'87* pp. 127–135.

Douglass, B. (1999). *Doing Hard Time: Developing Real-Time Systems with UML, Objects Frameworks and Patterns*, Addison-Wesley.

Dubois, E., Bois, P. D. and Zeippen, J. (1995). A formal requirements engineering method for real-time, concurrent, and distributed systems, *Proc. of the Real-Time Systems Conference RTS'95, Paris (France).*

Eckhardt, D., Caglayan, A., Knight, J., Lee, J., McAllister, D., Vouk, M. and Kelly, J. (1991). An experimental evaluation of software redundancy as a strategy for improving reliability, *IEEE Transactions on Software Engineering* **17**(7): 692–702.

Ericsson (1986). SDS80/A standardised computing system for Ada, *Document number L/BD, number = 5553*, Ericsson.

Evangelist, M., Francez, M. and Katz, S. (1989). Multiparty interactions for interprocess communication and synchronization, *IEEE Transactions on Software Engineering* **15**(11): 1417–1426.

Garman, J. (1981). The bug heard round the world, *Software Engineering Notes* **6**(3): 3–10.

Goel, A. and Bastini, F. (1985). Software reliability, *IEEE Transactions on Software Engineering* **SE-11**(12): 1409–1410.

Goldsack, S. and Finkelstein, A. (1991). Requirements engineering for real-time systems, *Software Engineering Journal* **6**(3): 101–15.

Gomaa, H. (1994). Software design methods for the design of large-scale real-time systems, *Journal of Systems and Software* **25**(2): 127–146.

Graham, I. (1994). *Object Oriented Methods*, 2nd edn, Addison-Wesley.

Graham, R. (1969). Bounds on multiprocessing timing anomalies, *SIAM J. Appl. Math.* **12**(2): 416–429.

Graham, R. et al. (1979). Optimization and approximation in deterministic sequencing and scheduling: A survey, *Ann. Discrete Math.* **5**: 287–326.

Gregory, S. and Knight, J. (1985). A new linguistic approach to backward error recovery, *The Fifteenth Annual International Symposium on Fault-Tolerant Computing Digest of Papers*, pp. 404–409.

Halbwachs, N., Caspi, P., Raymond, P. and Pilaud, D. (1991). The synchronous dataflow programming language Lustre, *Proceedings of IEEE*, pp. 1305–1320.

Harbour, M. G., Rivas, M. A. and Gutierrez, J. P. (1998). Implementing and using execution time clocks in Ada hard real-time applications, *Reliable Software Technologies - Ada Europe 98, Lecture Notes in Computer Science* **1411**: 90–101.

Hatton, L. (1997). N-version design versus one good version, *IEEE Software* **14**(6): 71–76.

Hecht, H. and Hecht, M. (1986a). Fault-tolerant software, *in* D. Pradhan (ed.), *Fault-Tolerant Computing Theory and Techniques Volume II*, Prentice Hall, pp. 659–685.

Hecht, H. and Hecht, M. (1986b). Software reliability in the systems context, *IEEE Transactions on Software Engineering* **SE-12**(1): 51–58.

Heitz, M. (1995). HOOD Reference Manual: Release 4.0, *HRM4-9/22/95*, HOOD Technical Group.

Herlihy, M. and Liskov, B. (1982). A value transmission method for abstract data types, *ACM TOPLAS* **4**(4): 527–551.

Hoare, C. (1974). Monitors - an operating system structuring concept, *CACM* **17**(10): 549–557.

Hoare, C. (1978). Communicating sequential processes, *CACM* **21**(8): 666–677.

Hoare, C. (1985). *Communicating Sequential Processes*, Prentice Hall International.

Hoogeboom, B. and Halang, W. (1992). The concept of time in the specification of real-time systems, *in* K. Kavi (ed.), *Real-Time Systems: Abstractions, Languages and Design Methodologies*, IEEE Computer Society Press, pp. 19–38.

Horning, J. J., Lauer, H. C., Melliar-Smith, P. M. and Randell, B. (1974). A program structure for error detection and recovery, *in* E. Gelenbe and C. Kaiser (eds), *Lecture Notes in Computer Science 16*, Springer-Verlag, pp. 171 – 187.

Hull, M., O'Donoghue, P. and Hagan, B. (1991). Development methods for real-time systems, *Computer Journal* **34**(2): 164–72.

IEEE (1995). Portable operating sysrem interface: Amendment 2: Threads extension [C language], *IEEE/1003.1c*, IEEE.

ISO/IEC JTC1/SC21/WG8 (1992). Open system interconnection - remote procedure call specification part 1: Model, *CD, number = 11578-1.2*, ISO/IEC JTC1/SC21/WG8.

Iverson, K. (1962). *A Programming Language*, Wiley New York.

J Consortium (2000). Real-time core extensions for the Java platform, *Revision 1.0.10*, J Consortium.

Jackson, K. (1986). Mascot 3 and Ada, *Software Engineering Journal* **1**(3): 121–135.

Jackson, M. (1975). *Principles of Program Design*, Academic Press Inc.

Jacobson, I., Booch, G. and Rumbaugh, J. (1999). *The Unified Software Develoment Process*, Addison-Wesley.

Jahanian, F. and Mok, A. (1986). Safety analysis of timing properties in real-time systems, *IEEE Transactions on Software Engineering* **12**(9): 890–904.

Jones, C. (1986). *Systematic Software Development Using VDM*, Prentice Hall.

Jones, M. (1997). What happened on Mars?, *http://www.cs.cmu.edu/afs/cs.cmu.edu/ project/art-6/www/mars.html*, Accessed 28/4/2000.

Joseph, M. and Pandya, P. (1986). Finding response times in a real-time system, *BCS Computer Journal* **29**(5): 390–395.

Joseph, M. (ed.) (1996). *Real-Time Systems: Specification, Verification and Analysis*, Prentice Hall.

Kemeny, J. et al. (1979). *Report of the President's Commission on the Accident at Three Mile Island*, Government Printing Office, Washington.

Kernighan, B. W. and Ritchie, D. M. (1978). *The C Programming Language*, Prentice Hall Inc., New Jersey.

Kim, T., Chang, N., Kim, N. and Shin, H. (1999). Scheduling garbage collector for embedded real-time systems, *Workshop on Languages, Compilers and Tools for Embedded Systems (LCTES'99), ACM SIGPLAN Notices*, pp. 55–64.

Kligerman, E. and Stoyenko, A. (1986). Real-Time Euclid: A language for reliable real-time systems, *IEEE Transactions on Software Engineering* **SE-12**(9): 941–949.

Knight, J., Leveson, N. and St.Jean, L. (1985). A large scale experiment in N-version programming, *Digest of Papers, The Fifteenth Annual International Symposium on Fault-Tolerant Computing*, Nichigan, USA, pp. 135–139.

Kopetz, H. (1997). *Real-Time Systems: Design Principles for Distributed Embedded Applications*, Kluwer International Series in Engineering and Computer Science.

Kramer, J., Magee, J., Sloman, M. and Lister, A. (1983). CONIC: an integrated approach to distributed computer control systems, *IEE Proceedings (Part E)*, pp. 1–10.

Lamport, L. (1978). Time, clocks, and the ordering of events in a distributed system, *CACM* **21**(7): 558–565.

Lamport, L. (1983). Specifying concurrent program modules, *Transactions on Programming Languages and Systems* **5**(2): 190–222.

Lamport, L., Shostak, R. and Pease, M. (1982). The Byzantine generals problem, *Transactions on Programming Languages and Systems* **4**(3): 382–401.

Lampson, B. and Redell, D. (1980). Experience with processes and monitors in Mesa, *CACM* **23**(2): 105–117.

Laprie, J. (1985). Dependable computing and fault tolerance: Concepts and terminology, *Digest of Papers, The Fifteenth Annual International Symposium on Fault-Tolerant Computing*, Michigan, USA, pp. 2–11.

Laprie, J. (1995). Dependable - its attributes, impairments and means, *in* B. Randell et al. (eds), *Predictable Dependable Computig Systems*, Springer.

Lauber, R. J. (1989). Forecasting real-time behaviour during software design using a CASE environment, *The Journal of Real-Time Systems* **1**: 61–76.

Lauer, H. and Needham, R. (1978). On the duality of operating system structure, *Proceedings of the Second International Symposium on Operating System Principles*, IRIA, pp. 3–19.

Lauer, H. and Satterwaite, E. (1979). The impact of Mesa on system design, *Proceedings of the 4th International Conference on Software Engineering*, IEEE, pp. 174–182.

Lawton, J. and France, N. (1988). The transformation of JSD specification into Ada, *Ada User* **8**(1): 29–44.

le Guernic, P., Gautier, T., le Borgne, M. and le Maire, C. (1991). Programming real applications in Signal, *Proceedings of IEEE*, pp. 1321–1313.

Lea, D. (1997). *Concurrent Programming in Java*, Addison Wesley.

Lee, I. and Gehlot, V. (1985). Language constructs for distributed real-time programming, *Proceedings of the Real-Time Systems Symposium*, IEEE Computer Society Press, pp. 57–56.

Lee, P. (1983). Exception handling in C programs, *Software - Practice and Experience* **13**(5): 389–406.

Lee, P., Ghani, N. and Heron, K. (1980). A recovery cache for the PDP-11, *IEEE Transactions on Computers* **C-29**(6): 546–549.

Lehman, M. and Belady, L. (1985). The characteristics of large systems, *Program Evolution - Processes of Software Change, APIC Studies in Data processing No. 27*, Academic Press, pp. 289–329.

Lehoczky, J. P., Sha, L. and Strosnider, J. K. (1987). Enhanced aperiodic responsiveness in a hard real-time environment, *Proceedings of the IEEE Real-Time Systems Symposium*, pp. 261–270.

Leung, J. and Whitehead, J. (1982). On the complexity of fixed-priority scheduling of periodic, real-time tasks, *Performance Evaluation (Netherlands)* **2**(4): 237–250.

Leveson, N. (1986). Software safety: Why, what and how, *ACM Computing Surveys* **18**(2): 125–163.

Leveson, N. and Harvey, P. (1983). Analyzing software safety, *IEEE Transactions on Software Engineering* **SE-9**(5): 569–579.

Lim, T. F., Pardyak, P. and Bershad, B. N. (1999). A memory-efficient real-time non-copying garbage collector, *Proceedings of the International Symposium on Memory Management (ISMM-98), ACM SIGPLAN Notices*, pp. 118–129.

Liskov, B. and Snyder, A. (1979). Exception handling in CLU, *IEEE Transaction on Software Engineering* **SE-5**(6): 546–558.

Liskov, B., Herlihy, M. and Gilbert, L. (1986). Limitations of remote procedure call and static process structure for distributed computing, *Proceedings of Thirteenth Annual ACM Symposium on Principles of Programming Languages*, St. Petersburg Beach, Florida, pp. 150–159.

Littlewood, B. and Strigini, L. (1993). Validation of ultrahigh dependability for software-based systems, *Communications of the ACM* **36**(11): 69–80.

Liu, C. and Layland, J. (1973). Scheduling algorithms for multiprogramming in a hard real-time environment, *JACM* **20**(1): 46–61.

Locke, C. (1992). Software architecture for hard real-time applications: cyclic executives vs. fixed priority executives, *Real-Time Systems* **4**(1): 37–53.

Lomet, D. (1977). Process structuring, synchronisation and recovery using atomic actions, *Proceedings ACM Conference Language Design for Reliable Software SIGPLAN*, pp. 128–137.

Lytz, R. (1995). Software metrics for the Boeing 777: a case study, *Software Quality Journal* **4**(1): 1–14.

Martin, D. (1982). Dissimilar software in high integrity applications in flight controls, *AGARD Symposium on Software for Avionics*, p. 36:1.

Matsuoka, S. and Yonezawa, A. (1993). Analysis of inheritance anomaly in object-oriented concurrent programming languages, *Research Directions in Concurrent Object-Oriented Programming*, MIT Press, pp. 107–150.

May, D. and Shepherd, R. (1984). Occam and the transputer, *Proc IFIP Workshop on Hardware Supported Implemention of Concurrent Languages in Distributed Systems*, Univ. of Bristol, UK.

McDermid, J. (1989). Assurance in high integrity software, *in* C. Sennett (ed.), *High Integrity Software*, Pitman.

Meyer, B. (1992). *Eiffel: The Language*, Prentice Hall.

Mok, A. and Dertouzos, M. (1978). Multiprocessor scheduling in a hard real-time environment, *Proc. 7th Texas Conf. Comput. Syst.*

Monarchi, D. and Puhr, G. (1992). A research typology for object-oriented analysis and design, *Communications of the ACM* **35**(9): 35–47.

Mullery, G. (1979). CORE - A method for controlled requirement specification, *IEEE Computer Society Press*.

Object Management Group (1999). Realtime CORBA joint revised submission, *OMG Document orbos/99-02-12*, Object Management Group.

Owicki, S. and Lamport, L. (1982). Proving liveness properties of concurrent programs, *Transactions on Programming Languages and Systems* **4**(4): 455–495.

Palencia Gutierrez, J. and Gonzalez Harbour, M. (1998). Schedulability analysis for tasks with static and dynamic offsets, *Proceedings of the 18th IEEE Real-Time Systems Symposium*, pp. 26–39.

Palencia Gutierrez, J. and Gonzalez Harbour, M. (1999). Exploiting precedence relations in the schedulability analysis of distributed real-time systems, *Proceedings of the 19th IEEE Real-Time Systems Symposium*, pp. 328–339.

Pease, M., Shostak, R. and Lamport, L. (1980). Reaching agreement in the presence of faults, *Journal of the ACM* **27**(2): 228–234.

Peterson, G. (1981). Myths about the mutual exclusion problem, *Information Processing Letters* **12**(3): 115–16.

Purtilo, J. and Jalote, P. (1991). An environment for developing fault-tolerant software, *IEEE Transactions on Software Engineering* **17**(2): 153–9.

Ramamritham, K. and Stankovic, J. (1984). Dynamic task scheduling in hard real-time distributed systems, *IEEE Software* **1**(3): 65–75.

Randell, B. (1975). System structure for software fault tolerance, *IEEE Transactions on Software Engineering* **SE-1**(2): 220–232.

Randell, B. (1982). *The Origins of Digital Computers: selected papers*, Springer Verlag.

Randell, B., Laprie, J.-C., Kopetz, H. and Littlewood(Eds.), B. (1995). *Predictably Dependable Computing Systems*, Springer.

Randell, B., Lee, P. and Treleaven, P. (1978). Reliability issues in computing system design, *ACM Computing Surveys* **10**(2): 123–165.

Real, J. and Wellings, A. J. (1999a). The ceiling protocol in multi-moded real-time systems, *Reliable Software Technologies - Ada-Europe 99, Lecture Notes in Computer Science* **1622**: 275–286.

Real, J. and Wellings, A. J. (1999b). Implementing mode changes and shared resources in Ada, *Proceedings 11th Euromicro Conference on Real-Time Systems*, IEEE Society Press, York, England, pp. 86–93.

Reason, J. (1979). Actions not as planned: The price of automation, *in Aspects of Consciousness ed G. Underwood and R. Stevens*.

Reeves, G. (1997). What really happened on mars? – authoritative account, *http://www.research.microsoft.com/~mbj/mars_pathfinder/authoritative_account.html*, Accessed 28/4/2000.

Rogers, P. and Wellings, A. J. (2000). An incremental recovery cache supporting software fault tolerance mechanisms, *Computer Systems Science and Engineering* **15**(1): 33–48.

Roos, J. (1991). Designing a real-time coprocessor for Ada tasking, *IEEE Design Test of Computers* **8**(1): 67–79.

Roscoe, A. (1985). Denotational semantics for occam, *Lecture Notes in Computer Science*, Vol. 197, Springer-Verlag.

Rouse, W. (1981). Human-computer interaction in the control of dynamic systems, *Computer Surveys* **13**(1): 71–99.

Rubira-Calsavara, C. and Stroud, R. (1994). Forward and backward error recovery in C++, *Object-Oriented Systems* **1**(1): 61–85.

Runner, D. and Warshawsky, E. (1988). Synthesizing Ada's ideal machine mate, *VLSI Systems Design* **9**(10): 30–39.

Saltzer, J., Reed, D. and Clark, D. (1984). End-to-end arguments in system design, *ACM Transactions on Computer Systems* **2**(4): 277–288.

Schneider, F. (1984). Byzantine generals in action: Implementing fail-stop processors, *Transactions on Computer Systems* **2**(2): 145–154.

Selic, B., Moore, A., Bjorkander, M., Gerhardt, M. and Watson, B. (2000). Response to the OMG RFP for schedulability, performance and time, *http://cgi.omg.org/cgi-bin/doc?ad/00-08-04*, Accessed 18/8/2000.

Sha, L., Rajkumar, R. and Lehoczky, J. P. (1990). Priority inheritance protocols: An approach to real-time synchronisation, *IEEE Transactions on Computers* **39**(9): 1175–1185.

Shrivastava, S. (1978). Sequential Pascal with recovery blocks, *Software - Practice and Experience* **8**(2): 177–186.

Shrivastava, S. (1979). Concurrent pascal with backward error recovery: Language features and examples, *Software - Practice and Experience* **9**(12): 1001–1020.

Shrivastava, S. and Banatre, J. (1978). Reliable resource allocation between unreliable processes, *IEEE Transactions on Software Engineering* **SE-4**(3): 230–240.

Shrivastava, S., Mancini, L. and Randell, B. (1987). On the duality of fault tolerant structures, *Lecture Notes in Computer Science*, Vol. 309, Springer-Verlag, pp. 19 – 37.

Siebert, F. (1999). Guaranteeing non-disruptiveness and real-time deadlines in an incremental garbage collector, *Proceedings of the International Symposium on Memory Management (ISMM-98), ACM SIGPLAN Notices*, pp. 118–129.

Silberschatz, A. and Galvin, P. (1994). *Operating System Concepts*, fourth edn, Addison-Wesley.

Sloman, M. and Kramer, J. (1987). *Distributed Systems and Computer Networks*, Prentice Hall.

Sloman, M., Magee, J. and Kramer, J. (1984). Building flexible distributed systems in Conic, *in* D. A. Duce (ed.), *Distributed Computing Systems Programme*, Peter Peregrinus Ltd., pp. 86–105.

Smedema, C., Medema, P. and Boasson, M. (1983). *The Programming Languages Pascal, Modula, CHILL, Ada*, Prentice Hall.

Spivey, M. (1989). *The Z Notation A Reference Manual*, Prentice Hall (see also http://spivey.oriel.ox.ac.uk/~mike/zrm/index.html) Accessed 19/10/2000.

Spuri, M. and Buttazzo, G. (1994). Efficient aperiodic service under earliest deadline scheduling, *Proceedings IEEE Real-Time Systems Symposium*, pp. 2–11.

Stankovic, J. (1988). Misconceptions about real-time computing: A serious problem for next generation systems, *IEEE Computer* **21**(10): 10–19.

Stankovic, J., Ramamritham, K. and Cheng, S. (1985). Evaluation of a flexible task scheduling algorithm for distributed hard real-time systems, *IEEE Trans. Computers* **34**(12): 1130–1143.

Sun Microsystems (2000). picoJava II datasheet, *http://www.sun.com/microelectronics/databook/datasheets.html*, Sun Microsystems.

Tanenbaum, A. S. (1998). *Computer Networks*, Prentice Hall, Englewood Cliffs, N.J.

Teichrow, D. and Hershey, E. (1977). PSL/PSA: A computer-aided technique for structured documentation and analysis of information processing systems, *IEEE Transactions on Software Engineering* **SE-3**(1): 41–48.

Tindell, K. and Clark, J. (1994). Holistic schedulability analysis for distributed hard real-time systems, *Euromicro Journal (Special Issue on Parallel Embedded Real-Time Systems)* **40**: 117–134.

Tindell, K., Burns, A. and Wellings, A. J. (1994). An extendible approach for analysing fixed priority hard real-time tasks, *Real-Time Systems* **6**(2): 133–151.

Tindell, K., Burns, A. and Wellings, A. J. (1995). Calculating controller area network (CAN) message response times, *Control Engineering Practice* **3**(8): 1163–1169.

US National Institute of Standards and Technology (1999). Requirements for real-time extensions for the Java platform, *Nistir*, US National Institute of Standards and Technology.

Venners, B. (1999). *Inside the Java 1.2 Virtual Machine*, Osborne McGraw-Hill.

Walker, W. and Cragon, H. (1995). Interrupt processing in concurrent processors, *Computer* **28**(6): 36–46.

Wegner, P. (1987). Dimensions of object-based language design, *ACM SIGPLAN Notices* **22**(12): 168–182.

Wellings, A. J. and Burns, A. (1996). Programming replicated systems in Ada 95, *Computer Journal* **39 5**: 362–373.

Wellings, A. J. and Burns, A. (1997). Implementing atomic actions in Ada 95, *IEEE Transactions on Software Engineering* **23**(2): 107–123.

Wellings, A. J., Johnson, B., Sanden, B., Kienzle, J., Wolf, T. and Michell, S. (2000). Integrating object-oriented programming and protected types in Ada 95, *ACM TOPLAS*.

Wellings, A. J., Keeffe, D. and Tomlinson, G. (1984). A problem with Ada and resource allocation, *Ada Letters* **3**(4): 112–123.

Werum, W. and Windauer, H. (1985). *Introduction to PEARL Process and Experiment Automation Realtime Language*, Friedr. Vieweg Sohn.

Whitaker, W. (1978). The U.S. department of defense common high order language effort, *ACM SIGPLAN Notices* **13**(2): 19–29.

Wirth, N. (1977a). Design and implementation of modula, *Software-Practice and Experience* **7**: 67–84.

Wirth, N. (1977b). Modula: a language for modular multiprogramming, *Software-Practice and Experience* **7**(1): 3–35.

Wirth, N. (1983). *Programming in Modula-2*, second edn, Springer-Verlag.

Wirth, N. (1988). The programming language Oberon, *Software - Practice and Experience* **18**(7): 671–690.

Wolf, T. (1998). *Replication on Non-Deterministic Objects*, Ph.D. thesis, Swiss Federal Institute of Technology in Lausanne, Switzerland.

Xerox Corporation (1985). Mesa language manual verson 5.0.

X/Open Company Ltd. (1996). *X/Open Guide: Architecture Neutral Distribution Format*, X/Open Company Ltd., UK.

Young, S. (1982). *Real Time Languages: Design and Development*, Ellis Horwood Publishers, Chichester.

Yuh-Jzer, J. and Smolka, S. A. (1996). A comprehensive study of the complexity of multiparty interaction, *Journal of the ACM* **43**(1): 75–115.

Index